Today's most **popular authors** have collaborated on this exciting new series, which combines **great literature** with remarkably **effective instruction,** bringing real writers and real tools together for real results.

CURRICULUM

Give your students

Real writers
unprecedented access to award-winning authors
(see page T2)

Real tools
remarkably effective tools for differentiated instruction
(see page T4)

Real results
built-in benchmarking to guarantee standards mastery and learning success   (see page T6)

> **This project is what I wish I'd had when I was in school . . . a resource where I could not only read really good writing, but also get a sense about how the authors actually felt!**

—Cornelius Eady
featured unit author

D1172010

TEACHER'S EDITION CONTENTS

TEACHER'S EDITION

PRENTICE HALL
LITERATURE

PENGUIN EDITION

WORLD MASTERPIECES
VOLUME II

Pearson Prentice Hall™ is a trademark of Pearson Education, Inc.
Pearson® is a registered trademark of Pearson plc.
Prentice Hall® is a registered trademark of Pearson Education, Inc.

Upper Saddle River, New Jersey
Boston, Massachusetts

ISBN 0-13-131766-0

2 3 4 5 6 7 8 9 10   09 08 07 06 05

CONTRIBUTING AUTHORS

The contributing authors guided the direction and philosophy of Prentice Hall Literature: Penguin Edition. Working with the development team, they helped to build the pedagogical integrity of the program and to ensure its relevance for today's teachers and students.

Kate **Kinsella**

Kate Kinsella, Ed.D., is a teacher educator in the Department of Secondary Education at San Francisco State University. She teaches coursework addressing academic language and literacy development in linguistically and culturally diverse classrooms. She maintains secondary classroom involvement by teaching an academic literacy class for adolescent English learners through the University's Step to College Program. She publishes and provides consultancy and training nationally, focusing upon responsible instructional practices that provide second language learners and less proficient readers in grades 4–12 with the language and literacy skills vital to educational mobility.

Dr. Kinsella is the program author for *Reading in the Content Areas: Strategies for Reading Success,* published by Pearson Learning and the lead program author for the 2002 Prentice Hall secondary language arts program *Timeless Voices: Timeless Themes.* She is the co-editor of the CATESOL Journal (CA Assn. of Teachers of ESL) and serves on the editorial board for the *California Reader.* A former Fulbright scholar, Dr. Kinsella has received numerous awards, including the prestigious Marcus Foster Memorial Reading Award, offered by the California Reading Association in 2002 to a California educator who has made a significant statewide impact on both policy and pedagogy in the area of literacy.

Sharon **Vaughn**

Sharon Vaughn, PH.D., is the H.E. Hartfelder/The Southland Corporation Regents Professor at the University of Texas and also director of the Vaughn Gross Center for Reading and Language Arts at the University of Texas (VGCRLA). As director of the VGCRLA, she leads more than five major initiatives, including The Central Regional Reading First Technical Assistance Center; the Three-Tier Reading Research Project; a bilingual-biliteracy (English/Spanish) intervention research study; the first through fourth grade Teacher Reading Academies that have been used for teacher education throughout Texas and the nation; and the creation of online professional development in reading for teachers and other interested professionals.

Dr. Vaughn has published more than ten books and over one hundred research articles. She is Editor in Chief of the *Journal of Learning Disabilities* and serves on the editorial board of more than ten research journals, including the *Journal of Educational Psychology,* the *American Educational Research Journal,* and the *Journal of Special Education.*

*To all those who seek truth, light, and wisdom.
After all, it is their hearts that turn to
the information in this book.*

CONTENTS

SECTION 1

SECTION 9

PREFACE

Essential oils are some of the oldest and most powerful therapeutic agents known. Most people today are unaware that they have an impressive, multimillennium history of use in healing and anointing throughout the ancient world. Dozens of essential oils are cited repeatedly in Judeo-Christian religious texts and records show they were used to treat virtually every ailment known to man at that time. Frankincense, myrrh, lotus, cedarwood, and sandalwood oils were widely used in ancient Egyptian purification and embalming rituals. Other oils, like cinnamon, clove and lemon, were highly valued as antiseptics hundreds of years before the development of today's synthetic medicines.

With the advance of antibiotics and prescription drugs during the last century, natural therapeutic agents, especially essential oils, have been largely overlooked. Only during the last two decades have essential oils begun a resurgence in popularity in the United States, as their broad-spectrum antibacterial and therapeutic action is rediscovered by many researchers and health-care professionals. No doubt part of the reason essential oils have been slow to emerge—especially in the United States—is because they were heavily extended and adulterated for commercial use, destroying their therapeutic biochemistry and making them useful only as air-freshening or flavoring compounds.

In their pure state, essential oils are some of the most concentrated natural extracts known, exhibiting significant and immediate antiviral, anti-inflammatory, antibacterial, and hormone-balancing effects. In clinical practice, they have been shown to have a profound influence on the central nervous system, helping to reduce or eliminate pain, release muscle tension and provide strong emotional uplift.

The chemical structure of an essential oil is such that it can rapidly penetrate cell membranes, travel throughout the blood and tissues, and enhance cellular function. For those health professionals who have worked regularly with quality essential oils on patients, it has become very clear that there is a powerful life force inherent in these substances, which gives them an unmatched ability to communicate and interact with cells in the human body.

For many there is no doubt that essential oils are ordained as medicines for mankind and will provide critical medical solutions in the future. They could very well be the missing link of modern health care, bringing allopathic and holistic practice together for optimal health in the 21st century.

Healthy-minded people the world over have learned the value of using high quality natural herbs. Interestingly, most therapeutic herbs can be distilled into an essential oil. The key difference is one of concentration. The essential oil can be from 100 to 10,000 times more concentrated – and therefore more potent – than the herb itself.

Even though they are many times more potent than natural herbs, essential oils--unlike prescription drugs--very rarely generate any negative side effects. This carries profound implications for those wanting to maintain or regain their health quickly AND naturally.

Sometimes the effects of administering essential oils are so dramatic that the patients themselves call it "miraculous." And while no one fully understands yet 'why' or 'how' essential oils provide such significant benefits, the fact is that they do. With pure essential oils, millions of people can find relief from disease, from infections, from pain, and even from mental difficulties. Their therapeutic potential is enormous and is only just beginning to be tapped.

ACKNOWLEDGMENTS

We wish to acknowledge D. Gary Young, ND, for his tremendous contribution to the rebirth of essential oils in North America. One of the pioneers in researching, cultivating, and distilling essential oils in North America, he has spent decades conducting clinical research on the ability of essential oils to combat disease and improve health. He has also developed new methods of application from which thousands of people have benefitted, especially his integration of therapeutic-grade essential oils with dietary supplements and personal care products. He is certainly one of the first, if not the first, to create these types of quality products.

Growing up as a farmer and rancher in Idaho, Gary developed a passion for the land, that has driven him to become one of the leading organic growers and distillers of essential oils in North America. With over 2,000 acres of land under cultivation in the US and Europe, he has set new standards for excellence that are redefining how therapeutic-grade essential oils are produced.

Gary's long experience as a grower, distiller, researcher, and alternative care practitioner not only gives him an unsurpassed insight into essential oils but also makes him an ideal spokesperson and educator on therapeutic properties of essential oils. Gary regularly travels throughout the world lecturing on the powerful potential of essential oils and how to produce therapeutic-grade essential oils that can consistently deliver results.

Much of the material contained in this book is derived from his research, lectures, and workshops, as well as the work of other practitioners and physicians who are at the forefront of understanding the clinical potential of essential oils to treat disease. To these researchers, the publisher is deeply indebted.

Hyssop

SECTION 1

German Chamomile

CHAPTER 1

Essential Oils: The Missing Link in Modern Medicine

Yesterday's Wisdom, Tomorrow's Destiny

Plants not only play a vital role in the ecological balance of our planet, but they have also been intimately linked to the physical, emotional, and spiritual well-being of mankind since the beginning of time.

The plant kingdom continues to be the subject of an enormous amount of research and discovery. At least 30 percent of prescription drugs in the United States are based on naturally occurring compounds from plants. Each year, millions of dollars are allocated to universities searching for new therapeutic agents that lie undiscovered in the bark, roots, flowers, seeds, and foliage of jungle canopies, river bottoms, forests, hillsides, and vast wilderness regions throughout the world.

As the most powerful part of the plant, essential oils and plant extracts have been woven into history since time immemorial. Essential oils have been used medicinally to kill bacteria, fungi, and viruses. They provide exquisite fragrances to balance mood, lift spirits, dispel negative emotions, and create a romantic atmosphere. They can stimulate the regeneration of tissue or stimulate nerves. They can even carry nutrients to, and oxygenate the cells.

What Is an Essential Oil?

Essential oils are aromatic volatile liquids distilled from shrubs, flowers, trees, roots, bushes, and seeds.

The chemistry of essential oils is very complex: each one may consist of hundreds of different and unique chemical compounds. Moreover, essential oils are highly concentrated and far more potent than dried herbs. The distillation process is what makes essential oils so concentrated. It often requires an entire plant or more to produce a single drop of distilled essential oil.

Essential oils are also different from vegetable oils such as corn oil, peanut oil, and olive oil. They are not greasy and do not clog the pores like many vegetable oils can.

Vegetable oils can become oxidized and rancid over time and are not antibacterial. Most essential oils, on the other hand, cannot go rancid and are powerful antimicrobials. Pressed oils and essential oils high in plant waxes such as patchouli, if not distilled properly, could go rancid after time, particularly if exposed to heat for extended periods of time.

Essential oils are substances that definitely deserve the respect of proper education. Users need to be fully versed in the chemistry and safety of the oils. However, this knowledge is not being taught at universities in the United States. There is a disturbing lack of institutional information, knowledge, and training on essential oils and the scientific approach to aromatherapy. Only in the Middle East, the Orient, and Europe, with their far longer history of using natural products and botanical extracts, can one obtain adequate instruction on the chemistry and therapy of essential oils.

The European communities have a tight framework of controls and standards concerning botanical extracts and who may administer them. Only practitioners with proper training and certification can practice aromatherapy. However, in the United States, the regulatory agencies have not recognized these disciplines or mandated the type and degree of training required to distribute and apply essential oils. This means that in the U.S. individuals can bill themselves as "aromatherapists" after a brief class in essential oils, and apply oils to people—even though they may not have the experience or training to properly understand and administer them. This may not only undermine and damage the credibility of the entire discipline of aromatherapy, but it can be dangerous to patients.

Corpus Callosum
Thalamus
Hypothalmus
Pineal Gland
Amygdala
Pituitary Gland
Cerebellum
Hippocampus
Brain Stem

Buccal Cavity

Limbic System

How aromatic molecules influence the emotional center of the brain

Aromatic Molecules

Olfactory Bulb

Glomeruli

Axon

Neuronal Cell Bodies

Olfactory Epithelium

Essential oils are not simple substances. They are mosaics of hundreds—or even thousands—of different chemicals. Any given essential oil may contain anywhere from 80 to 300 or more different chemical constituents. An essential oil like lavender is very complex with many of its constituents occurring in minute quantities—but all contributing to the oil's therapeutic effects to some degree. To understand these constituents and their functions requires years of study.

Even though an essential oil may be labeled as "basil" and have the botanical name Ocimum basilicum, it can have widely different therapeutic actions, depending on its chemistry. For example, basil high in linalool or fenchol is primarily used for its antiseptic properties. However, basil high in methyl chavicol is more anti-inflammatory than antiseptic. A third type, basil high in eugenol, has both anti-inflammatory and antiseptic effects.

Additionally, essential oils can be distilled or extracted in different ways that have dramatic effects on their chemistry and medicinal action. Oils derived from a second or third distillation of the same plant material are obviously not going to be as potent as oils extracted during the first distillation. Also, oils that are subjected to high heat and pressure have a distinctly simpler (and inferior) profile of chemical constituents, since excessive heat and temperature fractures and breaks down many of the delicate aromatic compounds within the oil—some of which are responsible for its therapeutic action. In addition, oils that are steam distilled are far different from those that are solvent extracted.

Of greatest concern is the fact that some oils are adulterated, engineered, or "extended" with the use of synthetic chemicals. For example, pure frankincense is often extended with colorless, odorless solvents such as diethylphthalate or dipropylene glycol. The only way to distinguish the "authentic" from the "adulterated" is to subject the essential oil to rigorous analytical testing using state-of-the-art gas chromatography, mass spectroscopy, and NMR (nuclear magnetic resonance).

However, even gas chromatography doesn't identify a natural chemical from a synthetic one. That is why it is very easy to engineer oils or extend poor quality oils to make them smell and look good.

Unfortunately, a large percentage of essential oils marketed in the United States fall in this adulterated category. When you understand the world of synthetic oils as well as low-grade oils cut with synthetic chemicals, you realize why unsuspecting people with their untrained noses don't know the difference.

Different Schools of Application

Therapeutic treatment using essential oils follows three different models or frameworks: French, German, and English.

The English model advocates diluting a small amount of essential oil in a vegetable oil and massaging the body for the purpose of relaxation and relieving stress.

The French model prescribes the ingestion and neat (undiluted) topical application of therapeutic-grade essential oils. A common form of internal use is to add a few drops of an essential oil to blue agave nectar or honey, a piece of bread, or a small amount of vegetable oil. Many French practitioners have found that taking the oils internally yields excellent benefits.

The German model focuses on inhalation of essential oils. Research has shown that the effect of fragrance and aromatic compounds on the sense of smell can exert strong effects on the brain—especially on the hypothalamus (the hormone command center of the body) and limbic system (the seat of emotions). Some essential oils high in sesquiterpenes, such as myrrh, sandalwood, cedarwood, vetiver, melissa, and frankincense, can dramatically increase oxygenation and activity in the brain. This may directly improve the function of many systems of the body.

Together, these three models show how versatile and powerful essential oils can be. By integrating all three models with Vita Flex, auricular technique, touch therapy, spinal touch, lymphatic massage, and Raindrop Technique, the best possible results may be obtained.

In some cases, inhalation of essential oils might be preferred over topical application, if the goal is to increase growth hormone secretion, induce weight loss, or balance mood and emotions. Sandalwood, peppermint, vetiver, lavender, and white fir oils are effective for inhalation.

In other cases, however, topical application of essential oils would produce better results, particularly in the case of spinal or muscle injuries or defects. Topically applied, marjoram is excellent for muscles, lemongrass for ligaments, and wintergreen for bones. For indigestion, a drop or two of peppermint oil taken orally may be very effective. However, this does not mean that peppermint cannot produce the same results when massaged on the stomach. In some cases, all three methods of application (topical, inhalation, and ingestion) are interchangeable and may produce similar benefits.

The ability of essential oils to act on both the mind and the body is what makes them truly unique among natural therapeutic agents. The fragrance of some essential oils can be very stimulating—both psychologically and physically. The fragrance of other essential oils may be calming and sedating, helping to overcome anxiety or hyperactivity. On a physiological level, essential oils may stimulate immune function and regenerate damaged tissue. Essential oils may also combat infectious disease by killing viruses, bacteria, and other pathogens.

Probably the two most common methods of essential oil application are cold-air diffusing and neat (undiluted) topical application. Other modes of application include incorporating essential oils into the disciplines of reflexology, Vita Flex, and acupressure. Combining these disciplines with essential oils enhances the healing response and often produces amazing results that can not be achieved by acupuncture or reflexology alone. Just 1–3 drops of an essential oil applied to an acupuncture meridian or Vita Flex point on the hand or foot can produce results within a minute or two.

Several years ago at a university in Europe, a professor well known in the field of aromatherapy commented that anyone who claims to cure diseases using essential oils is a quack. However, there are many people who are living proof that essential oils can be used to engineer recoveries from serious illness. Essential oils have been pivotal in helping many people live pain-free after years of intense pain. Patients have also witnessed firsthand how essential oils have helped with scoliosis and even restored hearing in those who were born deaf.

For example, a woman from Palisades Park, California, developed scoliosis after surviving polio as a teenager, which was further complicated by a serious fall and a dislocated shoulder. Suffering pain and immobility for 22 years, she had traveled extensively in a fruitless search to locate a practitioner who could permanently reset her shoulder. Upon learning about essential oils, she topically applied the oils of helichrysum and wintergreen, among others, to the shoulder. Within a short time she became pain free as the shoulder relocated. She was able to raise her arm over her head for the first time in 22 years.

When one sees such dramatic recoveries, it is difficult to discredit the value and the power of essential oils and the potential they hold.

Mankind's First Medicine

For many centuries essential oils and other aromatics were used for religious rituals, the treatment of illness, and other physical and spiritual needs.

Records dating back to 4500 BC describe the use of balsamic substances with aromatic properties for religious rituals and medical applications. Ancient writings tell of scented barks, resins, spices, and aromatic vinegars, wines, and beers that were used in rituals, temples, astrology, embalming, and medicine. The evidence suggests that the people of ancient times had a greater understanding of essential oils than we have today.

The Egyptians were masters in using essential oils and other aromatics in the embalming process. Historical records describe how one of the founders of "pharaonic" medicine was the architect Imhotep, who was the Grand Vizier of King Djoser (2780 - 2720 BC). Imhotep is often given credit for ushering in the use of oils, herbs, and aromatic plants for medicinal purposes.

Many hieroglyphics on the walls of Egyptian temples depict the blending of oils and describe hundreds of oil recipes.

An ancient papyrus found in the Temple of Edfu contained medicinal formulae and perfume recipes used by alchemists and high priests in blending aromatic substances for rituals.

The Egyptians may have been the first to discover the potential of fragrance. They created various aromatic blends for both personal use and for ceremonies performed in the temples and pyramids.

Well before the time of Christ, the ancient Egyptians collected essential oils and placed them in alabaster vessels. These vessels were specially carved and shaped for housing scented oils. In 1922, when King Tut's tomb was opened, some 50 alabaster jars designed to hold 350 liters of oils were discovered. Tomb robbers had stolen nearly all of the precious oils leaving the heavy jars behind. Some of them still contained oil traces. The robbers chose oils over a literal king's ransom in gold, showing how valuable the fragrant essential oils were to this ancient civilization.

In 1817 the Ebers Papyrus, a medical scroll over 870 feet long, was discovered. Dating back to 1500 BC, the scroll included over 800 different herbal prescriptions and remedies. Other scrolls described a high success rate in treating 81 different diseases. Many of the remedies contained myrrh and honey. Myrrh is still recognized for its ability to help with infections of the skin and throat and to regenerate skin tissue. Because of its effectiveness in preventing bacterial growth, myrrh was used for embalming.

The physicians of Ionia, Attia, and Crete (ancient civilizations based in the Mediterranean Sea) came to the cities of the Nile to increase their knowledge. At this time, the school of Cos was founded and was attended by Hippocrates (460-377 BC), whom the Greeks, with perhaps some exaggeration, named the "Father of Medicine."

The Romans purified their temples and political buildings by diffusing essential oils. They also used aromatics in their steam baths to both invigorate the flesh and ward off disease.

Early History of Essential Oil Extraction

Ancient cultures found that aromatic essences or oils could be extracted from the plant by a variety of methods. One of the oldest and crudest forms of extraction was known as enfleurage. Raw plant material (usually stems, foliage, bark, or roots) was crushed and mixed with olive oil or animal fat. Other vegetable oils were also used. In the case of cedar, for example, the bark was stripped from the trunk and branches, ground into a powder, soaked with olive oil, and placed in a wool cloth. The cloth was then heated. The heat pulled the essential oil out of the bark particles into the olive oil, and the wool was pressed to extract the essential oil. Sandalwood oil was also extracted in this fashion.

Enfleurage was also used to extract essential oils from flower petals. In fact, the French word *enfleurage* means literally "to saturate with the perfume of flowers." For example, petals from roses or jasmine were placed in goose or goat fat. The essential oil molecules were pulled from the petals into the fat, which was then processed to separate the essential oils from the fat. This ancient technique was among the most primitive forms of essential oil extraction.

Other extraction techniques were also used. Some of these included:
- Soaking plant parts in boiling water
- Cold-pressing
- Soaking in alcohol
- Steam distillation by passing steam through the plant material and condensing the steam to separate the oil from the plant.

Many ancient cosmetic formulas were created from a base of goat fat. Ancient Egyptians formulated eyeliners, eyeshadows, and other cosmetics this way. They also stained their hair and nails with a variety of ointments and perfumes. They probably used the same aromatic oils that were used in the temples. Such temple oils were commonly poured into evaporation dishes for fragrancing the chambers associated with sacred rituals and religious rites.

Fragrance "cones" made of wax and fragrant essential oils were worn by aristocratic Egyptian women who enjoyed the oils' rich scents as the cones melted with the heat of the day.

Ancient Arabians were another early culture that developed and refined a process of distillation. They perfected the extraction of rose oils and rose water, which were popular in the Middle East during the Byzantine Empire (330 AD - 1400 AD).

Biblical and Ancient References to Essential Oils

There are over 200 references to aromatics, incense, and ointments throughout the Old and New Testaments of the Bible. Aromatics such as frankincense, myrrh, galbanum, cinnamon, cassia, rosemary, hyssop, and spikenard were used for anointing and healing the sick. In Exodus, the Lord gave the following recipe to Moses for a holy anointing oil:

Myrrh	"five hundred shekels" (about 1 gallon)
Cinnamon	"two hundred and fifty shekels"
Calamus	"two hundred and fifty shekels"
Cassia	"five hundred shekels"
Olive Oil	"an hin" (about 1 1/3 gallons)

Psalms 133:2 speaks of the sweetness of brethren dwelling together in unity: "It is like the precious ointment upon the head, that ran down the beard, even Aaron's beard: that went down to the skirts of his garments." Another scripture that refers to anointing and the overflowing abundance of precious oils is Ecclesiastes 9:8: "Let thy garments be always white; and let thy head lack no ointment."

The Bible also lists an incident where an incense offering by Aaron stopped a plague. Numbers 16:46-50 records that Moses instructed Aaron to take a censer, add burning coals and incense, and to "go quickly into the congregation to make an atonement for them: for there is a wrath gone out from the Lord; the plague is begun." The Bible records that Aaron stood between the dead and the living and the plague was stayed. It is significant that according to the

biblical and Talmudic recipes for incense, three varieties of cinnamon were involved. Cinnamon is known to be highly antimicrobial, anti-infectious, and antibacterial. The incense ingredient listed as "stacte" is believed to be a sweet, myrrh-related spice, which would make it anti-infectious and antiviral as well.

The New Testament records that wise men presented the Christ child with frankincense and myrrh. There is another precious aromatic, spikenard, described in the anointing of Jesus:

> And being in Bethany in the house of Simon the leper, as he sat at meat, there came a woman having an alabaster box of ointment of spikenard very precious; and she brake the box, and poured it on his head. Mark 14:3.

The anointing of Jesus is also referred to in John 12:3:

> Then took Mary a pound of ointment of spikenard, very costly, and anointed the feet of Jesus, and wiped his feet with her hair: and the house was filled with the odour of the ointment.

Other Historical References

Throughout world history, fragrant oils and spices have played a prominent role in everyday life.

Napoleon is reported to have enjoyed a cologne water made of neroli and other ingredients so much that he ordered 162 bottles of it. After conquering Jerusalem, one of the things the Crusaders brought back to Europe was solidified essence of roses.

The 12th century herbalist, Hildegard of Bingen, used herbs and oils extensively in healing. This Benedictine nun founded her own convent and was the author of numerous works. Her book, Physica, has more than 200 chapters on plants and their uses for healing.

The Rediscovery

The reintroduction of essential oils into modern medicine first began during the late 19th and early 20th centuries.

During World War I, the use of aromatic essences in civilian and military hospitals became widespread. One physician in France, Dr. Moncière, used essential oils extensively for their antibacterial and wound-healing properties, and developed several kinds of aromatic ointments.

René-Maurice Gattefossé, PhD, a French cosmetic chemist, is widely regarded as the father of aromatherapy. He and a group of scientists began studying essential oils in 1907.

In his 1937 book, *Aromatherapy*, Dr. Gattefossé told the real story of his now-famous use of lavender essential oil to heal a serious burn. The tale has assumed mythic proportions in essential oil literature. His own words about this accident are even more powerful than what has been told over the years.

René-Maurice Gattefossé, PhD

Dr. Gattefossé was literally aflame — covered in burning substances — following a laboratory explosion in July, 1910. After he extinguished the flames by rolling on a grassy lawn, he wrote that "both my hands were covered with rapidly developing gas gangrene." He further reported that, "just one rinse with lavender essence stopped the gasification of the tissue. This treatment was followed by profuse sweating and healing which began the next day."

Robert B. Tisserand, editor of The International Journal of Aromatherapy, searched for Dr. Gattefossé's book for 20 years. A copy was located and Tisserand edited the 1995 reprint. Tisserand noted that Dr. Gattefossé's burns "must have been severe to lead to gas gangrene, a very serious infection."

Jean Valnet

Dr. Gattefossé shared his studies with his colleague and friend, Jean Valnet, a medical doctor practicing in Paris. Exhausting his supply of antibiotics as a physician in Tonkin, China, during World War II, Dr. Valnet began using therapeutic-grade essential oils on patients suffering battlefield injuries. To his surprise, they exerted a powerful effect in combating and counteracting infection. He was able to save the lives of many soldiers who might otherwise have died.

Two of Dr. Valnet's students, Dr. Paul Belaiche and Dr. Jean-Claude Lapraz, expanded his work. They clinically inves-

Dr. Jean-Calude Lapraz

tigated the antiviral, antibacterial, antifungal, and antiseptic properties in essential oils.

Dr Daniel Pénoël

In 1990, Dr Daniel Pénoël, a French medical doctor and Pierre Franchomme, a French biochemist, collaborated together to author the first reference book that catalogued the various medical properties of over 270 essential oils and how to use them in a clinical environment. Their work was based on Franchomme's laboratory experience and Pénoël's clinical experience administering the oils to his patients. The book, published in French, was titled *L'aromatherapie exactement*, and became the primary resource for dozens of authors world-wide in writing about the medical benefits of essential oils.

Because of the work of these doctors and scientists, the healing power of essential oils is again gaining prominence.

Today, it has become evident that we have not yet found permanent solutions for dreaded diseases such as the Ebola virus, hanta virus, AIDS, HIV, and new strains of tuberculosis and influenza. Essential oils may assume an increasingly important role in combating new mutations of bacteria, viruses, and fungi. More and more researchers are undertaking serious clinical studies on the use of essential oils to combat these types of diseases.

Research conducted at Weber State University in cooperation with D. Gary Young as well as other documented research, indicates that most viruses, fungi, and bacteria cannot live in the presence of many essential oils, especially those high in phenols, carvacrol, thymol, and terpenes. This, perhaps, offers a modern explanation why the Old Testament prophet Moses used aromatic substances to protect the Israelites from the plagues that decimated ancient Egypt. It may also help us understand why a notorious group of thieves, reputed to be spice traders and perfumers, was protected from the Black Plague as they robbed the bodies of the dead during the 15th century.

A vast body of anecdotal evidence (testimonials) suggests that those who use essential oils are less likely to contract infectious diseases. Moreover, oil users who do contract an infectious illness tend to recover faster than those using antibiotics.

CHAPTER 2

How Do Essential Oils Work?

Therapeutic-Grade Essential Oils

One of the factors that determines the purity of an oil is its chemical constituents. These constituents can be affected by a vast number of variables, including: the part(s) of the plant from which the oil was produced, soil condition, fertilizer (organic or chemical), geographical region, climate, altitude, harvesting methods, and distillation processes. For example, common thyme (Thymus vulgaris) produces several different chemotypes (biochemically unique variants within one species) depending on the conditions of its growth, climate, and altitude. One chemotype of thyme will yield an essential oil with high levels of thymol, depending on the time of year it is distilled. The later it is distilled in the growing season (ie., mid-summer or fall), the more thymol the oil will contain.

Proper cultivation assures that more specific chemotypes like Thymus vulgaris will maintain a good strain of thymol, where as with wildcrafting, you may produce linalol and eugenol thyme on the same mountainside.

An example of this was shown in studies at the University of Ege botany department in Izmir, Turkey where it was found that among Oreganum compactum plants within a 100 square foot radius, one plant would be very high in carvacrol and another would be high in another compound. Wildcrafting plants cannot guarantee the same chemotype even on the same hillside.

The key to producing a therapeutic-grade essential oil is to preserve as many of the delicate aromatic compounds within the essential oil as possible. Fragile aromatic chemicals are easily destroyed by high temperature and pressure, as well as contact with chemically reactive metals such as copper or aluminum. This is why all therapeutic-grade essential oils should be distilled in stainless steel cooking chambers at low pressure and low temperature.

The plant material should also be free of herbicides and other agrichemicals. These can react with the essential oil during distillation to produce toxic compounds. Because many pesticides are oil-soluble, they can also mix into the essential oil.

As we begin to understand the power of essential oils in the realm of personal, holistic healthcare, we will appreciate the necessity for obtaining the purest essential oils possible. No matter how costly pure essential oils may be, there can be no substitutes.

Although chemists have successfully recreated the main constituents and fragrances of some essential oils in the laboratory, these synthetic oils lack therapeutic benefits and may even carry risks. Why? Because essential oils contain hundreds of different chemical compounds, which, in combination, lend important therapeutic properties to the oil. Also, many essential oils contain molecules and isomers that are impossible to manufacture in the laboratory.

Anyone venturing into the world of therapy using essential oils must use the purest quality oils available. Inferior quality or adulterated oils most likely will not produce therapeutic results and could possibly be toxic. In Europe, a set of standards has been established that outlines the chemical profile and principal constituents that a quality essential oil should have. Known as AFNOR (Association French Normalization Organization Regulation) and ISO (International Standards Organization) standards, these guidelines help buyers differentiate between a therapeutic-grade essential oil and a lower grade oil with a similar chemical makeup and fragrance. **All of the therapeutic effects of the essential oils in this book are based on oils that have been graded according to AFNOR standards.**

Science and Application

Essential oils and human blood share several common properties: They fight infection, contain hormone-like compounds, and initiate regeneration. Working as the chemical defense mechanism of the plant, essential oils possess potent antibacterial, antifungal, and antiviral properties. They also ward off attacks by insects and animals. The ability of some essential oils to work as hormones helps them bring balance to many physiological systems of the human body. Oils like clary sage and sage that contain sclerol, for example, have an estrogenic action. Essential oils also play a role in initiating the regeneration process for the plant, the same way the blood does in the human body.

This similarity goes even deeper. Essential oils have a chemical structure that is similar to that found in human cells and tissues. This makes essential oils compatible with human protein and enables them to be readily identified and accepted by the body.

Essential oils have a unique ability to penetrate cell membranes and diffuse throughout the blood and tissues. The unique, lipid-soluble structure of essential oils is very similar to the makeup of our cell membranes. The molecules of essential oils are also relatively small, which enhances their ability to penetrate into the cells. When topically applied to the feet or elsewhere, essential oils can travel throughout the body in a matter of minutes.

The ability of some essential oils, like clove, to decrease the viscosity or thickness of the blood can also enhance circulation and immune function. Adequate circulation is vital to good health, since it affects the function of every cell and organ, including the brain.

Research indicates that when essential oils are diffused, they can increase atmospheric oxygen and provide negative ions, which in turn inhibits bacterial growth. This suggests that essential oils could play an important role in air purification and neutralizing odors. Because of their ionizing action, essential oils have the ability to break down potentially harmful chemicals and render them nontoxic.

In the human body, essential oils stimulate the secretion of antibodies, neurotransmitters, endorphins, hormones, and enzymes. Oils containing limonene have been shown to prevent and slow the progression of cancer. Other oils, like lavender, have

How Essential Oils are Formed in the Plant

CO_2 Carbon Dioxide

O_2 Oxygen

N Nitrogen NH_2^+ K^+ Na^+ Cl^- Mg^{++} S Sulfur

Minerals and carbons are combined with nitrogen in the soil to form amino acids in the plant. These amino acids form proteins that contribute to essential oil formation. Essential oils and amino acids like phenylalanine share a similar aromatic structure.

been shown to promote the growth of hair and increase the rate of wound healing. They increase the uptake of oxygen and ATP (adenosine triphosphate), the fuel for individual cells.

European scientists have studied the ability of essential oils to work as natural chelators, binding with heavy metals and petrochemicals and ferrying them out of the body.

Today approximately 300 essential oils are distilled or extracted, with several thousand chemical constituents and aromatic molecules identified and registered. The quantity, quality, and type of these aromatic compounds will vary depending on climate, temperature, and distillation factors. Ninety-eight percent of essential oils produced today are used in the perfume and cosmetic industry. Only about 2 percent are produced for therapeutic and medicinal applications.

Because essential oils are composites of hundreds of different chemicals, they can exert many different effects on the body. For example, clove oil can be simultaneously antiseptic and anaesthetic when applied topically. It can also be antitumoral. Lavender oil has been used for burns, insect bites, headaches, PMS, insomnia, stress, and hair growth.

Importantly, because of their complexity, essential oils do not disturb the body's natural balance or homeostasis: if one constituent exerts too strong an effect, another constituent may block or counteract it. Synthetic chemicals, in contrast, usually have only one action and often disrupt the body's homeostasis.

Using European AFNOR/ISO Standards to Identify Therapeutic-Grade Oils

As previously mentioned, one of the most reliable indicators of essential oil quality is the AFNOR (Association French Normalization Organization Regulation) or ISO certification. ISO is the International Standards Organization which has set standards for essential oils, adopted from AFNOR. This standard is more stringent and differentiates true top quality essential oils from similar oils with inferior chemistry (For more information, see Appendix A).

As Research Engineer at Centre National de la Recherche Scientifique (CNRS), Dr. Hervé Casabianca—who holds a doctors degree in organic chemistry—worked with many of the finest European scientists and doctors in helping to create the AFNOR standards, and was a voting member of AFNOR at the time of the standards' adoption.

Dr. Casabianca recognized that the primary constituents within an essential oil had to occur in certain percentages in order for the oil to have predictable therapeutic effects. He combined his studies with research conducted by other scientists and doctors to create the AFNOR certification.

Using these standards, many oils such as frankincense or lavender, can be checked to see if they do indeed have the proper balance of chemical constituents. If some constituents are too high or too low, the oils cannot be certified.

For example, the AFNOR standard for Lavandula angustifolia (true lavender) dictates that the level of linalool should range from 25 to 38 percent and the level of linalyl acetate should range between 25 and 34 percent. As long as the oil's marker compounds are within the specified ranges, it can be recognized as meeting AFNOR standards.

As a general rule, if two or more marker compounds in an essential oil fall outside the prescribed percentages, the oil does not meet the AFNOR standard.

A lavender oil produced in one region of France might have a slightly different chemistry than that grown in another region and as a result may not meet the standard. It may have excessive camphor levels (1.0 instead of 0.5), a condition that might be caused by distilling lavender that was too green. Or, the levels of lavandulol may be too low due to certain weather conditions at the time of harvest.

By comparing the gas chromatograph chemistry profile of a lavender essential oil with the AFNOR standard, one may also distinguish true lavender from various species of lavandin (hybrid lavender). Usually lavandin has high camphor levels, almost no lavandulol, and is easily identified. However, Tasmania produces a lavandin that yields an essential oil with naturally low camphor levels that mimics the chemistry of true lavender. Only by analyzing the chemical fingerprint of this Tasmanian lavandin using high resolution gas chromatography and comparing it with the AFNOR standard for genuine lavender can this hybrid lavender be identified.

Currently, there is no government agency responsible for certifying the quality of essential oils. The only recognized indication for quality in an essential oil is if it meets AFNOR or ISO standards. **The therapeutic effects discussed in this book can only be achieved using essential oils which meet the AFNOR standards.**

In the United States, few companies use the proper analytical equipment and methods to properly analyze essential oils. Most labs use equipment best-suited for synthetic chemicals—not for natural essential oil analysis. Young Living Essential Oils uses the proper equipment and has made serious efforts to adopt the European testing standards, widely regarded as the "gold standard" for testing essential oils. In addition to operating its analytical equipment on the same standard as the European laboratories, Young Living is continually expanding its analytical chemical library in order to perform more thorough chemical analysis.

Properly analyzing an essential oil by gas chromatography is a complex undertaking. The injection mixture, column diameter and length, and oven temperature must fall within certain parameters. Unless someone has gone to France and Turkey as Gary Young has and been trained in the analytical procedures of a gas chromatograph, they will not understand how to accurately test essential oils.

The column length should be at least 50 or 60 meters. However, almost all labs in the United States use a 30-meter column that is not long enough to achieve proper separation of all the essential oil constituents. While 30-meter columns are adequate for analyzing synthetic chemicals and marker compounds in vitamins, minerals, and herbal extracts, they are far too short to properly analyze the complex mosaic of natural chemicals found in an essential oil.

A longer column also enables double-phased ramping, which makes it possible to identify constituents that occur in very small percentages by increasing the separation of compounds. Without a longer column, it would be extremely difficult to identify these molecules, especially if they are chemically similar to each other or a marker compound.

While gas chromatography (GC) is an excellent tool for dissecting the anatomy of an essential oil, it does have limitations. Dr. Brian Lawrence, one of the foremost experts on essential oil chemistry, has commented that sometimes it can be difficult to distinguish between natural and synthetic compounds using GC analysis. If synthetic linalyl acetate is added to pure lavender, a GC analysis cannot really tell whether that compound is synthetic or natural, only that it is linalyl acetate. Adding a chiral column can help, however, in distinguishing between synthetic and natural oils. This addition allows the chemist to identify structural varieties of the same compound.

This is why oils must be analyzed by a chemist specially trained on the interpretation of a gas chromatograph chart. The chemist examines the entire chemical fingerprint of the oil to determine its purity and potency, measuring how various compounds in the oil occur in relation to each other. If some chemicals occur in higher quantities than others, these provide important clues to determine if the oil is adulterated or pure.

Adulteration is such a major concern that every batch of essential oil that comes into Young Living must be tested by highly trained independent European laboratories which utilize AFNOR standards. Batches that do not meet the standards are rejected and returned.

Adulteration of essential oils will become more and more common as the supply of top-quality essential oils dwindles and demand continues to increase. These adulterated essential oils will jeopardize the integrity of aromatherapy in the United States and may put many people at risk.

Adulterated Oils and Their Dangers

Today much of the lavender oil sold in America is the hybrid called lavandin, grown and distilled in China, Russia, France, and Tasmania. It is brought into France and cut with synthetic linalyl acetate to improve the fragrance. Then propylene glycol, DEP, or DOP (solvents that have no smell and increase the volume) are added and it is sold in the United States as lavender oil.

Often lavandin is heated to evaporate the camphor and then is adulterated with synthetic linalyl acetate. Most consumers don't know the difference, and are happy to buy it for $7 to $10 per half ounce in health food stores, beauty salons, grocery and department stores, and through mail order. This is one of the reasons why it is important to know about the integrity of the company or vendor from which you purchase your essential oils.

Frankincense is another example of a commonly adulterated oil. The frankincense resin that is sold in Somalia costs between $30,000 and $35,000 per ton. A great deal of time--12 hours or more--is required to properly steam-distill this essential oil from the resin, making the oil very expensive. Frankincense oil that sells for $25 per ounce or less is cheaply distilled with gum resins, alcohol, or other solvents, leaving the essential oil laden with harmful chemicals. Sadly, when these cut, synthetic, and adulterated oils cause rashes, burns, or other irritations, people wonder why they do not get the benefit they expected and conclude that essential oils do not have much value.

Some commercial statistics show that one large, U.S. corporation uses twice as much of a particular essential oil as is naturally grown and produced in the entire world! Where are these "phantom" essential oils coming from?

In France, production of true lavender oil (Lavandula angustifolia) dropped from 87 tons in 1967 to only 12 tons in 1998. During this same period the worldwide demand for lavender oil grew over 100 percent. So where did essential oil marketers obtain enough lavender to meet the demand? They probably used a combination of synthetic and adulterated oils. There are huge chemical companies on the east coast of the U.S. that specialize in creating synthetic chemicals that mimic every common essential oil. For every kilogram of pure essential oil that is produced, it is estimated there are between 10 and 100 kilograms of synthetic oil created.

Adulterated and mislabeled essential oils present dangers for consumers. One woman who had heard of the ability of lavender oil to heal burns used "lavender oil" purchased from a local health food store when she spilled boiling water on her arm. But the pain intensified and the burn worsened, so she later complained that lavender oil was worthless for healing burns. When her "lavender" oil was analyzed, it was found to be lavandin, the hybrid lavender that is chemically very different from pure Lavandula angustifolia. Lavandin contains high levels of camphor (12-18 percent) and can itself burn the skin. In contrast, true lavender contains virtually no camphor and has burn-healing agents not found in lavandin.

Adulterated oils that are cut with synthetic extenders can be very detrimental, causing rashes, burning, and skin irritations. Petrochemical solvents, such dipropylene glycol and diethylphthalate, can all cause allergic reactions, besides being devoid of any therapeutic effects.

Some people assume that because an essential oil is "100 percent pure," it will not burn their skin. This is not true. Some pure essential oils may cause skin irritation if applied undiluted. If you apply straight oregano oil to the skin of some people, it may cause severe reddening. Citrus and spice oils, like orange and cinnamon, may also produce rashes. Even the terpenes in conifer oils, like pine, may cause skin irritation on sensitive people.

Some writers have claimed that a few compounds, when isolated from the essential oil and tested in the lab, can exert toxic effects. Even so-called "nature-identical" essential oils (structured essential oils that have been chemically duplicated using 5 to 15 of the essential oil's primary chemical compounds in synthetic form) can produce unwanted side effects or toxicities. Isolated compounds may be toxic; however pure essential oils, in most cases, are not. This is because natural essential oils contain hundreds of different compounds, some of which balance and counteract each other's effects.

Many tourists in Egypt are eager to buy local essential oils, especially lotus oil. Vendors convince the tourists that the oils are 100 percent pure, going so far as to touch a lighted match to the neck of the oil container to show that the oil is not diluted with alcohol or other petrochemical solvents. However, this test provides no reliable indicator of purity. Many synthetic compounds can be added to an

essential oil that are not flammable, including propylene glycol. Or, flammable solvents can be added to a vegetable oil base that will cause it to catch fire. Some natural essential oils high in terpenes can be flammable.

Fact or Fiction: Myths and Misinformation

Much of the published information available on essential oils should be regarded with caution. Many aromatherapy books are merely compilations of two or three other books. The content is similar, only phrased and worded differently. Because the information has been copied from sources that have never been documented, the same misinformation repeatedly surfaces.

Many aromatherapy books claim that essential oils, such as clary sage, fennel, sage, and bergamot, can trigger an abortion. Several years ago, a rumor circulated about a laboratory research project in which the uterus of a rat was turned inside out and a cold drop of clary sage oil was applied to the exposed uterine wall. When this caused a contraction of the muscle, clary sage was labeled as abortion-causing. One must ask, what would have happened if cold water had been dropped on the exposed uterus? The uterine wall would likely have contracted in response. Following this reasoning, water could be labeled as abortion-causing as well.

The truth is that to our knowledge, there has never been a single documented case that clary sage, lemon, sage, or bergamot essential oils have caused an abortion. Sclareol, a compound in clary sage, is not an estrogen, although it can mimic estrogen if there is an estrogen deficiency. If there is not an estrogen deficiency, sclareol will not create more estrogen in the body. As a rule, essential oils bring balance to the human body.

The belief that pure essential oils will not leave a stain when poured on a tissue is also unfounded. Any essential oil high in waxes will leave stains. Oils like frankincense, cedarwood, clove, ylang ylang, blue cypress, or German chamomile may also leave a noticeable residue. However, an essential oil spiked with synthetic diluents or solvent may or may not leave a stain.

The Powerful Influence of Aromas on Both Mind and Body

The fragrance of an essential oil can directly affect everything from your emotional state to your lifespan.

When a fragrance is inhaled, the odor molecules travel up the nose where they are trapped by olfactory membranes that are well protected by the lining inside the nose. Each odor molecule fits like a little puzzle piece into specific receptor cell sites that line a membrane known as the olfactory epithelium. Each one of these hundreds of millions of nerve cells is replaced every 28 days. When stimulated by odor molecules, this lining of nerve cells triggers electrical impulses to the olfactory bulb in the brain. The olfactory bulb then transmits the impulses to the gustatory center (where the sensation of taste is perceived), the amygdala (where emotional memories are stored), and other parts of the limbic system of the brain. Because the limbic system is directly connected to those parts of the brain that control heart rate, blood pressure, breathing, memory, stress levels, and hormone balance, essential oils can have profound physiological and psychological effects.

The sense of smell is the only one of the five senses directly linked to the limbic lobe of the brain, the emotional control center. Anxiety, depression, fear, anger, and joy all emanate from this region. The scent of a special fragrance can evoke memories and emotions before we are even consciously aware of it. When smells are concerned, we react first and think later. All other senses (touch, taste, hearing, and sight) are routed through the thalamus, which acts as the switchboard for the brain, passing stimuli onto the cerebral cortex (the conscious thought center) and other parts of the brain.

The limbic lobe (a group of brain structures that includes the hippocampus and amygdala located below the cerebral cortex) can also directly activate the hypothalamus. The hypothalamus is one of the most important parts of the brain, acting as our hormonal control center. It releases chemical messengers that can affect everything from sex drive to energy levels. The production of growth hormones, sex hormones, thyroid hormones, and neurotransmitters such as serotonin, are all governed by the hypothalamus. Thus, the hypothalamus is referred to as the "master gland."

Essential oils—through their fragrance and unique molecular structure—can directly stimulate the limbic lobe and the hypothalamus. Not only can the inhalation of essential oils be used to combat stress and emotional trauma, but it can also stimulate the production of hormones from the hypothalamus. This results in increased thyroid hormones (our energy hormone) and growth hormones (our youth and longevity hormone).

Essential oils may also be used to reduce appetite and produce significant reductions in weight because of their ability to stimulate the ventro-medial nucleus of the hypothalamus, a section of the brain that governs our feeling of satiety or fullness following meals. In a large clinical study,[1] Alan Hirsch, MD, used fragrances, including peppermint, to trigger significant weight losses in a large group of patients who had previously been unsuccessful in any type of weight-management program. During the course of the six-month study involving over 3,000 people, the average weight loss exceeded 30 pounds. According to Dr. Hirsch, some patients actually had to be dropped from the study to avoid becoming underweight.

Another double-blind, randomized study by Hirsch[2] documents the ability of aroma to enhance libido and sexual arousal. When 31 male volunteers were subjected to the aromas of 30 different essential oils, each one exhibited a marked increase in arousal, based on measurements of brachial penile index and the measurement of both penile and brachial blood pressures. Among the scents that produced the most sexual excitement, was a combination of lavender and pumpkin fragrances. This study shows that fragrances enhance sexual desire by stimulating the amygdala, the emotional center of the brain.

In 1989, Dr. Joseph Ledoux at New York Medical University discovered that the amygdala plays a major role in storing and releasing emotional trauma.[3] From the studies of Dr. Hirsch and Dr. Ledoux the conclusion can be drawn that aromas may exert a profound effect in triggering a response from this almond-shaped neuro-structure.

---

1. Hirsch, AR, Inhalation of Odorants for Weight Reduction, Int J Obes, 1994, page 306

2. Alan R. Hirsch, MD, FACP, Dr. Hirsch's Guide to Scentsational Sex, Harper Collins, 1998 1993 Dec. 20;58(1-2):69-79

3. LeDoux, JE, Rationalizing Thoughtless Emotions, Insight, Sept. 1989

In studies conducted at Vienna and Berlin Universities, researchers found that sesquiterpenes, found in essential oils such as vetiver, patchouli, cedarwood, sandalwood and frankincense, can increase levels of oxygen in the brain by up to 28 percent (Nasel, 1992). Such an increase in brain oxygen may lead to a heightened level of activity in the hypothalamus and limbic systems of the brain, which can have dramatic effects on not only emotions, learning, and attitude, but also many physical processes of the body, such as immune function, hormone balance, and energy levels. High levels of sesquiterpenes also occur in melissa, myrrh, cedarwood, and clove oil.

People who have undergone nose surgery or suffer olfactory impairment may find it difficult or impossible to detect a complete odor. The same is true of people who use makeup, perfume, cologne, hair sprays, hair coloring, perms, or other products containing synthetic odors. These people may not derive the full physiological and emotional benefits of essential oils and their fragrances.

Proper stimulation of the olfactory nerves may offer a powerful and entirely new form of therapy that could be used as an adjunct against many forms of illness. Essential oils, through inhalation, may occupy a key position in this relatively unexplored frontier in medicine.

Chemical Sensitivities and Allergies

Occasionally, individuals beginning to use quality essential oils will suffer rashes or allergic reactions. This may be due to using an undiluted spice, conifer, or citrus oil, or it may be caused by an interaction of the oil with residues of synthetic, petroleum-based personal care products that have leached into the skin.

When using essential oils on a daily basis, it is imperative to avoid personal care products containing ammonium or hydrocarbon-based chemicals. These include quaternary compounds such as quaternariums and polyquaterniums. These compounds are commonly found in a variety of hand creams, mouthwashes, shampoos, antiperspirants, after-shave lotions, and hair-care products. In small concentrations they can be toxic and present the possibility of reacting with essential oils and producing chemical byproducts of unknown toxicity.

These chemicals can be fatal if ingested, especially benzalkonium chloride, which unfortunately is used in many personal care products on the market.

Other compounds that present concerns are sodium lauryl sulfate, propylene glycol—extremely common in everything from toothpaste to shampoo—and aluminum salts found in many deodorants.

Of particular concern are the potentially hazardous preservatives and synthetic fragrances that abound in virtually all modern personal-care products. Some of these include methylene chloride, methyl isobutyl ketone, and methyl ethyl ketone. These are not only toxic, but they can also react with some compounds in natural essential oils. The result can be a severe case of dermatitis or even septicemia (blood poisoning).

A classic case of a synthetic fragrance causing widespread damage occurred in the 1970s. AETT (acetylethyltetramethyltetralin) appeared in numerous brands of personal care products throughout the United States. Even after a series of animal studies revealed that it caused significant brain and spinal cord damage, the FDA refused to ban the chemical. Finally, the cosmetic industry voluntarily withdrew AFTT after allowing it to be distributed for years. How many other toxins masquerading as preservatives or fragrances are currently being used in personal care products?

Many chemicals are easily absorbed through the skin due to its permeability. One study found that 13 percent of BHT (butylated hydroxytoluene) and 49 percent of DDT (a carcinogenic pesticide) can be absorbed into the skin upon topical contact (Steinman, 1997). Once absorbed, they can become trapped in the fatty subdermal layers of skin where they can leach into the blood stream. These chemicals can remain trapped in fatty tissues underneath the skin for several months or years, where they harbor the potential of reacting with essential oils that may be topically applied later. The user may mistakenly assume that the threat of an interaction between oils and synthetic cosmetics used months before is small. However, a case of dermatitis is a possibility.

14

CHAPTER 3

The Chemistry of Essential Oils

Unlike synthetic chemicals, essential oil chemicals are diverse in their effects. No two oils are alike. Some constituents, such as aldehydes found in lavender and chamomile, are antimicrobial and calming. Eugenol, found in cinnamon and clove, is antiseptic and stimulating. Ketones, found in lavender, hyssop, and patchouli, stimulate cell regeneration and liquefy mucous. Phenols, found in oregano and thyme oil, are highly antimicrobial. Sesquiterpenes, predominant in vetiver, cedarwood, and sandalwood, are soothing to inflamed tissue and can also produce profound effects on emotions and hormonal balance.

The complex chemistry of essential oils makes them ideal for killing and preventing the spread of bacteria, since microorganisms have a difficult time mutating in the presence of so many different antiseptic compounds. At the March 2000 International Symposium in Grasse, France, Dr. Bérangere Arnal-Schnebelen presented a paper showing the antibacterial properties of essential oils against several infectious agents. Spanish oregano and cinnamon essential oils tested at above 95 percent efficiency against Candida albicans, E. coli, and a Streptococcus strain. This is significant as we face life-threatening, drug-resistant viruses and bacteria.

Key Chemical Constituents in Essential Oils and Their Effects

Constituent	Representative Oil	Effect
Ketones	Sage	mucolytic
Aldehydes	Lemongrass	calming
Esters	Lavender	balancing
Ethers	Tarragon	balancing
Alcohols	Ravensara	toning
Phenols	Savory	stimulant
Terpenes	Pine	stimulant

The essential oils of ravensara, melissa, oregano, mountain savory, clove, cumin, cistus, hyssop, and frankincense are highly antibacterial and contain immune supportive properties that have been documented by many researchers, such as Daniel Pénoël, MD and Pierre Franchomme. These oils are found in varying amounts in the immune support and antimicrobial essential blends presented later in this book (see Chapter 7).

UNDERSTANDING ESSENTIAL OIL CHEMISTRY

Basic Chemical Structure

The aromatic constituents of essential oils (i.e. terpenes, monoterpenes, phenols, aldehydes, etc.) are constructed from long chains of carbon and hydrogen atoms, which have a predominantly ring-like chemical structure. Links of carbon atoms form the backbone of these chains, with oxygen, hydrogen, nitrogen, sulfur, and other carbon atoms attached at various points of the chain.

Essential oils are chemically different from fatty oils (also known as fatty acids). In contrast to the simple linear carbon-hydrogen structure of fatty oils, essential oils have a far more complex ring structure and contain sulfur and nitrogen atoms that fatty oils do not have.

The terpenoids found in many essential oils are actually constructed out of the same basic building block—a five-carbon molecule known as isoprene.

When two isoprene units link together, they create a monoterpene; when three join, they create a sesquiterpene; and so on. Some of the largest molecules found in essential oils are triterpenoids, which consist of 30 carbon atoms or six isoprene

Vegetable Oil
Long Chain Carbon Structure
LAURIC ACID

The methyl end of the molecule

The acid end of the molecule

Eugenol—An aromatic molecule found in several essential oils including clove. Clove oil has been used as an antiseptic for many years.

units linked together. Carotenoids, which consist of 40 carbons or eight isoprene units, only occur in essential oils in tiny quantities because they are too heavy to be extracted via steam distillation.

Different molecules in an essential oil can exert different effects. For example, German chamomile (Matricaria recutita) contains azulene, a dark blue compound that has powerful anti-inflammatory compounds. German chamomile also contains bisobolol, a compound studied for its sedative and mood-balancing properties. There are other compounds in German chamomile that perform different functions, such as speeding up the regeneration process of tissue.

Chemotypes

A single species of plant can have several different chemotypes based on chemical composition. This means that basil (Ocimum basilicum) grown in one area might produce an essential oil with a completely different chemistry than a basil grown in another location. The plant's growing environment, such as soil pH and mineral content, can dramatically affect the plant's ultimate chemistry as well. Different chemotypes of basil are listed below:

Ocimum basilicum CT linalol fenchol
(Germany)
— antiseptic

Ocimum basilicum CT methyl chavicol
(Reunion, Comoro, or Egypt)
— anti-inflammatory

Ocimum basilicum CT eugenol (Madagascar)
— anti-inflammatory, pain-relieving

Another species of plant that occurs in a variety of different chemotypes is rosemary (Rosmarinus officinalis).

Rosmarinus officinalis CT camphor is obviously high in camphor. Camphor serves best as a general stimulant and works synergistically with other oils, such as pepper (Piper nigrum), and can be a powerful energy stimulant.

Rosmarinus officinalis CT cineol is rich in 1,8 cineol, which is used in other countries for pulmonary congestion and to help with the elimination of toxins from the liver and kidneys.

Rosmarinus officinalis CT verbenon is high in verbenon and is the most gentle of the rosemary chemotypes. It offers powerful regenerative properties and has outstanding benefits for skin care.

Thyme (Thymus vulgaris) also has several different chemotypes. Some of these are:

Thymus vulgaris CT thymol is germicidal and anti-inflammatory.

Thymus vulgaris CT linalool is anti-infectious.

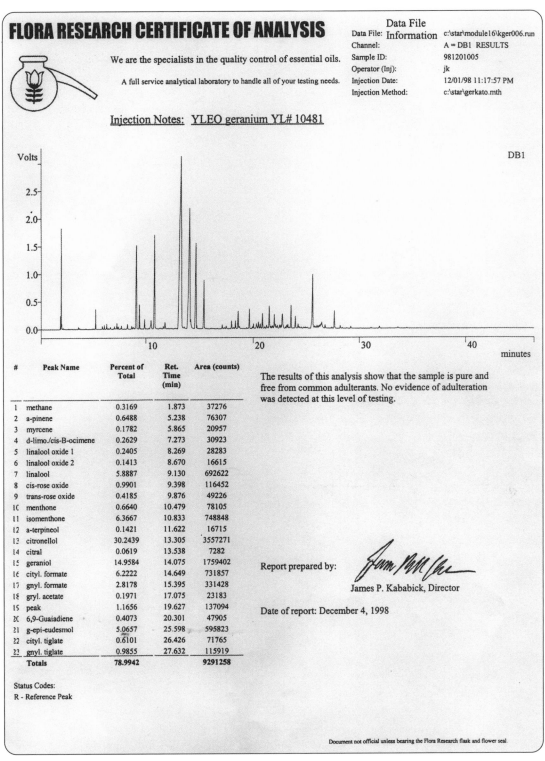

Sample of a gas chromatograph chemical profile.

CHAPTER 4

How to Safely Use Essential Oils

There are important guidelines to follow when using essential oils, especially if you are unfamiliar with the oils and their benefits. Many guidelines are listed below and are elaborated further throughout the chapter. However, no list of do's and don'ts can ever replace common sense. It is foolish to dive headlong into a pond when you don't know the depth of the water. The same is true when using essential oils. Start gradually, and patiently find what works best for you and your family members.

Basic Guidelines for Safe Use

Storage

1. Always keep a bottle of a pure vegetable oil (e.g., olive, almond, etc.) handy when using essential oils. Vegetable oils dilute essential oils if the essential oil(s) cause discomfort or skin irritation.

2. Keep bottles of essential oils tightly closed and store them in a cool location away from light. If stored properly, essential oils will maintain their potency for many years.

3. Keep essential oils out of reach of children. Treat them as you would any product for therapeutic use.

Usage

4. Essential oils rich in menthol (such as peppermint) should not be used on the throat or neck area of children under 18 months of age.

5. Angelica, bergamot, grapefruit, lemon, orange, tangerine, and other citrus oils are photosensitive and may cause a rash or dark pigmentation on skin exposed to direct sunlight or UV rays within 1–2 days after application.

6. Keep essential oils well away from the eye area and never put them directly into ears. Do not handle contact lenses or rub eyes with essential oils on your fingers. Even in minute amounts, many essential oils may damage contacts and will irritate eyes.

7. Pregnant women should always consult a health care professional when starting any type of health program. Avoid sage, fennel, and hyssop.

8. Epileptics and those with high blood pressure should consult their health care professional before using essential oils. Use extra caution with high ketone oils such as basil, rosemary, sage and tansy oils.

9. People with allergies should test a small amount of oil on an area of sensitive skin, such as the inside of the upper arm, for 30 minutes, before applying the oil on other areas of the body.

10. The bottom of the feet is one of the safest locations to apply essential oils topically.

11. Direct inhalation of essential oils (see page 25 on Direct Inhalation) can be a deep and intensive application method, particularly for respiratory congestion and illness. However, this method should not be used more than 10–15 times through the day without consulting a health professional. Also, inhalation of essential oils is NOT recommended for those with asthma conditions.

12. Before taking GRAS (Generally Regarded As Safe, listed in Appendix C) essential oils internally, test your reactions by diluting one drop of essential oil in one teaspoon of an oil-soluble liquid like blue agave, olive oil, or rice milk. If you intend to consume more than a few drops of diluted essential oil per day, we recommend first consulting a health professional.

13. Be aware that reactions to essential oils, both topically and orally, can be delayed as long as 2–3 days.

14. Never add more than 1–3 drops of undiluted essential oils directly to bath water. If more essential oil is desired, mix the oil first into bath salts or a bath gel base before adding to the bath water. Generally, never use more than 10 drops of essential oils in one bath.

   When essential oils are put directly into bath water without a dispersing agent, they can cause serious discomfort on sensitive skin because the essential oils tend to float, undiluted, on top of the water.

15. Keep essential oils away from open flames, sparks, or electricity. Some essential oils, including orange, fir, pine, and peppermint are potentially flammable (See Appendix G).

Before You Start

Always skin test an essential oil before using it. Each person's body is different, so apply oils to a small area first. Apply one oil or blend at a time. When layering oils that are new to you, allow enough time (3-5 minutes) for the body to respond before applying a second oil.

Exercise caution when applying essential oils to skin that has been exposed to cosmetics, personal care products, soaps, and cleansers containing synthetic chemicals. Some of them—especially petroleum-based chemicals—can penetrate and remain in the skin and fatty tissues for days or even weeks after use. Essential oils may react with such chemicals and cause skin irritation, nausea, headaches, or other uncomfortable effects.

Essential oils can also react with toxins built up in the body from chemicals in food, water, and work environment. If you experience a reaction to

CAUTION: Essential oils may sting if applied in or around the eyes. Some oils may be painful on mucous membranes unless diluted properly. Immediate dilution is strongly recommended if skin becomes painfully irritated or if oil accidentally gets into eyes. Flushing the area with a vegetable oil should minimize discomfort almost immediately. DO NOT flush with water! Essential oils are oil-soluble, not water-soluble. Water will only spread the oils over a larger surface, possibly worsening the problem.

essential oils, it may be wise to temporarily discontinue their use and start an internal cleansing program before resuming regular use of essential oils. In addition, double your water intake while using essential oils.

You may also want to try the following alternatives to a detoxification program to determine the cause of the problem:

- Dilute 1–3 drops of essential oil to 1/2 tsp. of massage oil, vegetable mixing oil, or any pure vegetable oil, such as almond or olive. More dilution may be needed, as necessary.

- Reduce the number of oils used at any time.

- Use single oils or oil blends, one at a time.

- Reduce the amount of oil used.

- Reduce the frequency of application.

- Drink more purified or distilled water.

- Ask your health care professional to monitor detoxification.

- Skin-test the diluted essential oil on a small patch of skin for 30 minutes. If any redness or irritation results, dilute the area immediately with a pure vegetable or massage oil. Then cleanse with soap and water.

- If skin irritation or other uncomfortable side effects persist, discontinue using the oil on that location and apply the oils on the bottoms of the feet.

You may also want to avoid using products that contain the following ingredients to eliminate potential problems:

- Cosmetics, deodorants, and skin care products containing aluminum, petrochemicals, or other synthetic ingredients.

- Perms, hair colors or dyes, and hair sprays or gels containing synthetic chemicals. Avoid shampoos, toothpaste, mouthwash, and soaps containing synthetic chemicals such as sodium laurel sulfate, propylene glycol, or lead acetate.

- Garden sprays, paints, detergents, and cleansers containing toxic chemicals and solvents.

You can use many essential oils anywhere on the body except on the eyes and in the ears. Other oils may irritate certain sensitive tissues. See recommended dilution rates in Appendix E.

Keep all essential oils out of reach of children and only apply to children under skilled supervision. If a child or infant swallows an essential oil:

- Administer a mixture of milk, cream, yogurt, or another safe, oil-soluble liquid.

- Call a Poison Control Center or seek immediate emergency medical attention if necessary.

NOTE: If your body pH is low (meaning that your system is very acidic), you also could have a negative reaction to the oils.

TOPICAL APPLICATION

Many oils are safe to apply directly to the skin. Lavender is safe to use on children without dilution. However, you must be sure what you are using is not lavandin labeled as lavender or genetically-altered lavender. When applying most other essential oils on children, dilute them with a carrier oil. For dilution, add 15–30 drops of essential oil to 1 oz. of a quality carrier oil as mentioned previously.

Carrier oils, such as a vegetable mixing oil, extend essential oils and provide more efficient use. When massaging, the vegetable oil helps lubricate the skin. Some excellent carrier oils include cold-pressed grapeseed, olive, wheat germ, and sweet almond oils, or a blend of any of these.

When starting an essential oil application, always apply the oil first to the bottom of the feet. This allows the body to become acclimated to the oil, minimizing the chance of a reaction. The Vita Flex foot charts (see Chapter 20) identify areas for best application. Start by applying 3–6 drops of a single or blended oil, spreading it over the bottom of each foot.

When applying essential oils to yourself, use 1–2 drops of oil on 2–3 locations twice a day. Increase to four times a day if needed. Apply the oil and allow it to absorb for 2–3 minutes before applying another oil or getting dressed (to avoid staining clothing).

As a general rule, when applying oils to yourself or another person for the first time, do not apply more than two single oils or blends at one time.

Massage

When mixing essential oil blends or diluting essential oils in a carrier oil, it is best to use containers made of glass or earthenware, rather than plastic. Plastic particles can leach into the oil and then into the skin once it is applied.

Before applying oils, wash hands thoroughly with soap and water.

Massage

Start by applying 2 drops of a single oil or blend on the skin and massaging it in. If you are working on a large area, such as the back, mix 1–3 drops of the selected essential oil into 1 tsp. of pure carrier oil (such as Enhanced V-6 Vegetable Oil Complex or a massage oil base (jojoba, almond, olive and/or grape seed)).

Keep in mind that many massage oils such as olive, almond, jojoba, or wheat germ oil may stain some fabrics.

Acupuncture

Licensed acupuncturists can dramatically increase the effectiveness of acupuncture by using essential oils. To start, place several drops of essential oil into the palm of your hand. Dip the acupuncture needle tip into the oil before inserting it. You can pre-mix several oils in your hand if you wish to use more than one oil.

> **Toothpick Application:**
> Dip end of wooden toothpick into oil and apply to mixtures when one drop of oil is too much.

Acupuncture

Acupressure

Acupressure

When performing acupressure treatment, apply 1–3 drops of essential oil to the acupressure point with finger. Using an auricular probe with a slender point to dispense oil can enhance the application. Start by pressing firmly and then releasing. Avoid applying pressure to any particular pressure point too long. You may continue along the acupressure points and meridians or use the reflexology or Vita Flex points as well. Once you have completed small point stimulations, massage the general area with the essential oil.

Warm Packs

For deeper penetration of an essential oil, use warm packs after applying oils. Dip a cloth in comfortably warm water. Wring the cloth out and place it on the location. Then cover the cloth loosely with a dry towel or blanket to seal in the heat. Allow the cloth to stand for 15–30 minutes. Remove the cloth immediately if there is any discomfort.

Cold Packs

Apply essential oils on the location, followed by cold water or ice packs when treating inflamed or swollen tissues. Frozen packages of peas or corn make excellent ice packs that will mold to the contours of the body part and will not leak. Keep the cold pack on until the swelling diminishes. For neurological problems, always use cold packs, never hot ones.

Layering

This technique consists of applying multiple oils one at a time. For example, place marjoram over a sore muscle, massage it into the tissue gently until the area is dry, and then apply a second oil, such as peppermint, until the oil is absorbed and the skin is dry. Then layer on the third oil, such as basil, and continue massaging.

Creating a Compress

- Rub 1–3 drops on the location, diluted or neat, depending on the oil used and the skin sensitivity at that location.

- Cover the location with a hot, damp towel.

- Cover the moist towel with a dry towel for 10–30 minutes, depending on individual need.

As the oil penetrates the skin, you may experience a warming or even a burning sensation, especially in areas where the greatest benefits occur. If burning becomes uncomfortable, apply a massage oil, vegetable mixing oil, or any pure vegetable oil such as olive or almond, to the location.

A second type of application is very mild and is suitable for children, or those with sensitive skin.

- Place 5-15 drops of essential oil into a basin filled with warm water.

- Water temperature should be approximately 100°F. (38°C.), unless the patient suffers neurological conditions; in this case, use cool water.

Applying a compress

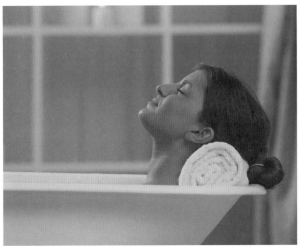

Bath

- Vigorously agitate the water and let it stand for 1 minute.

- Place a dry face cloth on top of the water to soak up oils that have floated to the surface.

- Wring out the water and apply the cloth on the location. To seal in the warmth, cover the location with a thick towel for 15–30 minutes.

Bath

Adding essential oils to bath water is challenging because oil does not mix with water. For even dispersion, mix 5–10 drops of essential oil in 1/4 cup of Epsom salts or bath gel base and then add this mixture under a running faucet. This method will help the oils disperse in the bath evenly and prevent stronger oils from stinging sensitive areas.

You can also use premixed bath gels and shampoos containing essential oils as a liquid soap in the shower or bath. Lather down with the bath gel, let it soak in, and then rinse. To maximize benefits, leave the soap or shampoo on the skin or scalp for several minutes to allow the essential oils to penetrate. You can create your own aromatic bath gels by placing 5–15 drops of essential oil in 1/2 oz. of an unscented bath gel base and then add to the bath water as described above.

Shower

Essential oils can be added to Epsom salts and used in the shower. There are special shower heads containing an attached receptacle that is filled with the essential oil/salts mixture. This allows essential oils to not only make contact with the skin, but also diffuses the fragrance of the oils into the air. The shower head receptacle can hold approximately 1/4 to 1/2 cup of bath salts.

Start by adding 5–10 drops of essential oil to 1/4 cup of bath salt. Fill the shower head receptacle with the oil/salt mixture. Make sure neither oils nor salts come in contact with the plastic seal on top of the receptacle. This should provide enough salt material for about 2–3 showers. Some shower heads have a bypass feature that allows the user to switch from aromatic salt water to regular tap water.

How to Enhance the Benefits of Topical Application

The longer essential oils stay in contact with the skin, the more likely they are to be absorbed. A high-quality lotion may be layered on top of the essential oils to reduce evaporation of the oils and enhance penetration. This may also help seal and protect cuts and wounds. Do not use ointments on burns until they are at least three days old.

DIFFUSING

Diffused oils alter the structure of molecules that create odors, rather than just masking them. They also increase oxygen availability, produce negative ions, and release natural ozone. Many essential oils such as lemongrass, orange, grapefruit, *Eucalyptus globulus*, tea tree, lavender, frankincense, and lemon, along with essential oil blends (Purification and Thieves), are extremely effective for eliminating and destroying airborne germs and bacteria.

A cold-air diffuser is designed to atomize a microfine mist of essential oils into the air, where they can remain suspended for several hours. Unlike aroma lamps or candles, a diffuser disperses essential oils without heating or burning, which can render the oil therapeutically less beneficial and even create toxic compounds. Burned oils may become carcinogenic. Research shows that cold air diffusing certain oils may:

- Reduce bacteria, fungus, mold, and unpleasant odors.

- Relax the body, relieve tension, and clear the mind.

- Help with weight management.

- Improve concentration, alertness, and mental clarity.

- Stimulate neurotransmitters.

- Stimulate secretion of endorphins.

- Stimulate growth hormone production and receptivity.

- Improve the secretion of IgA antibodies that fight candida.

- Improve digestive function.

- Improve hormonal balance.

- Relieve headaches.

Start by diffusing oils for 15–30 minutes a day. As you become accustomed to the oils and recognize their effects, you may increase the diffusing time to 1–2 hours per day.

Place the diffuser high in the room so that the oil mist falls through the air and removes the odor-causing substances.

By connecting your diffuser to a timer, you can gain better control over the length and duration of diffusing. For some respiratory conditions, you may diffuse the oils the entire night.

Cold-air diffuser

Do not use more than one blend at a time in a diffuser as this may alter the smell and the therapeutic benefit. However, a single oil may be added to a blend when diffusing.

Always wash the diffuser before using a different oil blend. Use alcohol, natural soap and warm water.

If you don't have a diffuser, you may add several drops of essential oil to a spray bottle, add 1 cup purified water, and shake. You can use this to mist your entire house, workplace, or car.

To freshen the air, use the following essential oil blend:

- 20 drops lavender
- 10 drops lemon
- 6 drops bergamot
- 5 drops lime
- 5 drops grapefruit

Diffuse neat, or mix with 1 cup of distilled water in a spray bottle; shake well before spraying.

Other Ways to Diffuse Oils

- Add essential oils to cedar chips to make your own potpourri.

- Put scented cedar chips in closets or drawers to deodorize them.

- Place any conifer essential oil such as spruce, fir (all varieties), cedar, or pine onto each log in the fireplace. As they burn, they will disperse an evergreen smell. This method has no therapeutic benefit, however.

- Put essential oil on cotton balls and place in your car or home air vents.

- Place a bowl of water with a few drops of oil on a wood stove.

- Dampen a cloth, apply essential oils to it, and place it near the intake duct of your heating and cooling system.

Humidifier and Vaporizer

Essential oils such as peppermint, lemon, Eucalyptus radiata, Melaleuca alternifolia, and frankincense make ideal additions to humidifiers or vaporizers.

NOTE: Test the oil in the vaporizer or humidifier first, some essential oils may damge the plastic parts of vaporizers.

Direct inhlation

OTHER USES

Direct Inhalation

- Place 2 or more drops into the palm of your left hand, and rub clockwise with the flat palm of your right hand. Cup your hands together over the nose and mouth and inhale deeply. (Do not touch your eyes!)

- Add several drops of an essential oil to a bowl of hot (not boiling) water. Inhale the steaming vapors that rise from the bowl. To increase the intensity of the oil vapors inhaled, drape a towel over your head and bowl before inhaling.

- Apply oils to a cotton ball, tissue, or handkerchief (do not use synthetic fibers or fabric) and place it in the air vent of your car.

- Inhale directly.

Indirect or Subtle Inhalation
(wearing as a perfume or cologne)

- Rub 2 or more drops of oil on your chest, neck, upper sternum, wrists, or under the nose and ears. Breathe in the fragrance throughout the day.

Vaginal Retention

For systemic health problems such as candida or vaginitis, vaginal retention is one of the best ways for the body to absorb essential oils.

- Mix 20–30 drops of essential oil in 2 tablespoons of carrier oil.

- Apply this mixture to a tampon (for internal infection) or sanitary pad (for external lesions). Insert and retain for 8 hours or overnight. Use tampons or sanitary pads made with organic cotton.

Rectal Retention

Retention enemas are the most efficient way to deliver essential oils to the urinary tract and reproductive organs. Always use a sterile syringe.

- Mix 15–20 drops of essential oil in a tablespoon of carrier oil.

- Place the mixture in a small syringe and inject into the rectum.

- Retain the mixture through the night (or longer for best results).

- Clean and disinfect the applicator after each use.

Water Distillers and Filters

You can apply oils like peppermint, lemon, clove, and cinnamon to the post-filter side of your water purifier. This will help purify the water.

Dishwashing Soap

To add fragrance or improve the antiseptic action of your liquid soap, add several drops of essential oils such as lavender, Melaleuca alternifolia, fir, spruce, pine, lemon, bergamot, and orange.

Cleaning and Disinfecting

A few drops of oil may be added to the dishwasher to help disinfect and purify. Some popular oils are pine, orange, tangerine, lemon, and peppermint, although any antibacterial oil would work well.

Painting

When painting, add 1 teaspoon of your favorite essential oil to one gallon of paint. Mix well. The oil will counteract the unpleasant smell of paint. Because essential oils are not fatty oils, they will not leave oil spots on the walls.

Laundry

Essential oils may be used to enhance the cleanliness and fragrance of your laundry. As unpleasant as it seems, dust mites live in your bedding, feeding from the dead skin cells you constantly shed. Recent research has shown that eucalyptus oil kills dust mites. To achieve effective dust mite control, add 25 drops of eucalyptus to each load, or approximately 1 tablespoon to a bottle of liquid laundry detergent.

You may also add several drops of essential oils to the rinse cycle, such as fir, spruce, juniper, lavender, cedarwood, wintergreen, or rosewood.

Instead of using toxic and irritating softening agents in the dryer, place a washcloth dampened with 10 drops of lavender, lemon, melaleuca, bergamot, or other essential oils. While the oils will not reduce static cling, they will impart a distinctive fragrance to the clothes.

Surface Cleansers: Counters, Furniture, etc.

Instead of purchasing standard household cleaners for surfaces, you can create your own natural, safe version by filling a plastic spray bottle with water and a squirt of dishwashing soap. Add 3 to 5 drops each of lavender, lemon, and pine essential oils. Shake the spray bottle well, and your homemade cleaner is ready to spray. This simple solution is extremely economical, yet it cleans and disinfects as well as any commercial cleaner.

Please keep in mind that some of the oils, if used directly, may stain some surfaces, such as linoleum.

Additional antibacterial and antiviral oils that are excellent for cleaning include cinnamon, clove, Eucalyptus globulus, thyme, juniper, Melaleuca alternifolia, spruce, lemongrass, and grapefruit.

Floors and Carpet

By combining essential oils with common household products, you can create your own nontoxic aromatic floor and carpet cleaners.

To clean non-carpeted floors, add 1/4 cup of white vinegar to a bucket of water. Then add 5–10 drops of lemon, pine, spruce, Melaleuca alternifolia, Thieves oil blend, or another suitable oil. If the floor is especially dirty, add several drops of dishwashing soap. This will clean even the dirtiest floor.

To make a carpet freshener, add 16–20 drops of essential oils to a cup of baking soda or borax powder. Mix well and place in a covered container overnight so that the oil can be absorbed. Sprinkle over your carpet the next day and then vacuum the powder up.

You may also saturate a disposable cloth or tissue with several drops of essential oil and place it into the collecting bag of your vacuum. This will diffuse a pleasant odor as you clean. If your vacuum collects dirt into water, simply add a few drops into the water reservoir before cleaning. This refreshes both the carpet and the room.

Insecticide and Repellent: Dust Mites, Fleas, Ticks, Ants, Spiders, etc.

Many of us use synthetic chemicals to deal with insects. Single oils such as lavender, lemon, peppermint, melaleuca, lemongrass, cypress, Eucalyptus globulus, cinnamon, thyme, basil, wintergreen, citronella, and the Purification and Thieves blends (see Chapter 30), effectively repel many types of insects including mites, lice, and fleas. Peppermint placed on entryways prevents ants from entering.

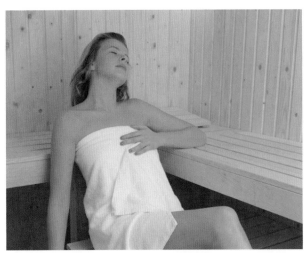

Hot tubs and saunas

If you need moth repellents for your linens and woolens, avoid toxic commercial mothballs made of naphthalene. Natural essential oils like citronella, lavender, lemongrass, Western red cedar, or rosemary can just as effectively repel moths and other insects. You can make a sachet by placing several drops of essential oil on a cotton ball. Wrap and tie this in a small handkerchief or square of cotton. Hang this cloth in storage areas or add it to your chest of linens. Refresh as often as necessary.

You can put this sachet in your bureau drawers to keep your clothes freshly scented. Lavender and rose are classic scents. For children's sleepwear, Roman chamomile is especially fragrant and relaxing. To scent stationery, stretch out an oil-scented cotton ball and place it in an envelope.

Hot Tubs and Saunas

Hot tubs, jacuzzis, and saunas act as reservoirs for germs, especially if used frequently. Lavender, cinnamon, clove, Eucalyptus globulus, thyme, lemon, or grapefruit can be used to disinfect and fragrance the water. Use 3 drops per person. For saunas, add several drops of rosemary, thyme, pine, or lavender to a spray bottle with water and then spray down the surfaces. Scented water can also be used to splash on hot sauna stones.

CAUTION: Some essential oils may damage plastic sauna/spa filters or hoses.

Deodorizing: Kitchens, Bathrooms, etc.

The kitchen and bathroom are often a source of odors and bacteria. Use the following mixtures to freshen, deodorize, and disinfect the air, work areas, cupboards, bathroom fixtures, sinks, tiles, woodwork, carpets, etc. These blends are safe for the family and the environment.

Since essential oils separate easily from water, always shake well and keep on shaking the bottle as you use these mixtures. They will deodorize and clean the air, instead of covering the odors.

Single oils:
Rosemary CT cineol with lemon, Eucalyptus globulus, and lavender

Blends:
Lavender with Purification

Recipe #1, Mix:
- 2 drops rosemary CT cineol
- 4 drops lemon
- 3 drops Eucalyptus globulus
- 4 drops lavender
- 1 cup water

Shake the mixture well and put it in a spray bottle.

Recipe #2, Mix:
- 3–4 drops lavender
- 5–6 drops Purification
- 1 cup water

Shake the mixture well and put it in a spray bottle.

Recipe #3, Mix:
- Pine with chamomile, Melaleuca alternifolia, lemongrass, or clove

Cooking

Many essential oils make excellent food flavorings. They are so concentrated that only 1–2 drops of an essential oil is equivalent to a full bottle (1–2 oz. size) of dried herbs.

As a general rule, spice oils impart a far stronger flavor than citrus oils do. For strong spice oils (such as oregano, nutmeg, cinnamon, marjoram, tarragon, wintergreen, thyme, or basil), you can dip a toothpick into the oils and stir food (after cooking) with the toothpick. This controls the amount of essential oil that is put into the food.

Cooking Tips:

- Ginger, cinnamon, clove, or nutmeg can be added to spice up gingersnap cookies. Use the toothpick application method.

- Lemon, orange, mandarin, or tangerine oil can be added to a regular sponge or bundt cake recipe.

- Peppermint or spearmint oil can be added to chocolate cake, brownie, or frosting recipes.

- Nutmeg, cinnamon, clove, or ginger oil can be used in pumpkin pie or spice cake recipes.

- Oregano, marjoram, thyme, or basil can be put in tomato sauces for spaghetti, pizza, ravioli, and lasagna recipes. Use the toothpick method of application.

- Lemon, clove, orange, tangerine, or peppermint oil can be added to enhance the flavor of puddings and fruit pies. Add 1-2 drops for 4–8 servings.

- Lavender, Roman chamomile, orange, tangerine, lemon, peppermint, wintergreen, or melissa can be used to make herbal teas. Mix 2 drops essential oil with 1 tsp. of blue agave nectar and stir into a cup of warm water.

- Lemon, orange, mandarin, tangerine, or peppermint can be mixed into a cool refreshing drink. Mix several drops of essential oil with 1 tsp. of blue agave nectar and add to a pitcher of cold water.

- Cinnamon, clove, lavender, basil, German or Roman chamomile, or lemon can be used to flavor blue agave nectar. Warm the blue agave until it becomes a thin liquid, then stir in your favorite oil.

Some oils that can be used as spices are: basil, cinnamon, clove, fennel, ginger, lemon, marjoram, nutmeg, oregano, peppermint, rosemary CT cineol, sage, spearmint, tarragon, coriander, grapefruit, mandarin, orange, wintergreen, black pepper, and thyme.

For recipes that serves 6–10 people, add 1–2 drops of an oil and stir in after cooking and just before serving, so the oil does not evaporate.

Internal and Oral Use as a Dietary Supplement

All essential oils that are Generally Regarded As Safe (GRAS) or certified as Food Additives (FA) by the FDA may be safely taken internally as dietary supplements (See GRAS and FA lists in Appendix C). But ingesting essential oils should only be done under the direction of a knowledgeable health professional.

In fact, many oils are actually more effective when taken orally in very small amounts. Essential oils should always be diluted in vegetable oil, blue agave nectar or rice milk prior to ingestion. More or less dilution may be required, depending on how strong the oil is. More potent oils, such as cinnamon, oregano, lemongrass, and thyme, will require far more dilution than relatively mild oils, and very mild oils like lavender or lemon may not need any dilution at all.

As a general rule, dilute 1 drop of essential oil in 1 tsp. of blue agave nectar or in at least 4 ounces of a beverage.

Usually no more than 2 or 3 drops should be ingested at one time (during any 4–8 hour period). Because essential oils are so concentrated, 1–2 drops are often sufficient to achieve significant benefits.

Essential oils are extremely concentrated, so they should be kept out of reach of infants and children. If a large quantity of oil is ingested at one time (more than 5 drops), contact your health care physician or a Poison Control Center immediately.

Essential oils should not be given as dietary supplements to children under six years of age. Parents should exercise caution before orally administering essential oils to any child, and again, oils should always be diluted prior to ingestion.

CHAPTER 5

Producing Therapeutic-Grade Essential Oils

Organic Herb Farming

The key to producing oils that are of genuine therapeutic quality starts with the proper cultivation of the herbs in the field.

• Plants should be grown on virgin land uncontaminated by chemical fertilizers, pesticides, fungicides, or herbicides. They should also be grown away from nuclear plants, factories, interstates, highways, and heavily-populated cities, if possible.

• Because robust, healthy plants produce higher quality essential oils, the soil should be nourished with enzymes, minerals, and organic mulch. The mineral content of the soil is crucial to the proper development of the plant, and soils that lack minerals result in plants that produce inferior oils.

• Land and crops should be watered with deep-well, reservoir, or watershed water. Mountain stream water is best because of its purity and high mineral content. Municipally treated water or secondary run-off water from residential and commercial areas can introduce undesirable chemical residues into the plant and the essential oil.

• Different varieties of plants produce different qualities of oils. Only those plants that produce the highest quality essential oil should be selected.

Distillation

The temperature and pressure levels during steam distillation can enhance or destroy the value of the oil. The operator of the distiller must have a full understanding of the value of essential oils in order to produce quality oils. If the pressure or temperature is too high, it may change the molecular structure of the fragrance molecule, altering the chemical constituents. For example, the distilling process for lavender should not exceed three pounds of pressure, and the temperature should not exceed 245° F.

- The timing of the harvest is one of the most important factors in the production of therapeutic-grade oils. If the plants are harvested at the wrong time of the season or even at the incorrect time of day, they may distill into a substandard essential oil. In some instances, changing harvest time, by even a few hours, can make a huge difference. For example, German chamomile harvested in the morning will produce an oil with far more azulene (a powerful anti-inflammatory compound) than chamomile harvested in the late afternoon.

- Other factors that should be taken into consideration during the harvest include the amount of dew on the leaves, the percentage of plant in bloom, and weather conditions during the two weeks prior to harvest.

- To prevent herbs from drying out prior to being distilled, distillers should be located as close to the field as possible. Transporting herbs to distillers hundreds or thousands of miles away heightens the risk of exposure to pollutants, dust, mold, and petrochemical residues.

Steam Distillation

Essential oils can be extracted from the plant by a variety of methods, including solvent extraction, carbon-dioxide extraction, and steam distillation. Steam distillation actually takes three forms. The first uses just water, where plant material is placed in boiling water. The rising steam and oils are captured and then separated. Clove oil is distilled this way. There is also a combination water/steam method where boiling water and steam are pushed through and around the plant matter (this is how nutmeg essential oil is distilled). The final method is straight steam, where steam is pushed through the plant material, picking up the essential oils. Lavender is distilled this way.

In each of these processes, as the steam rises, it ruptures the oil membranes in the plant and releases the essential oil. The steam, carrying the essential oil molecules, rises to a condenser, where the oil-steam mixture condenses and reliquefies. As the steam

Pressure/Temperature Chart for Distilling Several Therapeutic-Grade Essential Oils

Essential Oil	Starting Material	Oil Production	Optical Rotation	Pressure in pounds	Distilling Temp.	Distilling Time
Cypress	2000 lb	1 lb	24	0	220	24 hrs.
Pine	1000 lb	1 lb	2	0	180	8 hrs.
Myrtle	500 kl	1 kl	22	1-2	200	7-9 hrs.
Palmarosa	600 kl	1 kl	6	2	200	4 hrs.
Lemongrass	650 kl	17.5 kl	0	5	230	2.75 hrs.
Citronella	150 lb	1 lb	0	5	225	4.5 hrs.
Rosewood	500 kl	1 kl	-4	30	287	3 hrs.
Cinnamon	1300 lb	5 oz	0	5	225-235	9-24 hrs.
Clove	450 kl	5 lit	0	10	229	18 hrs.
Eucalyptus globulus	250 lb	1 lb	5	5	225	3-18 hrs.
Melaleuca alternifolia	1000 lb	10-15 lb	3	3	218	2-3 hrs.
Geranium	500 lb	6 lb	-8	1.2	200	1-3 hrs.

condenses back to water, the lighter essential oil collects and floats on the top. This mixture is then sent to a separator where the oil is separated from the water. The remaining water is referred to as hydrosol or floral water.

There are many variants in steam distillation. Subtle differences in equipment and processing conditions can translate into huge differences in essential oil quality. The size and material of the cooking chamber, the type of condenser and separator, and the degree of temperature and pressure can all have a huge impact on the oil. Distillation is as much a science as it is an art. If the pressure or temperature is too high, or if the cooking chambers are constructed from reactive materials, the oil may not be therapeutic grade.

Vertical steam distillation offers the greatest potential for protecting the therapeutic benefits and quality of essential oils. In ancient distillation, low pressure (5 pounds or lower) and low temperature were extremely important to produce the therapeutic benefits. Marcel Espieu, president of the Lavender Growers Association in Southern France, has long maintained that the best oil quality can only be produced when the pressure is zero pounds during distillation.

Temperature also has a distinct effect. At certain temperatures, the oil fragrance, as well as the chemical constituents, become altered. High pressures and high temperatures seem to cause a harshness in the oil. Even the oil pH and the electrical polarity are greatly affected.

For example, cypress requires a minimum of 24 hours of distillation at 265° F and 5 pounds of pressure to extract most of the therapeutically-active constituents. If distillation time is cut by only two hours, 18 to 20 constituents will be missing from the resulting oil.

However, most commercial cypress oil is distilled for only 2 hours and 15 minutes! This short distillation time allows the producer to cut costs and produces a cheaper oil, since money is saved on the fuel needed to generate the steam. It also causes less wear and tear on equipment. Sadly, it results in an oil with little or no therapeutic value.

In France, lavender produced commercially is often distilled for only 15 to 20 minutes at 155 pounds of pressure with a steam temperature

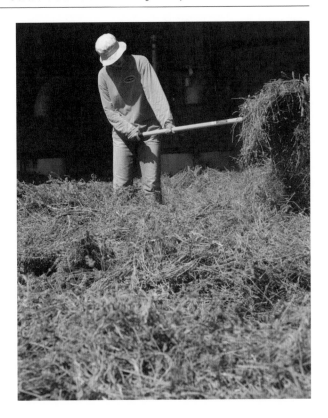

approaching 350° F. Although this high temperature, high pressure oil costs less to produce and is easily marketed, it is of poor quality. It retains few, if any, of the therapeutic properties of high-grade lavender distilled at zero pounds of pressure for a minimum of 1 hour and 15 minutes.

In many large commercial operations, distillers introduce chemicals into the steam distillation process to increase the volume of oil produced. Chemical trucks may even pump solvents directly into the boiler water. This expands oil production by as much as 18 percent. These chemicals inevitably leach into the distilling water and mix with the essential oil, fracturing the molecular structure of the oil and altering both its fragrance and therapeutic value. These chemicals remain in the oil after it is sold because it is impossible to completely separate them from the oil.

Another way that essential oil producers increase the quantity of the oil extracted is through redistillation. This refers to the repeated distillation of the plant material to maximize the volume of oil by using second, third, and fourth stages of steam distillation. Each successive distillation generates a weaker and less potent essential oil. Such essential oils are also degraded due to prolonged exposure to

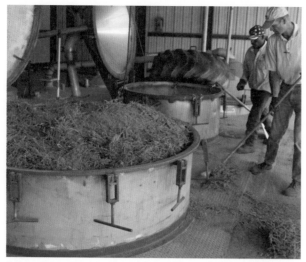

Commercial distillation chambers hold thousands of pounds of plant material.

water and heat used in the redistillation process. This water can hydrolize or oxidize the oil and begin to chemically break down the constituents responsible for its aroma and therapeutic properties.

Combining Traditional Steam Distillation with Modern Technology

Few people appreciate how chemically complex essential oils are. They are rich tapestries of literally hundreds of chemical components, some of which—even in small quantities—contribute important therapeutic benefits. The key to preserving as many as possible of these delicate aromatic constituents is to steam-distill plant material in small batches using low pressure and low heat. This is the traditional method of distillation that has been used for centuries in Europe but is being abandoned in favor of high-volume pressure cookers designed to operate at over 400° F and use over 50 pounds of pressure.

Even more important, the cooking chamber where the plants are distilled should be constructed of a non-reactive metal, preferably stainless steel, to reduce the possibility of the essential oil being chemically altered by more reactive metals such as aluminum or copper.

No solvents or synthetic chemicals should be used or added to the water used to generate steam because they might jeopardize the integrity of the essential oil. Even the addition of chemicals to water used in a closed-loop, heat-exchange system of the condenser can be risky, since there is no guarantee that they will

be completely isolated from the essential oil. It is unfortunate that many essential oils distilled commercially are processed using boiler water laden with chemicals and descaling agents.

Absolutely no pesticides, herbicides, fungicides, or agricultural chemicals of any kind should be used in the cultivation of herbs earmarked for distillation. These chemicals—even in minute quantities—can react with the essential oil and degrade its purity and quality and render it therapeutically less effective. During distillation, pesticide residue leaches out of the plant material, with the extracted essential oil.

Essential Oil Production

Producing pure essential oils is very costly. It often requires several hundred or even thousands of pounds of raw plant material to produce a single pound of essential oil. For example, it can take 2–3 tons of melissa plant material to produce one pound of melissa oil. Its extremely low yield explains why it sells for $9,000 to $15,000 per kilo. It takes 5,000 pounds of rose petals to produce approximately one pint of rose oil. It is not difficult to understand why these oils are so expensive.

The vast majority of oils are produced for the perfume industry, which is only interested in their aromatic qualities. High pressure, high temperatures, and the use of chemical solvents are used in this distillation process to produce greater quantities of oil in a shorter time. To most people, these oils carry a pleasant aroma, but they lack true therapeutic properties. Many of the important chemical constituents necessary to produce therapeutic results are either flashed off with the high heat or are not released from the plant material.

A Summary of the Benefits of Therapeutic-Grade Essential Oils

1. Essential oils are small enough in molecular size that they can quickly penetrate the tissues of the skin.

2. Essential oils are lipid-soluble and are capable of penetrating cell membranes, even if the membranes have hardened because of an oxygen deficiency. According to Jean Valnet, MD,

After condensation, separators isolate the oil from the floral water.

Different Forms of Essential Oil Production

Expressed oils are pressed from the rind of fruits, such as grapefruit, lemon, lime, mandarin, orange, and tangerine. Rich in terpene alcohols, expressed oils are not technically "essential oils," even though they are highly regarded for their therapeutic properties. Expressed oils should only be obtained from organically grown crops, since pesticide residues can become highly concentrated in the oil.

Steam distillation is the oldest and traditional method of extraction. Plant material is inserted into a cooking chamber, and steam is passed through it. After the steam is collected and condensed, it is run through a separator to collect the oil.

Solvent-extraction involves the use of oil-soluble solvents, such as hexane, di-methylene-chloride, and acetone.

Absolutes are technically not "essential oils" but are "essences." They are obtained from the grain alcohol extraction of a concrete, which is the solid waxy residue that is derived from the extraction of plant materials, usually flower petals. This method of extraction is used primarily for botanicals where the fragrance and therapeutic parts of the plant can only be unlocked using solvents. Jasmine and neroli are extracted this way.

essential oils can affect every cell of the body within 20 minutes and are then metabolized like other nutrients.

3. Essential oils, according to researchers at the University of Vienna, stimulate blood flow, which increases oxygen and nutrient delivery.

4. Essential oils are some of the most powerful known antioxidants as determined by the ORAC test developed at Tufts University.

5. Essential oils are antibacterial, antifungal, anti-infectious, antimicrobial, antiparasitic, antiviral, and antiseptic. Some essential oils have been shown to destroy all tested bacteria and viruses.

6. Essential oils may detoxify the cells and blood in the body.

7. Essential oils containing sesquiterpenes have the ability to pass the blood-brain barrier.

8. Essential oils are aromatic, and when diffused, may provide air purification by:

   • Increasing ozone and negative ions in the area.

   • Eliminating odors from cooking, bacteria, mold, animals, and other sources.

   • Filling the air with a fresh, aromatic scent.

9. Essential oils promote emotional, physical, and spiritual well-being.

Cutting resin drops from a Frankinsence tree

SECTION **2**

CHAPTER 6

Single Oils

This section describes over 80 single essential oils, including botanical information, therapeutic and traditional uses, chemical constituents of each oil, extraction method, cautions, and application instructions.

How to be Sure Your Essential Oils are Therapeutic Grade

How can you be sure that your essential oils are of therapeutic grade? Start by asking the following questions from your essential oil supplier:

Are the fragrances delicate, rich, and organic? Do they "feel" natural? Do the aromas vary from batch to batch as an indication that they are painstakingly distilled in small batches rather than industrially processed on a large scale?

Does your supplier subject each batch of essential oils through multiple chemical analyses to test for purity and therapeutic quality? Are these tests performed by independent labs?

Does your supplier grow and distill its own organically grown herbs?

Are the distillation facilities part of the farm where the herbs are grown (so oils are freshly distilled), or do herbs wait days to be processed and lose potency?

Does your supplier use low pressure and low temperature to distill essential oils so as to preserve all of their fragile chemical constituents? Are the distillation cookers fabricated from costly food-grade stainless steel alloys to reduce the likelihood of the oils chemically reacting with metal?

Does your supplier personally inspect the fields and distilleries where the herbs are grown and distilled? Do they verify that no synthetic or harmful solvents or chemicals are being used?

Do your essential oils meet AFNOR or ISO standards?

How many years has your supplier been doing all of this?

How to Maximize the Shelf Life of Your Essential Oils

The highest quality essential oils are bottled in dark glass. The reason for this is two-fold: glass is more stable than plastic and does not "breathe" the same way plastic does. Also, the darkness of the glass protects the oil from light that may chemically alter or degrade it over time.

After using an essential oil, keep the lid tightly sealed. Bottles that are improperly sealed can result in the loss of some of the lighter, lower-molecular-weight parts of the oil. In addition, over time, oxygen in the air reacts with and oxidizes the oil.

Essential oils should be stored away from light, especially sunlight—even if they are already stored in amber glass bottles. The darker the storage conditions, the longer your oil will maintian its orginal chemistry and quality.

Store essential oils in a cool location. Excessive heat can derange the molecular structure of the oil the same way ultraviolet light can.

Diluting Essential Oils

Most essential oils (EO) require dilution with a vegetable oil (VO) when being used either internally or externally. The amount of dilution depends on the essential oil. For example, oregano will require four times as much dilution as that of Roman chamomile. For more information on specific usage instructions for each essential oil, please see the preface to Chapter 30 "Personal Usage Guide" as well as Appendices E and S.

In this chapter the following abbreviations will be used to signify common dilutions: "Dilute 1 part EO with 1 part VO." In all cases, "EO" means Essential Oil and "VO" means Vegetable Oil. Vegetable Oils such the V6 Vegetable Oil Complex are specifically formulated to dilute essential oils and have a long shelf life (over two years) without going rancid.

Angelica

Angelica *(Angelica archangelica)*

Botanical Family: Apiaceae or Umbelliferae (parsley family)

Plant Origin: Belgium, France

Extraction Method: Steam distilled from seed/root.

Key Constituents:
Limonene (60-70%)
Alpha Pinene (5-8%
Alpha and Beta Phellandrene (3-6%)

Historical Data: Known as the "holy spirit root" or the "oil of angels" by the Europeans, angelica's healing powers were so strong that it was believed to be of divine origin. From the time of Paracelsus, it was credited with the ability to protect from the plague. The stems were chewed during the plague of 1660 to prevent infection. When burned, the seeds and roots were thought to purify the air.

Medical Properties: Anticoagulant, relaxant

USES: Throat/lung infections, indigestion, menstrual problems/PMS

Fragrant Influence: assisting in the release of pent-up negative feeling and restores memories to the point of origin before trauma or anger was experienced.

Application: Internal or as a Dietary Supplement: dilute 1 part EO with 1 part VO, put in a capsule and take up to three times daily or as needed; (1) apply 1-2 drops on location, (2) chakras/Vita Flex points, (3) directly inhale, (4) diffuse up to 30 minutes three times daily or as needed (see Appendices E and T).

Avoid applying to skin that will be exposed to direct sunlight or UV light within 24 hours.

Found In: Awaken, Forgiveness, Grounding, Harmony, and Surrender

Anise *(Pimpinella anisum)*

Botanical Family: Apiaceae or Umbelliferae (parsley family)

Plant Origin: Turkey

Extraction Method: Steam distilled from the seeds (fruit).

Key Constituents:
Trans-Anethol (85-95%)
Methyl Chavicol (2-4%)

ORAC: 333,700 µTE/100g

History: Listed in Dioscorides' De Materia Medica (A.D. 78), Europe's first authoritive guide to medicines, that became the standard reference work for herbal treatments for over 1,700 years.

Medical Properties: Digestive stimulatnt, anticoagulant, anesthetic/analgesic, antioxidant, diuretic, antitumoral

Anise

Balsam Fir

USES: Arthritis/rheumatism, cancer

Application: Dilute 1 part EO with 1 part VO, put in a capsule and take up to three times daily or as needed; (1) dilute 1 part EO with 1 part VO then apply on location, (2) chakras/Vita Flex points, (3) directly inhale, (4) diffuse up to 30 minutes three times daily, or (5) take as dietary supplemnt (see Appendices E and T)

Fragrant Influence: Opens emotional blocks and recharges vital energy.

Found In: Awaken, ComforTone, Detoxzyme, Di-Gize, Dream Catcher, Essentialzyme, ICP, ParaFree Softgels, Polyzyme, and Power Meal

Selected Research:

Ghelardini C, Galeotti N, Mazzanti G. "Local anaesthetic activity of monoterpenes and phenylpropanes of essential oils." *Planta Med.* 2001 Aug;67(6):564-6.

Chainy GB, Manna SK, Chaturvedi MM, Aggarwal BB. "Anethole blocks both early and late cellular responses transduced by tumor necrosis factor: effect on NF-kappaB, AP-1, JNK, MAPKK and apoptosis." *Oncogene.* 2000 Jun 8;19(25):2943-50.

Balsam Fir (Idaho) *(Abies balsamea)*

Botanical Family: Pinaceae (pine)

Plant Origin: Bonner's Ferry, Idaho

Extraction Method: Steam distilled from Leaves (needles) and branches.

Key Constituents:
  Alpha-Pinene (28-49%)
  Beta Pinene (14-24%)
  Camphene (13-20%)
  Limonene (13-20%)

ORAC: 20,500 µTE/100g

Historical Data: The fir tree—a tree commonly used as a christmas tree today—has been prized through the ages for its medicinal effects and ability to heal respiratory conditions and muscular and rheumatic pain.

Medical Properties: Anticoagulant, anti-inflammatory

USES: Throat/lung/sinus infections, fatigue. arthritis/rheumatism, urinary tract infections, scoliosis/lumbago/sciatica

Fragrant Influence: Grounding, stimulating to the mind, and relaxing to the body.

Application: Dilute 1 part EO with 1 part VO; (1) apply 2-4 drops on location or use neat in Raindrop Technique, (2) chakras/Vita Flex points, (3) directly inhale, (4) diffuse, or (5) take as dietary supplemnt (see Appendices E and T).

Bible References: (see additional Bible references in Appendix D)

2 Samuel 6:5—"And David and all the house of Israel played before the Lord on all manner of [instruments made of] fir wood, even on harps, and on psalteries, and on timbrels, and on cornets, and on cymbals."

Basil

1 Kings 5:8—"And Hiram sent to Solomon, saying, I have considered the things which thou sentest to me for: [and] I will do all thy desire concerning timber of cedar, and concerning timber of fir."

1 Kings 5:10—"So Hiram gave Solomon cedar trees and fir trees [according to] all his desire."

Found In: Animal Scents Ointment, Believe, BLM, En-R-Gee, Egyptial Gold, Gratitude, Sacred Mountain, Sacred Mountain Bar Soap, and Transformation

Basil *(Ocimum basilicum)*

Botanical Family: Lamiaceae or Labiatae (mint)

Plant Origin: India, Utah, France

Extraction Method: Steam distilled from leaves, stems, and flowers.

Key Constituents:
Methylchavicol (estragol) (40-80%)
Linalol (10-50%)
1,8 Cineole (1-7%)
Eugenol (1-10%)

ORAC: 54,000 μTE/100g

Historical Data: Used extensively in traditional Asian Indian medicine, basil's name is derived from "basileum," the Greek name for king. In the 16th century, the powdered leaves were inhaled to treat migraines and chest infections. The Hindu people put basil sprigs

on the chests of the dead to protect them from evil spirits. Italian women wore basil to attract possible suitors. It was listed in Hildegard's Medicine, a compilation of early German medicines by highly-regarded Benedictine herbalist Hildegard of Bingen (1098-1179).

Medical Properties: Powerful antispasmodic, antiviral, antibacterial, anti-inflammatory, muscle relaxant

USES: Migraines, throat/lung infections, insect bites

Fragrant Influence: Fights mental fatigue.

Application: Dilute 1 part EO with 4 parts VO; (1) apply 2-4 drops on location, temples, neck (2) chakras/Vita Flex points (crown of head, forehead, heart, and navel), (3) directly inhale, (4) diffuse, or (5) take as dietary supplement (see Appendices E and T).

Caution: Avoid use if epileptic.

Found In: Aroma Siez, Clarity, M-Grain.

Selected Research:

Fyfe L., et al. "Inhibition of *Listeria monocytogenes* and *Salmonella enteriditis* by combinations of plant oils and derivatives of benzoic acid: the development of synergistic antimicrobial combinations." *Int J Antimicrob Agents.* 1997;9(3):195-9.

Wan J, et al. "The effect of essential oils of basil on the growth of *Aeromonas hydrophila* and *Pseudomonas fluorescens*." *J Appl Microbiol.* 1998;84(2):152-8.

Lachowicz KJ, et al. "The synergistic preservative effects of the essential oils of sweet basil (*Ocimum basilicum* L.) against acid-tolerant food microflora." *Lett Appl Microbiol.* 1998;26(3):209-14.

Elgayyar M, et al., Antimicrobial activity of essential oils from plants against selected pathogenic and saprophytic microorganisms. *J Food Prot.* 2001 Jul;64(7):1019-24.

Bay Laurel

(see LAURUS NOBILIS)

Bergamot

Bergamot *(Citrus bergamia)*

Botanical Family: Rutaceae (citrus)

Plant Origin: Italy, Morroco

Extraction Method: Cold pressed from the rind, rectified and void of terpenes. Also produced by solvent extraction or vacuum distillation.

Key Constituents:
Limonene (30-45%)
Linaly Acetate (22-36%)
Linalol (3-15%)
Gamma-Terpinene (6-10%)
Beta-Pinene (5.5-9.5%)

Historical Data: It is believed that Christopher Columbus brought bergamot to Bergamo in Northern Italy from the Canary Islands. A mainstay in traditional Italian medicine, bergamot has been used in the Middle East for hundreds of years for skin conditions associated with an oily complexion. Bergamot is responsible for the distinctive flavor of the renowned Earl Grey Tea, and was used in the first genuine eau de cologne.

Medical Properties: Calming, hormonal support, antibacterial, antidepressant

USES: Agitation, depression, anxiety, intestinal parasites, insomnia, viral infections (Herpes, cold sores)

Fragrant Influence: Relieves anxiety; mood-lifting qualities.

Application: Dilute 1 part EO with 1 part VO; (1) apply 1-2 drops on location, (2) chakras/Vita Flex points, (3) directly inhale, (4) diffuse, or (5) take as dietary supplement (see Appendices E and T).

Cautions: Avoid applying to skin that will be exposed to sunlight or UV light within 36 hours.

Found In: Awaken, Clarity, Dragon Time Bath & Shower Gel, Dream Catcher, Evening Peace Bath & Shower Gel, Forgiveness, Genesis Hand & Body Lotion, Gentle Baby, Harmony, Joy, Prenolone, Prenolone +, Rosewood Moisturizing Conditioner, Rosewood Moisturizing Shampoo, and White Angelica.

Black Pepper *(Piper nigrum)*

(see PEPPER, BLACK)

Blue Cypress *(Callitris intratropica)*

(see CYPRESS, BLUE)

Blue Tansy *(Tanacetum annuum)*

(see TANSY, BLUE)

Blue Yarrow *(Achillea millefolium)*

(see YARROW, BLUE)

Cajeput *(Melaleuca leucadendron)*

Botanical Family: Myrtaceae (myrtle)

Plant Origin: Australia

Extraction Method: Steam distilled from leaves.

Key Constituents:
Eucalyptol (50-65%)
Alpha-Terpineol (7-13%)
Limonene (3-8%)
Alpha Pinene (1-3%)

ORAC: 37,600 µTE/100g

Historical Data: Traditionally used in Malaysia and other Indonesian islands, for respiratory/throat infections, headaches, rheumatism, toothache, skin conditions, and sore muscles. Cajeput derives its name from the Malaysian word for white tree.

Medical Properties: Antibacterial, antiparasitic, antispasmodic, anti-inflammatory, analgesic

USES: Throat/lung/sinus infections, urinary tract infections, coughs, intestinal problems

Application: Dietary Supplement: dilute 1 part EO with 1 part VO, put in a capsule and take up to three times daily or as needed; (1) dilute 1 drop EO with 1 drop VO, then apply on location, (2) chakras/Vita Flex points, (3) directly inhale, or (4) diffuse up to 30 minutes three times daily (see Appendices E and T).

Caution: Do not use synthetic cajeput, as it could cause further blistering and skin eruption.

Canadian Fleabane (*Conyza canadensis*)

(see FLEABANE, CANADIAN)

Cardamom (*Elettaria cardamomum*)

Botanical Family: Zingiberaceae (ginger)

Plant Origin: Guatemala, Sri Lanka

Extraction Method: Steam distilled from seeds.

Key Constituents:
Alpha Terpinyl Acetate (45-55%)
1,8 Cineol (Eucalyptol) (16-24%)
Linalol (4-7%)
Linalyl Acetate (3-7%)
Limonene (1-3%)

ORAC: 36,500 µTE/100g

Historical Data: Called "Grains of Paradise" since the Middle Ages, it has been used medicinally by Indian healers for millennia. One of the most prized spices in ancient Greece and Rome, cardamom was cultivated by the king of Babylon around the seventh century B.C.

It is mentioned in one of the oldest known medical records, Ebers Papyrus (dating from sixteenth century B.C.) an ancient Egyptian list of 877 prescriptions and recipes.

Cardamom

Medical Properties: Antispasmodic (neuromuscular), expectorant, antiparasitc (worms)

USES: Lung/sinus infection, indigestion, senility, headaches

Fragrant Influence: Uplifting, refreshing, and invigorating.

Application: Dietary Supplement: dilute 1 part EO with 1 part VO, put in a capsule and take up to three times daily; (1) Topical: dilute 1 part EO with 1 part VO, then apply on location, stomach, solar plexus, or thighs, (2) chakras/Vita Flex points, (3) directly inhale, (4) diffuse up to 30 minutes three times daily, or (5) take 4 drops as dietary supplement (see Appendices E and T).

Found In: Clarity and Transformation

Carrot Seed (*Daucus carota*)

Botanical Family: Apiaceae or Ubelliferae (parsley family)

Plant Origin: France

Extraction Method: Steam distilled from dried seeds.

Key Constituents:
Carotol (30-40%)
Alpha Pinene (12-16%)
Trans Beta Caryophyllene (6-10%)
Caryophyllene Oxide (3-5%)

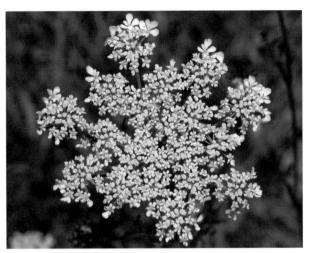

Carrot Seed

Historical Data: Traditionally used for kidney and digestive disorders and to relieve liver congestion.

Medical Properties: Antiparasitic, antiseptic, depurative, diuretic, vasodilatory

USES: Skin conditions (eczema, oily skin, psoriasis, wrinkles), water retention, liver problems

Application: Dilute 1 part EO with 1 part VO; (1) apply 1-2 drops on location, (2) chakras/Vita Flex points, or (3) take as dietary supplement (see Appendices E and T).

Found In: Animal Scents Ointment, GLF, Rose Ointment, and Juva Cleanse

Selected Research:

Friedman M, Henika PR, Mandrell RE. "Bactericidal activities of plant essential oils and some of their isolated constituents against Campylobacter jejuni, Escherichia coli, Listeria monocytogenes, and Salmonella enterica." *J Food Prot.* 2002 Oct;65(10):1545-60.

Cassia (*Cinnamomum cassia*)

Botanical Family: Lauraceae (laurel)

Plant Origin: China

Extraction Method: Steam distilled from branches, leaves and petioles. NOTE: While its aroma is similar to cinnamon, cassia is chemically and physically quite different.

Key Constituents:
Trans-Cinnamaldehyde (70-88%)
Trans-O-Methoxycinnamaldehyde (3-15%)
Coumarine (1.5-4%)
Cinnamyl Acetate (0-6%)

ORAC: 15,170 μTE/100g

Historical Data: Rich Biblical history. Mentioned in one of the oldest known medical records, Ebers Papyrus (dating from sixteenth century B.C.) an ancient Egyptian list of 877 prescriptions and recipes.

Medical Properties: Anti-inflammatory (COX2 inhibitor), antifungal, antibacterial, antiviral, anticoagulant

USES: Cataracts, fungal infections (ringworm, candida), atherosclerosis, arterosclerosis

Application: Dilute 1 part EO with 4 parts VO; (1) apply 1-2 drops on location, (2) chakras/Vita Flex points, (3) diffuse, or (4) take as dietary supplement (see Appendices E and T).

Caution: May irritate the nasal membranes if inhaled directly from diffuser or bottle.

Found In: Exodus II

Bible References: (See additional Bible references in Appendix D.)

Exodus 30:23,24,25—"Take thou also unto thee principal spices, of pure myrrh five hundred shekels, and of sweet cinnamon half so much, even two hundred and fifty shekels, And of sweet calamus two hundred and fifty shekels, And of **cassia** five hundred shekels, after the shekel of the sanctuary, and of oil olive an hin: And thou shalt make it an oil of holy ointment, an ointment compound after the art of the apothecary: it shall be an holy anointing oil."

Psalm 45:8—"All thy garments smell of myrrh, and aloes, and **cassia**, out of the ivory palaces, whereby they have made thee glad."

Selected Research:

Lee HS. "Inhibitory activity of Cinnamomum cassia bark-derived component against rat lens aldose reductase." *J Pharm Pharm Sci.* 2002 Sep-Dec;5(3):226-30.

Cassia

Walsh SE, et al., "Activity and mechanisms of action of selected biocidal agents on Gram-positive and -negative bacteria." *J Appl Microbiol.* 2003;94(2):240-7.

Lee HS, Kim BS, Kim MK. "Suppression effect of Cinnamomum cassia bark-derived component on nitric oxide synthase." *J Agric Food Chem.* 2002 Dec 18;50(26):7700-3.

Huss U, et al., "Screening of ubiquitous plant constituents for COX-2 inhibition with a scintillation proximity based assay." *J Nat Prod.* 2002 Nov;65(11):1517-21.

Friedman M, Henika PR, Mandrell RE. "Bactericidal activities of plant essential oils and some of their isolated constituents against Campylobacter jejuni, Escherichia coli, Listeria monocytogenes, and Salmonella enterica." *J Food Prot.* 2002 Oct;65(10):1545-60.

Lee HS, Ahn YJ. "Growth-Inhibiting Effects of Cinnamomum cassia Bark-Derived Materials on Human Intestinal Bacteria." *J Agric Food Chem.* 1998 Jan 19;46(1):8-12.

Inouye S, Yamaguchi H, Takizawa T. "Screening of the antibacterial effects of a variety of essential oils on respiratory tract pathogens, using a modified dilution assay method." *J Infect Chemother.* 2001 Dec;7(4): 251-4.

Cedar, Western Red *(Thuja plicata)*

Botanical Family: Cupressaceae

Plant Origin: Utah, Idaho, Canada

Extraction Method: Steam distilled from leaves and branches.

Key Constituents:
Alpha Thujone (70-80%)
Beta Thujone (4-7%)
Alpha Pinene (2-4%)
Sabinene (2-4%)

Historical Data: This oil is different from Canadian red ceder which is distlled from the bark of the same plant, Thuja plicata. This oil is not red in color, because it is derived from leaves.

Medical Properties: Antiseptic

USES: Throat/lung infections, urinary tract infections

Application: Dilute 1 part EO with 1 part VO; (1) apply 1-2 drops on location, (2) chakras/ Vita Flex points, (3) directly inhale, (4) diffuse, or (5) add to woodchips or place in closets/dressers to repel insects (see Appendices E and T).

Found In: KidScents Lotion

Cedarwood *(Cedrus atlantica)*

Botanical Family: Pinaceae (pine)

Plant Origin: Morocco, USA. *Cedrus atlantica* is the species most closely related to the biblical Cedars of Lebanon.

Extraction Method: Steam distilled from bark.

Key Constituents:
Alpha-Himachalene (10-20%)
Beta-Himachalene (35-55%)
Gamma-Himachalene (8-15%)
Delta-Cadinene (2-6%)

ORAC: 169,000 µTE/100g

Historical Data: Throughout antiquity, cedarwood has been used in medicines. The Egyptians used it for embalming the dead. It was used as both a traditional medicine and incense in Tibet.

Medical Properties: Combats hair loss (alopecia areata), antibacterial, lymphatic stimulatant

USES: Hair loss, arteriosclerosis, ADHD, skin problems (acne, eczema)

Fragrant Influence: Stimulates the limbic region of the brain (the center of emotions) stimulates the pineal gland, which releases melatonin. Terry Friedmann MD found in clinical tests that this oil was able to successfully treat ADD and ADHD (attention deficit disorders) in children. It is recognized for its calming, purifying properties.

Application: (1) Apply on location, (2) chakras/ Vita Flex points, (3) directly inhale, (4) diffuse, or (5) take as dietary supplement (see Appendices E and T).

Bible References: (See additional Bible references in Appendix D**).**

Leviticus 14:4—"Then shall the priest command to take for him that is to be cleansed two birds alive and clean, and cedar wood, and scarlet, and hyssop."

Leviticus 14:6—"As for the living bird, he shall take it, and the cedar wood, and the scarlet, and the hyssop, and shall dip them and the living bird in the blood of the bird [that was] killed over the running water."

Leviticus 14:49—"And he shall take to cleanse the house two birds, and cedar wood, and scarlet, and hyssop."

Found In: Australian Blue, Brain Power, Cel-Lite Magic Massage Oil, Egyptial Gold, Grounding, Highest Potential, Inspiration, Into The Future, KidScents Bath Gel, KidScents Lotion, Pepermint-Cedarwood Bar Soap, Sacred Mountain, Sacred Mountain Bar Soap, and SARA

Selected Research:

Hay IC, et al. "Randomized trial of aromatherapy. Successful treatment for alopecia areata." *Arch Dermatol.* 1998;134(11):1349-52.

Friedman M, Henika PR, Mandrell RE. "Bactericidal activities of plant essential oils and some of their isolated constituents against

Cedarwood

Campylobacter jejuni, Escherichia coli, Listeria monocytogenes, and Salmonella enterica." *J Food Prot.* 2002 Oct;65(10):1545-60.

Celery Seed *(Apium graveolens)*

Botanical Family: Apiaceae or Umbelliferae (parsley family)

Plant Origin: Europe

Extraction Method: Steam distilled from dried seeds.

Key Constituents:
Limonene (60-75%)
Alpha and Beta Selinene (14-20%)
Sednenolide (4-7%)

ORAC: 30,300 μTE/100g

Historical Data: Long recognized as helpful in digestion, liver cleansing, and urinary tract support. Also said to increase milk flow in nursing mothers.

Medical Properties: Antibacterial, antioxidant, antirheumatic, digestive aid, diuretic, liver protectant

USES: Arthritis/rheumatism, digestive problems, liver problems/hepatitis

Application: Dietary Supplement: dilute 1 part EO with 2 parts VO, put in a capsule and take up to three times daily or as needed; (1) apply on location, or (2) diffuse up to 1 hour three times daily (see Appendices E and T).

Celery Seed

German Chamomile

Found In: GLF, Juva Cleanse

Selected Research:

Friedman M, Henika PR, Mandrell RE. "Bactericidal activities of plant essential oils and some of their isolated constituents against Campylobacter jejuni, Escherichia coli, Listeria monocytogenes, and Salmonella enterica." *J Food Prot.* 2002 Oct;65(10):1545-60.

Zheng GQ, et al., "Chemoprevention of benzo[a]pyrene-induced forestomach cancer in mice by natural phthalides from celery seed oil." *Nutr Cancer.* 1993;19(1):77-86.

Chamomile (German) *(Matricaria recutita)*

Botanical Family: Asteraceae or Compositae (daisy)

Plant Origin: Utah, Idaho, Egypt, Hungary

Extraction Method: Steam distilled from flowers.

Key Constituents:
Chamazulene (2-5%)
Bisabolol Oxide A (32-42%)
Trans-Beta-Farnesene (18-26%)
Bisbolol Oxide B (3-6%)
Bisbolone Oxide A (3-6%)
Cis Spiro Ether (4-8%)

ORAC: 218,600 µTE/100g

Historical Data: Listed in Dioscorides' De Materia Medica (A.D. 78), Europe's first authoritive guide to medicines, that became the standard reference work for herbal treatments for over 1,700 years.

Medical Properties: Powerful antioxidant, (inhibits lipid peroxidation), antitumoral, anti-inflammatory, relaxant, anesthetic. Promotes digestion, liver, and gallbladder health

USES: Hepatitis/fatty liver, arteriosclerosis, insomnia, nervous tension, arthritis, carpal tunnel syndrome, skin problems (acne, eczema, scar tissue)

Fragrant Influence: Dispels anger, stabilizes emotions, and helps release emotions linked to the past. Soothes and clears the mind.

Application: Dietary Supplement: put 2 drops in a capsule, take three times daily or as needed; (1) Apply 2-4 drops on location, (2) chakras/Vita Flex points, (3) directly inhale, (4) diffuse up to 1 hour three times daily, or (5) take as dietary supplement (see Appendices E and T).

Found In: ART Day Activator, ART Night Reconstructor, ComforTone, EndoFlex, JuvaTone, and Surrender

Selected Research:

Burns E, et al., "The use of aromatherapy in intrapartum midwifery practice an observational study." *Complement Ther Nurs Midwifery.* 2000 Feb;6(1):33-4.

Rekka E, et al., "Synthesis of new azulene derivatives and study of their effect on lipid peroxidation and lipoxygenase activity." *Chem Pharm Bull* (Tokyo). 2002 Jul;50(7): 904-7.

Rekka EA, Kourounakis AP, Kourounakis PN. "Investigation of the effect of chamazulene on lipid peroxidation and free radical processes." *Res Commun Mol Pathol Pharmacol.* 1996 Jun;92(3):361-4.

Hernandez-Ceruelos A, Madrigal-Bujaidar E, de la Cruz C. "Inhibitory effect of chamomile essential oil on the sister chromatid exchanges induced by daunorubicin and methyl methanesulfonate in mouse bone marrow." *Toxicol Lett.* 2002 Sep 5;135(1-2):103-110.

Brehm-Stecher BF, Johnson EA. "Sensitization of Staphylococcus aureus and Escherichia coli to antibiotics by the sesquiterpenoids nerolidol, farnesol, bisabolol, and apritone." *Antimicrob Agents Chemother.* 2003 Oct;47(10):3357-60.

Chamomile (Roman) *(Chamaemelum nobile)*

Botanical Family: Asteraceae or Compositae (daisy)

Plant Origin: Utah, France

Extraction Method: Steam distilled from flowering top.

Key Constituents:
Isobutyl Angelate + Isamyl Methacrylate (30-45%)
Isoamyl Angelate (12-22%)
Methyl Allyl Angelate (6-10%)
Isobutyl n-butyrate (2-9%)
2-Methyl Butyl Angelate (3-7%)

ORAC: 240 µTE/100g

Historical Data: Used in Europe for skin regeneration. For centuries, mothers have used chamomile to calm crying children, combat digestive and liver ailments, and relieve toothaches.

Medical Properties: Relaxant, antispasmodic, anti-inflammatory, antiparasitic, nerve regenerative, anesthetic, detoxifies blood and liver

Roman Chamomile

USES: Relieves restlessness, anxiety, ADHD. depression, insomnia, skin conditions (acne, dermatitis, eczema)

Fragrant Influence: Because it is calming and relaxing, it can combat depression, insomnia, and stress. It minimizes anxiety, irritability, and nervousness. It may also dispel anger, stabilize the emotions, and help to release emotions that are linked to the past.

Application: (1) Apply 2-4 drops on location, ankles, or wrists (2) chakras/Vita Flex points, (3) directly inhale, (4) diffuse, or (5) take as dietary supplement (see Appendices E and T).

Found In: Awaken, Chelex Tincture, Clarity, Claraderm, Dragon Time Bath & Shower Gel, Evening Peace Bath & Shower Gel, Forgiveness, Genesis Hand & Body Lotion, Gentle Baby, Harmony, Joy, JuvaFlex, K&B Tincture, KidScents® Tender Tush, LemonSage Clarifying Conditioner, LemonSage Clarifying Shampoo, Motivation, M-Grain, Rehemogen tincture, Surrender, and Wolfberry Eye Cream.

Cinnamon Bark *(Cinnamomum verum)*

Botanical Family: Lauraceae (laurel)

Plant Origin: Sri Lanka, Madagascar, Ceylon

Extraction Method: Steam distilled from bark.

Key Constituents:
Trans-Cinnamaldehyde (40-50%)
Eugenol (20-30%)

Beta-Caryophyllene (3-8%)

Linalol (3-7%)

ORAC: 10,340 µTE/100g

History: Listed in Dioscorides' De Materia Medica (A.D. 78), Europe's first authoritive guide to medicines, that became the standard reference work for herbal treatments for over 1,700 years.

Cinnamon was reputed to be part of the "Marseilles Vinegar" or "Four Thieves Vinegar" used by grave-robbing bandits to protect themselves during the 15th century plague.

Medical Properties: Anti-inflammatory (COX2 inhibitor), powerfully antibacterial, antiviral, antifungal, anticoagulant, circulatory stimulant, stomach protectant (ulcers), antiparasitic (worms)

USES: Cardiovascular disease, infectious diseases, viral infections (Herpes etc), digestive complaints, ulcers, and warts

Fragrant Influence: Thought to attract wealth.

Application: Dilute 1 part EO with 4 parts VO; (1) apply 1-2 drops on location, (2) chakras/ Vita Flex points, (3) diffuse, or (4) take as dietary supplement (see Appendices E and T).

Cautions: May irritate the nasal membranes if inhaled directly from diffuser or bottle.

Found In: Abundance, Carbozyme, Christmas Spirit, Cinnamint Lip Balm, Dentarome, Dentarome Plus, Dentarome Ultra, Egyptian Gold, Exodus II, Gathering, Highest Potential, KidScents Toothpaste, Magnify Your Purpose, Mineral Essence, and Thieves, Thieves Bar Soap, Thieves, Household Cleaner, Thieves Foaming Hand Soap, Thieves Hard and Soft Lozenges, Thieves Spray, and Thieves Wipes

Bible Reference: (See additional Bible references in Appendix D)

Exodus 30:23—"Take thou also unto thee principal spices, of pure myrrh five hundred shekels, and of sweet cinnamon half so much, even two hundred and fifty shekels, and of sweet calamus two hundred and fifty shekels..."

Cinnamon

Proverbs 7:17—"I have perfumed my bed with myrrh, aloes, and cinnamon."

Song of Solomon 4:14—"Spikenard and saffron; calamus and cinnamon, with all trees of frankincense; myrrh and aloes, with all the chief spices:"

Selected Research:

Tantaoui-Elaraki A, et al. "Inhibition of growth and aflatoxin production in *Aspergillus parasiticus* by essential oils of selected plant materials." *J Environ Pathol Toxicol Oncol.* 1994;13(1):67-72.

Capasso R, Pinto L, Vuotto ML, Di Carlo G. "Preventive effect of eugenol on PAF and ethanol-induced gastric mucosal damage." *Fitoterapia.* 2000 Aug;71 Suppl 1:S131-7.

Lee HS, Kim BS, Kim MK. "Suppression effect of Cinnamomum cassia bark-derived component on nitric oxide synthase." *J Agric Food Chem.* 2002 Dec 18;50(26):7700-3.

Huss U, et al., "Screening of ubiquitous plant constituents for COX-2 inhibition with a scintillation proximity based assay." *J Nat Prod.* 2002 Nov;65(11):1517-21.

Pessoa LM, et al., "Anthelmintic activity of essential oil of Ocimum gratissimum Linn. and eugenol against Haemonchus contortus." *Vet Parasitol.* 2002 Oct 16;109(1-2):59-63.

Friedman M, Henika PR, Mandrell RE. "Bactericidal activities of plant essential oils and some of their isolated constituents against Campylobacter jejuni, Escherichia coli, Listeria monocytogenes, and Salmonella enterica." *J Food Prot.* 2002 Oct;65(10):1545-60.

Benencia F, Courreges MC. "In vitro and in vivo activity of eugenol on human herpes virus." *Phytother Res.* 2000 Nov;14(7):495-500.

Inouye S, Uchida K, Yamaguchi H. "In-vitro and in-vivo anti-Trichophyton activity of essential oils by vapour contact." *Mycoses.* 2001 May;44(3-4):99-107.

Inouye S, Yamaguchi H, Takizawa T. "Screening of the antibacterial effects of a variety of essential oils on respiratory tract pathogens, using a modified dilution assay method." *J Infect Chemother.* 2001 Dec;7(4):251-4.

Tantaoui-Elaraki A, Beraoud L. "Inhibition of growth and aflatoxin production in Aspergillus parasiticus by essential oils of selected plant materials." *J Environ Pathol Toxicol Oncol.* 1994;13(1):67-72.

Cistus

Application: (1) Apply 2-4 drops on location, (2) chakras/Vita Flex points, (3) directly inhale, (4) diffuse, or (5) take as 4 drops as dietary supplement (see Appendices E and T).

Found In: ImmuPower, ImmuneTune, and KidScents Tender Tush

Cistus *(Cistus ladanifer)* (known also as *Labdanum*)

Botanical Family: Cistaceae

Plant Origin: Spain

Extraction Method: Steam distilled from leaves/ branches.

Key Constituents:
Alpha Pinene (40-60%)
Camphene (2-5%)
Bornyl Acetate (3-6%)
Trans-Pinocarveol (3-6%)

ORAC: 3,860 µTE/100g

Historical Data: Cistus is also known as "rock rose" and has been studied for its effects on the regeneration of cells.

Medical Properties: Antiviral, antibacterial, antihemorrhagic, anti-inflammatory, supports sympathetic nervous system, immune stimulant

USES: Hemorrhages, arthritis

Fragrant Influence: Calming to the nerves, elevates the emotions.

Citronella *(Cymbopogon nardus)*

Botanical Family: Poaceae or Gramineae (grasses)

Plant Origin: Sri Lanka

Extraction Method: Steam distilled from aerial parts/leaves.

Key Constituents:
Geraniol (18-30%)
Limonene (5-10%)
Trans-Methyl Isoeugenol (4-10%)
Geranyl Acetate (5-10%)
Borneol (3-8%)

ORAC: 312,000 µTE/100g

Historical Data: Used by various cultures to treat intestinal parasites, menstrual problems, and as a stimulant. Historically used to sanitize and deodorize surfaces. Enhanced insect repelling properties when combined with cedarwood.

Medical Properties: Powerful antioxidant, antibacterial, antifungal, insect-repellent, anti-inflammatory, antispasmodic, antiparasitic (worms), relaxant

USES: Respiratory infections, muscle/nerve pain, digestive/intestinal problems, anxiety, skin problems (acne, eczema, oily skin), skin-penetration enhancer

Fragrant Influence: Refreshing and uplifting.

Application: Dietary Supplement: dilute 1 part EO with 1 part VO, put in a capsule and take up to three times daily or as needed; (1) dilute 1 part EO with 1 part VO, then apply on location, (2) chakras/Vita Flex points, (3) directly inhale, (4) diffuse up to 30 minutes three times daily, or (5) take as dietary supplement (see Appendices E and T).

Found In: Animal Scents Shampoo and Purification

Selected Research:

Mutalik S, Udupa N. Effect of some penetration enhancers on the permeation of glibenclamide and glipizide through mouse skin. *Pharmazie.* 2003 Dec;58(12):891-4.

Kumaran AM, et al., Geraniol, the putative anthelmintic principle of Cymbopogon martinii. *Phytother Res.* 2003 Sep;17(8):957.

Carnesecchi S, et al., "Geraniol, a component of plant essential oils, sensitizes human colon cancer cells to 5-fluorouracil treatment." *IARC Sci Publ.* 2002;156:407-9.

Carnesecchi S, et al., "Perturbation by geraniol of cell membrane permeability and signal transduction pathways in human colon cancer cells." *J Pharmacol Exp Ther.* 2002 Nov;303(2):711-5.

Umezu T, et al., "Anticonflict effects of rose oil and identification of its active constituents." *Life Sci.* 2002 Nov 22;72(1):91-102.

Choi HS, Song HS, Ukeda H, Sawamura M. "Radical-scavenging activities of citrus essential oils and their components: detection using 1,1-diphenyl-2-picrylhydrazyl." *J Agric Food Chem.* 2000 Sep;48(9):4156-61.

Citrus Hystrix / Combava

Citrus Hystrix / Combava (also known as Kaffir lime)

Botanical Family: Rutaceae

Plant Origin: Indochina, Malaysia

Extraction Method: Steam distilled from leaves.

Key Constituents:
Citronnellal (65-80%)
Linalol (3-6%)
Citronnellol (2-5%)
Isopulegol ((2-4%)

ORAC: 69,200 µTE/100g

Historical Data: Studies at Kinki University in Japan found that it has strong anti-inflammatory properties. Other research has shown that it combats depression.

Medical Properties: Anti-inflammatory, antidepressant, relaxant, rich in citronellal which possesses calmative properties

USES: Stress, anxiety, trauma

Application: (1) Dilute 1 part EO with 1 part VO, then apply on location, (2) chakras/Vita Flex points, (3) directly inhale, (4) diffuse up to 30 minutes three times daily, or (5) take as dietary supplement (see Appendices E and T).

Found In: Trauma Life

Clary Sage

Clary Sage *(Salvia sclarea)*

Botanical Family: Lamiaceae or Labiatae (mint)

Plant Origin: Utah, France

Extraction Method: Steam distilled from flowering plant.

Key Constituents:
Linalyl Acetate (56-78%)
Linalol (7-24%)
Germacrene D (2-12%)
Sclareol (.4-3%)

ORAC: 221,000 µTE/100g

Historical Data: Recent medical data indicates that it naturally raises estrogen and progesterone levels.

Medical Properties: Anticoagulant, antioxidant, antidiabetic, estrogen-like, antifungal, antispasmodic, relaxant, cholesterol-reducing, antitumoral, anesthetic

USES: Leukemia, menstrual discomforts/PMS, hormonal imbalance, insomnia, circulatory problems, high cholesterol

Fragrant Influence: Enhances one's ability to dream and is very calming and stress-relieving.

Application: Dilute 1 part EO with 1 part VO; (1) apply on location, feet, ankles, wrists, (2) chakras/Vita Flex points, (3) directly inhale, (4) diffuse, or (5) take as dietary supplement (see Appendices E and T), (6) Rub 6-8 drops on lower back during PMS.

Found In: Cel-Lite Magic Massage Oil, CortiStop Women's, Dragon Time, Dragon Time Bath & Shower Gel, Dragon Time Massage Oil, Estro Tincture, Evening Peace Bath & Shower Gel, FemiGen, Into The Future, Lady Sclareol, Lavender Volume Conditioner, Lavender Volume Shampoo, Prenolone, Prenolone Plus, Rosewood Moisturizing Conditioner, Rosewood Moisturizing Shampoo, and SclarEssence

Selected Research:

Dimas K, et al., "The effect of sclareol on growth and cell cycle progression of human leukemic cell lines." *Leuk Res.* 1999 Mar;23(3):217-34.

Yasui K, "Synthesis of manool-related labdane diterpenes as platelet aggregation inhibitors." *Chem Pharm Bull* (Tokyo). 1993 Oct;41(10):1698-707.

Burns E, et al., "The use of aromatherapy in intrapartum midwifery practice an observational study." *Complement Ther Nurs Midwifery.* 2000 Feb;6(1):33-4.

Clove *(Syzygium aromaticum)*

Botanical Family: Oleaceae

Plant Origin: Madagascar, Spice Islands

Extraction Method: Steam distilled from flower bud and stem.

Key Constituents:
Eugenol (75-87%)
Eugenol Acetate (8-15%)
Beta-Carophyllene (2-7%)

ORAC: 1,078,700 µTE/100g

Historical Data: The people on the island of Ternate were free from epidemics until the 16th century, when Dutch conquerors destroyed the clove trees that flourished on the islands. Many of the islanders died from the epidemics that followed.

Cloves were reputed to be part of the "Marseilles Vinegar" or "Four Thieves Vinegar" used by grave-robbing bandits to protect themselves during the 15th century plague.

Clove was listed in Hildegard's Medicine, a compilation of early German medicines by highly-regarded Benedictine herbalist Hildegard of Bingen (1098-1179).

Healers in Chinia and India have used clove buds since ancient times as part of their treatments.

Eugenol, clove's principal constituent, was used in the dental industry for years to numb gums.

Courmont et al. demonstrated that a solution of .05% eugenol from clove oil was sufficient to kill the tuberculosis bacillus (Gattefossé, 1990).

Medical Properties: Anti-aging, antitumoral, antimicrobial, antifungal, antiviral, analgesic/anesthetic, antioxidant, anticoagulant, anti-inflammatory, stomach protectant (ulcers), antiparasitic (worms), anticonvulsant

USES: Anti-aging, cardiovacular disease, arthritis/ rheumatism, hepatitis, intestinal parasites/ infections, for numbing all types of pain, throat/sinus/lung infections, cataracts, ulcers, lice, toothache, acne

Fragrant Influence: A mental stimulant; encourages sleep, stimulates dreams, and creates a sense of protection and courage.

Application: Dilute 1 part EO with 4 parts VO; (1) apply 2-4 drops on location, gums, or mouth, (2) chakras/Vita Flex points, (3) diffuse, or (4) take as dietary supplement (see Appendices E and T).

For tickling cough, put a drop on back of tongue.

Cautions: Anticoagulant properties can be enhanced when combined with Warfarin, aspirin, etc.

Found In: Abundance, AromaGuard Meadow Mist, AromaGuard Mountain Mist, BLM, Carbozyme, Dentarome Toothpaste, Dentarome Plus Toothpaste, Dentarome Ultra Toothpaste, En-R-Gee, Essentialzyme, ImmuPower, K&B Tincture, KidScents Toothpaste, Longevity, Longevity Softgels, Melrose, PanAway, Para Free Softgels, Thieves, Thieves Foaming Hand Soap,

Clove

Thieves Household Cleaner, Thieves Lozenges (hard), Thieves Lozenges (soft), Thieves Spray, Thieves Wipes, and Transformation

Selected Research:

Nishijima H, et al. "Mechanisms mediating the vasorelaxing action of eugenol, a pungent oil, on rabbit arterial tissue." *Jpn J Pharmacol.* 1999 Mar;79(3):327-34.

Jayashree T, et al. "Antiaflatoxigenic activity of eugenol is due to inhibition of lipid peroxidation." *Lett Appl Microbiol.* 1999; 28(3):179-83.

Wie MB, et al. "Eugenol protects neuronal cells from excitotoxic and oxidative injury in primary cortical cultures." *Neurosci Lett.* 1997: 4:225(2):93-6.

Capasso R, et al., "Preventive effect of eugenol on PAF and ethanol-induced gastric mucosal damage." *Fitoterapia.* 2000 Aug;71 Suppl 1:S131-7.

Lahlou S, et al., "Cardiovascular Effects of Eugenol, a Phenolic Compound Present in Many Plant Essential Oils, in Normotensive Rats." *J Cardiovasc Pharmacol.* 2004 Feb;43(2):250-257.

Mutalik S, Udupa N. "Effect of some penetration enhancers on the permeation of glibenclamide and glipizide through mouse skin." *Pharmazie.* 2003 Dec;58(12):891-4.

Olasupo NA, et al., "Activity of natural antimicrobial compounds against Escherichia coli and Salmonella enterica serovar Typhimurium." *Lett Appl Microbiol.* 2003; 37(6):448-51.

Miyazawa M, Hisama M. "Antimutagenic activity of phenylpropanoids from clove (Syzygium aromaticum)." *J Agric Food Chem.* 2003 Oct 22;51(22):6413-22.

Yang YC, Lee SH, Lee WJ, Choi DH, Ahn YJ. "Ovicidal and adulticidal effects of Eugenia caryophyllata bud and leaf oil compounds on Pediculus capitis." *J Agric Food Chem.* 2003 Aug 13;51(17):4884-8.

Ingvast-Larsson JC, Axen VC, Kiessling AK. "Effects of isoeugenol on in vitro neuromuscular blockade of rat phrenic nerve-diaphragm preparations." *Am J Vet Res.* 2003 Jun;64(6):690-3.

Kim SS, et al., "Eugenol suppresses cyclooxygenase-2 expression in lipopolysaccharide-stimulated mouse macrophage RAW264.7 cells." *Life Sci.* 2003 Jun 6;73 (3):337-48.

Nadin G, Goel BR, Yeung CA, Glenny AM. "Pulp treatment for extensive decay in primary teeth." *Cochrane Database Syst Rev.* 2003;(1):CD003220.

Kim EH, Kim HK, Ahn YJ. "Acaricidal activity of clove bud oil compounds against Dermatophagoides farinae and Dermatophagoides pteronyssinus (Acari: Pyroglyphidae)." *J Agric Food Chem.* 2003 Feb 12;51(4):885-9.

Lee HS. "Inhibitory activity of Cinnamomum cassia bark-derived component against rat lens aldose reductase." *J Pharm Pharm Sci.* 2002 Sep-Dec;5(3):226-30.

Huss U, et al., "Screening of ubiquitous plant constituents for COX-2 inhibition with a scintillation proximity based assay." *J Nat Prod.* 2002 Nov;65(11):1517-21.

Pessoa LM, et al., "Anthelmintic activity of essential oil of Ocimum gratissimum Linn. and eugenol against Haemonchus contortus." *Vet Parasitol.* 2002 Oct 16;109(1-2):59-63.

Friedman M, Henika PR, Mandrell RE. "Bactericidal activities of plant essential oils and some of their isolated constituents against Campylobacter jejuni, Escherichia coli, Listeria monocytogenes, and Salmonella enterica." *J Food Prot.* 2002 Oct;65(10):1545-60.

Sayyah M, Valizadeh J, Kamalinejad M. "Anticonvulsant activity of the leaf essential oil of Laurus nobilis against pentylenetetrazole- and maximal electroshock-induced seizures." *Phytomedicine.* 2002 Apr;9(3):212-6.

Lee KG, Shibamoto T. "Inhibition of malonaldehyde formation from blood plasma oxidation by aroma extracts and aroma components isolated from clove and eucalyptus." *Food Chem Toxicol.* 2001 Dec;39(12): 1199-204.

Vazquez BI, Fente C, Franco CM, Vazquez MJ, Cepeda A. "Inhibitory effects of eugenol and thymol on Penicillium citrinum strains in culture media and cheese." *Int J Food Microbiol.* 2001 Jul 20;67(1-2):157-63.

Atsumi T, et al., "Reactive oxygen species generation and photo-cytotoxicity of eugenol in solutions of various pH." *Biomaterials.* 2001 Jun;22(12):1459-66.

Benencia F, Courreges MC. "In vitro and in vivo activity of eugenol on human herpesvirus." *Phytother Res.* 2000 Nov;14 (7):495-500.

Teissedre PL, Waterhouse AL. "Inhibition of oxidation of human low-density lipoproteins by phenolic substances in different essential oils varieties." *J Agric Food Chem.* 2000 Sep;48(9):3801-5.

Vidhya N, Devaraj SN. "Antioxidant effect of eugenol in rat intestine." *Indian J Exp Biol.* 1999 Dec;37(12):1192-5.

Ahmed M, et al., "Analgesic principle from Abutilon indicum." *Pharmazie.* 2000 Apr; 55(4):314-6.

Kelm MA, Nair MG, Strasburg GM, DeWitt DL. "Antioxidant and cyclooxygenase inhibitory phenolic compounds from Ocimum sanctum Linn." *Phytomedicine.* 2000 Mar;7(1):7-13.

Nishijima H, et al., "Mechanisms mediating the vasorelaxing action of eugenol, a pungent oil, on rabbit arterial tissue." *Jpn J Pharmacol.* 1999 Mar;79(3):327-34.

Jayashree T, Subramanyam C. "Antiaflatoxigenic activity of eugenol is due to inhibition of lipid peroxidation." *Lett Appl Microbiol.* 1999 Mar;28(3):179-83.

Rao M, Kumar MM, Rao MA. "In vitro and in vivo effects of phenolic antioxidants against cisplatin-induced nephrotoxicity." *J Biochem* (Tokyo). 1999 Feb;125(2):383-90.

Uchida M, Nakajin S, Toyoshima S, Shinoda M. "Antioxidative effect of sesamol and related compounds on lipid peroxidation." *Biol Pharm Bull.* 1996 Apr;19(4):623-26.

Zhao ZS, O'Brien PJ. "The prevention of CCl4-induced liver necrosis in mice by naturally occurring methylenedioxybenzenes." *Toxicol Appl Pharmacol.* 1996 Oct;140 (2):411-21.

Nagababu E, Lakshmaiah N. "Inhibition of xanthine oxidase-xanthine-iron mediated lipid peroxidation by eugenol in liposomes." *Mol Cell Biochem.* 1997 Jan;166(1-2):65-71.

Nagababu E, Sesikeran B, Lakshmaiah N. "The protective effects of eugenol on carbon tetrachloride induced hepatotoxicity in rats." *Free Radic Res.* 1995 Dec;23(6):617-27.

Reddy AC, Lokesh BR. "Effect of curcumin and eugenol on iron-induced hepatic toxicity in rats." *Toxicology.* 1996 Jan 22;107(1):39-45.

Zheng GQ, Kenney PM, Lam LK. "Sesquiterpenes from clove (Eugenia caryophyllata) as potential anticarcinogenic agents." *J Nat Prod.* 1992 Jul;55(7):999-1003.

"Inhibitory effect of eugenol on non-enzymatic lipid peroxidation in rat liver mitochondria." *Biochem Pharmacol.* 1992 Jun 9;43(11):2393-400.

Combava

(See CITRUS HYSTRIX)

Copaiba (Copal)

Copaiba (Copal) *(Copaifera reticulata/langsdorfii)*

Botanical Family: Fabaceae (alt. Leguminosae)

Plant Origin: Brazil

Extraction Method: Tapped directly from tree

Chemical Constituents:
Delta-Elemene (2-3%)
Alpha-Cubebene (1%)
Alpha-Copaene (2-4%)
Beta-Elemene (1-2%)
Beta-Caryophyllene (39-42%)
Trans-Alpha-Bergamotene (3-5%)
Germacrene D (4-6%)
Beta-Bisabolene (1%)
Delta-Cadinene (2-3%)

Note: The word "Copal" is derived from the Spanish word for incense (copelli) and can refer to any number of different resinous gums or exudates from trees in Malaysia and South America. Copals are known as black (Protium copal), white (blanco) (Bursera bipinnata), gold (oro) (H. courbaril), and Brazilian (Copaifera langsforfii or reticulata). Only the Brazilian copal or copaiba has a GRAS distinction in the U.S. and has the most published research on its anti-inflammatory effects. It is the only essential oil tapped directly from the tree; it is not distilled. The other copals are distilled from hardened resin.

Historical Data: Healers and *curanderos* in the Amazon use copaiba resin for all types of pain and inflammatory disorders, both internal (stomach ulcers and cancer) and external (skin disorders and insect bites). In Peruvian traditional medicine, three or four drops of the resin are mixed with a spoonful of honey and taken as a natural sore throat remedy. It is also employed in Peruvian and Brazilian herbal medicine systems as an anti-inflammatory and antiseptic for the urinary tract (cystitis, bladder, and kidney disorders), and in the treatment of urinary problems, stomach ulcers, syphilis, tetanus, bronchitis, and tuberculosis.

In Brazilian herbal medicine the resin is highly regarded as a strong antiseptic and expectorant for the respiratory tract (including bronchitis and sinusitis) and as an antiseptic gargle. It is a popular home-remedy in Brazil for sore throats and tonsillitis (1/2 teaspoon of resin is added to warm water).

Medical Properties: Anti-inflammatory (powerful), mucolytic, anti-ulcer, antiseptic.

USES: pain relief (strong anti-inflammatory), arthritis, rheumatism, skin disorders, insect bites, stomach distress, urinary disorders, sore throat

Application: Diffuse, directly inhale, or apply topically. Add to food or soy/rice milk as dietary supplement.

Safety Data: Approved as a food additive in the U.S.

Selected Research:

Gomes, N. M., "Antinociceptive activity of Amazonian Copaiba oils." *J. Ethnopharmacol.* 2007 Feb; 109(3): 486-92.

Paiva, L. A., et al. "Anti-inflammatory effect of kaurenoic acid, a diterpene from Copaifera langsdorffi on acetic acid-induced colitis in rats." Vascul. *Pharmacol.* 2002 Dec; 39(6):303-7.

Veiga, V. F., et al. "Phytochemical and antioedematogenic studies of commercial copaiba oils available in Brazil." *Phytother. Res.* 2001; 15(6): 476–80.

Ghelardini, C., et al. "Local anaesthetic activity of beta-caryophyllene." *Farmaco.* 2001; 56(5-7): 387-9.

Cilantro (from which corriander Essential Oil is made)

Basile, A. C., et al. "Anti-inflammatory activity of oleoresin from Brazilian Copaifera." *J. Ethnopharmacol.* 1988; 22: 101–9.

Fernandes, R. M., Contribuicao para o conhecimento do efito antiiinflamatorio e analgesico do balsamo de copaiba e alguns de seus constituintes quimicos. Thesis, 1986. Federal University of Rio de Janeiro.

Lima, S. R., et al. "In vivo and in vitro studies on the anticancer activity of Copaifera multijuga Hayne and its fractions." *Phytother. Res.* 2003 Nov; 17(9): 1048-53.

Found in: Deep Relief Roll-on, Breathe Again Roll-on

Coriander *(Coriandrum sativum)*

Botanical Family: Apiaceae or Umbelliferae (parsley)

Plant Origin: Russia

Extraction Method: Steam distilled from seeds (fruit).

Chemical Constituents:
Linalol (65-78%)
Alpha-Pinene (3-7%)
Camphor (4-6%)
Gamma-Terpinene (2-7%)
Limonene (2-5%)
Geranyl Acetate (1-3.5%)
Geraniol (0.5-3%)

ORAC: 298,300 µTE/100g

Historical Data: Coriander seeds were found in the ancient Egyptian tomb of Ramses II. This oil has been researched at Cairo University for its effects in lowering glucose and insulin levels and supporting pancreatic function. It has also been studied for its effects in strengthening the pancreas.

Medical Properties: Anti-inflammatory, sedative, analgesic

USES: Diabetes, arthritis or intestinal problems

Fragrant Influence: Soothing and calming.

Application: Dilute 1 part EO with 1 part VO; (1) apply 2-4 drops on location, (2) chakras/Vita Flex points, (3) directly inhale, (4) diffuse, or (5) take as dietary supplement (see Appendices E and T).

Selected Research:

Delaquis PJ, et al., "Antimicrobial activity of individual and mixed fractions of dill, cilantro, coriander and eucalyptus essential oils." *Int J Food Microbiol.* 2002 Mar 25;74(1-2):101-9.

Elgayyar M, et al., "Antimicrobial activity of essential oils from plants against selected pathogenic and saprophytic microorganisms." *J Food Prot.* 2001 Jul;64(7):1019-24.

Found In: Longevity

Cumin *(Cuminum cyminum)*

Botanical Family: Apiaceae or Umbelliferae (parsley)

Plant Origin: Egypt

Extraction Method: Steam distilled from seeds.

Key Constituents:
Cuminaldehyde (16-22%)
Gamma-Terpinene (16-22%)
Beta-Pinene (12-18%)
Para-Mentha-1,3 &1,4-dien-7-al (25-35%)
Para-Cymene (3-8%)

ORAC: 82,400 µTE/100g

Historical Data: The Hebrews used cumin as an antiseptic for circumcision.

Cumin Seed Pods

Medical Properties: Antitumoral, anti-inflammatory, antioxidant, antiviral, digestive aid, liver protectant, immune stimulant

USES: Cancer, infectious disease, digestive problems

Application: Dietary Supplement: dilute 1 part EO with 4 parts VO, put in a capsule and take 1 daily or as directed by a health professional; (1) dilute 1 drop with 4 drops vegetable oil, test on small area of skin or the underside of arm, then apply, (2) chakras/Vita Flex points, (3) directly inhale, (4) diffuse up to 10 minutes three times daily, or (5) take as dietary supplement (see Appendices E and T).

Found In: Detoxzyme

Caution: Dilute before applying to skin. Avoid direct sunlight or UV rays for up to 12 hours after applying.

Selected Research:

Ramakrishna Rao R, Platel K, Srinivasan K. "In vitro influence of spices and spice-active principles on digestive enzymes of rat pancreas and small intestine." *Nahrung.* 2003 Dec;47(6):408-12.

Singh G, et al., "Studies on essential oils: part 10; antibacterial activity of volatile oils of some spices." *Phytother Res.* 2002 Nov; 16(7):680-2.

Dhandapani S, et al., "Hypolipidemic effect of Cuminum cyminum L. on alloxan-induced diabetic rats." *Pharmacol Res.* 2002 Sep; 46(3):251-5.

Krishnakantha TP, Lokesh BR. "Scavenging of superoxide anions by spice principles." *Indian J Biochem Biophys.* 1993 Apr;30(2):133-4.

Reddy AC, Lokesh BR. "Studies on spice principles as antioxidants in the inhibition of lipid peroxidation of rat liver microsomes." *Mol Cell Biochem.* 1992 Apr;111(1-2):117-24.

Banerjee S, et al., "Influence of certain essential oils on carcinogen-metabolizing enzymes and acid-soluble sulfhydryls in mouse liver." *Nutr Cancer.* 1994;21(3):263-9.

Tantaoui-Elaraki A, Beraoud L. "Inhibition of growth and aflatoxin production in Aspergillus parasiticus by essential oils of selected plant materials." *J Environ Pathol Toxicol Oncol.* 1994;13(1):67-72.

Cypress *(Cupressus sempervirens)*

Botanical Family: Cupressaceae (cypress)

Plant Origin: France, Spain

Extraction Method: Steam distilled from branches.

Key Constituents:
Alpha-Pinene (40-65%)
Beta-Pinene (0.5-3%)
Delta-3-Carene (12-25%)
Limonene (1.8-5%)
Cedrol (0.8-7%)
Myrcene (1-3.5%)
Manoyle Oxide
Iso-pimaradiene
Karahanaenone

ORAC: 24,300 µTE/100g

Historical Data: The Phoenicians and Cretans used cypress for building ships and bows, while the Egyptians made sarcaphagi from the wood. The Greeks used cypress to carve statues to their gods. The Greek word '*sempervirens*' for which the botanical name is derived means "live forever." The tree

Cypress

shares its name with the island of Cypress, where it is used for worship. Legend says the cross of Jesus was made from cypress wood. It is often planted in graveyards.

Medical Properties: Improves circulation and strengthens blood capillaries; anti-infectious, antispasmodic; discourages fluid retention

USES: Diabetes, circulatory disorders, cancer (Jean Valnet, M.D.), grounding, stabilizing

Fragrant Influence: Eases the feeling of loss and creates a sense of security and grounding. Also helps heal emotional trauma, calms, soothes anger, and helps life flow better. Can help soothe irritating coughs and minor chest discomfort.

Application: Dilute 1 part EO with 1 part VO; (1) apply 2-4 drops on location or massaging toward center of body, (2) chakras/Vita Flex points, (3) directly inhale, (4) diffuse, or (5) take as dietary supplement (see Appendices E and T).

Bible Reference:

Isaiah 44:14—"He heweth him down cedars, and taketh the cypress and the oak, which he strengtheneth for himself among the trees of the forest: he planteth an ash, and the rain doth nourish it."

Found In: Aroma Life, Aroma Siez, BodyGize, Cel-Lite Magic Massage Oil, HRT Tincture, Power Meal, and R.C.

Selected Research:

Karkabounas S, et al., Effects of Cupressus sempervirens cone extract on lipid parameters in Wistar rats. *In Vivo.* 2003 Jan-Feb; 17(1):101-3.

Cypress, Blue *(Callitris intratropica)*

Botanical Family: Cypressaceae

Plant Origin: Australia

Extraction Method: Steam distillation from the leaves and wood of the tree.

Key Constituents:
Alpha, Beta, Gamma Eudesmols (18-30%)
Guaiol (8-18%)
Bulnesol (5-15%)
Alpha, Beta and Delta Selinenes (5-10%)

ORAC: 73,100 µTE/100g

Historical Data: Blue cypress in ancient times was used for incense, perfume and embalming.

Medical Properties: Anti-inflammatory, anti-viral

USES: Viral infections (Herpes simplex, herpes zoster, cold sores, human papilloma virus etc.)

Application: (1) apply 2-4 drops on location, dilution not required except for the most sensitive skin, (2) chakras/Vita Flex points, (3) directly inhale, or (4) diffuse up to 1 hour three times daily (see Appendices E and T).

Found In: Australian Blue, Brain Power, Essential Beauty Syrum – Dry Skin, and Highest Potential

Davana *(Artemisia pallens)*

Botanical Family: Asteraceae or Compositae (daisy)

Extraction Method: Steam distilled from flowers and leaves

Chemical Constituents:
Cis-davanone (35-40%)
Trans-davanone (4-6%)
Isodavanone (2-4%)
Nerol (8-12%)
Geraniol (4-6%)

Historical Data: Grows in the same areas of India as sandalwood. Has been used in India for diabetes, digestive problems (expels parasites), fighting infections and calming anger. It has been recommended as an aphrodisiac, and is often used in perfumery. It has a very rich, concentrated aroma and is usually used only in very small quantities. It should always be diluted because it is high in ketones. The aroma tends to develop differently depending on the individual chemistry of the person wearing the oil.

Medical Properties: Anti-infectious, antiviral, aphrodisiac, anthelmintic, calmative

USES: Skin infections, headaches, emotional stress, worm infestations, sugar metabolism

Application: Dilute at least 50-50 with vegetable oil and apply 1-2 drops on location or on chakras/vitaflex points. Davana is usually used as a complement in very small amounts in essential oil blends.

Found In: Trauma Life, Essential Beauty Serums

Dill *(Anethum graveolens)*

Botanical Family: Apiaceae or Umbelliferae (parsley)

Plant Origin: Austria, Hungary

Extraction Method: Steam distilled from whole plant.

Key Constituents:
Carvone (30-45%)
Limonene (15-25%)
Alpha- and Beta-Phellandrenes (20-35%)

ORAC: 35,600 µTE/100g

Historical Data: The dill plant is mentioned in the Papyrus of Ebers from Egypt (1550 B.C.). Roman gladiators rubbed their skin with dill before each match. Listed in Dioscorides' De Materia Medica (A.D. 78), Europe's first authoritive guide to medicines, that became the standard reference work for herbal treatments

Dill

for over 1,700 years. It was listed in Hildegard's Medicine, a compilation of early German medicines by highly-regarded Benedictine herbalist Hildegard of Bingen (1098-1179).

Medical Properties: Antidiabetic, Antispasmodic, antibacterial, expectorant, pancreatic stimulant, insulin/blood sugar regulator

USES: Diabetes, digestive problems, liver deficiencies

Fragrant Influence: Calms the autonomic nervous system and, when diffused with Roman chamomile, combats ADHD.

Application: Dilute 1 part EO with 1 part VO; (1) apply 2-4 drops on location or abdomen, (2) chakras/Vita Flex points, (3) directly inhale, (4) diffuse, or (5) take as dietary supplement (see Appendices E and T).

Selected Research:

Lis-Balchin M, Hart S. A preliminary study of the effect of essential oils on skeletal and smooth muscle in vitro. *J Ethnopharmacol.* 1997 Nov;58(3):183-7.

Delaquis PJ, et al., Antimicrobial activity of individual and mixed fractions of dill, cilantro, coriander and eucalyptus essential oils. *Int J Food Microbiol.* 2002 Mar 25;74(1-2):101-9.

Douglas, Fir

(see FIR, DOUGLAS)

Elemi *(Canarium luzonicum)*

Botanical Family: Burseraceae (frankincense)

Plant Origin: Philippines

Extraction Method: Steam distilled from the gum/resin of the tree.

Key Constituents:
Limonene (40-72%)
Alpha-Phellandrene (10-24%)
Sabinene (3-8%)
Elemol (1-25%)

Historical Data: Elemi has been used in Europe for hundreds of years in salves for skin and is included in celebrated healing ointments, such as *baum paralytique.* Used by a 17th century physician, J. J. Wecker, on the battle wounds of soldiers, elemi belongs to the same botanical family as frankincense *(Boswellia carteri)* and myrrh *(Commiphora myrrha).* The Egyptians used elemi for embalming, and subsequent cultures (particularly in Europe) used it for skin care and for reducing fine lines, wrinkles, and skintone.

Medical Properties: Antispasmodic, anti-inflammatory, antimicrobial, antiseptic

USES: Muscle/nerve pain, skin problems (scars, acne, wrinkles), can be grounding and used to clear the mind

Fragrant Influence: Its spicy incense-like fragrance is very conducive toward meditation. Can be grounding and used to clear the mind.

Application: (1) Apply 2-4 drops on location, (2) chakras/Vita Flex points, (3) directly inhale, or (4) diffuse (see Appendices E and T), (5) If used as a dietary supplement, put one drop in a capsule and take or put 1 drop in 4 fl. oz. of liquid (rice milk, etc.).

Found In: Ortho Sport Massage Oil

Eucalyptus Citriodora *(Eucalyptus citriodora)*

Botanical Family: Myrtaceae (myrtle)

Plant Origin: China

Extraction Method: Steam distilled from leaves.

Key Constituents:
Citronellal (75-85%)
Neo-isopulegol + Isopulegol (0-10%)

ORAC: 83,000 µTE/100g

Historical Data: Traditionally used to perfume linen closets and as an insect repellent.

Medical Properties: Analgesic, antiviral, antibacterial, antifungal, expectorant, and insecticidal

USES: Fungal infections (ringworm, Candida), respiratory infections, viral infections (Herpes, shingles)

Application: Dilute 1 part EO with 1 part VO, then apply on location; (1) apply 2-4 drops on location, (2) chakras/Vita Flex points, (3) directly inhale, or (4) diffuse up to 30 minutes three times daily (see Appendices E and T).

Found In: R.C.

Selected Research:

Silva J, et al., Analgesic and anti-inflammatory effects of essential oils of Eucalyptus. *J Ethnopharmacol.* 2003 Dec;89(2-3):277-83.

Ohno T, et al., Antimicrobial activity of essential oils against Helicobacter pylori. *Helicobacter.* 2003 Jun;8(3):207-15.

Ramsewak RS, In vitro antagonistic activity of monoterpenes and their mixtures against 'toe nail fungus' pathogens. *Phytother Res.* 2003 Apr;17(4):376-9.

Low D, Rawal BD, Griffin WJ. Antibacterial action of the essential oils of some Australian Myrtaceae with special references to the activity of chromatographic fractions of oil of Eucalyptus citriodora. *Planta Med.* 1974 Sep;26(2):184-5.

Eucalyptus Dives *(Eucalyptus dives)*

Botanical Family: Myrtaceae (myrtle)

Plant Origin: Australia

Extraction Method: Steam distilled from leaves.

Key Constituents:
Alpha- and Beta-Phellandrene (23-30%)
Piperitone (35-45%)
Para-Cymene (6-10%)
Alpha-Thujen (2-6%)
Terpinene-4-ol (3-6%)

Medical Properties: Mucolytic, diuretic, antibacterial

USES: Hypertension, throat/lung/sinus infections

Fragrant Influence: Has a fresh, invigorating aroma that helps clear sinus and brochi.

Application: Dilute 1 part EO with 1 part VO; (1) apply 2-4 drops on location, (2) chakras/Vita Flex points, or (3) diffuse (see Appendices E and T).

Selected Research:

Delaquis PJ, et al., Antimicrobial activity of individual and mixed fractions of dill, cilantro, coriander and eucalyptus essential oils. *Int J Food Microbiol.* 2002 Mar 25;74(1-2):101-9.

Eucalyptus Globulus *(Eucalyptus globulus)*

Botanical Family: Myrtaceae (myrtle)

Plant Origin: China

Extraction Method: Steam distilled from leaves.

Key Constituents:
1,8 Cineole (Eucalyptol) (58-80%)
Alpha Pinene (10-22%)
Limonene (1-8%)
Para-Cymene (1-5%)
Trans-Pinocarveol (1-5%)
Aromadendrene (1-5%)
Globulol (0.5-1.5%)

ORAC: 2,400 µTE/100g

Historical Data: For centuries, Australian Aborigines used the disinfecting leaves to cover wounds. Shown by laboratory tests to be a powerful antimicrobial agent, *E. globulus* contains a high percentage of eucalyptol (a key ingredient in many antiseptic mouth rinses). Often used for the respiratory system. Eucalyptus has been investigated for its powerful insect repellent effects (Trigg, 1996). Eucalyptus trees have been planted throughout parts of North Africa to successfully block the spread of malaria. According to Jean Valnet, M.D., a solution of 2 percent eucalyptus oil sprayed in the air will kill 70 percent of airborne staph bacteria. Some doctors still use solutions of eucalyptus oil in surgical dressings.

Medical Properties: Expectorant, mucolytic, antimicrobial, antibacterial, antifungal, antiviral, anti-aging

USES: Respiratory/sinus infections, decongestant, rheumatism/arthritis, soothe sore muscles

Fragrant Influence: It promotes health, well-being, purification, and healing.

Application: Dilute 1 part EO with 1 part VO; (1) apply 2-4 drops on location, (2) chakras/Vita Flex points, (3) directly inhale, (4) diffuse, or (5) take as dietary supplement (see Appendices E and T).

Found In: Chelex Tincture, Dentarome Ultra Toothpaste, Ortho Sport Massage Oil, and R.C.

Selected Research:

Tovey ER, et al. "A simple washing procedure with eucalyptus oil for controlling house dust mites and their allergens in clothing and bedding." *J Allergy Clin Immunol.* 1997; 100(4):464-6.

Weyers W, et al. "Skin absorption of volatile oils. Pharmacokinetics." *Pharm Unserer Zeit.* 1989;18(3):82-6.

Zanker KS, et al. "Evaluation of surfactant-like effects of commonly used remedies for colds." *Respiration.* 1980;39(3):150-7.

Lee KG, Shibamoto T. Inhibition of malonaldehyde formation from blood plasma oxidation by aroma extracts and aroma components isolated from clove and eucalyptus. *Food Chem Toxicol.* 2001 Dec;39(12):1199-204.

Eucalyptus Polybractea (*Eucalyptus polybractea*)

Botanical Family: Myrtaceae (myrtle)

Plant Origin: Australia

Extraction Method: Steam distilled from leaves.

Key Constituents:
1,8 Cineole (Eucalyptol) (60-80%)
Limonene (1-5%)
Para-Cymene (1-5%)
Alpha-Pinene (1-5%)

Medical Properties: antiviral, antibacterial, anti-inflammatory, expectorant, mucolytic, and insect repellent

USES: Acne, urinary tract/bladder infections, viral infections (Herpes)

Application: Dilute 1 part EO with 1 part VO; (1) Apply 2-4 drops on location, (2) chakras/Vita Flex points, (3) diffuse or put in humidifier, or (4) take as dietary supplement (see Appendices E and T).

Eucalyptus Radiata (*Eucalyptus radiata*)

Botanical Family: Myrtaceae (myrtle)

Plant Origin: Australia

Extraction Method: Steam distilled from leaves.

Key Constituents:
1,8 Cineole (Eucalyptol) (60-75%)
Alpha Terpineol (5-10%)
Limonene (4-8%)
Alpha Pinene (2-6%)

Medical Properties: Antibacterial, antiviral, expectorant, anti-inflammatory

USES: Respiratory/sinus infections, viral infections, fights Herpes simplex when combined with bergamot

Application: Dilute 1 part EO with 1 part VO; (1) apply 2-4 drops on location, (2) chakras/ Vita Flex points, (3) directly inhale, (4) diffuse or put in humidifier (see Appendices E and T).

Found In: AromaGuard Mountain Mist Deodorant, Carbozyme, Dentarome Toothpaste, Dentarome Plus Toothpaste, Dentarome Ultra Toothpaste, KidScents Toothpaste, Raven, R.C., Thieves, Thieves Bar Soap, Thieves Foaming Hand Soap, Thieves Household Cleaner, Thieves Lozenges (hard), Thieves Lozenges (soft), Thieves Spray, and Thieves Wipes

Fennel

Fennel *(Foeniculum vulgare)*

Botanical Family: Apiaceae or Umbelliferae (parsley)

Plant Origin: Hungary

Extraction Method: Steam distilled from the crushed seeds (fruit).

Key Constituents:
Trans-Anethol (60-80%)
Fenchone + Linalol (12-16%)
Alpha-Pinene (3-5%)
Methyl Chavicol (2-5%)

ORAC: 238,400 µTE/100g

Historical Data: Believed to ward off evil spirits and to protect against spells cast by witches during medieval times. Sprigs were hung over doors to fend off evil phantasms. For hundreds of years, fennel seeds have been used as a digestive aid and to balance menstrual cycles. It is mentioned in one of the oldest known medical records, Ebers Papyrus (dating from sixteenth century B.C.) an ancient Egyptian list of 877 prescriptions and recipes.

It was listed in Hildegard's Medicine, a compilation of early German medicines by highly-regarded Benedictine herbalist Hildegard of Bingen (1098-1179).

Medical Properties: Antidiabetic, anti-inflammatory, antitumoral, estrogen-like, digestive aid, antiparasitic (worms), antiseptic, antispasmodic, analgesic, increases metabolism

USES: Diabetes, cancer, obesity, arthritis/ rheumatism, urinary tract infection, fluid retention, intestinal parasites, menstrual problems/PMS, digestive problems

Application: Dilute 1 part EO with 1 part VO; (1) apply 2-4 drops on location, (2) chakras/Vita Flex points, (3) directly inhale, (4) diffuse, or (5) take as dietary supplement (see Appendices E and T).

Cautions: Avoid using if epileptic.

Found In: ComforTone, CortisStop-Women's, Detoxzyme, Di-Gize, Dragon Time, Dragon Time Bath & Shower Gel, Dragon Time Massage Oil, Essentialzyme, Estro Tincture, Femi Gen, ICP, JuvaFlex, K&B Tincture, Mister, Para Free Softgels, Power Meal, Prenolone, Prenolone Plus, ProGen, Progessence, and SclarEssence

Selected Research: Fyfe L, et al. "Inhibition of *Listeria monocytogenes* and *Salmonella enteriditis* by combinations of plant oils and derivatives of benzoic acid: the development of synergistic antimicrobial combinations." *Int J Antimicrob Agents.* 1997;9(3):195-9.

Lis-Balchin M, Hart S. A preliminary study of the effect of essential oils on skeletal and smooth muscle in vitro. *J Ethnopharmacol.* 1997 Nov;58(3):183-7.

Chainy GB, Manna SK, Chaturvedi MM, Aggarwal BB. Anethole blocks both early and late cellular responses transduced by tumor necrosis factor: effect on NF-kappaB,

Douglas Fir

AP-1, JNK, MAPKK and apoptosis. *Oncogene.* 2000 Jun 8;19(25):2943-50.

Haze S, Sakai K, Gozu Y. et al., Effects of fragrance inhalation on sympathetic activity in normal adults. *Jpn J Pharmacol.* 2002 Nov;90(3):247-53.

Fir, Douglas *(Pseudotsuga menziesii)*

Botanical Family: Abietaceae

Plant Origin: Idaho

Extraction Method: Steam-distilled

Chemical Constituents:
Alpha Pinene (25-40%)
Beta Pinene (7-15%)
Limonene (6-11%)
Bornyl Acetate (8-15%)

ORAC: 69,000 µTE/100g

Medical Properties: Antitumoral, antioxidant, anti-fungal, pain relieving

USES: Respiratory/sinus infections

Application: Dilute 1 part EO with 1 part VO; (1) apply 2-4 drops on location, (2) chakras/Vita Flex points, (3) directly inhale, or (4) diffuse (see Appendices E and T).

Found In: Evergreen Essence and Regenlone

Fir, Balsam (Idaho)

(See BALSAM FIR, IDAHO)

Fir, White *(Abies concolor)*

Botanical Family: Pinaceae

Plant Origin: Idaho

Extraction Method: Steam-distilled

Key Constituents:
Alpha Pinene (8-12%)
Beta Pinene (20-30%)
Camphene (7-15%)
Bornyl Acetate (11-16%)
Delta Cadinene (2-7%)

ORAC: 47,900 µTE/100g

Medical Properties: Anti-tumoral, anti-cancerous, anti-oxidant, pain relieving

USES: Respiratory infections, anti-fungal

Application: Dilute 1 part EO with 1 part VO; (1) apply 2-4 drops on location, (2) chakras/Vita Flex points, (3) directly inhale, or (4) diffuse (see Appendices E and T).

Found In: AromaGuard Mountain Mint Deodorant, Australian Blue, Evergreen Essence, Grounding, Highest Potential, ImmuneTune, and Into the Future

Fleabane, Canadian *(Conyza canadensis)*

Botanical Family: Asteraceae or Compositae (daisy)

Plant Origin: Canada

Extraction Method: Steam distilled from stems, leaves, and flowers (aerial parts).

Key Constituents:
Limonene (60-75%)
Cis Alpha Bergamotene (5-11%)
Trans Beta Ocimene (3-7%)

ORAC: 26,700 µTE/100g

Medical Properties: Stimulates liver and pancreas, anti-aging (stimulates growth hormone), antirheumatic, antispasmodic, vasodilating, reduces blood pressure

USES: Hypertension, hepatitis, accelerated aging

Application: Dilute 1 part EO with 1 part VO; (1) apply 2-4 drops on location, (2) chakras/ Vita Flex points, (3) directly inhale, (4) diffuse, or (5) take as dietary supplement (see Appendices E and T).

Found In: CortiStop-Women's, Progessence, ThermaBurn, Ultra Young, and Ultra Young Plus

Frankincense *(Boswellia carteri)*

Botanical Family: Burseraceae (Frankincense)

Plant Origin: Somalia/Spain

Extraction Method: Steam distilled from gum/resin.

Key Constituents:
Alpha-Pinene (28-49%)
Limonene (10-16%)
Sabinene (3-7%)
Myrcene (8-12%)
Beta Caryophyllene (3-7%)
Alpha Thuyene (4-8%)
Paracymene (2-5%)

ORAC: 630 µTE/100g

Historical Data: Also known as "olibanum," or "Oil from Lebanon" the name frankincense is derived from the Medieval French word for "real incense." Frankincense is considered the "holy anointing oil" in the Middle East and has been used in religious ceremonies for thousands of years. It was well known during the time of Christ for its anointing and healing powers and was one of the gifts given to Christ at His birth. "Used to treat every conceivable ill known to man," frankincense was valued more than gold during ancient times, and only those with great wealth and abundance possessed it. It is mentioned in one of the oldest known medical records, Ebers Papyrus (dating from sixteenth century B.C.) an ancient Egyptian list of 877 prescriptions and recipes.

Medical Properties: Antitumoral, immuno-stimulant, antidepressant, muscle relaxing

USES: Depression, cancer, respiratory infections, inflammation, immune-stimulating

Frankincense

Fragrant Influence: Increases spiritual awareness, promotes meditation, improves attitude and uplifts spirits.

Frankincense contains sesquiterpenes which stimulate the limbic system of the brain (the center of memory and emotions) and the hypothalamus, pineal and pituitary glands. The hypothalamus is the master gland of the human body, producing many vital hormones including thyroid and growth hormone.

Application: (1) Apply 2-4 drops on location, (2) chakras/Vita Flex points, (3) directly inhale, (4) diffuse, (5) when using as a dietary supplement, dilute 1 drop os frankincense in 4 drops V-6 or olive oil and put in a capsule - take 1 capsule before each meal or as desired (see Appendices E and T).

Found In: 3 Wise Men, Abundance, Acceptance, ART Day Activator, Art Cleanser, ART Night Repair, Awaken, Believe, Boswellia Wrinkle Cream, Brain Power, ClaraDerm, CortiStop-Women's, Exodus, Egyptian Gold, Exodus II, Forgiveness, Gathering, Gratitude, Harmony, Highest Potential, Humility, ImmuPower, Inspiration, Into The Future, KidScents Tender Tush, Longevity, Longevity Softgels, Therma-Burn, Transformation, Trauma Life, Valor, Valor Bar Soap, and Wolfberry Eye Cream

Bible References: There are over 52 references to frankincense (considering that "incense" is translated from the Hebrew/Greek "frankincense" and is referring to the same oil). (See additional Bible references in Appendix D)

Exodus 30:34—"And the Lord said unto Moses, Take unto thee sweet spices, stacte, and onycha, and galbanum; these sweet spices with pure frankincense: of each shall there be a like weight:"

Leviticus 2:1—"And when any will offer a meat offering unto the Lord, his offering shall be of fine flour; and he shall pour oil upon it, and put frankincense thereon:"

Leviticus 2:2—"And he shall bring it to Aaron's sons the priests: and he shall take thereout his handful of the flour thereof, and of the oil thereof, with all the frankincense thereof; and the priest shall burn the memorial of it upon the altar, to be an offering made by fire, of a sweet savour unto the Lord:"

Selected Research:

Michie, C.A., et al. "Frankincense and myrrh as remedies in children." *J R Soc Med.* 1991;84(10):602-5.

Wang, L.G., et al. "Determination of DNA topoisomerase II activity from L1210 cells--a target for screening antitumor agents." *Chung Kuo Yao Li Hsueh Pao.* 1991;12(2):108-14.

Lis-Balchin M, Hart S. A preliminary study of the effect of essential oils on skeletal and smooth muscle in vitro. *J Ethnopharmacol.* 1997 Nov;58(3):183-7.

Crowell PL.Prevention and therapy of cancer by dietary monoterpenes. *J Nutr.* 1999 Mar;129(3):775S-778S.

Galbanum *(Ferula gummosa)*

Botanical Family: Apiaceae or Umbelliferae

Plant Origin: France, Iran

Extraction Method: Steam distilled from gum/resin derived from stems and branches.

Key Constituents:
Alpha-Pinene (5-21%)
Beta-Pinene (40-70%)
Delta-3-Carene (2-16%)
Myrcene (2.5-3.5%)
Sabinene (0.3-3%)

ORAC: 26,200 µTE/100g

Historical Data: Mentioned in Egyptian papyri and the Old Testament (Exodus 30:34) it was esteemed for its medicinal and spiritual properties. Dioscorides, an ancient Roman historian, records that galbanum was used for its antispasmodic, diuretic, and pain-relieving properties.

Medical Properties: Antiseptic, analgesic, and light antispasmodic, anti-inflammatory, circulatory stimulant, anticonvulsant

USES: Digestive problems (diarrhea), nervous tension, rheumatism, skin conditions (scar tissue, wrinkles)

Fragrant Influence: Harmonic and balancing, amplifies spiritual awareness and meditation. When combined with frankincense or sandalwood, the frequency rises dramatically.

Application: Dietary Supplement: dilute 1 part galbanium with 1 part vegetable oil, put in a capsule and take up to three times daily or as needed; (1) apply 2-4 drops on location, (2) chakras/Vita Flex points, (3) directly inhale, (4) diffuse up to 1 hour three times daily, or (5) take as dietary supplement (see Appendices E and T)

Found In: Exodus II, Gathering, Gratitude, and Highest Potential

Bible Reference: Exodus 30:34—"And the Lord said unto Moses, Take unto thee sweet spices, stacte, and onycha, and galbanum; these sweet spices with pure frankincense: of each shall there be a like weight:"

Selected Research:

Vaziri A. Antimicrobial action of galbanum. *Planta Med.* 1975 Dec;28(4):370-3.

Sayyah M, Mandgary A, Kamalinejad M. Evaluation of the anticonvulsant activity of the seed acetone extract of Ferula gummosa Boiss. against seizures induced by pentylenetetrazole and electroconvulsive shock in mice. *J Ethnopharmacol.* 2002 Oct;82(2-3):105-9.

Sadraei H, et al., Spasmolytic activity of essential oil and various extracts of Ferula gummosa Boiss. on ileum contractions. *Phytomedicine.* 2001 Sep;8(5):370-6.

Geranium *(Pelargonium graveolens)*

Botanical Family: Geraniaceae

Plant Origin: Egypt, India

Extraction Method: Steam distilled from the flowers and leaves.

Key Constituents:
Citronellol + Nerol (35-50%)
Citronnellyl Formate (9-15%)
Geraniol (5-10%)
6,9-Guaiadene (4-8%)
Isomenthone (4-8%)

Historical Data: Geranium has been used for centuries for regenerating and healing skin conditions.

Medical Properties: Antispasmodic, anti-oxidant, antitumoral, anti-inflammatory, hemostatic (stops bleeding), antibacterial, antifungal, improves blood flow, liver and pancreas stimulant, dilates bile ducts for liver detoxification, helps cleanse oily skin; revitalizes skin cells

USES: Hepatitis/fatty liver (Jean Valnet, M.D.), skin conditions (dermatitis, eczema, psoriasis, acne, vitiligo), fungal infections (ringworm), viral infections (Herpes, shingles), hormone imbalances, circulatory problems (improves blood flow), menstrual problems/PMS

Fragrant Influence: Helps release negative memories and eases nervous tension. It balances the emotions, lifts the spirit, and fosters peace, well-being, and hope.

Application: (1) Apply 2-4 drops on location, (2) chakras/Vita Flex points, (3) directly inhale, (4) diffuse, or (5) when using as a dietary supplement, dilute 1 drop os geranium in 4 drops V-6 or olive oil and put in a capsule - take 1 capsule before each meal or as desired. (see Appendices E and T).

Found In: Acceptance, Animal Scents Ointment, Animal Scents Shampoo, AromaGuard Meadow Mist Deodorant, Awaken, Boswellia Wrinkle Cream, Clarity, Dragon Time Bath & Shower Gel, EndoFlex, Envision, Evening Peace Bath & Shower Gel, Forgiveness, Gathering, Genesis Hand & Body Lotion, Gentle Baby, Harmony, Highest Potential,

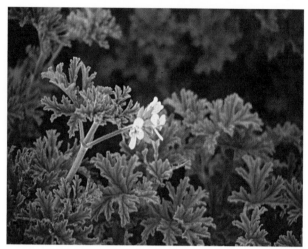

Geranium

Humility, Joy, JuvaFlex, JuvaTone, K&B Tincture, KidScents Lotion, Lady Sclareol, Lemon-Sage Clarifying Conditioner, Lemon-Sage Clarifying Shampoo, Melaleuca-Geranium Bar Soap, Prenolone, Prenolone Plus, Progessence, Release, Rosewood Moisturizing Conditioner, Rosewood Moisturizing Shampoo, SARA, Trauma Life, White Angelica, and Wolfberry Eye Cream

Selected Research:

Lis-Balchin, M., et al. "Antimicrobial activity of Pelargonium essential oils added to a quiche filling as a model food system." *Lett Appl Microbiol.* 1998;27(4):207-10.

Lis-Balchin, M., et al. "Comparative antibacterial effects of novel Pelargonium essential oils and solvent extracts." *Lett Appl Microbiol.* 1998;27(3):135-41.

Fang, H.J., et al. "Studies on the chemical components and anti-tumour action of the volatile oils from Pelargonium graveoleus." *Yao Hsueh Hsueh Pao.* 1989;24(5):366-71.

Thompson JD, et al., Qualitative and quantitative variation in monoterpene co-occurrence and composition in the essential oil of Thymus vulgaris chemotypes. *J Chem Ecol.* 2003 Apr;29(4):859-80.

Carnesecchi S, et al., Geraniol, a component of plant essential oils, sensitizes human colon cancer cells to 5-fluorouracil treatment. *IARC Sci Publ.* 2002;156:407-9.

Carnesecchi S, et al., Perturbation by geraniol of cell membrane permeability and signal transduction pathways in human colon cancer cells. *J Pharmacol Exp Ther*. 2002 Nov;303(2):711-5.

Choi HS, Song HS, Ukeda H, Sawamura M. Radical-scavenging activities of citrus essential oils and their components: detection using 1,1-diphenyl-2-picrylhydrazyl. *J Agric Food Chem*. 2000 Sep;48(9):4156-61.

Dorman HJ, Deans SG. Antimicrobial agents from plants: antibacterial activity of plant volatile oils. *J Appl Microbiol*. 2000 Feb;88(2):308-16.

Ginger *(Zingiber officinale)*

Botanical Family: Zingiberaceae (ginger)

Plant Origin: India, China

Extraction Method: Steam distilled from rhizomes/root.

Key Constituents:
Zingiberene + Alpha-Selinene (25-40%)
Beta-Sesquiphellandrene +
  Delta-Cadinene (7-14%)
Beta-Phellandrena +
  1,8 Cineol + Limonene (8-15%)
AR Curcumene (5-11%)

ORAC: 99,300 µTE/100g

Historical Data: Traditionally used to combat nausea. Women in the West African country of Senegal weave belts of ginger root to restore their mates' sexual potency.

Medical Properties: Anti-inflammatory, anticoagulant, digestive aid, anesthetic, expectorant

USES: Rheumatism/arthritis, digestive disorders, respiratory infections/congestion, muscular aches/pains, nausea

Fragrant Influence: Gentle, stimulating, endowing physical energy, and courage.

Application: Dilute 1 part EO with 1 part VO; (1) apply 2-4 drops on location, (2) chakras/ Vita Flex points, (3) directly inhale, (4) diffuse, or (5) take as dietary supplement (see Appendices E and T).

Ginger Root

Cautions: Anticoagulant properties can be enhanced when combined with Warfarin, aspirin, etc.

Found In: Abundance, ComforTone, Di-Gize, ICP, Magnify Your Purpose, Ultra Young, Ultra Young Plus

Selected Research:

Martins AP, Essential oil composition and antimicrobial activity of three Zingiberaceae from S.Tome e Principe. *Planta Med*. 2001 Aug;67(6):580-4.

Nurtjahja-Tjendraputra E, et al., Effective anti-platelet and COX-1 enzyme inhibitors from pungent constituents of ginger. *Thromb Res*. 2003;111(4-5):259-65.

Baliga MS, Jagetia GC, Rao SK, Babu K. Evaluation of nitric oxide scavenging activity of certain spices in vitro: a preliminary study. *Nahrung*. 2003 Aug;47(4):261-4.

Kirana C, et al., Antitumor activity of extract of Zingiber aromaticum and its bioactive sesquiterpenoid zerumbone. *Nutr Cancer*. 2003;45(2):218-25.

Ippoushi K, et al., [6]-Gingerol inhibits nitric oxide synthesis in activated J774.1 mouse macrophages and prevents peroxynitrite-induced oxidation and nitration reactions. *Life Sci*. 2003 Nov 14;73(26):3427-37.

Goldenrod

Goldenrod *(Solidago canadensis)*

Botanical Family: Asteraceae

Plant Origin: Canada

Extraction Method: Steam distilled from flowering tops.

Key Constituents:
Germacrene D (22-35%)
Alpha-Pinene (10-18%)
Myrcene (8-15%0
Sabinene (5-11%)
Limonene (6-12%)

ORAC: 61,900 µTE/100g

Historical Data: The genus name, solidago, comes from the Latin solide, which means 'to make whole'. During the Boston Tea Party, when English tea was dumped into Boston Harbor, Colonists drank goldenrod tea instead, which gave it the nickname 'Liberty Tea'.

Medical Properties: Diuretic, anti-inflammatory, anti-hypertensive, liver stimulant

USES: Hypertension, liver congestion, hepatitis/ fatty liver, circulatory conditions, urinary tract/bladder conditions

Application: Dilute 1 part EO with 1 part VO; (1) apply 2-4 drops on location or compress, (2) chakras/Vita Flex points, (3) directly inhale, (4) diffuse, or (5) take as dietary supplement (see Appendices E and T).

Selected Research:

Yarnell E. Botanical medicines for the urinary tract. *World J Urol.* 2002 Nov; 20(5):285-93. Epub 2002 Oct 17.

Grapefruit *(Citrus paradisi)*

Botanical Family: Rutaceae (citrus)

Plant Origin: South Africa, and California. (Grapefruit is a hybrid between *Citrus maxima* and *Citrus sinensis*.)

Extraction Method: Cold pressed from rind.

Key Constituents:
Limonene (88-95%)
Myrcene (1-4%)

ORAC: 22,600 µTE/100g

Medical Properties: Antitumoral, metabolic stimulant, antiseptic, detoxifying, diuretic, fat-dissolving, cleansing for kidneys, lymphatic and vascular system, antidepressant. Rich in limonene, which has been extensively studied for its ability to combat tumor growth in over 50 clinical studies.

USES: Alzheimers, fluid retention. depression, obesity, liver disorders, anxiety, cellulite

Fragrant Influence: Refreshing and uplifting. A 1995 Mie University study found that citrus fragrances boosted immunity, induced relaxation, and reduced depression.

Application: Dilute 1 part EO with 1 part VO; (1) apply 2-4 drops on location, (2) chakras/ Vita Flex points, (3) directly inhale, (4) diffuse, or (5) take as dietary supplement (see Appendices E and T).

Cautions: Avoid applying to skin that will be exposed to sunlight or UV light within 24 hours.

Found In: BodyGize, Cel-Lite Magic Massage Oil, Citrus Fresh, GLF, Power Meal, and Super C

Selected Research:

Haze S, Sakai K, Gozu Y. et al., Effects of fragrance inhalation on sympathetic activity in normal adults. *Jpn J Pharmacol.* 2002 Nov;90(3):247-53.

Miyazawa M, Tougo H, Ishihara M. Inhibition of acetylcholinesterase activity by essential oil from Citrus paradisi. *Nat Prod Lett.* 2001;15(3):205-10.

Niijima A, Nagai K. Effect of olfactory stimulation with flavor of grapefruit oil and lemon oil on the activity of sympathetic branch in the white adipose tissue of the epididymis. *Exp Biol Med (Maywood).* 2003 Nov;228(10):1190-2.

Wattenberg LW, et al., Inhibition of carcinogenesis by some minor dietary constituents. *Princess Takamatsu Symp.* 1985;16:193-203.

Alderman GG, Marth EH. Inhibition of growth and aflatoxin production of Aspergillus parasiticus by citrus oils. *Z Lebensm Unters Forsch.* 1976 Apr 28;160(4):353-8.

Fisher JF et al., A new coumarin from grapefruit peel oil. *Tetrahedron.* 1967 Jun;23(6):2523-8.

Crowell PL. Prevention and therapy of cancer by dietary monoterpenes. *J Nutr.* 1999 Mar;129(3):775S-778S.

Komori T, et al., Application of fragrances to treatments for depression. *Nihon Shinkei Seishin Yakurigaku Zasshi.* 1995 Feb;15(1): 39-42. Japanese.

Helichrysum *(Helichrysum italicum)*

Botanical Family: Asteraceae or Compositae (daisy)

Plant Origin: Yugoslavia, Corsica, Croatia, Spain

Extraction Method: Steam distilled from flower.

Key Constituents:
Neryl Acetate (25-35%)
Gamma Curcuneme (9-15%)
Limonene (8-13%)
Neryl Propionate (3-7%)
Alpha Pinene (3-8%)
Beta-Caryophyllene (1-5%)
Linalol (1-4%)
Nerol (2-5%)

ORAC: 1,700 µTE/100g

Helichrysum

Medical Properties: Anticoagulant, anesthetic, antispasmodic, antiviral, liver protectant / detoxifier / stimulant, chelates chemicals and toxins, regenerates nerves

USES: Herpes virus, Arteriosclerosis, atherosclerosis, hypertension, blood clots, liver disorders, circulatory disorders, skin conditions (eczema, psoriasis scar tissue, varicose veins)

Fragrant Influence: Uplifting to the subconscious.

Application: (1) Apply 2-4 drops on location, temple, forehead, back of neck, or outside of ear, (2) chakras/Vita Flex points, (3) directly inhale, (4) diffuse, or (5) take as dietary supplement (see Appendices E and T).

Found In: Aroma Life, Awaken, Brain Power, CardiaCare, Chelex, ClaraDerm Spray, Forgiveness, GLF, Juva Cleanse, Juva Flex, M-Grain, PanAway, and Trauma Life

Selected Research:

Nostro A, et al., Evaluation of antiherpesvirus-1 and genotoxic activities of Helichrysum italicum extract. *New Microbiol.* 2003 Jan;26(1):125-8.

Sala A, Anti-inflammatory and antioxidant properties of Helichrysum italicum. *J Pharm Pharmacol.* 2002 Mar;54(3):365-71.

Schinella GR, et al., Antioxidant activity of anti-inflammatory plant extracts. *Life Sci.* 2002 Jan 18;70(9):1023-33.

Hyssop

Hyssop *(Hyssopus officinalis)*

Botanical Family: Lamiaceae or Labiatae (mint)

Plant Origin: France, Hungary

Extraction Method: Steam distilled from stems/leaves.

Key Constituents:
Beta Pinene (13.5-23%)
Sabinene (2-3%)
Pinocamphone (5.5-17.5%)
Iso-Pinochamphone (34.5-50%)
Gemacrene D (2-3%)
Limonene (1-4%)

ORAC: 20,900 µTE/100g

Historical Data: While there is some uncertainty that *Hyssopus officinalis* is the same species of plant as the hyssop referred to in the Bible, there is no question that *H. officinalis* has been used medicinally for almost a millennium for its antiseptic properties. It has also been used for opening the respiratory system.

Medical Properties: Mucolytic, decongestant, anti-inflammatory, regulates lipid metabolism, antiviral, antibacterial, and antiparasitic

USES: Respiratory infections/congestion, parasites (expelling worms), viral infections, and circulatory disorders

Fragrant Influence: Stimulates creativity and meditation.

Application: Dilute 1 part EO with 1 part VO; (1) apply 2-4 drops on location, (2) chakras/

Vita Flex points, (3) directly inhale, (4) diffuse, or (5) take as dietary supplement (see Appendices E and T).

Cautions: Avoid use if epileptic.

Found In: Awaken, Egyptian Gold, Exodus, Exodus II, GLF, Harmony, ImmuPower, Relieve It, and White Angelica

Bible References: (See additional Bible references in Appendix D).

Exodus 12:22— "And ye shall take a bunch of hyssop, and dip it in the blood that is in the bason, and strike the lintel and the two side posts with the blood that is in the bason; and none of you shall go out at the door of his house until the morning."

Leviticus 14:4—"Then shall the priest command to take for him that is to be cleansed two birds alive and clean, and cedar wood, and scarlet, and hyssop:"

Leviticus 14:6—"As for the living bird, he shall take it, and the cedar wood, and the scarlet, and the hyssop, and shall dip them and the living bird in the blood of the bird that was killed over the running water:"

Selected Research:

Lu M, et al., Muscle relaxing activity of Hyssopus officinalis essential oil on isolated intestinal preparations. *Planta Med.* 2002 Mar;68(3):213-6.

Idaho Tansy *(Tanacetum vulgare)*

(See TANSY, IDAHO)

Jasmine Absolute *(Jasminum officinale)*

Botanical Family: Oleaceae (olive)

Plant Origin: India

Extraction Method: Absolute extraction from flower. Jasmine is actually an "essence" not an essential oil. The flowers must be picked at night to maximize fragrance.

NOTE: One pound of jasmine oil requires about 1,000 pounds of jasmine or 3.6 million fresh unpacked blossoms. The blossoms must be collected before sunrise, or much of the fragrance will have evaporated. The quality of the blossoms may also be compromised if they are crushed. A single pound of pure jasmine oil may cost between $1,200 to $4,500. In contrast, synthetic jasmine oils can be obtained for $3.50 per pound, but they do not possess the same therapeutic qualities as the pure oil.

Key Constituents:
Benzyl Acetate (18-28%)
Benzyl Benzoate (14-21%)
Linalol (3-8%)
Phytol (6-12%)
Isophytol (3-7%)
Squalene (3-7%)

Historical Data: Nicknamed as the "queen of the night" and "moonlight of the grove." For centuries, women have treasured jasmine for its beautiful, seductive fragrance.

Medical Properties: Uplifting, antidepressant, stimulating, antibacterial

USES: Anxiety, depression, menstrual problems/ PMS, skin problems (eczema, wrinkles, greasy), frigidity

Fragrant Influence: Uplifting, counteracts hopelessness, nervous exhaustion, anxiety, depression, indifference, and listlessness. University researchers in Japan found that diffusing certain aromas in an office environment dramatically improved mental accuracy and concentration. Diffused lemon resulted in 54 percent fewer errors, jasmine 33 percent fewer errors, and lavender 20 percent fewer errors. When aromas were diffused during test taking, scores increased by as much as 50 percent.

Application: (1) Apply 2-4 drops on location, (2) chakras/Vita Flex points, (3) directly inhale, or (4) diffuse (see Appendices E and T).

Found In: Awaken, Clarity, Dragon Time, Dragon Time Bath & Shower Gel, Dragon Time Massage Oil, Evening Peace Bath & Shower Gel, Forgiveness, Genesis Hand & Body Lotion, Gentle Baby, Harmony, Highest Potential, Inner Child, Into The Future, Joy, Lady Sclareol, Lavender Volume Conditioner, Lavender Volume Shampoo, Sensation Hand & Body Lotion, Sensation Massage Oil, and Sensation Bath & Shower Gel

Juniper

Selected Research:

Friedman M, Henika PR, Mandrell RE. Bactericidal activities of plant essential oils and some of their isolated constituents against Campylobacter jejuni, Escherichia coli, Listeria monocytogenes, and Salmonella enterica. *J Food Prot.* 2002 Oct;65(10):1545-60.

Juniper *(Juniperus osteosperma* and *J. scopulorum)*

Botanical Family: Cupressaceae (cypress)

Plant Origin: Utah

Extraction Method: Steam distilled from aerial parts.

Key Constituents:
Alpha-pinene (20-40%)
Sabinene (3-18%)
Myrcene (1-6%)
Camphor (10-18%)
Limonene (3-8%)
Bornyl Acetate (12-20%)
Terpinene-4-ol (3-8%)

ORAC: 250 µTE/100g

Historical Data: Bundles of juniper berries were hung over doorways to ward off witches during medieval times. It has been used for centuries as a diuretic. Until recently, French hospital wards burned sprigs of juniper and rosemary to protect from infection.

Medical Properties: Antiseptic, digestive cleanser/stimulant, purifying, detoxifying, increases circulation through the kidneys and promotes excretion of toxins, promotes nerve regeneration

USES: Skin conditions (acne, eczema), liver problems, urinary/bladder infections, fluid retention

Fragrant Influence: Juniper evokes feelings of health, love, and peace and may help to elevate one's spiritual awareness.

Application: Dilute 1 part EO with 1 part VO; (1) apply 2-4 drops on location, (2) chakras/ Vita Flex points, (3) directly inhale, (4) diffuse, or (5) take as dietary supplement (see Appendices E and T).

Found In: 3 Wise Men, Awaken, Cel-Lite Magic Massage Oil, Di-Gize, Dream Catcher, En-R-Gee, Grounding, Hope, Into the Future, K&B Tincture, Morning Start Bar Soap, Morning Start Bath & Shower Gel, Neurogen, and Ortho Ease Massage Oil

Bible Reference:

Job 30:45—"Who cut up mallows by the bushes, and juniper roots for their meat."

Selected Research:

Takacsova M, et al. "Study of the antioxidative effects of thyme, sage, juniper and oregano." *Nahrung.* 1995;39(3):241-3.

Laurus Nobilis (*Laurus nobilis-Bay Laurel*)

Botanical Family: Lauraceae

Plant Origin: Croatia

Extraction Method: Steam distilled from leaves and twigs.

Key Constituents:
Alpha-Pinene (4-10%)
Beta-Pinene (3-8%)
Sabinene (4-12%)
Linalol (4-16%)
1,8 Cineol(Eucalyptol) (35-50%)
Eugenol + Terpenyl Acetate (10-18%)

ORAC: 98,900 µTE/100g

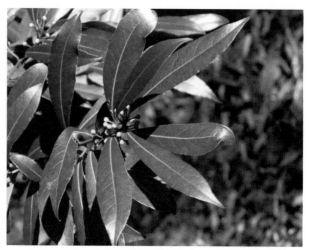

Laurus Nobilis

Historical Data: Both the leaves and the black berries were also used to alleviate indigestion, and loss of appetite. During the Middle Ages, it was used for angina, migraine, heart palpitations, and liver and spleen complaints.

Medical Properties: Antimicrobial, expectorant, mucolytic, antibacterial (Staph, Strep, *E. coli*), antifungal (Candida), anticoagulant, anticonvulsant

USES: Nerve regeneration, arthritis (rheumatoid), and oral infections (gingivitis), respiratory infections, viral infections

Application: Dilute 1 part EO with 1 part VO; (1) apply 2-4 drops on location or abdomen, (2) chakras/Vita Flex points, (3) directly inhale, (4) diffuse, or (5) take as dietary supplement (see Appendices E and T).

Found In: Exodus Softgels, and ParaFree Softgels

Selected Research:

Sayyah M, Valizadeh J, Kamalinejad M. Anticonvulsant activity of the leaf essential oil of Laurus nobilis against pentylenetetrazole- and maximal electroshock-induced seizures. *Phytomedicine.* 2002 Apr;9(3):212-6.

Lavandin

Lavender

Lavandin *(Lavandula* x *hybrida)*

Botanical Family: Lamiaceae or Labiatae (mint)

Plant Origin: France

Extraction Method: Steam distilled from the flowering top

Key Constituents:
Linalyl acetate (28-35%)
Linalol (30-38%)
Camphor (5-12%)
Limonene + 1,8 Cineol (Eucalyptol) (2-8%)
Borneol (2-6%)
Terpinene-4-ol (2-7%)
Lavandulyl Acetate (1-5%)

Historical Data: Also known as *Lavandula* x *intermedia*, lavandin is a hybrid plant developed by crossing true lavender with spike lavender or aspic (*Lavandula latifolia*). It has been used to sterilize the animal cages in veterinary clinics and hospitals throughout Europe.

Medical Properties: Antibacterial, antifungal

USES: Lavandin is a stronger antiseptic than Lavandula officinialis. Its greater penetrating qualities make it well suited to help with respiratory, circulatory, and muscular conditions

Fragrant Influence: Similar calming effects as lavender.

Application: (1) Apply 2-4 drops on location, (2) chakras/Vita Flex points, (3) directly inhale, or (4) diffuse (see Appendices E and T).

Cautions: Avoid using for burns; instead use lavender.

Found In: Animal Scents Shampoo, Purification, and Release

Lavender *(Lavandula angustifolia)*

Botanical Family: Lamiaceae or Labiatae (mint)

Plant Origin: Utah, Idaho, France

Extraction Method: Steam distilled from flowering top.

Key Constituents:
Linalyl Acetate (24-45%)
Linalol (25-38%)
Cis-beta-Ocimene (4-10%)
Trans-beta Ocimene (1.5-6%)
Terpinene-4-ol (2-6%)

ORAC: 360 µTE/100g

Historical Data: The French scientist René Gattefossé was the first to discover lavender's ability to promote tissue regeneration and speed wound healing when he severely burned his arm in a laboratory accident. Today, lavender is one of the few essential oils to still be listed in the British Pharmacopoeia.

Medical Properties: Antiseptic, antifungal, analgesic, antitumoral, anticonvulsant, vasodilating, relaxant, anti-inflammatory, reduces blood fat/cholesterol, combats excess sebum on skin

USES: Respiratory infections, high blood pressure, arteriosclerosis, menstrual problems/PMS, skin conditions (perinial repair, acne, eczema, psoriasis, scarring stretch marks), burns, hair loss, insomnia, nervous tension

Fragrant Influence: Calming, relaxing, and balancing, both physically and emotionally. University researchers in Japan found that diffusing certain aromas in an office environment dramatically improved mental accuracy and concentration. Diffused lemon resulted in 54 percent fewer errors, jasmine 33 percent fewer errors, and lavender 20 percent fewer errors. When aromas were diffused during test taking, scores increased by as much as 50 percent. Has been documented to improve concentration and mental acuity.

University of Miami researchers found that inhalation of lavender oil increased beta waves in the brain, suggesting heightened relaxation. It also reduced depression and improved cognitive performance (Diego et al., 1998). A 2001 Osaka Kyoiku University study found that lavender reduced mental stress and increased alertness (Motomura et al., 2001).

Application: (1) Apply 2-4 drops on location, (2) chakras/Vita Flex points, (3) directly inhale, (4) diffuse, or (5) take as dietary supplement (see Appendices E and T).

Cautions: True lavender is often extended with hybrid lavender or synthetic linalol and linalyl acetate.

Found In: Aroma Siez, AromaGuard Meadow Mist Deodorant, Awaken, Brain Power, Claraderm, Dragon Time, Dragon Time Bath & Shower Gel, Dragon Time Massage Oil, Egyptian Gold, Envision, Estro Tincture, Forgiveness, Gathering, Gentle Baby, Harmony, Highest Potential, KidScents Tender Tush, Lavaderm Cooling Mist, Lavender Volume Conditioner, Lavender Volume Shampoo, Lavender-Rosewood Bar Soap, Mister, Motivation, M-Grain, Orange Blossom Facewash, Progen, R.C., Relaxation Massage Oil, Sandalwood Moisture Cream, SARA, Surrender, Trauma Life, and Wolfberry Eye Cream

Selected Research:

Larrondo JV, et al. "Antimicrobial activity of essences from labiates." *Microbios.* 1995; 82(332):171-2.

Guillemain J, et al. "Neurodepressive effects of the essential oil of *Lavandula angustifolia* Mill." *Ann Pharm Fr.* 1989;47(6):337-43.

Kim HM, et al. "Lavender oil inhibits immediate-type allergic reaction in mice and rats." *J Pharm Pharmacol.* 1999;51(2):221-6.

Siurin SA. Effects of essential oil on lipid peroxidation and lipid metabolism in patients with chronic bronchitis. *Klin Med (Mosk).* 1997;75(10):43-5.

Nikolaevskii VV, et al., Effect of essential oils on the course of experimental atherosclerosis, *Patol Fiziol Eksp Ter.* 1990 Sep-Oct;(5):52-3.

Holmes C, et al., Lavender oil as a treatment for agitated behaviour in severe dementia: a placebo controlled study. *Int J Geriatr Psychiatry.* 2002 Apr;17(4):305-8.

Inouye S, Uchida K, Yamaguchi H. In-vitro and in-vivo anti-Trichophyton activity of essential oils by vapour contact. *Mycoses.* 2001 May;44(3-4):99-107.

Morris N. The effects of lavender (Lavendula angustifolium) baths on psychological well-being: two exploratory randomised control trials. *Complement Ther Med.* 2002 Dec;10(4):223-8.

Louis M, Kowalski SD. Use of aromatherapy with hospice patients to decrease pain, anxiety, and depression and to promote an increased sense of well-being. *Am J Hosp Palliat Care.* 2002 Nov-Dec;19(6):381-6.

Cornwell S, Dale A. Lavender oil and perineal repair. *Mod Midwife.* 1995 Mar;5(3):31-3.

Yamada K, Mimaki Y, Sashida Y. Anticonvulsive effects of inhaling lavender oil vapour. *Biol Pharm Bull.* 1994 Feb;17(2): 359-60.

Ghelardini C, et al., Local anaesthetic activity of the essential oil of Lavandula angustifolia. *Planta Med.* 1999 Dec;65(8):700-3.

Motomura N, Sakurai A, Yotsuya Y. Reduction of mental stress with lavender odorant. *Percept Mot Skills.* 2001 Dec;93(3):713-8.

Ledum (*Ledum groenlandicum*)

Botanical Family: Ericaceae

Plant Origin: North America (Canada)

Extraction Method: Steam distilled from flowering tops.

Key Constituents:
Limonene (20-35%)
Cis- and Trans-Paramenth1(7%)
   8 Diene 8-ol (12-17%)
Cis- and Trans-Paramenthatriene
   1,3,8 (8-15%)

Historical Data: Known colloquially as "Labrador tea," ledum is a strongly aromatic herb that has been used for centuries in folk medicine. The native people of Eastern Canada used this herb for tea, as a general tonic, and to treat a variety of kidney-related problems. Ledum has helped protect the native people of North America against scurvy for more than 5,000 years. The Cree used it for fevers and colds.

Medical Properties: Anti-inflammatory, anti-tumoral, antibacterial, diuretic, liver-protectant

USES: Liver problems/hepatitis/fatty liver, obesity, and water retention

Application: (1) Apply 2-4 drops on location, (2) chakras/Vita Flex points, (3) directly inhale, (4) diffuse, or (5) take as dietary supplement (see Appendices E and T).

Found In: GLF, and JuvaCleanse

Lemon (*Citrus limon*)

Botanical Family: Rutaceae (citrus)

Plant Origin: California, Italy

Extraction Method: Cold pressed from rind. It takes 3,000 lemons to produce 1 kilo of oil.

Lemon

Key Constituents:
Limonene (59-73%)
Gamma-Terpinene (6-12%)
Beta-Pinene (7-16%)
Alpha-Pinene (1.5-3%)
Sabinene (1.5-3%)

ORAC: 660 µTE/100g

Historical Data: Research by Jean Valnet, M.D., showed that vaporized lemon oil can kill meningococcus bacteria in 15 minutes, typhoid bacilli in one hour, *Staphylococcus aureus* in two hours, and *Pneumococcus* bacteria within three hours. Even a 0.2% solution of lemon oil can kill diphtheria bacteria in 20 minutes and inactivate tuberculosis bacteria. Lemon oil has been widely used in skin care to cleanse skin and reduce wrinkles and combat acne. Lemon has shown to have antidepressant effects in research done by Komori, et al., 1995.

Medical Properties: Antitumoral, antiseptic, improves microcirculation, and immune stimulant (increases white blood cells), improves memory, relaxation. Rich in limonene, which has been extensively studied for its ability to combat tumor growth in over 50 clinical studies.

USES: Circulatory problems, arteriosclerosis, obesity, parasites, urinary tract infections, varicose veins, anxiety, hypertension, digestive problems, acne

Fragrant Influence: It promotes clarity of thought and purpose with a fragrance that is invigorating, enhancing, and warming. University researchers in Japan found that diffusing certain aromas in an office environment dramatically improved mental accuracy and concentration. Diffused lemon resulted in 54 percent fewer errors, jasmine 33 percent fewer errors, and lavender 20 percent fewer errors. When aromas were diffused during test taking, scores increased by as much as 50 percent.

A 1995 Mie University study found that citrus fragrances boosted immunity, induced relaxation, and reduced depression.

Application: Dilute 1 part EO with 1 part VO; (1) apply 2-4 drops on location, (2) chakras/Vita Flex points, (3) directly inhale, (4) diffuse, or (5) take as dietary supplement (see Appendices E and T).

Cautions: Avoid applying to skin that will be exposed to sunlight or UV light within 24 hours.

Found In: AlkaLime, Animal Scents Shampoo, AromaGuard Meadow Mist Deodorant, AromaGuard Mountain Mist Deodorant, Awaken, BodyGize, Carbozyme, CardiaCare, Citrus Fresh, Clarity, Dentarome Toothpaste, Dentarome Plus Toothpaste, Dentarome Ultra Toothpaste, Dragon Time Bath & Shower Gel, Evening Peace Bath & Shower Gel, Genesis Hand & Body Lotion, Forgiveness, Gentle Baby, Harmony, HRT, ImmuneTune, Joy, JuvaTone, KidScents Shampoo, KidScents Toothpaste, Lemon-Sage Shampoo, Lemon-Sage Conditioner, Lemon-Sandalwood Bar Soap, Mineral Essence, Ningxia Red, Orange Blossom Face Wash, Power Meal, Raven, Super C, Surrender, Thieves, Thieves Bar Soap, Thieves Foaming Hand Soap, Thieves Household Cleaner, Thieves Lozenges (hard), Thieves Lozenges (soft), Thieves Spray, Thieves Wipes, and Transformation

Selected Research:

Lu XG, et al., D-limonene induces apoptosis of gastric cancer cells. *Zhonghua Zhong Liu Za Zhi.* 2003 Jul;25(4):325-7.

Nishino H et al. Cancer Chemoprevention by Phytochemicals and their Related Compounds. *Asian Pac J Cancer Prev.* 2000;1(1): 49-55.

Parija T, Das BR. Involvement of YY1 and its correlation with c-myc in NDEA induced hepatocarcinogenesis, its prevention by d-limonene. *Mol Biol Rep.* 2003 Mar;30(1):41-6.

Uedo N, et al., Inhibition by D-limonene of gastric carcinogenesis induced by N-methyl-N'-nitro-N-nitrosoguanidine in Wistar rats. *Cancer Lett.* 1999 Apr 1;137(2):131-6.

Hakim IA, Harris RB, Ritenbaugh C. Citrus peel use is associated with reduced risk of squamous cell carcinoma of the skin. *Nutr Cancer.* 2000;37(2):161-8.

Asamoto M, et al., Mammary carcinomas induced in human c-Ha-ras proto-oncogene transgenic rats are estrogen-independent, but responsive to d-limonene treatment. *Jpn J Cancer Res.* 2002 Jan;93(1):32-5.

Guyton KZ, Kensler TW. Prevention of liver cancer. Curr Oncol Rep. 2002 Nov;4(6):464-70.

Bradlow HL, Sepkovic DW. Diet and breast cancer. *Ann N Y Acad Sci.* 2002 Jun;963: 247-67.

Niijima A, Nagai K. Effect of olfactory stimulation with flavor of grapefruit oil and lemon oil on the activity of sympathetic branch in the white adipose tissue of the epididymis. *Exp Biol Med (Maywood).* 2003 Nov;228(10):1190-2.

Wattenberg LW, et al., Inhibition of carcinogenesis by some minor dietary constituents. *Princess Takamatsu Symp.* 1985;16:193-203.

Alderman GG, Marth EH. Inhibition of growth and aflatoxin production of Aspergillus parasiticus by citrus oils. *Z Lebensm Unters Forsch.* 1976 Apr 28;160(4):353-8.

Crowell PL. Prevention and therapy of cancer by dietary monoterpenes. *J Nutr.* 1999 Mar;129(3):775S-778S.

Komori T, et al., Application of fragrances to treatments for depression. *Nihon Shinkei Seishin Yakurigaku Zasshi.* 1995 Feb;15(1): 39-42. Japanese.

Lemongrass

Lemongrass *(Cymbopogon flexuosus)*

Botanical Family: Poaceae or Gramineae (grasses)

Plant Origin: India, Guatemala

Extraction Method: Steam distilled from herb/leaves.

Key Constituents:
Geranial (35-45%)
Geraniol (5-10%)
Neral (25-40%)
Trans-beta-Caryophyllene (2-6%)

ORAC: 1,780 µTE/100g

Historical Data: Lemongrass is used for purification and digestion. Research was published in *Phytotherapy Research* on topically applied lemongrass for its powerful antifungal properties.

Medical Properties: Antifungal, antibacterial, antiparasitic, anti-inflammatory, regenerates connective tissues and ligaments, dilates blood vessels, improves circulation, promotes lymph flow

USES: Bladder infection, respiratory/sinus infection, digestive problems, parasites, torn ligaments/muscles, fluid retention, varicose veins, Salmonella

Fragrant Influence: Promotes psychic awareness and purification.

Application: Dilute 1 part EO with 4 parts VO; (1) apply 1-2 drops on location, (2) chakras/ Vita Flex points, (3) directly inhale, (4) diffuse, or (5) take as dietary supplement (see Appendices E and T).

Found In: Be-Fit, Di-Gize, En-R-Gee, ICP, Inner Child, Morning Start Bar Soap, Morning Start Bath Gel, MultiGreens, NeuroGen, Ortho Ease Massage Oil, Ortho Sport Massage Oil, Purification, Super C, and Super Cal

Selected Research:

Pattnaik S, et al. "Antibacterial and antifungal activity of ten essential oils in vitro." *Microbios.* 1996;86(349):237-46.

Inouye S, Yamaguchi H, Takizawa T. Screening of the antibacterial effects of a variety of essential oils on respiratory tract pathogens, using a modified dilution assay method. *J Infect Chemother.* 2001 Dec;7(4):251-4.

Lorenzetti BB, et al. "Myrcene mimics the peripheral analgesic activity of lemongrass tea." *J Ethnopharmacol.* 1991;34(1):43-8.

Elson CE, et al. "Impact of lemongrass oil, an essential oil, on serum cholesterol." *Lipids.* 1989;24(8):677-9.

Friedman M, Henika PR, Mandrell RE. Bactericidal activities of plant essential oils and some of their isolated constituents against Campylobacter jejuni, Escherichia coli, Listeria monocytogenes, and Salmonella enterica. *J Food Prot.* 2002 Oct;65(10):1545-60.

Venturini ME, Blanco D, Oria R. In vitro antifungal activity of several antimicrobial compounds against Penicillium expansum. *J Food Prot.* 2002 May;65(5):834-9.

Inouye S, Uchida K, Yamaguchi H. In-vitro and in-vivo anti-Trichophyton activity of essential oils by vapour contact. *Mycoses.* 2001 May;44(3-4):99-107.

Lime *(Citrus aurantifolia)*

Botanical Family: Rutaceae (citrus)

Plant Origin: Native to South Asia (Ivory Coast)

Extraction Method: Cold expression from the rind of the unripe fruit

Lime

Mandarin

Key Constituents:
Limonene & Eucalyptol (50-60%)
Gamma Terpinene (10-15%)
Beta Pinene (8-12%)
Alpha Pinene (2-5%)

ORAC: 26,200 µTE/100g

Historical Data: Primarily used in skin care, and in supporting and strengthening the respiratory and immune systems.

Medical Properties: Antirheumatic, antiviral and antibacterial

USES: Skin conditions (acne, herpes), decongests the lymphatic system, insect bites, respiratory problems

Application: Dietary Supplement: dilute 1 part EO with 1 part VO, then put in a capsule and take up to three times daily or as needed; (1) Topical: dilute 1 part EO with 1 part VO, then apply on location, (2) chakras/Vita Flex points, (3) directly inhale, (4) diffuse up to 30 minutes three times daily, or (5) take as dietary supplement (see Appendices E and T).

Cautions: Avoid applying to skin that will be exposed to sunlight or UV light within 48 hours.

Found In: AlkaLime, Bodygize, KidScents® MightyVites, LemonSage Clarfiying Conditioner, and LemonSage Clarifying Shampoo

Selected Research:

Crowell PL.Prevention and therapy of cancer by dietary monoterpenes. *J Nutr.* 1999 Mar;129(3):775S-778S.

Mandarin (*Citrus reticulata*)

Botanical Family: Rutaceae (citrus)

Plant Origin: Madagascar, Italy

Extraction Method: Cold pressed from rind.

Key Constituents:
Limonene (65-75%)
Gamma-Terpinene (16-22%)
Alpha-Pinene (2-3%)
Beta-Pinene (1.2-2%)
Myrcene (1.5-2%)

ORAC: 26,500 µTE/100g

Historical Data: This fruit was traditionally given to Imperial Chinese officials named the Mandarins.

Medical Properties: Light antispasmodic, digestive tonic (digestoid), antifungal, and stimulates gallbladder. Rich in limonene, which has been extensively studied for its ability to combat tumor growth in over 50 clinical studies.

USES: Digestive problems, fluid retention, insomnia, anxiety, intestinal problems, skin problems (congested and oily skin, scars, acne), stretch marks (when combined with either jasmine, lavender, sandalwood, and/or frankincense)

Fragrant Influence: It is appeasing, gentle, and promotes happiness.

Application: Dilute 1 part EO with 1 part VO; (1) apply 2-4 drops on location, (2) chakras/

Manuka

Vita Flex points, (3) directly inhale, (4) diffuse, or (5) take as dietary supplement (see Appendices E and T).

Cautions: Avoid applying to skin that will be exposed to sunlight or UV light within 24 hours.

Found In: Awaken, Bodygize, Citrus Fresh, Dragon Time Bath & Shower Gel, Joy, and KidScents® MightyVites

Selected Research:

A 1995 Mie University study found that citrus fragrances boosted immunity, induced relaxation, and reduced depression.

Komori T, et al., Application of fragrances to treatments for depression. *Nihon Shinkei Seishin Yakurigaku Zasshi.* 1995 Feb;15(1): 39-42. Japanese

Manuka *(Leptospermum scoparium)*

Botanical Family: Myrtaceae

Plant Origin: New Zealand and Australia

Extraction Method: Steam distillation of chopped leaves and small stems

Key Constituents:
Leptospermone (17-18%)
Flavesone (6-7%)
Isoleptospermone (5-6%)
Copaene (4-5%)
Beta Cubebene (2-4%)
Caryophyllene (1-3%)
AlphaPinene (1-1.5%)

ORAC: 106,200 uTE/100g

Historical data: Similar to tea tree oil but warmer, richer and milder, manuka oil has long been used in treatment of skin, foot and hair problems. Like tea tree it is antibacterial, antiviral AND antifungal, so it can help in eliminating a wide variety of problems. Research suggests that manuka is more potent in fighting bacteria and fungi than tea tree oil. 'Manuka' is the Maori name for the bushy tree from which the oil is produced.

Medical Properties: antibacterial, antifungal, anti-inflammatory, anti-acne. Although research is on-going, many believe Manuka has potential in fighting antibiotic resistant organisms, such as MRSA. A leading German aromatherapist reports that the Manuka aroma is psychologically very beneficial for people who suffer from stress and anxiety. Its skin healing properties are exceptional.

USES: Skin infections, acne, bedsores, mild sunburn, fungal infections, itching, respiratory infections, sore throats, pain relief in muscles and joints, athletes foot and ringworm, dandruff, body odor, cold sores, dermatitis, rhinitis, tonsillitis, stress relief, sleep aid

Application:
2-4 drops on affected area, 1-3 times daily

Selected Research:

Cooke, A. MD, Cawthron Institute, An investigation into the Antimicrobial Properties of Manuka and Kanuka Oil, February 1991

Perry, N.B.; Brennan, N.J.; Van Klink, J.W.; Harris, W.; Douglas, M.H.; McGimsey, J.A.; Smallfield, M.B.; Anderson, R.E. Essential Oils from New Zealand—Manuka and Kanuka: chemotaxonomy of Leptospermum. *Phytochemistry,* 1997, 44, 1485-1494

Porter, N.G.; Smale, P.E.; Nelson M.A.; Hay, A.J.; Van Klink, J.W.; Dean, C.M. Variability in essential oil chemistry and plant morphology within a Leptospermum scoparium population. New Zealand *Journal of Botany,* 1998, 35, 125-133.

Marjoram

Melaleuca

Marjoram *(Origanum majorana)*

Botanical Family: Lamiaceae or Labiatae (mint)

Plant Origin: France, Egypt

Extraction Method: Steam distilled from leaves.

Key Constituents:
Terpinene-4-ol (25-35%)
Gamma-Terpinene (12-20%)
Linalol +Cis-4-Thujanol (3-8%)
Alpha-Terpinene (6-13%)
Alpha-Terpineol (2-6%)
Sabinene (2-6%)

ORAC: 130,900 µTE/100g

Historical Data: Marjoram was known as the "herb of happiness" to the Romans and "joy of the mountains" to the Greeks. It was believed to increase longevity. Listed in Dioscorides' De Materia Medica (A.D. 78), Europe's first authoritive guide to medicines, that became the standard reference work for herbal treatments for over 1,700 years. It was listed in Hildegard's Medicine, a compilation of early German medicines by highly-regarded Benedictine herbalist Hildegard of Bingen (1098-1179).

Medical Properties: Its muscle-soothing properties help relieve body and joint discomfort. May also help soothe the digestive tract and is a general relaxant. Antibacterial, antifungal, vasodilator, lowers blood pressure, promotes intestinal peristalsis, expectorant, mucolytic.

USES: Arthritis/rheumatism, muscle/nerve pain, headaches, circulatory disorders, respiratory infections, menstrual problems/PMS, fungal infections, ringworm, shingles, sores, spasms, and fluid retention

Fragrant Influence: Assists in calming the nerves.

Application: Dilute 1 part EO with 1 part VO; (1) apply 2-4 drops on location, (2) chakras/ Vita Flex points, (3) directly inhale, (4) diffuse, or (5) take as dietary supplement (see Appendices E and T).

Found In: Aroma Life, Aroma Siez, Cardia-Care, Dragon Time, Dragon Time Bath & Shower Gel, M-Grain, Ortho Ease Massage Oil, R.C., and Super Cal

Melaleuca Alternifolia *(Melaleuca alternifolia)*

(See TEA TREE)

Melaleuca Cajeput

(See CAJEPUT)

Melaleuca Ericifolia *(Melaleuca ericifolia)*

Botanical Family: Myrtaceae (myrtle)

Plant Origin: Australia

Extraction Method: Steam distilled from leaves and branches.

Key Constituents:

Alpha-Pinene (5-10%)

1,8 Cineol + Beta Phellandrene (18-28%)

Alpha-Terpineol (1-5%)

Para-Cymene (1-6%)

Linalol (34-45%)

Aromadendrene (2-6%)

ORAC: 61,100 µTE/100g

Medical Properties: Powerful antibacterial, antifungal, antiviral, antiparasitic, anti-inflammatory

USES: Herpes virus, respiratory/sinus infections

Application: Dilute 1 part EO with 1 part VO; (1) apply 2-4 drops on location, temples, wrists, throat, face, or chest (2) chakras/Vita Flex points, (3) directly inhale, (4) diffuse, or (5) take as dietary supplement (see Appendices E and T).

Found In: Melaleuca-Geranium Bar Soap

Selected Research:

Stablein JJ, Bucholtz GA, Lockey RF. Melaleuca tree and respiratory disease. *Ann Allergy Asthma Immunol.* 2002 Nov;89 (5):523-30.

Farag RS, et al., Chemical and biological evaluation of the essential oils of different Melaleuca species. *Phytother Res.* 2004 Jan;18(1):30-5.

Melaleuca Quinquenervia

(See NIAOULI)

Melissa *(Melissa officinalis)*

(Also known as lemon balm)

Botanical Family: Lamiaceae or Labiatae (mint)

Plant Origin: Utah, Idaho, France

Extraction Method: Steam distilled from aerial parts before flowering.

Key Constituents:

Geranial (25-35%)

Neral (18-28%)

Beta Caryophyllene (12-19%)

Melissa

ORAC: 134,300 µTE/100g

Historical Data: Anciently, melissa was used for nervous disorders and many different ailments dealing with the heart or the emotions. It was also used to promote fertility. Melissa was the main ingredient in Carmelite water, distilled in France since 1611 by the Carmelite monks. Dr. Dietrich Wabner, a professor at the Technical University of Munich, reported that a one-time application of true melissa oil led to complete remission of Herpes Simplex lesions.

Medical Properties: Anti-inflammatory, antiviral, relaxant, and hypotensive

USES: Viral infections (herpes etc.), depression, anxiety, and insomnia

Fragrant Influence: Brings out gentle characteristics within people. It is calming and uplifting and balances emotions. It removes emotional blocks and instills a positive outlook on life.

Application: (1) Apply 2-4 drops on location, (2) chakras/Vita Flex points, (3) directly inhale, (4) diffuse up to 1 hour three times daily, (5) Dietary Supplement: put 2 drops of melissa in a capsule, take three times daily or as needed, (6) Topical: apply 2-4 drops directly to affected area as needed, dilution not required except for extremely sensitive skin (see Appendices E and T).

Found In: Awaken, Brain Power, Forgiveness, Hope, Humility, MultiGreens, and White Angelica

Mountain Savory

Selected Research: Yamasaki K, et al. "Anti-HIV-1 activity of herbs in Labiatae." *Biol Pharm Bull.* 1998;21(8):829-33.

Larrondo JV, et al. "Antimicrobial activity of essences from labiates." *Microbios.* 1995;82 (332):171-2.

Kucera LS, et al. "Antiviral activities of extracts of the lemon balm plant." *Ann NY Acad Sci.* 1965 Jul 30;130(1):474-82.

Sadraei H, Ghannadi A, Malekshahi K. Relaxant effect of essential oil of Melissa officinalis and citral on rat ileum contractions. *Fitoterapia.* 2003 Jul;74(5):445-52.

Mountain Savory *(Satureja montana)*

Botanical Family: Lamiaceae or Labiatae (mint)

Plant Origin: France

Extraction Method: Steam distilled from flowering plant.

Key Constituents:
Carvacrol (22-35%)
Thymol (14-24%)
Gamma-Terpinene (8-15%)
Carvacrol Methyl Ether (4-9%)
Beta-Caryophyllene (3-7%)

ORAC: 11,300 µTE/100g

Historical Data: Mountain savory has been used historically as a general tonic for the body.

Medical Properties: Strong antibacterial, antifungal, antiviral, antiparasitic, immune stimulant, and anti-inflammatory action

USES: Viral infections (Herpes, HIV, etc.), scoliosis/lumbago/back problems

Fragrant Influence: Revitalizes and stimulates the nervous system. It is a powerful energizer and motivator.

Application: Dilute 1 part EO with 4 parts VO; (1) apply 2-4 drops on location, (2) chakras/Vita Flex points, (3) diffuse, or (4) take as dietary supplement (see Appendices E and T).

Found In: ImmuPower, Surrender

Selected Research:

Yamasaki K, et al. "Anti-HIV-1 activity of herbs in Labiatae." *Biol Pharm Bull.* 1998; 21(8):829-33.

Panizzi L, et al. "Composition and antimicrobial properties of essential oils of four Mediterranean Lamiaceae." *J Ethnopharmacol.* 1993;39(3):167-70.

Radonic A, Milos M. "Chemical composition and in vitro evaluation of antioxidant effect of free volatile compounds from Satureja montana L." *Free Radic Res.* 2003 Jun;37(6):673-9.

Mugwort *(Artemisia vulgaris)*

Botanical Family: Asteraceae (Daisy)

Plant Origin: Canada

Extraction Method: Steam distilled from leaves and roots

Key Constituents:
Sabinene (9-14%)
Myrcene (20-25%)
Limonene & Beta Phellandrene (1-5%)
Alpha- and Beta-Thujone (8-12%)
Germacrene D (4-8%)

Historical Data: Used by Chinese in moxibustion. Was worn to protect against evil spirits in 14th century England. Introduced by the Portuguese to the French in the 1800s where it became known as a cure for blindness and other diseases. Has been placed under pillows to produce vivid dreams.

Myrrh

Medical Properties: Antibacterial, antifungal, antiparasitic, gastrointestinal regulator

USES: Intestinal complaints, worm infestations, headaches, muscle spasms, circulatory problems, menstrual problems/PMS, dysentery, gout

Application: Dilute 1 part EO with 1 part VO; (1) apply 1-2 drops on location, (2) chakras/ Vita Flex points, (3) diffuse, or (4) take as dietary supplement (see Appendices E and T).

Found In: ComforTone, Inspiration

Selected Research:

Friedman M, Henika PR, Mandrell RE. Bactericidal activities of plant essential oils and some of their isolated constituents against Campylobacter jejuni, Escherichia coli, Listeria monocytogenes, and Salmonella enterica. *J Food Prot*. 2002 Oct;65(10): 1545-60.

Myrrh *(Commiphora myrrha)*

Botanical Family: Burseraceae (Frankincense)

Plant Origin: Somalia

Extraction Method: Steam distilled from gum/ resin.

Key Constituents:
Lindestrene (30-45%)
Curzerene (17-25%)
Furanoendesma-1,3-diene (4-8%)
Methoxyfuronogermacrene (5-9%)
Beta- and Gamma-Elemenes (3-6%)

ORAC: 379,800 µTE/100g

Historical Data: It is mentioned in one of the oldest known medical records, Ebers Papyrus (dating from sixteenth century B.C.) an ancient Egyptian list of 877 prescriptions and recipes. The Arabian people used myrrh for many skin conditions, such as chapped and cracked skin and wrinkles. It was listed in Hildegard's Medicine, a compilation of early German medicines by highly-regarded Benedictine herbalist Hildegard of Bingen (1098-1179).

Medical Properties: Powerful antioxidant, antitumoral, anti-inflammatory, antiviral, anti-parasitic, analgesic/anesthetic

USES: Diabetes, cancer, hepatitis, fungal infections (Candida, ringworm, eczema), tooth/gum infections, skin conditions (chapped, cracked, wrinkles, stretch marks)

Fragrant Influence: Promotes spiritual awareness and is uplifting. It contains sesquiterpenes which stimulate the limbic system of the brain (the center of memory and emotions) and the hypothalamus, pineal and pituitary glands. The hypothalamus is the master gland of the human body, producing many vital hormones including thyroid and growth hormone.

Application: (1) Apply 2-4 drops on location, (2) chakras/Vita Flex points, (3) directly inhale, (4) diffuse, or (5) take as dietary supplement (see Appendices E and T).

Found In: Abundance, Animal Scents Ointment, Boswellia Wrinkle Cream, ClaraDerm Mist, Egyptian Gold, Exodus II, Gratitude, Hope, Humility, Protec, Rose Ointment, Sandalwood Moisture Cream, Thyromin, and White Angelica

Bible References: (See additional Bible references in Appendix D).

Genesis 37:25—"And they sat down to eat bread: and they lifted up their eyes and looked, and behold, a company of Ishmelites came from Gilead with their camels bearing spicery and balm and myrrh, going to carry it down to Egypt."

Genesis 43:11—"And their father Israel said unto them, If it must be so now, do this; take of the best fruits in the land in your vessels, and carry down the man a present, a little balm, and a little honey, spices, and myrrh, nuts, and almonds:"

Exodus 30:23—"Take thou also unto thee principal spices, of pure myrrh five hundred shekels, and of sweet cinnamon half so much, even two hundred and fifty shekels, and of sweet calamus two hundred and fifty shekels,"

Selected Research:

Tipton DA, In vitro cytotoxic and anti-inflammatory effects of myrrh oil on human gingival fibroblasts and epithelial cells. *Toxicol In Vitro.* 2003 Jun;17(3):301-10.

Al-Awadi FM, et al. "Studies on the activity of individual plants of an antidiabetic plant mixture." *Acta Diabetol Lat.* 1987;24(1):37-41.

Dolara P, et al. "Analgesic effects of myrrh." *Nature.* 1996 Jan 4;379(6560):29.

Michie CA, et al. "Frankincense and myrrh as remedies in children." *J R Soc Med.* 1991;84(10):602-5.

Anderson C, et al., Evaluation of massage with essential oils on childhood atopic eczema. *Phytother Res.* 2000 Sep;14(6):452-6.

al-Harbi MM, et al., Anticarcinogenic effect of Commiphora molmol on solid tumors induced by Ehrlich carcinoma cells in mice. *Chemotherapy.* 1994 Sep-Oct;40(5):337-47.

Qureshi S, et al., Evaluation of the genotoxic, cytotoxic, and antitumor properties of Commiphora molmol using normal and Ehrlich ascites carcinoma cell-bearing Swiss albino mice. *Cancer Chemother Pharmacol.* 1993;33(2):130-8.

Dolara P, Corte B. Local anaesthetic, anti-bacterial and antifungal properties of sesquiterpenes from myrrh. *Planta Med.* 2000 May;66(4):356-8.

Myrtle

Myrtle *(Myrtus communis)*

Botanical Family: Myrtaceae (myrtle)

Plant Origin: Tunisia

Extraction Method: Steam distilled from leaves.

Key Constituents:
Alpha Pinene (45-60%)
1,8 Cineol (Eucalyptol) (17-27%)
Limonene (5-11%)
Linalol (2-5%)

ORAC: 25,400 μTE/100g

Historical Data: Myrtle has been researched by Dr. Daniel Pénoël for normalizing hormonal imbalances of the thyroid and ovaries, as well as balancing the hypothyroid. It has also been researched for its soothing effects on the respiratory system.

Medical Properties: Antimutagenic, liver stimulant, prostate and thyroid stimulant, sinus/lung decongestant, antispasmodic

USES: Thyroid problems, throat/lung/sinus infections, prostate problems, skin irritations (acne, blemishes, bruises, oily skin, psoriasis, etc.), muscle spasms

Fragrant Influence: Elevating and euphoric.

Application: Dilute 1 part EO with 1 part VO; (1) apply 2-4 drops on location, (2) chakras/ Vita Flex points, (3) directly inhale, (4) diffuse or put in humidifier, or (5) take as dietary supplement (see Appendices E and T).

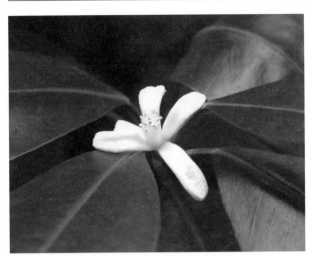

Neroli

Found In: EndoFlex, Inspiration, JuvaTone, Mister, ProGen, Purification, R.C., Super Cal, ThermaBurn, and Thyromin

Bible Reference: (See additional Bible references in Appendix D).

Nehemiah 8:15—"And that they should publish and proclaim in all their cities, and in Jerusalem, saying, Go forth unto the mount, and fetch olive branches, and pine branches, and myrtle branches, and palm branches, and branches of thick trees, to make booths, as it is written."

Isaiah 41:19—"I will plant in the wilderness the cedar, the shittah tree, and the myrtle, and the oil tree; I will set in the desert the fir tree, and the pine, and the box tree together:"

Isaiah 55:13—"Instead of the thorn shall come up the fir tree, and instead of the brier shall come up the myrtle tree: and it shall be to the Lord for a name, for an everlasting sign that shall not be cut off."

Selected Research:

Hayder N, et al., Antimutagenic activity of aqueous extracts and essential oil isolated from Myrtus communis. *Pharmazie.* 2003 Jul;58(7):523-4.

Monti D, et al., Effect of different terpene-containing essential oils on permeation of estradiol through hairless mouse skin. *Int J Pharm.* 2002 Apr 26;237(1-2):209-14.

Neroli Absolute *(Citrus sinensis)*

Botanical Family: Rutaceae (citrus)

Plant Origin: Tunisia

Extraction Method: Absolute extraction from flowers of the orange tree.

Key Constituents:
Linalol (28-44%)
Limonene (9-18%)
Beta-Pinene (7-17%)
Linalyl Acetate (3-15%)
Trans-Ocimene (3-8%)
Alpha Terpineol (2-5.5%)
Trans-Nerolidol (1-5%)
Myrcene (1-4%)

Historical Data: Highly regarded by the ancient Egyptians for its ability to heal the mind, body, and spirit.

Medical Properties: Antiparasitic, digestive tonic, antidepressive, and hypotensive (lowers blood pressure)

USES: Hypertension, anxiety, depression, hysteria, insomnia, skin conditions (scars, stretch marks, thread veins, wrinkles)

Fragrant Influence: A natural relaxant used to treat depression and anxiety. It strengthens and stabilizes the emotions and uplifts and inspires the hopeless, encouraging confidence, courage, joy, peace, and sensuality. It brings everything into focus at the moment.

Application: Dietary Supplement: dilute 1 part EO with 1 part VO, put in a capsule and take up to three times daily or as needed. Topical Use: Dilution not required except for the most sensitive skin; (1) apply 2-4 drops on location, (2) chakras/Vita Flex points, (3) directly inhale, or (4) diffuse up to 1 hour three times daily (see Appendices E and T).

Found In: Acceptance, Awaken, Humility, Inner Child, and Present Time

Niaouli *(Melaleuca quinquenervia)*

Botanical Family: Myrtaceae (myrtle)

Plant Origin: Australia

Niaouli

Nutmeg

Extraction Method: Steam distilled from leaves and twigs.

Key Constituents:
1,8 Cineole + Limonene (55-70%)
Alpha-Pinene (7-15%)
Beta-Pinene (2-6%)
Viridiflorol (2-6%)

ORAC: 18,600 µTE/100g

Medical Properties: Male hormone-like, anti-inflammatory, antibacterial, antiviral, and antiparasitic (amoeba and parasites in the blood), vasodilating, skin penetration enhancer (hormones)

USES: Hypertension, urinary tract/bladder infections, respiratory/sinus infections and allergies

Application: Dilute 1 part EO with 1 part VO; (1) apply 2-4 drops on location, (2) chakras/ Vita Flex points, (3) directly inhale, or (4) diffuse (see Appendices E and T).

Found In: Melrose

Selected Research:

Monti D, et al., Effect of different terpene-containing essential oils on permeation of estradiol through hairless mouse skin. *Int J Pharm.* 2002 Apr 26;237(1-2):209-14.

Groppo FC, et al., Antimicrobial activity of garlic, tea tree oil, and chlorhexidine against oral microorganisms. *Int Dent J.* 2002 Dec;52(6):433-7.

Stablein JJ, Bucholtz GA, Lockey RF. Melaleuca tree and respiratory disease. *Ann Allergy Asthma Immunol.* 2002 Nov;89 (5): 523-30.

Nutmeg *(Myristica fragrans)*

Botanical Family: Myristicaceae (myrtle)

Plant Origin: Tunisia, Indonesia

Extraction Method: Steam distilled from fruits and seeds.

Key Constituents:
Sabinene (14-29%)
Beta-Pinene (13-18%)
Alpha-Pinene (15-28%)
Limonene (2-7%)
Gamma-Terpinene (2-6%)
Terpinene-4-ol (2-6%)
Myristicine (5-12%)

ORAC: 158,100 µTE/100g

Historical Data: It was listed in Hildegard's Medicine, a compilation of early German medicines by highly-regarded Benedictine herbalist Hildegard of Bingen (1098-1179).

Recently the University of Ibadan revealed that nutmeg has potent anti-inflammatory and anticoagulant action.

Medical Properties: Anti-inflammatory, anticoagulant, antiseptic, antiparasitic, analgesic, liver protectant, stomach protectant (ulcers) and circulatory stimulant, adrenal stimulant, muscle relaxing, increases production of growth hormone/melatonin

USES: Rheumatism/arthritis, cardiovascular disease, hypertension, hepatitis, ulcers, digestive disorders, antiparasitic, nerve pain, fatigue/exhaustion, neuropathy. It is also used for its adrenal cortex-like activity which helps support the adrenal glands for increased energy.

Application: Dilute 1 part EO with 2 parts VO; (1) apply 1-2 drops on location, (2) chakras/ Vita Flex points, (3) directly inhale, (4) diffuse, or (5) take as dietary supplement (see Appendices E and T).

Found In: Be-Fit, EndoFlex, En-R-Gee, Magnify Your Purpose, Para Free Softgels, Power Meal, and ThermaBurn

Selected Research:

OA Olajide et al., Biological effects of Myristica fragrans (nutmeg) extract. *Phytother Res.* 1999 Jun;13(4):344-5.

Valero M, Salmeron MC. Antibacterial activity of 11 essential oils against Bacillus cereus in tyndallized carrot broth. *Int J Food Microbiol.* 2003 Aug 15;85(1-2):73-81.

Ramsewak RS, et al., In vitro antagonistic activity of monoterpenes and their mixtures against 'toe nail fungus' pathogens. *Phytother Res.* 2003 Apr;17(4):376-9.

Morita T, et al., Hepatoprotective effect of myristicin from nutmeg (Myristica fragrans) on lipopolysaccharide/d-galactosamine-induced liver injury. *J Agric Food Chem.* 2003 Mar 12;51(6):1560-5.

Grover JK, et al., Pharmacological studies on Myristica fragrans--antidiarrheal, hypnotic, analgesic and hemodynamic (blood pressure) parameters. *Methods Find Exp Clin Pharmacol.* 2002 Dec;24(10):675-80.

Capasso R, Pinto L, Vuotto ML, Di Carlo G. Preventive effect of eugenol on PAF and ethanol-induced gastric mucosal damage. *Fitoterapia.* 2000 Aug;71 Suppl 1:S131-7.

Ram A, et al., Hypolipidaemic effect of Myristica fragrans fruit extract in rabbits. *J Ethnopharmacol.* 1996 Dec;55(1):49-53.

Orange

Lis-Balchin M, Hart S. A preliminary study of the effect of essential oils on skeletal and smooth muscle in vitro. *J Ethnopharmacol.* 1997 Nov;58(3):183-7.

Rashid A, Misra DS. Antienterotoxic effect of Myristica fragrans (nutmeg) on enterotoxigenic Escherichia coli. *Indian J Med Res.* 1984 May;79:694-6.

Sherry CJ, Burnett RE. Enhancement of ethanol-induced sleep by whole oil of nutmeg. *Experientia.* 1978 Apr 15;34(4):492-3.

Dietz WH Jr, Stuart MJ. Nutmeg and prostaglandins. *N Engl J Med.* 1976 Feb 26;294(9):503.

Banerjee S, et al., Influence of certain essential oils on carcinogen-metabolizing enzymes and acid-soluble sulfhydryls in mouse liver. *Nutr Cancer.* 1994;21(3):263-9.

Dorman HJ, Deans SG. Antimicrobial agents from plants: antibacterial activity of plant volatile oils. *J Appl Microbiol.* 2000 Feb;88(2):308-16.

Orange *(Citrus sinensis)*

Botanical Family: Rutaceae (citrus)

Plant Origin: USA, South Africa, Italy, China

Extraction Method: Cold pressed from rind.

Chemical Constituents:
Limonene (85-96%)
Myrcene (0.5-3%)

ORAC: 1,890 µTE/100g

Medical Properties: Antitumoral, relaxant, anticoagulant, circulatory stimulant. Rich in limonene, which has been extensively studied for its ability to combat tumor growth in over 50 clinical studies.

USES: Arteriosclerosis, hypertension, cancer, insomnia, and complexion (dull and oily), fluid retention, and wrinkles

Fragrant Influence: Uplifting and antidepressant. A 1995 Mie University study found that citrus fragrances boosted immunity, induced relaxation, and reduced depression.

Application: Dilute 1 part EO with 1 part VO; (1) apply 2-4 drops on location, (2) chakras/ Vita Flex points, (3) directly inhale, (4) diffuse, or (5) take as dietary supplement (see Appendices E and T).

Cautions: Avoid applying to skin that will be exposed to sunlight or UV light within 24 hours.

Found In: Abundance, Awaken, Bodygize, Christmas Spirit, CinnaMint Lip Balm, Citrus Fresh, Envision, Harmony, Immune-Tune, Inner Child, Into The Future, KidScents® MightyVites, KidScents Toothpaste, Lady Sclareol, Longevity, Longevity Softgels, Peace & Calming, Power Meal, SARA, Super C, Super C Chewables, and Thieves Lozenges (soft)

Selected Research:

Lu XG, et al., D-limonene induces apoptosis of gastric cancer cells. *Zhonghua Zhong Liu Za Zhi.* 2003 Jul;25(4):325-7.

Nishino H et al. Cancer Chemoprevention by Phytochemicals and their Related Compounds. *Asian Pac J Cancer Prev.* 2000;1(1):49-55.

Parija T, Das BR. Involvement of YY1 and its correlation with c-myc in NDEA induced hepatocarcinogenesis, its prevention by d-limonene. *Mol Biol Rep.* 2003 Mar;30(1):41-6.

Bodake HB, Panicker KN, Kailaje VV, Rao KV. Chemopreventive effect of orange oil on the development of hepatic preneoplastic lesions induced by N-nitrosodiethylamine in rats: an ultrastructural study. *Indian J Exp Biol.* 2002 Mar;40(3):245-51.

Uedo N, et al., Inhibition by D-limonene of gastric carcinogenesis induced by N-methyl-N'-nitro-N-nitrosoguanidine in Wistar rats. *Cancer Lett.* 1999 Apr 1;137(2):131-6.

Hakim IA, Harris RB, Ritenbaugh C. Citrus peel use is associated with reduced risk of squamous cell carcinoma of the skin. *Nutr Cancer.* 2000;37(2):161-8.

Asamoto M, et al., Mammary carcinomas induced in human c-Ha-ras proto-oncogene transgenic rats are estrogen-independent, but responsive to d-limonene treatment. *Jpn J Cancer Res.* 2002 Jan;93(1):32-5.

Guyton KZ, Kensler TW. Prevention of liver cancer. *Curr Oncol Rep.* 2002 Nov;4(6): 464-70.

Bradlow HL, Sepkovic DW. Diet and breast cancer. *Ann N Y Acad Sci.* 2002 Jun;963: 247-67.

Wattenberg LW, et al., Inhibition of carcinogenesis by some minor dietary constituents. *Princess Takamatsu Symp.* 1985;16:193-203.

Alderman GG, Marth EH. Inhibition of growth and aflatoxin production of Aspergillus parasiticus by citrus oils. *Z Lebensm Unters Forsch.* 1976 Apr 28; 160(4):353-8.

Crowell PL.Prevention and therapy of cancer by dietary monoterpenes. *J Nutr.* 1999 Mar;129(3):775S-778S.

Komori T, et al., Application of fragrances to treatments for depression. *Nihon Shinkei Seishin Yakurigaku Zasshi.* 1995 Feb;15(1): 39-42. Japanese

Oregano *(Origanum compactum)*

Botanical Family: Lamiaceae or Labiatae (mint)

Plant Origin: US, France, Germany, Turkey

Extraction Method: Steam distilled from leaves.

Key Constituents:
Carvacrol (60-75%)
Gamma-Terpinene (3.5-8.5%)

Oregano

Para-Cymene (5.5-9%)
Beta Caryophyllene (2-5%)
Myrcene (1-3%)
Thymol (0-5%)

ORAC: 15,300 µTE/100g

Historical Data: Listed in Hildegard's Medicine, a compilation of early German medicines by highly-regarded Benedictine herbalist Hildegard of Bingen (1098-1179).

Medical Properties: Anti-aging, powerful antiviral, antibacterial, antifungal, antiparasitic, anti-inflammatory, immune stimulant

USES: Arthritis/rheumatism respiratory infectious diseases, infections/tuberculosis, digestive problems

Fragrant Influence: Creates a feeling of security.

Application: Dilute 1 part EO with 4 parts VO; (1) apply 1-2 drops on location (or neat as in Raindrop Technique), (2) chakras/Vita Flex points, (3) diffuse, or (4) take as dietary supplement (see Appendices E and T).

Caution: High in phenols, oregano may irritate the nasal membranes or skin if inhaled directly from diffuser or bottle, or applied neat.

Found In: ImmuPower, Ortho Sport Massage Oil, and Regenolone

Selected Research:

Friedman M, Henika PR, Mandrell RE. Bactericidal activities of plant essential oils and some of their isolated constituents against Campylobacter jejuni, Escherichia coli, Listeria monocytogenes, and Salmonella enterica. *J Food Prot.* 2002 Oct;65(10): 1545-60.

Papageorgiou G, et al., Effect of dietary oregano oil and alpha-tocopheryl acetate supplementation on iron-induced lipid oxidation of turkey breast, thigh, liver and heart tissues. *J Anim Physiol Anim Nutr (Berl).* 2003 Oct;87(9-10):324-35.

Elgayyar M, et al., Antimicrobial activity of essential oils from plants against selected pathogenic and saprophytic microorganisms. *J Food Prot.* 2001 Jul;64(7):1019-24.

Tantaoui-Elaraki A, Beraoud L. Inhibition of growth and aflatoxin production in Aspergillus parasiticus by essential oils of selected plant materials. *J Environ Pathol Toxicol Oncol.* 1994;13(1):67-72.

Dorman HJ, Deans SG. Antimicrobial agents from plants: antibacterial activity of plant volatile oils. *J Appl Microbiol.* 2000 Feb; 88(2):308-16.

Palmarosa (*Cymbopogon martinii*)

Botanical Family: Poaceae or Gramineae (grasses)

Plant Origin: India

Extraction Method: Steam distilled from leaves.

Key Constituents:
Geraniol (70-85%)
Geranyl Acetate (6-10%)
Linalol (3-7%)

ORAC: 127,800 µTE/100g

Historical Data: A relative of lemongrass, palmarosa was used in temple incense by the ancient Egyptians.

Medical Properties: Antibacterial, antifungal, antiviral, supports heart and nervous system, stimulates new skin cell growth, regulates sebum production in skin

USES: Fungal infections/Candida, cardiovascular/circulatory diseases, digestive problems, skin problems (acne, eczema)

Fragrant Influence: Creates a feeling of security. It also helps to reduce stress and tension and promotes recovery from nervous exhaustion.

Application: Dilute 1 part EO with 1 part VO, put in a capsule and take up to three times daily; (1) apply 2-4 drops on location, dilution not required except for the most sensitive skin, (2) chakras/Vita Flex points, (3) directly inhale, (4) diffuse up to 1 hour three times daily, or (5) take as dietary supplement (see Appendices E and T).

Found In: Animal Scents Ointment, Awaken, Clarity, Dragon Time Bath & Shower Gel, Evening Peace Bath & Shower Gel, Forgiveness, Genesis Hand & Body Lotion, Gentle Baby, Harmony, Joy, and Rose Ointment

Selected Research:

Friedman M, Henika PR, Mandrell RE. Bactericidal activities of plant essential oils and some of their isolated constituents against Campylobacter jejuni, Escherichia coli, Listeria monocytogenes, and Salmonella enterica. *J Food Prot.* 2002 Oct;65(10):1545-60.

Kumaran AM, et al., Geraniol, the putative anthelmintic principle of Cymbopogon martinii. *Phytother Res.* 2003 Sep;17(8):957.

Prashar A, et al., Antimicrobial action of palmarosa oil (Cymbopogon martinii) on Saccharomyces cerevisiae. *Phytochemistry.* 2003 Jul;63(5):569-75

Carnesecchi S, et al., Geraniol, a component of plant essential oils, sensitizes human colon cancer cells to 5-fluorouracil treatment. *IARC Sci Publ.* 2002;156:407-9.

Carnesecchi S, et al., Perturbation by geraniol of cell membrane permeability and signal transduction pathways in human colon cancer cells. *J Pharmacol Exp Ther.* 2002 Nov;303(2):711-5.

Umezu T, et al., Anticonflict effects of rose oil and identification of its active constituents. *Life Sci.* 2002 Nov 22;72(1):91-102.

Choi HS, Song HS, Ukeda H, Sawamura M. Radical-scavenging activities of citrus essential oils and their components: detection using 1,1-diphenyl-2-picrylhydrazyl. *J Agric Food Chem.* 2000 Sep;48(9):4156-61.

Palo Santo

Palo Santo *(Bursera graveolens)*

Botanical Family: Burseracae

Plant Origin: Ecuador

Extraction Method: Steam-distilled from bark, wood, branches

Key Constitutents:
Limonene (55-65%)
Alpha-Terpineol (8-12%)
Menthofuran (5-8%)
(Constituents can vary depending on whether the wood is harvested from coastal or inland areas, and if the trunk is red or white.)

Historical Data: Palo Santo comes from the same botanical family as frankincense, although it is found in South America. Like frankincense, Palo Santo is known as a spiritual oil, with a deep-rooted tradition in which it was used by the Incas to purify and cleanse the air of negative energies. Even its Spanish name reflects how highly this oil was regarded: Palo Santo means "holy or sacred wood."

Applications: Diffuse or apply topically. Should be diluted 50-50.

Cautions: If pregnant or under a doctor's care, consult your physician

Patchouli *(Pogostemon cablin)*

Botanical Family: Lamiaceae or Labiatae (mint)

Plant Origin: Indonesia

Extraction Method: Steam distilled from flowers.

Key Constituents:
Patchoulol (25-35%)
Alpha-Bulnesene (14-20%)
Alpha-Guaiene + Seychellene (15-25%)
Alpha-Patchoulene (5-9%)

ORAC: 49,400 µTE/100g

Medical Properties: Relaxant, digestive aid that combats nausea, anti-inflammatory, anti-microbial, prevents wrinkles/chapped skin, relieves itching

USES: Hypertension, skin conditions (eczema, acne), fluid retention, Listeria infection

Application: (1) apply 2-4 drops on location, (2) chakras/Vita Flex points, (3) directly inhale, (4) diffuse, or (5) take as dietary supplement (see Appendices E and T)

Fragrant Influence: A relaxant that clarifies thoughts, allowing the discarding of jealousies, obsessions, and insecurities.

Found In: Abundance, Animal Scents Ointment, Di-Gize, Magnify Your Purpose, Orange Blossom Face Wash, Peace & Calming, and Rose Ointment

Selected Research:

Friedman M, Henika PR, Mandrell RE. Bactericidal activities of plant essential oils and some of their isolated constituents against Campylobacter jejuni, Escherichia coli, Listeria monocytogenes, and Salmonella enterica. *J Food Prot.* 2002 Oct;65(10):1545-60.

Haze S, Sakai K, Gozu Y. et al., Effects of fragrance inhalation on sympathetic activity in normal adults. *Jpn J Pharmacol.* 2002 Nov;90(3):247-53.

Black Pepper

Pepper, Black *(Piper nigrum)*

Botanical Family: Piperaceae

Plant Origin: Madagascar, Ceylon, England

Extraction Method: Steam distilled from fruit/berries.

Key Constituents:
Beta Caryophyllene (25-35%)
Limonene (8-12%)
Sabinene (5-10%)
Alpha and Beta Pinenes (10-15%)

ORAC: 79,700 µTE/100g

Historical Data: Used by the Egyptians in mummification as evidenced by the discovery of black pepper in the nostrils and abdomen of Ramses II. Indian monks ate several black peppercorns a day to to give them endurance during their arduous travels. In ancient times pepper was as valuable as gold or silver. When the barbarian Goth tribes of Europe vanquished Rome in 410 A.D., they demanded 3,000 pounds of pepper as well as other valuables as a ransom. Traditional Chinese healers used pepper to treat cholera, malaria, and digestive problems.

Medical Properties: Analgesic, stimulates metabolism, antifungal

USES: Obesity, arthritis. digestive problems, fatigue, nerve/muscle pain, fungal infections

Fragrant Influence: Stimulating, energizing and empowering. A 2002 study found that fragrance inhalation of pepper oil induced a 1.7-fold increase in plasma adrenaline concentration (Haze et al.).

Application: Dilute 1 part EO with 1 part VO; (1) apply 2-4 drops on location, (2) chakras/ Vita Flex points, (3) directly inhale, (4) diffuse, or (5) take as dietary supplement (see Appendices E and T).

Found In: Awaken, Dream Catcher, En-R-Gee, and Relieve It

Selected Research: Unnikrishnan MC, et al. "Tumour reducing and anticarcinogenic activity of selected spices." *Cancer Lett.* 1990;51(1):85-9.

Haze S, Sakai K, Gozu Y. et al., Effects of fragrance inhalation on sympathetic activity in normal adults. *Jpn J Pharmacol.* 2002 Nov;90(3):247-53.

Tantaoui-Elaraki A, Beraoud L. Inhibition of growth and aflatoxin production in Aspergillus parasiticus by essential oils of selected plant materials. *J Environ Pathol Toxicol Oncol.* 1994;13(1):67-72.

Dorman HJ, Deans SG. Antimicrobial agents from plants: antibacterial activity of plant volatile oils. *J Appl Microbiol.* 2000 Feb;88(2):308-16.

Haze S, Sakai K, Gozu Y. Effects of fragrance inhalation on sympathetic activity in normal adults. *Jpn J Pharmacol.* 2002 Nov;90(3):247-53.

Peppermint (*Mentha piperita*)

Botanical Family: Lamiaceae or Labiatae (mint)

Plant Origin: North America, Mediterranean area, Great Britain

Extraction Method: Steam distilled from leaves and stems.

Key Constituents:
Menthol (34-44%)
Menthone (12-20%)
Menthofurane (4-9%)
1.8 Cineol (Eucalyptol) (2-5%)
Pulegone (2-5%)
Menthyl Acetate (4-10%)

Peppermint

ORAC: 37,300 μTE/100g

Historical Data: Reputed to be part of the "Marseilles Vinegar" or "Four Thieves Vinegar" used by grave-robbing bandits to protect themselves during the 15th century plague. A highly regarded digestive stimulant. Jean Valnet, M.D., used peppermint to treat liver and respiratory diseases.

Medical Properties: Anti-inflammatory, antitumoral, antiparasitic (worms), antibacterial, antiviral, antifungal, gallbladder/digestive stimulant, pain-reliever, curbs appetite

USES: Rheumatism/arthritis, respiratory infections (pneumonia, tuberculosis, etc), obesity, viral infections (Herpes simplex, herpes zoster, cold sores, human papilloma virus etc.), fungal infections/Candida, digestive problems, headaches, nausea, skin conditions (itchy skin, varicose veins, eczema, psoriasis, dermatitis), scoliosis/lumbago/back problems

Fragrant Influence: Purifying and stimulating to the conscious mind. Dr. William N. Dember of the University of Cincinnati found that inhaling peppermint oil increased mental accuracy by 28 percent.

Alan Hirsch, M.D. researched peppermint's stimulation of the brain's satiety center (ventromedial nucleus of the hypothalamus) to curb appetite. When inhaled, it improves/ restores sense of taste by stimulating the trigeminal nerve. University of Kiel researchers found that peppermint blocked headache pain in a double-blind placebo-controlled cross-over study.

Application: Dilute 1 part EO with 2 parts VO; (1) apply 1-2 drops on location, abdomen, temples (2) chakras/Vita Flex points, (3) directly inhale, (4) diffuse, or (5) take as dietary supplement (see Appendices E and T).

To improve concentration, alertness, and memory, place 1-2 drops on the tongue. Inhale 5-10 times a day to curb appetite.

Cautions: Avoid contact with eyes, mucus membranes, sensitive skin, or fresh wounds or burns. Do not apply to infants younger than 18 months of age.

Found In: Aroma Siez, AromaGuard Mountain Mint Deodorant, BLM Powder, CinnaMint Lip Balm, Clarity, ComforTone, CortiStop - Woman's Dentarome Toothpaste, Dentarome Plus Toothpaste, Dentarome Ultra Toothpaste, Di-Gize, Digest & Cleanse Softgels, Essentialzyme, Essentialzyme, KidScents Mightyzyme, KidScents Toothpaste, M-Grain, Mineral Essence, Mister, Morning Start Bar Soap, Morning Start Bath & Shower Gel, NeuroGen, Ortho Ease Massage Oil, Ortho Sport Massage Oil, PanAway, Peppermint-Cedarwood Bar Soap, Polyzyme, ProGen, R.C., Raven, Regenolone, Relaxation Massage Oil, Relieve It, Satin Facial Scrub-Mint, SclarEssence, TheraBurn, Therma-Mist, Thieves Lozenges (hard), Thieves Lozenges (soft), Thyromin, and Transformation.

Selected Research:

Gobel H, et al. "Effect of peppermint and eucalyptus oil preparations on neurophysiological and experimental algesimetric headache parameters." *Cephalalgia.* 1994; 14(3):228-34.

Juergens UR, Stober M, Vetter H. The anti-inflammatory activity of L-menthol compared to mint oil in human monocytes in vitro: a novel perspective for its therapeutic use in inflammatory diseases. *Eur J Med Res.* 1998 Dec 16;3(12):539-45.

Samman MA, et al. "Mint prevents shamma-induced carcinogenesis in hamster cheek pouch." *Carcinogenesis.* 1998;19(10):1795-801.

Schuhmacher A, Reichling J, Schnitzler P. Virucidal effect of peppermint oil on the enveloped viruses herpes simplex virus type 1 and type 2 in vitro. *Phytomedicine.* 2003; 10(6-7):504-10.

Samarth RM, et al., Mentha piperita (Linn) leaf extract provides protection against radiation induced alterations in intestinal mucosa of Swiss albino mice. *Indian J Exp Biol.* 2002 Nov;40(11):1245-9.

Mimica-Dukic N, et al., Antimicrobial and antioxidant activities of three Mentha species essential oils. *Planta Med.* 2003 May; 69(5):413-9.

Edris AE, Farrag ES. Antifungal activity of peppermint and sweet basil essential oils and their major aroma constituents on some plant pathogenic fungi from the vapor phase. *Nahrung.* 2003 Apr;47(2):117-21.

Shkurupii VA, et al., Efficiency of the use of peppermint (Mentha piperita L) essential oil inhalations in the combined multi-drug therapy for pulmonary tuberculosis. *Probl Tuberk.* 2002;(4):36-9.

Iscan G, et al., Antimicrobial screening of Mentha piperita essential oils. *J Agric Food Chem.* 2002 Jul 3;50(14):3943-6.

Imai H, et al., Inhibition by the essential oils of peppermint and spearmint of the growth of pathogenic bacteria. *Microbios.* 2001;106 Suppl 1:31-9.

Petitgrain *(Citrus sinensis)*

Botanical Family: Rutaceae (citrus)

Plant Origin: Paraguay

Extraction Method: Steam distilled from leaves and twigs.

Key Constituents:
Linalyle Acetate (40-55%)
Linalol (15-30%)
Alpha Terpineol (3.5-7.5%)
Geranyl Acetate (2-5%)
Geraniol (2-4.5%)

ORAC: 73,600 µTE/100g

Pine

Historical Data: Petitgrain derives its name from the extraction of the oil, which at one time was from the green unripe oranges when they were still about the size of a cherry.

Medical Properties: Antispasmodic, anti-inflammatory, relaxant, re-establishes nerve equilibrium

USES: Insomnia, anxiety, muscle spasms

Fragrant Influence: Uplifting and refreshing to the senses; it clears confusion, reduces mental fatigue and depression. Stimulates the mind and improves memory.

Application: Dietary Supplement: put 2 drops in a capsule, take three times daily or as needed; (1) apply 2 drops on location, dilution not required except for the most sensitive skin, (2) chakras/Vita Flex points, (3) directly inhale, or (4) diffuse up to 1 hour three times daily (see Appendices E and T).

Pine *(Pinus sylvestris)*

Botanical Family: Pinaceae (pine)

Plant Origin: Austria, USA, Canada

Extraction Method: Steam distilled from needles.

Key Constituents:
Alpha Pinene (55-70%)
Beta Pinene (3-8%)
Limonene (5-10%)
Delta 3 Carene (6-12%)

Historical Data: Pine was first investigated by Hippocrates, the father of Western medicine, for its benefits to the respiratory system. In 1990, Dr. Pénoël and Dr. Franchomme described pine oil's antiseptic properties in their medical textbook. Pine is used in massage for stressed muscles and joints. It shares many of the same properties as *Eucalyptus globulus*, and the action of both oils is enhanced when blended. Native Americans stuffed mattresses with pine needles to repel lice and fleas. It was used to treat lung infections and even added to baths to revitalize those suffering from mental or emotional fatigue.

Medical Properties: Hormone-like, antidiabetic, cortisone-like, antiseptic, lymphatic stimulant

USES: Throat/lung/sinus infections, rheumatism/arthritis, skin parasites, urinary tract infection

Fragrant Influence: Relieves anxiety and revitalizes mind, body, and spirit. It also has an empowering, yet grounding fragrance.

Application: Dilute 1 part EO with 1 part VO; (1) apply 2-4 drops on location, (2) chakras/Vita Flex points, (3) directly inhale, or (4) diffuse (see Appendices E and T).

Cautions: Avoid any pine oils adulterated with turpentine, a low-cost, but potentially hazardous filler.

Found In: Grounding, ImmuneTune, LemonSage Clarifying Conditioner, LemonSage Clarifying Shampoo, and R.C.

Bible Reference: Nehemiah 8:15—"And that they should publish and proclaim in all their cities, and in Jerusalem, saying, Go forth unto the mount, and fetch olive branches, and pine branches, and myrtle branches, and palm branches, and branches of thick trees, to make booths, as it is written."

Isaiah 41:19—"I will plant in the wilderness the cedar, the shittah tree, and the myrtle, and the oil tree; I will set in the desert the fir tree, and the pine, and the box tree together:"

Isaiah 60:13—"The glory of Lebanon shall come unto thee, the fir tree, the pine tree, and the box together, to beautify the place of my sanctuary; and I will make the place of my feet glorious."

Ravensara (*Ravensara aromatica*)

Botanical Family: Lauraceae

Plant Origin: Madagascar, Austria

Extraction Method: Steam distilled from leaves.

Key Constituents:
Limonene + Eucalyptol (50-65%)
Sabinene (6-12%)
Alpha-Terpineol (5-11%)
Alpha Pinene (4-9%)
Beta-Pinene (1-5%)

ORAC: 890 µTE/100g

Historical Data: Ravensara is referred to by the people of Madagascar as "the oil that heals." It is antimicrobial and supporting to the nerves and respiratory system.

Medical Properties: Antitumoral, antiviral, antibacterial

USES: Herpes virus/viral infections (including colds), throat/lung infections, hepatitis, shingles, cancer, and pneumonia

Application: (1) Apply 2-4 drops on location, (2) chakras/Vita Flex points, (3) directly inhale, or (4) diffuse (see Appendices E and T).

Found In: ImmuPower, ImmuneTune, and Raven

Selected Research:

Raharivelomanana PJ, Terrom GP, Bianchini JP, Coulanges Study of the antimicrobial action of various essential oils extracted from Malagasy plants. II: Lauraceae. *Arch Inst Pasteur Madagascar.* 1989;56(1):261-71.

Rosalina

(See MELALEUCA ERICIFOLIA)

Rose (*Rosa damascena*)

Botanical Family: Rosaceae

Plant Origin: Bulgaria, Turkey

Extraction Method: Therapeutic-grade oil is steam distilled from flower (a two-part process). NOTE: The Bulgarian *Rosa damascena* (high in citronellol) is very different from Morrocan *Rosa centifolia* (high in phenyl ethanol). They have different colors, aromas, and therapeutic actions.

Key Constituents:
Citronellol (34-44%)
Geraniol (12-28%)
Nerol (6-9%)
Phenylethylic Alcohol (0-2%)

ORAC: 160,400 µTE/100g

Historical Data: Rose has been used for the skin for thousands of years. The Arab physician, Avicenna, was responsible for first distilling rose oil, eventually authoring an entire book on the healing attributes of the rose water derived from the distillation of rose. Throughout much of ancient history, the oil was produced by enfleurage, a process of pressing the petals along with a vegetable oil to extract the essence. Today, however, almost all rose oils are solvent extracted.

Medical Properties: Anti-inflammatory, relaxant, reduces scarring, anti-ulcer

USES: Hypertension, anxiety, viral infections (Herpes simplex), skin conditions (scarring, wrinkles), ulcers

Fragrant Influence: Its beautiful fragrance is intoxicating and aphrodisiac-like. It helps bring balance and harmony, allowing one to overcome insecurities. It is stimulating and elevating to the mind, creating a sense of well-being.

Application: (1) Apply 2-4 drops on location, (2) chakras/Vita Flex points, (3) directly inhale, (4) diffuse, or (5) take as dietary supplement (see Appendices E and T).

Found In: Awaken, Egyptian Gold, Envision, Forgiveness, Gathering, Gentle Baby, Harmony, Highest Potential, Humility, Joy, SARA, Rose Ointment, Trauma Life, and White Angelica

Selected Research:

Sysoev NP "The effect of waxes from essential-oil plants on the dehydrogenase activity of the blood neutrophils in mucosal trauma of the mouth." *Stomatologiia* 1991;70(1):12-3.

Mahmood N, et al. "The anti-HIV activity and mechanisms of action of pure compounds isolated from Rosa damascena." *Biochim Biophys Res Commun.* 1996;229(1):73-9.

Umezu T, et al., Anticonflict effects of rose oil and identification of its active constituents. *Life Sci.* 2002 Nov 22;72(1):91-102.

Haze S, Sakai K, Gozu Y. et al., Effects of fragrance inhalation on sympathetic activity in normal adults. *Jpn J Pharmacol.* 2002 Nov;90(3):247-53.

Boyanova L, Neshev G. Inhibitory effect of rose oil products on Helicobacter pylori growth in vitro: preliminary report. *J Med Microbiol.* 1999 Jul;48(7):705-6.

Rosemary *(Rosmarinus officinalis* CT cineol)

Botanical Family: Labiatae

Plant Origin: Tunisia, Morocco, Spain

Extraction Method: Steam distilled from leaves.

Key Constituents:
1,8 Cineol (Eucalyptol) (38-55%)
Camphor (5-15%)
Alpha-Pinene (9-14%)
Beta-Pinene (4-9%)
Camphene (2.5-6%)
Borneol (1.5-5%)
Limonene (1-4%)

ORAC: 330 µTE/100g

Historical Data: Rosemary was part of the "Marseilles Vinegar" or "Four Thieves Vinegar" used by grave-robbing bandits to protect themselves during the 15th century plague. The name of the oil is derived from the Latin words for dew of the sea (ros + marinus).

Rosemary

According to folklore history, rosemary originally had white flowers; however, they turned red after the Virgin Mary laid her cloak on the bush. Since the time of ancient Greece (about 1,000 B.C.), rosemary was burned as incense. Later cultures believed that it warded off devils, a practice that eventually became adopted by the sick who then burned rosemary to protect against infection.

It was listed in Hildegard's Medicine, a compilation of early German medicines by highly-regarded Benedictine herbalist Hildegard of Bingen (1098-1179).

Until recently, French hospitals used rosemary to disinfect the air.

Medical Properties: Liver-protecting, anti-tumoral, antifungal, antibacterial, antiparasitic, enhances mental clarity/concentration

USES: Infectious disease, liver conditions/hepatitis, throat/lung infections, hair loss (alopecia areata), impaired memory/Alzheimers

Fragrant Influence: Helps overcome mental fatigue and improves mental clarity and focus. University of Miami scientists found that inhaling rosemary boosted alertness, eased anxiety, and amplified analytic and mental ability.

Application: Dilute 1 part EO with 1 part VO; (1) apply 2-4 drops on location, (2) chakras/Vita Flex points, (3) directly inhale, (4) diffuse, or (5) take as dietary supplement (see Appendices E and T).

Caution: Do not use on children under 4 years of age. Avoid using on person with high blood pressure.

Found In: AromaGuard Meadow Mist Deodorant, AromaGuard Mountain Mint Deodorant, Be-Fit, Carbozyme, Chelex, Clarity, ComfortTone, Dentarome Toothpaste, Dentarome Plus Toothpaste, Dentarome Ultra Toothpaste, En-R-Gee, ICP, JuvaFlex, JuvaTone, KidScents Toothpaste, Melrose, Morning Start Bar Soap, Morning Start Bath & Shower Gel, MultiGreens, Polyzyme, Purity, Rehemogen, Thieves, Thieves Bar Soap, Thieves Foaming Hand Soap, Thieves Household Cleaner, Thieves Lozenges (hard), Thieves Lozenges (soft), Thieves Spray, and Thieves Wipes

Selected Research:

Larrondo JV, et al. "Antimicrobial activity of essences from labiates." *Microbios.* 1995; 82(332):171-2.

Panizzi L, et al. "Composition and antimicrobial properties of essential oils of four Mediterranean Lamiaceae." *J Ethnopharmacol.* 1993;39(3):167-70.

Diego MA, et al. "Aromatherapy positively affects mood, EEG patterns of alertness and math computations." *Int J Neurosci.* 1998; 96(3-4):217-24.

Moss M, Cook J, Wesnes K, Duckett P. Aromas of rosemary and lavender essential oils differentially affect cognition and mood in healthy adults. *Int J Neurosci.* 2003 Jan;113(1):15-38.

Fahim FA, et al., Allied studies on the effect of Rosmarinus officinalis L. on experimental hepatotoxicity and mutagenesis. *Int J Food Sci Nutr.* 1999 Nov;50(6):413-27.

Tantaoui-Elaraki A, Beraoud L. Inhibition of growth and aflatoxin production in Aspergillus parasiticus by essential oils of selected plant materials. *J Environ Pathol Toxicol Oncol.* 1994;13(1):67-72.

Rosewood *(Aniba rosaeodora)*

Botanical Family: Lauraceae

Plant Origin: Brazil

Extraction Method: Steam distilled from wood.

Key Constituents:
Linalol (70-90%)
Alpha-Terpineol (2-7%)
Alpha-Copaene (trace-3%)
1,8 Cineole (Eucalyptol) (trace-3%)
Geraniol (0.5-2.5%)

ORAC: 113,200 µTE/100g

Medical Properties: Antibacterial, antiviral, antiparasitic, antifungal, stimulant, improves skin elasticity.

USES: Fungal infections/Candida, skin conditions (eczema, psoriasis)

Fragrant Influence: Empowering and emotionally stabilizing.

Application: (1) Apply 2-4 drops on location, (2) chakras/Vita Flex points, (3) directly inhale, (4) diffuse, or (5) take as dietary supplement (see Appendices E and T).

Found In: Acceptance, Animal Scents Ointment, AromaGuard Meadow Mist Deodorant, Awaken, Believe, Clarity, Dragon Time Bath & Shower Gel, Evening Peace Bath & Shower Gel, Forgiveness, Genesis Hand & Body Lotion, Gentle Baby, Gratitude, Harmony, HRT, Humility, Inspiration, Joy, KidScents Lotion, KidScents Tender Tush, Lady Sclereol, Lavender-Rosewood Bar Soap, Magnify Your Purpose, Relaxation Massage Oil, Rose Ointment, Rosewood Moisturizing Conditioner, Rosewood Moisturizing Shampoo, Sandalwood Moisture Cream, Sensation, Sensation Bath & Shower Gel, Sensation Hand & Body Lotion, Sensation Massage Oil, Valor, Valor Bar Soap, White Angelica, and Wolfberry Eye Cream

Sage

Sandalwood

Sage *(Salvia officinalis)*

Botanical Family: Lamiaceae or Labiatae (mint)

Plant Origin: Spain, Croatia, France

Extraction Method: Steam distilled from leaves.

Key Constituents:
Alpha-Thuyone (18-43%)
Beta-Thuyone (3-8.5%)
1,8 Cineole (Eucalyptol) (5.5-13%)
Camphor (4.5-24.5%)
Camphene (1.5-7%)
Alpha-Pinene (1-6.5%)
Alpha-Humulene (0-12%) α β.

ORAC: 14,800 µTE/100g

Historical Data: Known as "herba sacra" or sacred herb by the ancient Romans, sage's name, *Salvia*, is derived from the word for "salvation." Sage has been used in Europe for oral infections and skin conditions. It has been recognized for its benefits of strengthening the vital centers and supporting metabolism.

Medical Properties: Antitumoral, hormone regulating, estrogen-like, antifungal, antiviral, circulatory stimulant, gallbladder stimulant

USES: Menstrual problems/PMS, estrogen, progesterone, and testosterone deficiencies, liver problems

Fragrant Influence: Mentally stimulating and helps combat despair and mental fatigue. Sage strengthens the vital centers of the body, balancing the pelvic chakra where negative emotions from denial and abuse are stored.

Application: Dilute 1 part EO with 1 part VO; (1) apply 2-4 drops on location, (2) chakras/ Vita Flex points, (3) directly inhale, (4) diffuse, or (5) take as dietary supplement (see Appendices E and T).

Cautions: Avoid if epileptic. Avoid use on persons with high blood pressure.

Found In: Dragon Time Bath & Shower Gel, Dragon Time Massage Oil, EndoFlex, Envision, FemiGen, K&B Tincture, LemonSage Clarifying Conditioner, LemonSage Clarifying Shampoo, Magnify Your Purpose, Mister, Prenolone, Prenolone Plus, Progessence, ProGen, and Protec

Selected References:

Gali-Muhtasib HU, Affara NI. Chemopreventive effects of sage oil on skin papillomas in mice. *Phytomedicine.* 2000 Apr;7(2):129-36.

Sandalwood *(Santalum album)*

Botanical Family: Santalaceae (sandalwood)

Plant Origin: India

Extraction Method: Steam distilled from wood.

Key Constituents:
Alpha-Santalol (47-55%)
Beta-Santalol (19-23%)

ORAC: 160 µTE/100g

Historical Data: Used for centuries in Ayurvedic medicine for skin revitalization, yoga, and meditation. Listed in Dioscorides' De Materia Medica (A.D. 78), Europe's first authoritive guide to medicines, that became the standard reference work for herbal treatments for over 1,700 years.

Recent research at Brigham Young University documented its ability to inhibit many types of cancerous cells.

Medical Properties: Antitumoral, antiviral, immune stimulant

USES: Cancer, viral infections (Herpes simplex, Herpes zoster, cold sores, human papilloma virus etc.), skin conditions (acne, wrinkles, scars etc.)

Fragrant Influence: Enhances deep sleep, may help remove negative programming from the cells. It is high in sesquiterpenes that stimulate the pineal gland and the limbic region of the brain, the center of emotions. The pineal gland is responsible for releasing melatonin, a powerful immune stimulant and antitumoral agent. Can be grounding and stabilizing.

Application: (1) Apply 2-4 drops on location, (2) chakras/Vita Flex points, (3) directly inhale, (4) diffuse, or (5) take as dietary supplement (see Appendices E and T).

Found In: 3 Wise Men, Acceptance, ART Day Activator, ART Gentle Foaming Cleanser, ART Night Repair, Awaken, Boswellia Wrinkle Cream, Brain Power, Dream Catcher, Evening Peace Bath & Shower Gel, Forgiveness, Gathering, Harmony, Highest Potential, Inner Child, Inspiration, KidScents Tender Tush, Lady Sclareol, Lemon-Sandalwood Bar Soap, Magnify Your Purpose, Release, Sandalwood Moisture Cream, Transformation, Trauma Life, Ultra Young, Ultra Young +, and White Angelica

Selected References:

Benencia F, et al. "Antiviral activity of sandalwood oil against herpes simplex viruses-1 and -2." *Phytomedicine*. 1999;6(2):119-23

Dwivedi C, et al. "Chemopreventive effects of sandalwood oil on skin papillomas in mice." *Eur J Cancer Prev*. 1997;6(4):399-401.

Spearmint

Spanish Sage *(Sage lavanduli folia)*

Found In: Awaken, Harmony, Lady Sclareol, and SclarEssence

Spearmint *(Mentha spicata)*

Botanical Family: Lamiaceae or Labiatae (mint)

Plant Origin: Utah, China

Extraction Method: Steam distilled from leaves.

Key Constituents:
Carvone (45-55%)
Limonene (15-25%)
Cis-Dihydrocarvone (5-10%)

ORAC: 540 µTE/100g

Medical Properties: Increases metabolism, anti-inflammatory, antiseptic, mucolytic, gallbladder stimulant, digestive aid.

USES: Obesity, intestinal/digestive disorders, Hepatitis

Fragrant Influence: Opens and releases emotional blocks and brings about a feeling of balance and a lasting sense of well-being.

Application: Dilute 1 part EO with 2 parts VO; (1) apply 2-4 drops on location, (2) chakras/Vita Flex points, (3) directly inhale, (4) diffuse, or (5) take as dietary supplement (see Appendices E and T).

Found In: CinnaMint Lip Balm, Citrus Fresh, EndoFlex, GLF, KidScents Toothpaste, Relaxation Massage Oil, ThermaBurn, ThermaMist, and Thyromin

Selected Research:

Imai H, et al., Inhibition by the essential oils of peppermint and spearmint of the growth of pathogenic bacteria. *Microbios.* 2001;106 Suppl 1:31-9.

Spikenard *(Nardostachys jatamansi)*

Botanical Family: Valerianaceae

Plant Origin: India

Extraction Method: Steam distilled from roots.

Key Constituents:
Calarene (22-35%)
Beta-Ionene (4-8%)
Beta-Maaliene (4-9%)
Aristoladiene (3-7%)

ORAC: 54,800 µTE/100g

Historical Data: Highly regarded in India as a medicinal herb. It was the one of the most precious oils in ancient times, used only by priests, kings, or high initiates. References in the New Testament describe how Mary of Bethany used a salve of spikenard to anoint the feet of Jesus before the Last Supper. According to Dietrich Gumbel, Ph.D. it strengthens heart and improves circulation.

Medical Properties: Antibacterial, antifungal, anti-inflammatory, relaxant, immune stimulant

USES: Insomnia, menstrual problems/PMS, heart arrhythmias, nervous tension

Fragrant Influence: Relaxing, soothing, and helps nourish and regenerate the skin.

Application: (1) Apply 2-4 drops on location, (2) chakras/Vita Flex points, (3) directly inhale, (4) diffuse, or (5) take as dietary supplement (see Appendices E and T).

Found In: Animal Scents Shampoo Exodus, Egyptian Gold, Exodus II, and Humility

Bible References: (See additional Bible references in Appendix D).

Song Of Solomon 1:12—"While the king sitteth at his table, my spikenard sendeth forth the smell thereof."

Song Of Solomon 4:13—"Thy plants are an orchard of pomegranates, with pleasant fruits; camphire, with spikenard,"

Song Of Solomon 4:14—"Spikenard and saffron; calamus and cinnamon, with all trees of frankincense; myrrh and aloes, with all the chief spices:"

Selected Research:

Friedman M, Henika PR, Mandrell RE. Bactericidal activities of plant essential oils and some of their isolated constituents against Campylobacter jejuni, Escherichia coli, Listeria monocytogenes, and Salmonella enterica. *J Food Prot.* 2002 Oct;65(10):1545-60.

Spruce *(Picea mariana)*

Botanical Family: Pinaceae (pine)

Plant Origin: Canada

Extraction Method: Steam distilled from branches, needles, and twigs.

Key Constituents:
Bornyl Acetate (18-28%)
Camphene (17-25%)
Alpha Pinene (12-19%)
Beta Pinene (4-8%)
Delta-3-Carene (5-10%)
Limonene (2-7%)
Santene (1-5%)
Tricyclene (1-5%)

Historical Data: The Lakota Indians used spruce to strengthen their ability to communicate with the Great Spirit.

Traditionally, it was believed to possess the frequency of prosperity.

Medical Properties: Antispasmodic, antiparasitic, antiseptic, anti-inflammatory, hormone-like, cortisone-like; immune stimulant

USES: Arthritis/rheumatism, fungal infections (Candida), sinus/respiratory infections, sciatica/lumbago

Fragrant Influence: Releases emotional blocks, bringing about a feeling of balance and grounding.

Application: Dilute 1 part EO with 1 part VO; (1) apply 2-4 drops on location, (2) chakras/Vita Flex points, (3) directly inhale, (4) diffuse, or (5) take as dietary supplement (see Appendices E and T)

Found In: 3 Wise Men, Abundance, Awaken, Christmas Spirit, Envision, Gathering, Grounding, Harmony, Highest Potential, Hope, Inner Child, Inspiration, Motivation, Present Time, R.C., Relieve It, Sacred Mountain, Sacred Mountain Bar Soap, Surrender, Trauma Life, Valor, and White Angelica

Tamanu *(Calophyllum inophyllum)* (NOT an essential oil, but rather a fatty acid)

Botanical Family: Bintangor

Plant Origin: Tahiti

Extraction Method: Extracted by a cold pressed method from the nut of the Polynesian Tamanu tree.

Key Constituents: (all of these constituents are fatty acid compounds – NOT essential oil compounds)
Oleic acid (35-39%)
Linoleic Acid (30-35%)
Palmitic Acid (12-14%)
Stearic Acid (12-14%)

Historical Data: The natives of Tahiti believed tamanu oil was "sacred" gift of nature. The Tahitian women used the oil as a moisturizing natural cosmetic on their faces and bodies. It was also used as sunburn protection.

Medical Properties: Used on scalp for healthy hair. When mixed with helichrysum it is affective on burns and wounds. Also the oil is used for a natural sunscreen.

Tangerine

Application: (1) apply 2-4 drops on location or (2) take as dietary supplement (see Appendices E and T).

Tangerine *(Citrus reticulata)*

Botanical Family: Rutaceae (citrus)

Plant Origin: Brazil

Extraction Method: Cold pressed from rind.

Key Constituents:
Limonene (85-93%)
Beta-Phellandrene+Cis-Beta-Ocimene (2-5%)
Myrcene (1-4%)

Medical Properties: Antitumoral, relaxant, antispasmodic, digestive aid, and circulatory enhancer. Rich in limonene, which has been extensively studied for its ability to combat tumor growth in over 50 clinical studies.

USES: Obesity, anxiety, insomnia, irritability, liver problems, digestive problems, parasites, and fluid retention

Fragrant Influence: Promotes happiness, calming, helps with anxiety and nervousness. A 1995 Mie University study found that citrus fragrances boosted immunity, induced relaxation, and reduced depression.

Application: Dilute 1 part EO with 1 part VO; (1) apply 2-4 drops on location, (2) chakras/Vita Flex points, (3) directly inhale, (4) diffuse, or (5) take as dietary supplement (see Appendices E and T)

Tansy

Found In: Awaken, Bodygize, Citrus Fresh, ComforTone, Dream Catcher, Inner Child, KidScents Shampoo, Peace & Calming, Relaxation Massage Oil, and Super C

Selected Research:

Wattenberg LW, et al., Inhibition of carcinogenesis by some minor dietary constituents. *Princess Takamatsu Symp.* 1985;16:193-203.

Alderman GG, Marth EH. Inhibition of growth and aflatoxin production of Aspergillus parasiticus by citrus oils. *Z Lebensm Unters Forsch.* 1976 Apr 28;160(4):353-8.

Crowell PL. Prevention and therapy of cancer by dietary monoterpenes. *J Nutr.* 1999 Mar;129(3):775S-778S.

Komori T, et al., Application of fragrances to treatments for depression. *Nihon Shinkei Seishin Yakurigaku Zasshi.* 1995 Feb;15(1): 39-42. Japanese

Tansy, Blue (*Tanacetum annuum*)

Botanical Family: Asteraceae or Compositae (daisy)

Plant Origin: Morocco

Extraction Method: Steam distilled from flowering plant.

Key Constituents:
Camphor (10-17%)
Sabinene (10-17%)
Beta-Pinene (5-10%)
Myrcene (7-13%)
Alpha-Phellandrene (5-10%)
Para-Cymene (3-8%)
Chamazulene (3-6%)

ORAC: 68,800 µTE/100g

Medical Properties: Anti-inflammatory, analgesic/ anesthetic, anti-itching, relaxant, hormone-like

Application: Dietary Supplement: Put 2 drops in a capsule and take three times daily or as needed; (1) apply 2-4 drops on location, dilution not required except for the most sensitive skin, (2) chakras/Vita Flex points, (3) directly inhale, or (4) diffuse up to 1 hour three times daily (see Appendices E and T).

Found In: Acceptance, Australian Blue, Awaken, Dragon Time Bath & Shower Gel, Dream Catcher, Evening Peace Bath & Shower Gel, Highest Potential, JuvaFlex, JuvaTone, KidScents Shampoo, KidScents Tender Tush Ointment, Peace & Calming, Release, SARA, Valor, and Valor Bar Soap

Tansy, Idaho (*Tanacetum vulgare*)

Botanical Family: Asteraceae or Compositae (daisy)

Plant Origin: Idaho, Morroco

Extraction Method: Steam distilled from leaves and stems.

Key Constituents:
Beta Thujone (65-80%)
Camphor (3-8%)
Sabinene (1-4%)
Germacrene D (3-7%)

Historical Data: This antimicrobial oil has been used extensively as an insect repellent. According to E. Joseph Montagna's P.D.R. on herbal formulas, it may help numerous skin conditions and tone the entire system.

Tarragon

Tea Tree

Medical Properties: Analgesic, anticoagulant, immune stimulant, insect repellent

USES: Arteriosclerosis, hypertension, arthritis/rheumatism

Application: Dilute 1 part EO with 1 part VO; (1) apply 2-4 drops on location, (2) chakras/Vita Flex points, (3) directly inhale, or (4) diffuse (see Appendices E and T)

Cautions: Do not use if pregnant.

Found In: ImmuPower, Into The Future, Lady Sclareol, and ParaFree Softgels

USES: Instestinal disorders, urinary tract infection, nausea, menstrual problems/PMS

Fragrant Influence: May help alleviate deep depression.

Application: Dilute 1 part EO with 1 part VO; (1) apply 2-4 drops on location, (2) chakras/Vita Flex points, or (3) take as dietary supplement (see Appendices E and T)

Caution: Avoid use if epileptic.

Found In: ComforTone, Di-Gize, Essentialzyme, and ICP

Tarragon *(Artemisia dracunculus)*

Botanical Family: Asteraceae or Compositae (daisy)

Plant Origin: Italy

Extraction Method: Steam distilled from leaves.

Key Constituents:
Methyl Chavicol (Estragole) (68-80%)
Trans-Beta Ocimene (6-12%)
Cis-Beta-Ocimene (6-12%)
Limonene (2-6%)

ORAC: 37,900 µTE/100g

Medical Properties: Antispasmodic, anti-inflammatory, antifermentation, antiparasitic, digestive aid

Tea Tree *(Melaleuca alternifolia)*

Botanical Family: Myrtaceae (myrtle)

Plant Origin: Australia, France

Extraction Method: Steam distilled from leaves.

Key Constituents:
Terpinenol-4 (30-45%)
Gamma Terpinene (10-28%)
Alpha-Terpinene (5-13%)
1,8 Cineole (Eucalyptol) (0-15%)
Alpha-Terpineol (1.5-8%)
Para-Cymene (0.5-12%)
Limonene (0.5-4%)
Aromadendrene (trace-7%)
Delta-Cadinene (trace-8%)
Alpha Pinene (1-6%)

Historical Data: Highly regarded as an antimicrobial and antiseptic essential oil. It has high levels of terpinenol-4.

Medical Properties: Powerful antibacterial, antifungal, antiviral, antiparasitic, anti-inflammatory action

USES: Fungal infections (Candida, ringworm), sinus/lung infections), tooth/gum disease, water retention/hypertension, skin conditions (acne, sores)

Fragrant Influence: Promotes cleansing and purity.

Application: Dilute 1 part EO with 1 part VO; (1) apply 2-4 drops on location, (2) chakras/Vita Flex points, (3) directly inhale, (4) diffuse, or (5) take as dietary supplement (see Appendices E and T).

Found In: Animal Scents Ointment, AromaGuard Meadow Mist Deodorant, Claraderm Mist, Melaleuca-Geranium Bar Soap, Melrose, ParaFree Softgels, Purification, Rehemogen Tincture, and Rose Ointment

Selected Research:

Syed TA, et al. "Treatment of toenail onychomycosis with 2% butenafine and 5% *Melaleuca alternifolia* (tea tree) oil in cream." *Trop Med Int Health*. 1999;4(4):284-7.

Hammer KA, et al. "In vitro susceptibilities of lactobacilli and organisms associated with bacterial vaginosis to *Melaleuca alternifolia* (tea tree) oil." *Antimicrob Agents Chemother*. 1999;43(1):196.

Concha JM, et al. 1998 William J. Stickel Bronze Award. "Antifungal activity of *Melaleuca alternifolia* (tea-tree) oil against various pathogenic organisms." *J Am Podiatr Med Assoc*. 1998;88(10):489-92.

Groppo FC, et al., Antimicrobial activity of garlic, tea tree oil, and chlorhexidine against oral microorganisms. Int Dent J. 2002 Dec;52(6):433-7.

Stablein JJ, Bucholtz GA, Lockey RF. Melaleuca tree and respiratory disease. Ann Allergy Asthma Immunol. 2002 Nov;89(5): 523-30.

Thyme

Thyme *(Thymus vulgaris)*

Botanical Family: Lamiaceae or Labiatae (mint), also known as Red Thyme

Plant Origin: Mediterranean area

Extraction Method: Steam distilled from leaves, stems, and flowers.

Key Constituents:
Thymol (37-55%)
Para-cymene (14-28%)
Gamma-Terpinene (4-11%)
Linalol (3-6.5%)
Carvacrol (0.5-5.5%)
Myrcine (1-2.8%)

ORAC: 15,960 µTE/100g

Historical Data: It is mentioned in one of the oldest known medical records, Ebers Papyrus (dating from sixteenth century B.C.) an ancient Egyptian list of 877 prescriptions and recipes. The Egyptians used thyme for embalming. Listed in Dioscorides' De Materia Medica (A.D. 78), Europe's first authoritative guide to medicines, that became the standard reference work for herbal treatments for over 1,700 years.

Thyme was listed in Hildegard's Medicine, a compilation of early German medicines by highly-regarded Benedictine herbalist Hildegard of Bingen (1098-1179).

Medical Properties: Anti-aging, highly antimicrobial, antifungal, antiviral, antiparasitic. A solution of thyme's most active ingredient, thymol, is used in many over-the-counter products such as mouthwash and vapor rubs because of its purifying agents.

USES: Infectious diseases, cardiovascular disease, Alzheimers disease, hepatitis

Fragrant Influence: It may be beneficial in helping to overcome fatigue and exhaustion after illness.

Application: Dilute 1 part EO with 4 parts VO; (1) apply 1-2 drops on location, (2) chakras/ Vita Flex points, (3) diffuse, or (4) take as dietary supplement (see Appendices E and T).

Caution: May irritate the nasal membranes or skin if inhaled directly from diffuser or bottle, or applied neat.

Found In: Dentarome Ultra, Longevity, Longevity Softgels, Ortho Ease Massage Oil, Ortho Sport Massage Oil, ParaFree Softgels, and Rehemogen

Selected Research:

Panizzi L, et al. "Composition and antimicrobial properties of essential oils of four Mediterranean Lamiaceae." *J Ethnopharmacol.* 1993;39 (3):167-70.

Youdim KA, Deans SG. Dietary supplementation of thyme (Thymus vulgaris L.) essential oil during the lifetime of the rat: its effects on the antioxidant status in liver, kidney and heart tissues. *Mech Ageing Dev.* 1999 Sep 8;109(3):163-75.

Youdim KA, et al. "Beneficial effects of thyme oil on age-related changes in the phospholipid C20 and C22 polyunsaturated fatty acid composition of various rat tissues." *Biochim Biophys Acta.* 1999;1438(1):140-6.

Youdim KA, Deans SG. Effect of thyme oil and thymol dietary supplementation on the antioxidant status and fatty acid composition of the ageing rat brain. *Br J Nutr.* 2000 Jan;83(1):87-93.

Inouye S, et al. "Antisporulating and respiration- inhibitory effects of essential oils on filamentous fungi." *Mycoses.* 1998;41(9-10): 403-10.

Tsuga

Friedman M, Henika PR, Mandrell RE. Bactericidal activities of plant essential oils and some of their isolated constituents against Campylobacter jejuni, Escherichia coli, Listeria monocytogenes, and Salmonella enterica. *J Food Prot.* 2002 Oct;65(10):1545-60.

Venturini ME, Blanco D, Oria R. In vitro antifungal activity of several antimicrobial compounds against Penicillium expansum. *J Food Prot.* 2002 May;65(5):834-9.

Inouye S, Yamaguchi H, Takizawa T. Screening of the antibacterial effects of a variety of essential oils on respiratory tract pathogens, using a modified dilution assay method. *J Infect Chemother.* 2001 Dec;7(4):251-4.

Lee KG, Shibamoto T. Inhibition of malonaldehyde formation from blood plasma oxidation by aroma extracts and aroma components isolated from clove and eucalyptus. *Food Chem Toxicol.* 2001 Dec; 39(12):1199-204.

Vazquez BI, Fente C, Franco CM, Vazquez MJ, Cepeda A. Inhibitory effects of eugenol and thymol on Penicillium citrinum strains in culture media and cheese. *Int J Food Microbiol.* 2001 Jul 20;67(1-2):157-63.

Teissedre PL, Waterhouse AL. Inhibition of oxidation of human low-density lipoproteins by phenolic substances in different essential oils varieties. *J Agric Food Chem.* 2000 Sep;48(9):3801-5.

Valerian Root

Inouye S, Uchida K, Yamaguchi H. In-vitro and in-vivo anti-Trichophyton activity of essential oils by vapour contact. *Mycoses.* 2001 May;44(3-4):99-107.

Tantaoui-Elaraki A, Beraoud L. Inhibition of growth and aflatoxin production in Aspergillus parasiticus by essential oils of selected plant materials. *J Environ Pathol Toxicol Oncol.* 1994;13(1):67-72.

Dorman HJ, Deans SG. Antimicrobial agents from plants: antibacterial activity of plant volatile oils. *J Appl Microbiol.* 2000 Feb;88(2):308-16.

Tsuga *(Tsuga canadensis)*

Botanical Family: Pinaceae

Plant Origin: Canada

Extraction Method: Steam distilled from needles and twigs of the conifer tree commercially known as hemlock.

Key Constituents:
Alpha- and Beta-Pinenes (18-25%)
Camphene (12-18%)
Limonene + Beta Phellandrene (3-7%)
Bornyl Acetate (28-38%)
Tricyclene (4-8%)
Myrcene (1-3%)

ORAC: 7,100 µTE/100g

Medical Properties: Analgesic, antirheumatic, blood cleanser, stimulant

USES: Respiratory conditions, kidney/urinary infections, skin conditions, venereal diseases

Application: Dilute 1 part EO with 1 part VO; (1) apply 2-4 drops on location, (2) chakras/Vita Flex points, (3) directly inhale, (4) diffuse, or (5) take as dietary supplement (see Appendices E and T).

Valerian *(Valeriana officinalis)*

Botanical Family: Valerianaceae

Plant Origin: Belgium, Croatia

Extraction Method: Steam distilled from root.

Key Constituents:
Bornyl Acetate (32-44%)
Camphene + Alpha-Fenchene (24-34%)
Alpha-Pinene (4-8%)
Beta-Pinene (2-6%)
Isobicycolgermacrenol (3-6%)
Myrtenyl Acetate (1-5%)

ORAC: 6,200 µTE/100g

Historical Data: During the last three decades, valerian has been clinically investigated for its tranquilizing properties. Researchers have pinpointed the sesquiterpenes, valerenic acid and valerone as the active constituents that exert a calming effect on the central nervous system. The German Commission E has pronounced valerian to be an effective treatment for restlessness and for sleep disturbances resulting from nervous conditions. insomnia, indigestion, migraine, restlessness, and tension.

Medical Properties: Sedative and tranquilizing to the central nervous system

USES: Insomnia, anxiety

Fragrant Influence: Calming, relaxing, grounding, and emotionally balancing.

Application: (1) Apply 2-4 drops on location, (2) chakras/Vita Flex points, (3) directly inhale, (4) diffuse, or (5) take as dietary supplement (see Appendices E and T).

Found In: Trauma Life

Selected Research:

Wagner J, et al. "Beyond benzodiazepines: alternative pharmacologic agents for the treatment of insomnia." *Ann Pharmacother.* 1998;32(6):680-91.

Vetiver *(Vetiveria zizanioides)*

Botanical Family: Poaceae or Gramineae (grasses)

Plant Origin: Haiti

Extraction Method: Steam distilled from root.

Key Constituents:
Isovalencenol (11-15%)
Khusenol (6-11%)
Alpha Vetivone (3-6%)
Beta Vetivone (3-6%)
Nootkatone (2-5%)
Khusimone (3-6%)

ORAC: 74,300 µTE/100g

Historical Data: It is well known for its anti-inflammatory properties and traditionally used for arthritic symptoms.

Medical Properties: Antiseptic, antispasmodic, relaxant, circulatory stimulant

USES: ADHD, anxiety, rheumatism/arthritis, depression (including postpartum), insomnia, skin care (oily, aging, acne, wrinkles)

Fragrant Influence: Psychologically grounding, calming, and stabilizing. It helps us cope with stress and recover from emotional trauma. Terry Friedmann, MD found in clinical tests that this oil was able to successfully treat ADD and ADHD (attention deficit disorders) in children.

Found In: Lady Sclareol, Melaleuca-Geranium Bar Soap, Ortho Ease Massage Oil, Ortho Sport Massage Oil, ParaFree Softgels, and Thieves Fresh Essence Mouthwash

Application: (1) Apply 2-4 drops on location, (2) chakras/Vita Flex points, (3) directly inhale, (4) diffuse, or (5) take as dietary supplement (see Appendices E and T).

Wintergreen

Western Red Cedar

(See CEDAR, WESTERN RED)

Wintergreen *(Gaultheria procumbens)*

Botanical Family: Ericaceae

Plant Origin: China, North America

Extraction Method: Steam distilled from leaves and bark.

Key Constituent:
Methyl Salicylate (90+%)

ORAC: 101,800 µTE/100g

Historical Data: Leaves have been chewed to increase respiratory capacity by Native Americans when running long distances and performing difficult labor. Settlers in early America had their children chew the leaves for several weeks each spring to prevent tooth decay. Wintergreen was used as a substitute for Black Tea during the Revolutionary War.

Medical Properties: Anticoagulant, antispasmodic, highly anti-inflammatory, vasodilator, analgesic/anesthetic, reduces blood pressure, all types of pain. Methyl Salicylate, the principal constituent of wintergreen oil, has been incorporated into numerous linaments and ointments for muskoskeletal problems. The oil is also used as a flavoring agent in candies and chewing gums.

USES: Arthritis/rheumatism, muscle/nerve pain, hypertension, arteriosclerosis, hepatitis/fatty liver

Fragrant Influence: It stimulates and increases awareness in all levels of the sensory system.

Application: Dilute 1 part EO with 2 parts VO; (1) apply 1-2 drops on location, (2) chakras/Vita Flex points, (3) directly inhale, (4) diffuse, or (5) take as dietary supplement (see Appendices E and T).

Cautions: Avoid use if epileptic. Anticoagulant properties can be enhanced when used with Warfarin or aspirin.

Found In: Be-Fit, BLM Softgels, BLM Powder, Dentarome Toothpaste, Dentarome Ultra Toothpaste, Ortho Ease Massage Oil, Ortho Sport Massage Oil, PanAway, Raven, Regenolone, Rosewood Moisturizing Conditioner, Rosewood Moisturizing Shampoo, and Super Cal

Selected Research:

Ichiyama RM, et al., Effects of topical analgesics on the pressor response evoked by muscle afferents. *Med Sci Sports Exerc.* 2002 Sep;34(9):1440-5.

Battino M, In vitro antioxidant activities of mouthrinses and their components. *J Clin Periodontol.* 2002 May;29(5):462-7.

Charles CH, et al., Effect of an essential oil-containing dentifrice on dental plaque microbial composition. *Am J Dent.* 2000 Sep;13(Spec No):26C-30C.

Yu D et al., Caries inhibition efficacy of an antiplaque/antigingivitis dentifrice. *Am J Dent.* 2000 Sep;13(Spec No):14C-17C.

Joss JD, LeBlond RF. Potentiation of warfarin anticoagulation associated with topical methyl salicylate. *Ann Pharmacother.* 2000 Jun;34(6):729-33.

Trautmann M, Peskar BM, Peskar BA. Aspirin-like drugs, ethanol-induced rat gastric injury and mucosal eicosanoid release. *Eur J Pharmacol.* 1991 Aug 16;201(1):53-8.

Yarrow, Blue (*Achillea millefolium*)

Botanical Family: Asteraceae or Compositae (daisy)

Plant Origin: Commoro, USA, Europe, Asia

Extraction Method: Steam distilled from flowers, leaves, and stems.

Key Constituents:
Chamazulene (12-19%)
Trans-Beta-Caryophyllene (4-8%)
Germacrene D (4-8%)
Camphor (4-9%)
Sabinene (3-7%)
Beta-Pinene (3-7%)
1,8 Cineol (Eucalyptol) (2-6%)

ORAC: 55,900 μTE/100g

Historical Data: The Greek Achilles, hero of the Trojan War, was said to have used the yarrow herb to help cure the injury to his Achilles tendon. Yarrow was considered sacred by the Chinese, who recognized the harmony of the Yin and Yang energies within it. It has been said that the fragrance of yarrow makes possible the meeting of heaven and earth. Yarrow was used by Germanic tribes for the treatment of battle wounds.

Medical Properties: Anti-inflammatory, hormone-like, combats scarring, prostate support

USES: Prostate problems, menstrual problems/PMS, varicose veins

Fragrant Influence: Balancing highs and lows, both external and internal, yarrow simultaneously inspires and grounds us. Useful during meditation and supportive to intuitive energies. Reduces confusion and ambivalence.

Application: Dietary Supplement: put 2 drops in a capsule, take three times daily or as needed; (1) apply 2-4 drops on location, dilution not required except for the most sensitive skin, (2) chakras/Vita Flex points, (3) directly inhale, or (4) diffuse up to 1 hour three times daily (see Appendices E and T).

Found In: Dragon Time, Dragon Time Massage Oil, Mister, Prenolone, Prenolone Plus, ProGen, and Progessence

Ylang Ylang

Ylang Ylang *(Cananga odorata)*

Botanical Family: Annonaceae (custard-apple)

Plant Origin: Commoro

Extraction Method: Steam distilled from flowers. Flowers are picked early in the morning to maximize oil yield. The highest quality oil is drawn from the first distillation and is known as ylang ylang complete. The last distillation, known as the tail, is of inferior quality and is called "cananga."

Key Constituents:
Germacrene D (15-20%)
Alpha Farnesene (8-12%)
Benzyl Acetate (9-15%)
Benzyl Benzoate (3-6%)
Linalol (6-10%)
Methyl Paracresol (5-9%)
Isoeugenol (3-5%)
Cinnamyl acetate (3-5%)

ORAC: 130,000 µTE/100g

Historical Data: Ylang ylang means "flower of flowers." The flowers have been used to cover the beds of newlywed couples on their wedding night. Traditionally used in hair formulas to promote thick, shiny, lustrous hair.

Medical Properties: Antispasmodic, vasodilating, antidiabetic, anti-inflammatory, anti-parasitic, regulates heartbeat

USES: Cardiac arrhythmia, cardiac problems, anxiety, hypertension, depression, hair loss, intestinal problems

Fragrant Influence: Balances male-female energies, enhances spiritual attunement, combats anger, combats low self-esteem, and increases focus of thoughts, filters out negative energy. Restores confidence and peace.

Application: Dilute 1 part EO with 1 part VO; (1) apply 2-4 drops on location, (2) chakras/ Vita Flex points, (3) directly inhale, (4) diffuse, or (5) take as dietary supplement (see Appendices E and T).

Caution: Use sparingly if you have low blood pressure.

Found In: Aroma Life, Australian Bue, Awaken, Boswellia Wrinkle Cream, CardiaCare, Clarity, Dragon Time Bath & Shower Gel, Dragon Time Massage Oil, Dream Catcher, Evening Peace Bath & Shower Gel, FemiGen, Forgiveness, Gathering, Genesis Hand & Body Lotion, Gentle Baby, Gratitude, Grounding, Harmony, Highest Potential, HRT, Humility, Inner Child, Into The Future, Joy, Lady Sclareol, LemonSage Clarifying Conditioner, LemonSage Clarifying wash, Motivation, Peace & Calming, Prenolone, Prenolone Plus, Progressence, Present Time, Release, Sacred Mountain, SARA, Sensation, Sensation Bath & Shower Gel, Sensation Hand and Body Lotion, Sensation Massage Oil, and White Angelica

Yarrow and Fennel

SECTION 3

This section describes specific blends that were formulated after years of research for both physical and emotional health. Each of these blends is formulated to maximize the synergistic effect between various oil chemistries and harmonic frequencies. When chemistry and frequency coincide, noticeable physical, spiritual, and emotional benefits can be attained.

It is important to remember that essential oils may be irritating to those with sensitive skin. Avoid eye contact. In case of accidental contact, put a few drops of any pure vegetable oil (i.e. V-6 Enhanced Vegetable Oil Complex, olive, etc.) in the eye and call your doctor if necessary. Avoid using water to dilute or rinse.

All essential oils, including blends, should be stored in a cool, dark place to avoid the harmful effects of light to some of the fragile components.

Abundance

Increases the attraction of abundance and success. It enhances the frequency of the energy field that surrounds us through stimulation of the somatides. Somatides transmit frequency from the cells to the environment when stimulated through fragrance and thoughts. This frequency creates the "law of attraction," a harmonic magnetic energy field around oneself.

When focusing on issues of abundance and inhaling this oil, a memory link to the RNA template is created where memory is blueprinted and permanently transcribed.

Ingredients:

Myrrh *(Commiphora myrrha)* possesses the frequency of wealth according to legends and is referenced throughout the Old and New Testaments ("A bundle of myrrh is my well-beloved unto me... " Song of Solomon 1:13). It

was also part of a formula the Lord gave to Moses (Exodus 30:22-27). It was used traditionally in the royal palaces by the queens during pregnancy and birthing.

Cinnamon Bark *(Cinnamomum verum)* is the oil of wealth from the Orient and part of the formula the Lord gave to Moses (Exodus 30:22-27). It was regarded by the emperors of China and India to have great value; their wealth was measured by the amount of oil they possessed. It was believed to attract wealth and abundance.

Frankincense *(Boswellia carteri)* was valued more than gold during ancient times, and only those with great wealth and abundance possessed it. It is considered a holy anointing oil in the Middle East and has been used in religious ceremonies for thousands of years. Frankincense contains sesquiterpenes which stimulate and elevate the mind, overcoming stress and despair.

Patchouli *(Pogostemon cablin)* is used by East Indians to fragrance their clothing and homes to attract abundance. Legends say that patchouli represented money and those who possessed it were considered wealthy. It is also relaxing and helps clarify thoughts.

Orange *(Citrus sinensis)* brings joy, security, peace, and happiness to those who possess it.

Clove *(Syzygium aromaticum)* is an oil from the Orient associated with great abundance; those who possessed it were considered wealthy.

Ginger *(Zingiber officinale)* was highly prized in ancient times. It amplifies the law of attraction.

Spruce *(Picea mariana)* was traditionally, believed to possess the frequency of prosperity. Helps relieve emotional blocks bringing about a sense of balance.

Applications:

For topical use, dilute 1 part Abundance with 1 part vegetable oil (e.g. olive, V-6 Enhanced Vegetable Oil Complex). Apply 1-2 drops on location.

Diffuse, directly inhale, or add 2-4 drops to bath water. Apply 1 to 2 drops over heart, on wrists, neck, and temples. Put 2 drops on a wet cloth and put in clothes dryer. May stain white fabrics. Put 4-8 drops on a cotton ball and locate on heater vents.

For aromatic use, diffuse up to 30-45 min. daily. Avoid contact with eyes.

Use Release first to release emotions that prevent us from receiving abundance. Follow with Acceptance, Believe, Envision, Into the Future, Joy, Magnify Your Purpose, Motivation or Valor.

Acceptance

Stimulates the mind, compelling us to open and accept new things, people, or relationships in life, allowing one to reach a higher potential. It also helps to overcome procrastination and denial.

Ingredients:

Neroli (*Citrus sinensis*) was used by the ancient Egyptians for healing the mind, body, and spirit. It is stabilizing and strengthening to the emotions, promoting peace, confidence, and awareness. It brings everything into focus.

Sandalwood (*Santalum album*) is high in sesquiterpene compounds which stimulate the pineal gland and the limbic region of the brain, the center of emotions and memory. Used traditionally in yoga and meditation. May help remove negative programming in the cells.

Blue Tansy (*Tanacetum annuum*) helps cleanse the liver and lymphatic system helping to overcome anger and negative emotions. Promotes a feeling of self-control.

Rosewood (*Aniba rosaeodora*) is high in linalool, which has a relaxing, empowering effect.

Geranium (*Pelargonium graveolens*) helps balance hormones and discharge toxins from the liver, where fear and anger are stored.

Frankincense (*Boswellia carteri*) is considered a holy anointing oil and has been used in religious ceremonies for thousands of years. It stimulates the limbic part of the brain, which elevates the mind, helping to overcome stress and despair. It is used in European medicine to combat depression.

Carrier Oil: Almond

Applications:

Diffuse or add 1-2 drops to bath water. Apply over heart and thymus, on wrists, behind ears, on neck and temples.

Aroma Life

Improves cardiovascular, lymphatic, and circulatory systems. Lowers high blood pressure and reduces stress.

Ingredients:

Helichrysum (*Helichrysum italicum*) improves circulation and reduces blood viscosity. It is anticoagulant, regulates cholesterol, stimulates liver cell function, and reduces plaque deposits from the veins and arteries.

Ylang Ylang (*Cananga odorata*) used traditionally to balance heart function and treat tachycardia (rapid heart beat) and high blood pressure. Combats insomnia.

Marjoram (*Origanum majorana*) helps regenerate smooth muscle tissue, and assists in relieving muscle spasms. it calms nervous tension. Has diuretic-like action.

Cypress (*Cupressus sempervirens*) improves circulation and lymphatic drainage. It reduces edema and water retention. It strengthens the vascular system.

Carrier Oil: Organic Sesame (*Sesamum indicum*) Seed

Application:

For topical use, apply 4 drops on location (heart, abdomen or in conjunction with Raindrop Technique) as needed.

Diffuse, directly inhale, or add 2-4 drops to bath water. Apply 1 to 2 drops over heart and along spine from first to fourth thoracic vertebrae (which correspond to the cardiopulmonary nerves). Dilute 1:15 with vegetable oil for a full-body massage.

Aroma Siez

An advanced complex of anti-inflammatory, muscle-relaxing essential oils that promote circulation and treat spasmed, tight, inflamed, aching muscles resulting from injury, fatigue, or stress. It also relieves headaches.

Ingredients:

Basil *(Ocimum basilicum)* combats muscle spasms and inflammation. It is relaxing to both striated and smooth muscles (involuntary muscles such as those found in the heart and digestive system).

Marjoram *(Origanum majorana)* helps regenerate smooth muscle tissue, and assists in relieving spasms, sprains, bruises, migraine headaches and calming the nerves. It is antibacterial and antiseptic.

Lavender *(Lavandula angustifolia)* relieves muscle spasms/sprains/pains, headaches, inflammation, anxiety, burns, and skin conditions (psoriasis) preventing scarring, and stretch marks. It is hypotensive, anti-infectious, anticoagulant.

Peppermint *(Mentha piperita)* has powerful pain-blocking, anti-inflammatory, and antispasmodic properties. A 1994 double-blind, placebo-controlled, randomized cross-over study at the University of Kiel in Germany found that peppermint oil had a significant analgesic effect (Gobel et al., 1994).

Cypress *(Cupressus sempervirens)* is antibacterial, antimicrobial, antiseptic, and improves circulation and lymphatic drainage. It reduces edema and water retention. It strengthens the vascular system.

Applications:

See label. For topical use, dilute 1 drop of Aroma Siez with 1 drop V-6 or olive oil. Apply to affected area as needed.

Apply on location to sore muscles, ligaments or areas of poor circulation. Use with Raindrop Technique.

Possible skin sensitivity.

Australian Blue

Includes a rare Australian aromatic called blue cypress, a part of the aboriginal pharmacopoeia for thousands of years. Distilled from the wood of *Callitris intratropica*, the Northern Cypress Pine, which has antiviral properties. Its aromatic influence uplifts and inspires while simultaneously grounding and stabilizing.

Ingredients:

Blue Cypress *(Callitris intratropica)* contains guaiol and guaiazulene, strong anti-inflammatory and antiviral compounds. Oral traditions indicate that the aboriginal Tiwi people of northern Australia used resins from the bark of blue cypress as a skin wash for sores and cuts. It's also used to relieve pain and repel insects.

Ylang Ylang *(Cananga odorata)* increases relaxation; balances male and female energies. It also restores confidence and equilibrium.

Cedarwood *(Cedrus atlantica)* is high in sesquiterpenes, which can stimulate the limbic part of the brain, the center of emotions and memory. It stimulates the pineal gland, which releases melatonin, thereby improving thoughts, cognition, and memory. Cedarwood is also very grounding emotionally.

Blue Tansy *(Tanacetum annuum)* is anti-inflammatory. Emotionally, it combats anger and negative emotions and promotes a feeling of self-control.

White Fir *(Abies concolor)* is antimicrobial, antiseptic, antiarthritic, and stimulating. It supports the body and reduces the symptoms of arthritis, rheumatism, bronchitis, coughs, sinusitis. It creates a feeling of grounding, anchoring, and empowerment.

Application:

Diffuse, directly inhale, or add 2-4 drops to bath water. Apply 1 to 2 drops on wrists, neck, temples, or foot Vita Flex points. Dilute 1:15 with vegetable oil for a full-body massage. May also be diffused for up to 1 hour daily.

Awaken

Enhances inner self knowledge in order to make desirable transitions assisting to reach one's highest potential. Stimulates the creativity of the right brain, amplifying the function of pineal and pituitary glands in balancing the energy centers of the body. Helps open up our true and complete selves.

Ingredients: *(A blend of five other blends)*

Joy produces a uplifting, magnetic energy that brings joy to the heart. It inspires romance and helps overcome grief and depression.

Forgiveness helps release negative memories. It helps people move past emotional barriers, enabling them to achieve higher awareness and compelling them to forgive and let go.

Present Time has an empowering fragrance, which gives a feeling of being "in the moment." One can only go forward and progress when in the present time.

Dream Catcher helps open the mind and enhance dreams and visualization, promoting greater potential for realizing your dreams and staying on your path. It also protects you from negative dreams that might cloud your vision.

Harmony promotes physical and emotional healing by bringing about a harmonic balance to the energy centers of the body. It reduces stress and creates a feeling of well-being.

Carrier Oil: Almond

Applications:

Diffuse, directly inhale, or add 2-4 drops to bath water. Apply 1 to 2 drops over heart, on wrists, neck, temples, forehead, or foot Vita Flex points. Dilute 1:15 with vegetable oil for a full-body massage. Put 2 drops on a wet cloth and put in clothes dryer. Put 4-8 drops on cotton ball and locate on vents. For clearing allergies, rub over sternum.

Possible sun sensitivity

Believe

Helps to release the unlimited potential everyone possesses, making it possible to more fully experience health, happiness, and vitality. Restores feelings of hope.

Ingredients:

Idaho Balsam Fir *(Abies balsamea)* opens emotional blocks and recharges vital energy. Gives a feeling of strength and inner peace.

Rosewood *(Aniba rosaeodora)* is high in linalool, which has a relaxing, empowering effect. A very grounding oil.

Frankincense *(Boswellia carteri)* is considered a holy anointing oil in the Middle East and has been used in religious ceremonies for thousands of years. Stimulates the limbic part of the brain, elevating the mind and helping to overcome stress and despair. It is used in European medicine to combat depression.

Applications:

Dilute 1 part EO to 1 part vegetable oil.

Directly inhale, or add 2-4 drops to bath water. Apply 1 to 2 drops over heart, on wrists, neck, temples, forehead, or foot Vita Flex points. Dilute 1:15 with vegetable oil for a full-body massage. Put 2 drops on a wet cloth and put in clothes dryer. Put 4-8 drops on cotton ball and locate on vents.

May also be diffused up to 30 minutes daily.

Possible skin sensitivity.

Brain Power

Promotes deep concentration and channels physical energy into mental energy. It also increases mental potential and clarity, and long-term use may retard the aging process. Many of the oils in this blend are high in sesquiterpene compounds that increase activity in the pineal, pituitary, and hypothalamus glands and thereby increase output of growth hormone and melatonin. The oils also help dissolve petrochemicals that congest the receptor sites, clearing the "brain fog" that people experience due to exposure to synthetic petrochemicals in food, skin and hair care products, and air.

Ingredients:

Frankincense (*Boswellia carteri*) stimulates the limbic part of the brain, which elevates the mind, helping to overcome stress and despair. It is used in European medicine to combat depression.

Sandalwood *(Santalum album)* is high in sesquiterpene compounds which stimulate the pineal gland and the limbic region of the brain, the center of our emotions and memory. Used traditionally in yoga and meditation.

Melissa *(Melissa officinalis)* stimulates the limbic part of the brain, the emotional center of memories. It removes emotional blocks and instills a positive outlook on life.

Cedarwood *(Cedrus atlantica)* is high in sesquiterpenes, which can stimulate the limbic part of the brain, the center of emotions and memory. It stimulates the pineal gland, which releases melatonin, thereby improving thoughts, cognition, and memory.

Blue Cypress *(Callitris intratropica)* improves circulation and increases the flow of oxygen to the brain, stimulating the amygdala, pineal gland, pituitary gland, and hypothalamus.

Lavender *(Lavandula angustifolia)* has been documented to improve concentration and mental acuity. University of Miami researchers found that inhalation of lavender oil increased beta waves in the brain, suggesting heightened relaxation. It also reduced depression and improved cognitive performance (Diego et al., 1998). Research during a 2001 Osaka Kyoiku University study found that lavender reduced mental stress and increased alertness (Motomura et al., 2001).

Helichrysum *(Helichrysum italicum)* helps improve circulation and stimulate optimum nerve function. Enhances awareness and cognition and helps release feelings of anger, that allows one to gain focus and concentration.

Applications:
Diffuse, directly inhale, or add 2-4 drops to bath water. Apply 1 to 2 drops on back of neck, throat, temples, or under nose. Apply 1 or 2 drops with a finger on insides of cheeks in mouth. Put 2 drops on a wet cloth and put in clothes dryer. Put 4-8 drops on cotton ball and locate on vents.

Possible skin sensitivity.

Breathe Again Roll-on

This supercharged version of the R.C. blend is packaged in a convenient dispenser for easy use whenever throat or nasal congestion strikes. Contains four different eucalyptus oils and five additional essential oils, all known for their ability to relax airways, make breathing easier and reduce coughing. In addition, these oils have anti-inflammatory characteristics.

Ingredients:

Eucalyptus Staigeriana, also known as Lemon Iron Bark or Lemon-Scented Ironbark, has a lemon-scented aroma and is antiviral, antiseptic, expectorant, anti-inflammatory and a digestive stimulant. It is not cineol-rich, so can be used people with sensitive skin.

Eucalyptus Globulus is fantastic on skin ailments (burns, blisters, wounds, insect bites, lice, and skin infections), as well as in combatting the effects of colds and the flu. There is also a history of eucalyptus essential oil being applied to sore muscles and joints.

Eucalyptus Radiata is commonly known as "narrow-leaved Peppermint" and contains a high percentage of cineol, also known as eucalyptol, popularly used to relieve colds and congestion. It is less harsh than other eucalyptus oils, more pleasant to inhale and less likely to irritate the skin. It can also be used on sore muscles and joints and also as an antiseptic. It has a crisp, clean, camphorous aroma with back notes of citrus/floral.

Eucalyptus Blue (Azul) *(Eucalyptus ssp.)* has the highest antiseptic cineol content and therefore is one of the strongest antiseptics among the Eucalyptus. It can also be used to combat the effects of colds and flu. Has a fresh, camphorous aroma with a hint of peppermint.

Bay Laurel *(Laurus nobilis)* is anti-infectious, antibacterial, antiviral, anti-fungal, anti-parasitic, antiseptic, anti-nausea, and a tonic. Laurus nobilis oil is used as a sedative for whooping cough and toothaches in India. It can help relieve symptoms of bronchitis, skin disease, cholera, & diarrhea. It has also been used as a circulatory stimulant.

Peppermint *(Mentha piperita)* is a powerful anti-inflammatory and antiseptic for the respiratory system. It is used to treat bronchitis and pneumonia. High in menthol and menthone, it helps suppress coughs and clears lung and nasal congestion.

Copaiba *(Copaifera reticulata (langsdorfii))* is commonly used in anti-inflammatory recipes prescribed by Amazonian traditional medical practitioners. It can also be effective in reducing muscle spasms.

Myrtle *(Myrtus communis)* is a wonderfully mild and gentle respiratory treatment, sometimes recommended for treating asthma attacks and respiratory problems with children. Myrtle has a mildly sedative action, which can make it useful in treating insomnia and nervous conditions. It is non-irritating and non-sensitizing, which makes it an appropriate oil to treat children and the elderly in cases of respiratory afflictions, chronic lung conditions, colds, infections, etc.

Manuka *(Leptospermum scopulorum)*, similar to Tea Tree oil, but much less medicinal in aroma, this healing oil is honey scented. It is anti-bacterial, anti-fungal and anti-viral. It is also proven effective against both strep and staph infections. Experimental use has shown it helpful in dealing with the symptoms of chronic fatigue.

Coconut Oil *(Cocos nucifera),* and **Rose Hip Seed Oil** *(Rosa rubiginosa)*

Application:

Apply to throat, neck or chest every 15-30 minutes for up to four applications for relief of symptoms related to colds, coughs or sinus/lung congestion.

Christmas Spirit

A purifying blend of evergreen, citrus, and spice, reminiscent of winter holidays, that brings joy, peace, happiness, and security.

Ingredients:

Orange *(Citrus sinensis)* is elevating to the mind and body, bringing security, joy, and peace.

Cinnamon Bark *(Cinnamomum verum)* is the oil of wealth from the Orient and part of the formula the Lord gave Moses (Exodus 30:22-27). Emperors of China and India measured their wealth partly by the amount of cinnamon they possessed. Traditionally, it was thought to have a frequency that attracted wealth and abundance. It is highly antiviral, antifungal, and antibacterial. Can bring back memories of wassail, home-cooked food, and all fond memories of the holidays.

Spruce *(Picea mariana)* helps the respiratory and nervous systems. It is anti-infectious, antiseptic, and anti-inflammatory. Its aromatic influences help to open and release emotional blocks, bringing about a feeling of balance and grounding. Traditionally, spruce oil was believed to possess the frequency of prosperity. This oil brings memories of Christmas trees and makes the whole house feel more like home during the holidays.

Application:

Dilute 1 part EO to 1 part vegetable oil.

Diffuse, directly inhale, or add 2-4 drops to bath water. Apply 1 to 2 drops over heart, on wrists, neck, temples, or foot Vita Flex points. Dilute 1:15 with vegetable oil for a full-body massage. Put 2 drops on a wet cloth and put in clothes dryer. Put 4-8 drops on cotton ball and locate on vents. Add to cedar chips for dresser drawers.

Add a few drops to wood before putting in fireplace.

Splash a few drops on your paper vacuum cleaner bag for a treat when cleaning house.

Possible sun/skin sensitivity.

Citrus Fresh

Stimulates the right brain to amplify creativity and well-being as well as eradicate anxiety. Works well as an air purifier. University researchers in Japan found that diffusing a citrus fragrance in an office environment improved mental accuracy and concentration by 54 percent. When diffused, it adds a clean, fresh scent to any environment.

Ingredients:

Orange *(Citrus sinensis)* is elevating to the mind and body, bringing security, joy, and peace. It is high in limonene which prevents DNA damage. Has anticoagulant properties.

Tangerine *(Citrus reticulata)* contains esters and aldehydes that are sedating and calming, combating anxiety and nervousness. It is high in limonene which prevents DNA damage.

Lemon *(Citrus limon)* has an extremely cleansing smell. This oil helps purify and uplift.

Mandarin *(Citrus reticulata)* has sedative and slightly hypnotic properties, mandarin combats insomnia, stress and irritability. It is high in limonene which prevents DNA damage. Has anticoagulant properties.

Grapefruit *(Citrus paradisi)* decongesting and fat-dissolving. It is high in limonene which prevents DNA damage. Has anticoagulant properties. This aroma can be very calming and bring a sense of wholeness.

Spearmint *(Mentha spicata)* oil helps support the respiratory, glandular, and nervous systems. With its hormone-like activity, it helps open and release emotional blocks and bring about a feeling of balance. It is antispasmodic, anti-infectious, anti-parasitic, antiseptic, and anti-inflammatory. It has also been used to increase metabolism to burn fat.

Application:
Dilute 1 part EO to 1 part vegetable oil.

A favorite for diffusing or directly inhale, or add 2-4 drops to bath water. Apply 1 to 2 drops on edge of ears, wrists, neck, temples, or foot VitaFlex points. Dilute 1:15 with vegetable oil for a full-body massage. Put 2 drops on a wet cloth and put in clothes dryer. Put 4-8 drops on cotton ball and locate on vents. Can also be ingested.

Possible sun/skin sensitivity.

Clarity

Promotes a clear mind and amplifies mental alertness. Improves mental activity and vitality, and increases energy when overly tired. Brings the spirit and mind back into focus.

Ingredients:

Cardamom *(Elettaria cardamomum)* is uplifting, refreshing, and invigorating. It may be beneficial for clearing confusion. In a study done by Dember, et al., 1995, cardamom was found to enhance performance accuracy.

Rosemary *(Rosmarinus officinalis* CT cineol*)* helps overcome mental fatigue, stimulates

memory and opens the conscious mind. University of Miami scientists found that inhaling rosemary boosted alertness, eased anxiety, and amplified analytic and mental ability.

Peppermint *(Mentha piperita)* Dr. William N. Dember of the University of Cincinnati found that inhaling peppermint oil increased mental accuracy by 28 percent. Stimulation to the mind and senses.

Basil *(Ocimum basilicum)* alleviates mental fatigue and muscle spasms.

Bergamot *(Citrus bergamia)* is simultaneously uplifting and calming, with a unique ability to relieve anxiety, stress, and tension.

Geranium *(Pelargonium graveolens)* is antispasmodic, relaxant, anti-inflammatory, and is uplifting.

Jasmine *(Jasminum officinale)* is stimulating to the mind and improves concentration.

Lemon *(Citrus limon)* is stimulating and invigorating. A 1995 Mie University study found that citrus fragrances boosted immunity, induced relaxation, and reduced depression.

Palmarosa *(Cymbopogon martinii)* is stimulating and revitalizing, enhancing both the nervous and cardiovascular system.

Roman Chamomile *(Chamaemelum nobile)* combats restlessness, tension, and insomnia. It purges toxins from liver where anger is stored. It also clears mental blocks.

Rosewood *(Aniba rosaeodora)* is high in linalool, which has a relaxing, empowering effect. It is also very grounding and strengthening.

Ylang Ylang *(Cananga odorata)* helps bring about a sense of relaxation and balance.

Application:
Dilute 1 part EO to 1 part vegetable oil.
Possible sun/skin sensitivity.

Diffuse, directly inhale, or add 2-4 drops to bath water. Apply 1 to 2 drops on edge of ears, wrists, neck, forehead, temples, or foot Vita Flex points (brain = large toe).

Add Brain Power, Palo Santo, lemon, or peppermint to enhance effects of Clarity.

Deep Relief Roll-on

Formulated for the convenient relief of muscle soreness and tension. Soothes sore joints and ligaments, helps calm stressed nerves and reduces inflammation. This powerful blend contains nine essential oils, most of which are for their anti-inflammatory and pain-relieving characteristics. The convenient roll-on tube provides for highly portable, convenient, no-mess application.

Ingredients:

Peppermint *(Menthe piperita)* has been found to relieve surface pain and tension/discomfort of the neck and head. It is also a highly regarded herb for soothing stomach discomfort.

Lemon *(Citrus limon)* is stimulating and invigorating. A 1995 Mie (Japan) University study found that citrus fragrances boosted immunity, induced relaxation and reduced depression.

Idaho Balsam Fir *(Abies balsamea)* has been prized through the ages for its medicinal effects and its ability to soothe muscular and rheumatic pain. Like other conifer oils, its aroma is grounding, stimulating to the mind and relaxing to the body.

Copaiba *(Copaifera langsdorfii)* is commonly used in anti-inflammatory recipes prescribed by Amazonian traditional medical practitioners. It can also be effective in reducing muscle spasms.

Clove *(Syzygium aromaticum)* has been used for decades as a natural anesthetic in dentistry. It was one of the ingredients in the original "Four Thieves Vinegar" that protected grave-robbing bandits during the 15th century plague. It has been shown to be extremely antioxidant as well as analgesic, anesthetic and anti-inflammatory.

Wintergreen *(Gaultheria procumbens)* is strongly anti-inflammatory and antispasmodic. It is analgesic and reduces all types of pain.

Helichrysum *(Helichrysum italicum)* has been extensively studied in Europe for its unusual abilities to improve circulation, regenerate tissue and relieve pain.

Vetiver *(Vetiveria zizanoides)* is well-known for its anti-inflammatory properties and is traditionally used to relieve symptoms of arthritis.

Palo Santo *(Bursera graveolens)* is known as a spiritual oil. Harvested in Ecuador, this oil has some similarities to frankincense and has traditionally been used to purify and cleanse the spirit from negative energies.

Fractionated and Virgin Coconut Oils
(Cocos nucifera)

Application:

Apply generously on location every fifteen minutes for up to four applications. For head tension, apply over temples and on forehead.

Keep out of reach of children. Do not ingest this blend. If pregnant, nursing, taking medication, or have a medical condition, consult a health care practitioner prior to use.

Di-Gize

Relieves digestive problems including indigestion, heartburn, gas, and bloating. Combats candida and parasite infestation.

Ingredients:

Tarragon *(Artemisia dracunculus)* is antiseptic and combats intestinal parasites and urinary tract infection. It is antispasmodic, anti-inflammatory, anti-infectious, and prevents fermentation.

Ginger *(Zingiber officinale)* has been traditionally used to combat nausea and gastro-intestinal fermentation. It is antispasmodic, antiseptic, and combats indigestion.

Peppermint *(Mentha piperita)* is one of the most highly regarded herbs for improving digestion and combating parasites. It relaxes the smooth muscles of the intestinal tract and promotes peristalsis. It kills bacteria, yeasts, fungi, and mold.

Juniper *(Juniperus osteosperma* and *J. scopulorum)* works as a powerful detoxifier and cleanser and amplifies kidney function.

Fennel *(Foeniculum vulgare)* is antiseptic and stimulating to the gastrointestinal system. It is antispasmodic, antiseptic, and used for flatulence and nausea. It promotes digestion and prevents fermentation.

Lemongrass *(Cymbopogon flexuosus)* has been documented to have powerful antifungal properties. It is vasodilating, anti-inflammatory, and improves digestion.

Anise *(Pimpinella anisum)* is antispasmodic, antiseptic, stimulates and increases bile flow. Combats spastic colitis, indigestion, and intestinal pain.

Patchouli *(Pogostemon cablin)* is powerful digestive aid that combats nausea. Antimicrobial, anti-inflammatory, and reduces fluid retention.

Application:

Dilute 1 part EO to 4 parts V-6 or vegetable oil.

Massage or place as a compress on the stomach. Apply to Vita Flex points on feet/ankles for stomach and intestines.

For internal use, dilute as directed above and take 1 capsule before each meal or as desired.

Possible skin sensitivity.

Dragon Time

Relieves PMS symptoms and menstrual discomforts including cramping and irregular periods. Combats mood swings and headaches caused by hormonal imbalance.

Ingredients:

Clary Sage *(Salvia sclarea)* balances the hormones. It contains natural sclareol, a phytoestrogen that mimics estrogen function. It helps with menstrual cramps, PMS, and circulatory problems.

Blue Yarrow *(Achillea millefolium)* balances hormones and reduces inflammation.

Lavender *(Lavandula angustifolia)* is relaxant that combats anxiety, headaches, and PMS symptoms.

Jasmine *(Jasminum officinale)* is used for muscle spasms, frigidity, depression, and nervous exhaustion. Brings out the feminine attributes.

Fennel *(Foeniculum vulgare)* is antiseptic and antispasmodic. It has estrogen-like activity and hormone-like activity.

Marjoram *(Origanum majorana)* relieves muscle spasm and calms nerves. It relieves menopausal symptoms as well as painful periods.

Application:

Dilute 1 part EO to 1 part vegetable oil.

Diffuse, directly inhale, or add 2-4 drops to bath water. Apply 1 to 2 drops on wrists, neck, temples, or foot Vita Flex points. Dilute 1:15 with vegetable oil for a full-body massage. Apply with a hot compress or directly over lower abdomen, across lower back, or on location of pain. May also be used on both sides of ankles and feet.

Possible skin sensitivity.

Dream Catcher

Opens the mind to enhance dreams and visualizations, promoting greater potential for realizing your dreams and staying on your path. It also protects you from negative dreams that might cloud your vision.

Ingredients:

Sandalwood *(Santalum album)* is high in sesquiterpene compounds which stimulate the pineal gland and the limbic region of the brain, the center of our emotions and memory. Used traditionally in yoga and meditation. Enhances deep sleep.

Blue Tansy *(Tanacetum annuum)* helps to overcome anger and negative emotions promoting a feeling of self-control.

Juniper *(Juniperus osteosperma* and *J. scopulorum)* elevates spiritual awareness to create feelings of love and peace. Juniper has also been used to cleanse the spirit.

Bergamot *(Citrus bergamia)* is simultaneously uplifting and calming, with a unique ability to relieve anxiety, stress, and tension.

Anise *(Pimpinella anisum)*

Tangerine *(Citrus reticulata)* combats anxiety and nervousness. A 1995 Mie University study found that the application of citrus fragrance to depressive patients made it possible to markedly reduce doses of antidepressants. Researchers also found that citrus fragrances boosted immunity. Extremely uplifting and calming.

Ylang Ylang *(Cananga odorata)* increases relaxation, balances male and female energies, and also restores confidence and equilibrium. Alleviates insomnia.

Pepper, Black *(Piper nigrum)* stimulates the endocrine system and increases energy.

Application:

Dilute 1 part EO to 1 part vegetable oil.

Diffuse up to 1 hour three times daily.

Directly inhale, or add 2-4 drops to bath water (most effective before and during sleep). Apply on forehead, ears, throat, under nose, eyebrows, and base of neck. Use during meditation, in saunas, or just before sleeping.

For topical use, dilute 1 drop with V-6 or olive oil, then apply to affected area as needed

Possible sun/skin sensitivity.

Caution: Avoid direct sunlight or UV rays for 12 hours after applying product.

Note: If unpleasant dreams occur, continue to use since subconscious memories and thoughts will still need to be resolved. Hold on to your dreams and visualize them into reality. It may be helpful to write down your dreams upon arising.

Egyptian Gold

Combining the most valuable essences of the Middle East and Central Europe, this blend offers a truly enchanting aromatic effect that stimulates simultaneously the central nervous system, the immune system and the respiratory system.

Ingredients:

Hyssop *(Hyssopus officinalis)* is anti-inflammatory, antiparasitic, anti-infectious, and decongestant. Great for opening up the respiratory system.

Frankincense *(Boswellia carteri)* is considered a holy anointing oil in the Middle East. It stimulates the hypothalamus to amplify immunity. Research at Ponce University shows that it inhibits breast cancer and enhances DNA repair. In ancient times, it was well-known for its healing powers, and was reportedly used to treat every conceivable ill. Considered a gift of the highest caliber during the time of Christ.

Spikenard *(Nardostachys jatamansi)* was used by Mary of Bethany to anoint the feet of Jesus. Strengthens immunity and hypothalmus function.

Myrrh *(Commiphora myrrha)* is antimicrobial and antimutagenic. It is referenced in the Old and New Testaments (*A bundle of myrrh is my well-beloved unto me...* Song of Solomon 1:13). Its high levels of sesquiterpenes stimulate the hypothalamus and the pituitary and amplify immune response. It possesses the frequency of wealth according to legends.

Cinnamon Bark *(Cinnamomum verum)* is part of the formula the Lord gave Moses (Exodus 30:22-27). It is antibacterial, antiparasitic, antiviral, and antifungal. Researchers, including J. C. Lapraz, MD, found that viruses could not live in the presence of cinnamon oil.

Lavender *(Lavandula angustifolia)* is relaxing and grounding. University of Miami researchers found that inhalation of lavender oil increased beta waves in the brain, suggesting heightened relaxation. It also reduced depression and improved cognitive performance (Diego et al., 1998). A 2001 Osaka Kyoiku University study found that lavender reduced mental stress and increased alertness (Motomura et al., 2001).

Rose *(Rosa damascena)* has the highest frequency among essential oils. It creates a sense of balance, harmony, and well-being and elevates the mind. It creates a magnetic energy that attracts love and brings joy to the heart.

Cedarwood *(Cedrus atlantica)* is high in sesquiterpenes, which can stimulate the limbic part of the brain, the center of emotions and memory. It stimulates the pineal gland, which releases melatonin, thereby improving thoughts, cognition, and memory.

Idaho Balsam Fir *(Abies balsamea)* has been researched for its ability to kill airborne germs and bacteria. As a confer oil, it creates a feeling of grounding, anchoring and empowerment.

Application:

For dietary, topical or aromatic use. When using as a supplement, dilute one drop of essential oil with 4 drops of pure vegetable oil (V-6, olive, etc.) and put in a capsule. Then take one capsule before each meal or as desired.

Diffuse, directly inhale, or add 2-4 drops to bath water. Apply 1 to 2 drops over heart, on wrists, neck, temples, or foot Vita Flex points. Dilute 1:15 with vegetable oil for a full-body massage. Put 2 drops on a wet cloth and put in clothes dryer. Put 4-8 drops on cotton ball and locate on vents.

Possible skin sensitivity.

EndoFlex

Amplifies metabolism and vitality, and creates hormonal balance.

Ingredients:

Spearmint *(Mentha spicata)* used to increase metabolism to burn fat. With its hormone-like activity, it supports the nervous and glandular systems. Spearmint is antispasmodic, antiseptic, and anti-inflammatory. It is also highly invigorating and stimulating.

Sage *(Salvia officinalis)* strengthens the vital centers. The Lakota Indians used sage for purification, healing and to dispel negative emotions.

Geranium *(Pelargonium graveolens)* assists in balancing hormones. It is antispasmodic, relaxant, anti-inflammatory, antibacterial, antifungal, and stimulates the liver and pancreas.

Myrtle *(Myrtus communis)* helps normalize hormonal imbalances of the thyroid and ovaries.

German Chamomile *(Matricaria recutita)* is highly anti-inflammatory and liver-protecting.

Nutmeg *(Myristica fragrans)* supports the adrenal glands for increased energy. It is powerfully stimulating and energizing.

Carrier Oil: Organic Sesame Seed

Application:

Diffuse up to 30 minutes three times daily, directly inhale, or add 2-4 drops to bath water

Apply over lower back, thyroid, kidneys, liver, feet, glandular areas, and foot Vita Flex points for these organs.

For use as a dietary supplement, dilute with 1 drop of V-6 or olive oil, put in capsule, and take up to 3 times per day or as needed.

For topical use, dilute 1 drop of EndoFlex with 1 drop of V-6 or olive oil. Apply to affected area. Use as needed.

En-R-Gee

Increases vitality, circulation, and alertness in the body.

Ingredients:

Rosemary *(Rosmarinus officinalis* CT cineol*)* helps overcome mental fatigue, stimulating memory and opens the conscious mind. University of Miami scientists found that inhaling rosemary boosted alertness, eased anxiety, and amplified analytic and mental ability.

Juniper *(Juniperus osteosperma* and *J. scopulorum)* detoxifies and cleanses and improves nerve and kidney function. It elevates spiritual awareness.

Lemongrass *(Cymbopogon flexuosus)* increases blood circulation and vasodilation.

Nutmeg *(Myristica fragrans)* supports the adrenal glands for increased energy. It is powerfully stimulating and energizing.

Balsam Fir (Idaho) *(Abies balsamea)* is stimulating and empowering.

Clove *(Syzygium aromaticum)* a powerful general stimulant.

Pepper, Black *(Piper nigrum)* stimulates the endocrine system and increases energy in all systems of the body.

Application:

Dilute 1 part EO to 2 parts vegetable oil.

Diffuse, directly inhale, or add 2-4 drops to bath water. May also be used with Raindrop Technique.

For topical use, dilute as indicated above and apply on desired location or on temples, back of neck, forehead, or on chakra/Vita Flex points.

For aromatic use, diffuse or humidify for 15-20 minutes daily.

Enhance effects by rubbing En-R-Gee on feet and Awaken on temples.

Possible skin sensitivity.

Caution: Avoid contact with mucous membranes or sensitive skin. Not intended for use on children

Envision

Renews faith in the future, stimulates creative and intuitive abilities, and amplifies emotional fortitude to achieve your goals and dreams. It helps reawaken internal drive and independence and overcome the fear of experiencing new dimensions.

Ingredients:

Sage *(Salvia officinalis)* strengthens the vital centers. The Lakota Indians used sage for purification, healing and to dispel negative emotions. Known as a sacred herb by the Romans.

Geranium *(Pelargonium graveolens)* helps release negative memories, thereby opening and elevating the mind.

Orange *(Citrus sinensis)* is elevating to the mind and body. A 1995 Mie University study documented the ability of citrus fragrances to combat depression and induce relaxation.

Rose *(Rosa damascena)* possesses the highest frequency of the oils. It creates a sense of balance, harmony, and well-being and elevates the mind. Rose creates a magnetic energy that attracts love and brings joy to the heart.

Lavender *(Lavandula angustifolia)* has been documented to improve concentration and mental acuity. University of Miami researchers found that inhalation of lavender oil increased beta waves in the brain, suggesting heightened relaxation. It also reduced depression and improved cognitive performance (Diego et al., 1998). A 2001 Osaka Kyoiku University study found that lavender reduced mental stress and increased alertness (Motomura et al., 2001). It can also be very relaxing and combats nervous tension.

Spruce *(Picea mariana)* helps to open and release emotional blocks, bringing about a feeling of balance and grounding. Traditionally, spruce oil was believed to possess the frequency of prosperity.

Application:

Diffuse, directly inhale, or add 2-4 drops to bath water. Apply 1 to 2 drops on forehead, edge of ears, wrists, neck, temples, or foot Vita Flex points. Put 2 drops on a wet cloth and put in clothes dryer. Put 4-8 drops on cotton ball and locate on vents.

Essential Beauty Serum

(See Chapter 13)

Evergreen Essence

Similar to Sacred Mountain, it is spiritually uplifting with deep and longlasting emotional influences. Dispels depression and melancholy. This blend is a favorite during the Thanksgiving and Christmas holiday season.

Ingredients:

Spruce *(Picea mariana)* helps to open and release emotional blocks, creating a feeling of balance and grounding. Traditionally, spruce oil was believed to possess the frequency of prosperity.

Fir *(Abies alba)* antiseptic, antiarthritic, and stimulating. It creates a feeling of grounding, anchoring, and empowerment.

Pine *(Pinus sylvestris)* helps reduce stress, relieve anxiety, and energize the entire body.

Also contains: Colorado Blue Spruce, Ponderosa Pine, Red Fir, Black Pine, Piñon Pine, Lodge Pole Pine, Scotch Pine, Western Red Cedar, White Fir

Application:

Dilute 1 part EO to 1 part vegetable oil.

Diffuse, directly inhale, or add 2-4 drops to bath water. Apply 1 to 2 drops on edge of ears, wrists, neck, temples, or foot Vita Flex points. Dilute 1:15 with vegetable oil for a full-body massage. Put 2 drops on a wet cloth and put in clothes dryer. Put 4-8 drops on cotton ball and locate on vents or at the base of Christmas tree.

Great for diffusing, add a few drops to a log prior to burning, or splash a few drops on a paper vacuum cleaner bag before vacuuming

Possible skin sensitivity.

Exodus II

Some researchers believe that these aromatics were used by Moses to protect the Israelites from a plague. Modern science shows that these oils contain immune-stimulating and antimicrobial compounds. Because of the complex chemistry of essential oils, it is very difficult for viruses and bacteria to mutate and acquire resistance to them.

Ingredients:

Cassia (*Cinnamomum cassia*) is anti-infectious, antibacterial, and anticoagulant. It was part of the formula the Lord gave Moses (Exodus 30:22-27) for the holy anointing oil.

Hyssop (*Hyssopus officinalis*) is anti-inflammatory, antiparasitic, anti-infectious, and decongestant.

Frankincense (*Boswellia carteri*) is considered a holy anointing oil in the Middle East. It stimulates the hypothalamus to amplify immunity. Research at Ponce University shows that it inhibits breast cancer and enhances DNA repair. In ancient times, it was well-known for its healing powers, and was reportedly used to treat every conceivable ill.

Spikenard (*Nardostachys jatamansi*) was used by Mary of Bethany to anoint the feet of Jesus. Strengthens immunity and hypothalmus function.

Galbanum (*Ferula gummosa*) prized for healing since Biblical times. (And the Lord said unto Moses, Take unto thee sweet spices, stacte, and onycha, and galbanum; sweet spices with pure frankincense: Exodus 30:34).

Myrrh (*Commiphora myrrha*) is antimicrobial and antimutagenic. It is referenced in the Old and New Testaments (*A bundle of myrrh is my well-beloved unto me...* Song of Solomon 1:13). Its' high levels of sesquiterpenes stimulate the hypothalamus and the pituitary and amplify immune response.

Cinnamon Bark (*Cinnamomum verum*) is part of the formula the Lord gave Moses (Exodus 30:22-27). It is antibacterial, antiparasitic, antiviral, and antifungal. Researchers, including J. C. Lapraz, MD, found that viruses could not live in the presence of cinnamon oil.

Calamus (*Acorus calamus*) is part of the formula the Lord gave Moses (Exodus 30:22-27). It is antispasmodic, and anti-inflammatory (gastrointestinal).

Carrier Oil: Olive oil.

Application:

Diffuse, directly inhale, or add 2-4 drops to bath water. Apply 1 to 2 drops on ears, wrists, foot Vita Flex points, or along spine raindrop-style.

For topical use, dilute 1 drop of Exodus II with 4 drops of V-6 or olive oil, test on the underside of arm before regular use. Apply to affected area as needed.

For aromatic use, diffuse up to 10 minutes three times daily.

Possible skin sensitivity.

Caution: Not intended for children under 12 years of age unless directed by a health professional.

Forgiveness

Helps one to release hurt feelings, insults, and negative emotions. Also helps release negative memories, allowing one to move past emotional barriers and attain higher awareness, assisting them to forgive and let go.

Ingredients:

Rose (*Rosa damascena*) has the highest frequency among essential oils. It creates a sense of balance, harmony, and well-being and elevates the mind. It creates a magnetic energy that attracts love and brings joy to the heart.

Melissa (*Melissa officinalis*) brings out gentleness. It is calming and balancing to the emotions, affecting the limbic part of the brain, the emotional center of memories. Helps alleviate depression, hypertension, and anxiety.

Helichrysum (*Helichrysum italicum*) helps release feelings of anger, promoting forgiveness.

Angelica (*Angelica archangelica*) helps to calm emotions and to bring memories back to the point of origin before trauma or anger was experienced, helping to let go negative feelings.

Frankincense (*Boswellia carteri*) is considered a holy anointing oil in the Middle East and has been used in religious ceremonies for thousands of years. Stimulates the limbic part of the brain, elevating the mind and helping to overcome stress and despair. It is used in European medicine to combat depression.

Sandalwood (*Santalum album*) is high in sesquiterpene compounds which stimulate the pineal gland and the limbic region of the brain, the center of emotions and memory. Used traditionally in yoga and meditation. May help remove negative programming in the cells.

Lavender *(Lavandula angustifolia)* is relaxing and grounding. University of Miami researchers found that inhalation of lavender oil increased beta waves in the brain, suggesting heightened relaxation. It also reduced depression and improved cognitive performance (Diego et al., 1998). A 2001 Osaka Kyoiku University study found that lavender reduced mental stress and increased alertness (Motomura et al., 2001).

Bergamot *(Citrus bergamia)* is simultaneously uplifting and calming, with a unique ability to relieve anxiety, stress, and tension.

Geranium *(Pelargonium graveolens)* assists in balancing hormones, with antidepressant, uplifting, and tension-relieving properties.

Jasmine *(Jasminum officinale)* has therapeutic effects, both emotional and physical. Is uplifting, an antidepressant, and counteracts indifference, frigidity, and hopelessness.

Lemon *(Citrus limon)* is stimulating and invigorating, promoting a deep sense of well-being. A 1995 Mie University study found that citrus fragrances boosted immunity, induced relaxation, and reduced depression.

Palmarosa *(Cymbopogon martinii)* is stimulating and revitalizing, enhancing both the nervous and cardiovascular system. Creates a feeling of security.

Roman Chamomile *(Chamaemelum nobile)* combats restlessness, tension, and opens mental blocks. It purges toxins from the liver where anger is stored.

Rosewood *(Aniba rosaeodora)* is high in linalool, which has a relaxing, empowering effect. It is also very grounding and strengthening.

Ylang Ylang *(Cananga odorata)* increases relaxation; balances male and female energies. It also restores confidence and equilibrium.

Carrier Oil: Organic Sesame Seed

Application:
Diffuse, directly inhale, or add 2-4 drops to bath water. Apply 1 to 2 drops behind ears, on wrists, neck, temples, navel, solar plexus, or heart. Dilute 1:15 with vegetable oil for a full-body massage. Put 4-8 drops on cotton ball and locate on vents.

Possible sun/skin sensitivity.

Caution: Avoid contact with eyes

Gathering

This blend was created to help us overcome the bombardment of chaotic energy that alters our focus and takes us off our path toward higher achievements. Galbanum, a favorite oil of Moses, has a strong effect when blended with frankincense and sandalwood in gathering our emotional and spiritual thoughts, helping us to achieve our potential. These oils helps increase the oxygen around the pineal and pituitary gland, bringing greater harmonic frequency to receive the communication we desire. This blend helps bring people together on a physical, emotional, and spiritual level for greater focus and clarity. It helps one stay focused, grounded, and clear in gathering one's potential for self-improvement.

Ingredients:

Galbanum *(Ferula gummosa)* was used for both medicinal and spiritual purposes. When combined with frankincense and sandalwood, its frequency increases dramatically. (And the Lord said unto Moses, Take unto thee sweet spices, stacte, and onycha, and galbanum; sweet spices with pure frankincense: Exodus 30:34).

Frankincense *(Boswellia carteri)* is considered a holy anointing oil in the Middle East and has been used in religious ceremonies for thousands of years. Stimulates the limbic part of the brain, elevating the mind and helping to overcome stress and despair. It is used in European medicine to combat depression. Helps connect us with our greater powers.

Sandalwood *(Santalum album)* is high in sesquiterpene compounds which stimulate the pineal gland and the limbic region of the brain, the center of emotions and memory. Used traditionally in yoga and meditation. Can be very grounding and stabilizing.

Rose *(Rosa damascena)* has the highest frequency among essential oils. It creates a sense of balance, harmony, and well-being and elevates the mind. It creates a magnetic energy that attracts love and brings joy to the heart.

Lavender *(Lavandula angustifolia)* is relaxant and grounding and improves concentration and mental acuity. University of Miami researchers found that inhalation of lavender oil increased beta waves in the brain, suggesting heightened relaxation. It also reduced depression and improved cognitive performance (Diego et al., 1998). A 2001 Osaka Kyoiku University study found that lavender reduced mental stress and increased alertness (Motomura et al., 2001).

Cinnamon Bark *(Cinnamomum verum)* is the oil of wealth from the Orient and part of the formula the Lord gave to Moses (Exodus 30:22-27). It has been traditionally used to release malice or spite.

Spruce *(Picea mariana)* helps to open and release emotional blocks, creating a feeling of balance and grounding. Traditionally, spruce oil was believed to possess the frequency of prosperity.

Ylang Ylang *(Cananga odorata)* increases relaxation; balances male and female energies. It also restores confidence and equilibrium and balance.

Geranium *(Pelargonium graveolens)* stimulates nerves and assists in balancing hormones. Its' aromatic influence helps release negative memories, thereby opening and elevating the mind.

Application:

Dilute 1 part EO to 1 part vegetable oil.
Possible skin sensitivity.

Diffuse, directly inhale, or add 2-4 drops to bath water. Apply 1 to 2 drops on edge of ears, wrists, neck, or temples. May also be applied to spine Raindrop Technique-style. Dilute 1:15 with vegetable oil for a full-body massage. Put 2 drops on a wet cloth and put in clothes dryer. Put 4-8 drops on cotton ball and locate on vents.

Use Forgiveness on navel, Sacred Mountain on crown (to clear negative attitudes), Valor on crown or feet, Three Wise Men on crown, Clarity on temples, and Dream Catcher.

Gentle Baby

Comforting, soothing, relaxing, and beneficial for reducing stress during pregnancy. It helps reduce stretch marks and scar tissue and rejuvenates the skin, improves elasticity and reduces wrinkles.

It is particularly soothing to dry, chapped skin and diaper rash. Skin issues improved when using Gentle Baby with Rose Ointment over the top of it.

Ingredients:

Geranium *(Pelargonium graveolens)* has been used for centuries for skin care. It revitalizes tissue and nerves and has relaxant, anti-inflammatory, anti-infectious effects.

Rosewood *(Aniba rosaeodora)* is soothing and nourishing to the skin, enhancing skin elasticity, and is antibacterial and antifungal.

Lemon *(Citrus limon)* increases microcirculation and lymphatic function. Its fragrance is stimulating, invigorating and antidepressant. (Komori, et al., 1995).

Lavender *(Lavandula angustifolia)* is known as the universal oil. It is beneficial for skin conditions, such as burns, rashes, and psoriasis and prevents scarring and stretch marks. It is relaxing, grounding, and combats depression.

Jasmine *(Jasminum officinale)* is beneficial for dry, greasy, irritated, or sensitive skin. Also brings out femininity and helps with depression and nervous exhaustion.

Roman Chamomile *(Chamaemelum nobile)* combats restlessness, insomnia, muscle tension, and inflammation.

Bergamot *(Citrus bergamia)* is simultaneously uplifting and calming, with a unique ability to relieve anxiety, stress, and tension.

Ylang Ylang *(Cananga odorata)* increases relaxation; balances male and female energies. It also restores confidence and equilibrium.

Palmarosa *(Cymbopogon martinii)* combats candida, rashes, and scaly and flaky skin. It stimulates new cell growth, as it moisturizes and promotes healing. It is antimicrobial. It also helps reduce tension and helps recovery from nervous exhaustion.

Rose *(Rosa damascena)* used for the skin for thousands of years, it promotes healthy skin, reduces scarring, and promotes elasticity.

Application:

Dilute 1 part EO to 1 part vegetable oil.
Possible sun sensitivity.

Diffuse or apply on location for dry, chapped skin or diaper rash. Apply over mother's abdomen, on feet, lower back, face, and neck areas. Dilute with vegetable oil for body massage and for applying on baby's skin.

For Pregnancy and Delivery: Use for massage throughout entire pregnancy for relieving stress and anxiety, and to prevent scarring and creating serenity. Massage on the perineum to help it stretch for easier birthing.

GLF

The initials of this essential oil blend stand for Gall bladder/Liver Flush. It is formulated with oils that help to cleanse and restore liver and gall bladder function when taken in capsules as a dietary supplement.

Ingredients:

Grapefruit rind *(Citrus paradise)*— decongesting and fat-dissolving. It is high in limonene which prevents DNA damage and has anticoagulant properties.

Helichrysum *(Helichrysum italicum)*l— stimulates liver cell function and removes plaque from veins and arteries.

Celery seed *(Apium graveolens)*—a powerful liver cleanser

Ledum *(Ledum groenlandicum)*— shown in clinical studies to strengthen the liver and improve bile function

Hyssop *(hyssopus officinalis)*—is a decongestant that is also anti-inflammatory, antiparasitic and anti-infectious

Spearmint *(Mentha spicata)*—antispasmodic, anti-infectious, antiparasitic, antiseptic and anti-inflammatory. It has also been used to increase metabolism to burn fat.

Application:

Dilute 80-20 in a quality vegetable oil and fill a 00 size capsule. Take 2 capsules daily to support a detoxification and cleansing routine focused on the liver and gall bladder.

Gratitude

This delightful blend is designed to elevate, soothe and bring relief to the body while helping to foster a grateful attitude. It is also nourishing and supportive to the skin. The New Testament tells us that on one occasion Christ healed 10 lepers (Luke 17:12-19), but only one returned to express his thanks. This blend embodies the spirit of that one and only grateful leper.

Ingredients:

Idaho Balsam Fir *(Abies balsamea)* opens emotional blocks and recharges vital energy.

Frankincense *(Boswellia carteri)* is considered a holy anointing oil in the Middle East and has been used in religious ceremonies for thousands of years. Stimulates the limbic part of the brain, elevating the mind and helping to overcome stress and despair. It is used in European medicine to combat depression.

Myrrh *(Commiphora myrrha)* is referenced throughout the Old and New Testaments constituting a part of a holy anointing formula given Moses (Exodus 30:22-27). It has one of the highest levels of sesquiterpenes, a class of compounds that can stimulate the hypothalamus, pituitary, and amygdala, the control center for emotions and hormone release in the brain. It possesses the frequency of wealth according to legends.

Galbanum *(Ferula gummosa)* was used for both medicinal and spiritual purposes. It is antimicrobial and supporting to the body. When combined with frankincense and sandalwood, its frequency increases dramatically. (And the Lord said unto Moses, Take unto thee sweet spices, stacte, and onycha, and galbanum; sweet spices with pure frankincense: Exodus 30:34).

Ylang Ylang *(Cananga odorata)* increases relaxation; balances male and female energies. It also restores confidence and equilibrium.

Rosewood *(Aniba rosaeodora)* is soothing and nourishing to the skin, enhancing skin elasticity, and is antibacterial and antifungal. It gives feelings of being grounded and strengthened.

Application:
Possible skin sensitivity.

Diffuse, directly inhale, or add 2-4 drops to bath water. Apply 1 to 2 drops behind ears, over heart, on wrists, base of neck, temples, or base of spine. Put 4-8 drops on cotton ball and locate on vents.

Diffuse, directly inhale, or add 2-4 drops to bath water. Apply 1 to 2 drops behind ears, on wrists, base of neck, temples, or base of spine. Put 4-8 drops on cotton ball and locate on vents.

Grounding

Creates a feeling of solidarity and balance. It stabilizes and grounds us in order to cope constructively with reality. When we're hurting emotionally, we may wish to leave this physical existence. When this happens, it is easy to make poor choices that lead to unhealthy relationships and unwise business decisions. We seek to escape because we do not have anchoring or awareness to know how to deal with our emotions.

Ingredients:

Spruce *(Picea mariana)* helps to open and release emotional blocks, creating a feeling of balance and grounding.

White Fir *(Abies concolor)* creates a feeling of grounding, anchoring, and empowerment.

Ylang Ylang *(Cananga odorata)* increases relaxation; balances male and female energies. It also restores confidence and equilibrium.

Pine *(Pinus sylvestris)* helps reduce stress, relieve anxiety, and energize the entire body. Has a grounding, yet empowering aromatic effect.

Cedarwood *(Cedrus atlantica)* is high in sesquiterpenes, which can stimulate the limbic part of the brain, the center of emotions and memory. It stimulates the pineal gland, which releases melatonin, thereby improving thoughts, cognition, and memory. Cedarwood has been used for stabilizing and grounding oneself.

Angelica *(Angelica archangelica)* helps to bring memories back to the point of origin before trauma or anger was experienced, helping us to release negative feelings.

Juniper *(Juniperus osteosperma* and *J. scopulorum)* elevates spiritual awareness creating feelings of love and peace.

Application:
Dilute 1 part EO to 1 part vegetable oil.
Possible sun/skin sensitivity.

Harmony

Promotes physical and emotional healing by creating a harmonic balance for the energy centers of the body. It brings us into harmony with all things, people, and cycles of life. It is beneficial in reducing stress and amplifying well-being. Combats feelings of discord. It is also uplifting and elevating to the mind creating a positive attitude.

Ingredients:

Geranium *(Pelargonium graveolens)* stimulates nerves and assists in balancing hormones. Its aromatic influence helps release negative memories, thereby opening and elevating the mind. It purges toxins from the liver where anger is stored.

Rosewood *(Aniba rosaeodora)* is high in linalool, which has a relaxing, empowering effect. It is very grounding and strengthening.

Lavender *(Lavandula angustifolia)* a relaxant that helps overcome insomnia, headaches, and anxiety. Gives a feeling of overall well-being.

Sandalwood *(Santalum album)* is high in sesquiterpenes, which stimulate the pineal gland and the limbic region of the brain, the center of our emotions. Used traditionally in yoga and meditation. May help remove negative programming in the cells.

Frankincense *(Boswellia carteri)* stimulates the limbic part of the brain, elevating the mind and helping to overcome stress and despair. It is used in European medicine to combat depression. Used for meditation and prayer.

Orange *(Citrus sinensis)* is elevating to the mind and body. A 1995 Mie University study documented the ability of citrus fragrances to combat depression and induce relaxation. Orange fragrance brings feelings of security.

Lemon *(Citrus limon)* is stimulating and invigorating, promoting a deep sense of well-being. A 1995 Mie University study found that citrus fragrances boosted immunity, induced relaxation, and reduced depression.

Angelica (*Angelica archangelica*) helps to bring memories back to the point of origin before trauma or anger was experienced, helping us to release negative feelings.

Hyssop (*Hyssopus officinalis*) is very balancing for emotions. Can also be spiritually uplifting.

Spanish Sage (*Salvia lavandulifolia*) is high in limonene which prevents DNA damage.

Jasmine (*Jasminum officinale*) is uplifting and relieves anxiety and hopelessness. It also helps with nervous exhaustion and frigidity.

Roman Chamomile (*Chamaemelum nobile*) combats restlessness, tension, insomnia. It purges toxins from liver where anger is stored.

Bergamot (*Citrus bergamia*) is simultaneously uplifting and calming, with a unique ability to relieve anxiety, stress, and tension.

Ylang Ylang (*Cananga odorata*) increases relaxation; balances male and female energies. It also restores confidence and equilibrium.

Palmarosa (*Cymbopogon martinii*) is stimulating and revitalizing, enhancing both the nervous and cardiovascular system.

Rose (*Rosa damascena*) has the highest frequency among essential oils. It creates a sense of balance, harmony, and well-being and also elevates the mind. It creates a magnetic energy that attracts pure love and brings joy to the heart.

Spruce (*Picea mariana*) helps to open and release emotional blocks, creating a feeling of balance and grounding. Traditionally, spruce oil was believed to possess the frequency of prosperity.

Application:

Dilute 1 part EO to 1 part vegetable oil.

Diffuse, directly inhale, or add 2-4 drops to bath water. Dilute 1:15 with vegetable oil for a full-body massage. Put 4-8 drops on cotton ball and locate on vents. Add 2 drops to a wet cloth and put in clothes dryer.

For topical use, apply 1-2 drops on edge of ears, wrists, neck, temples, over heart, or chakra/Vita Flex points.

For aromatic use directly inhale as needed or diffuse/humidify for 20-25 minutes daily.

Possible sun/skin sensitivity.

Highest Potential

Combines powerful emotional blends with the most exotic essential oil aromas, jasmine and ylang ylang and potent Biblical oils of frankincense, galbanum, cedarwood and sandalwood.

Helps you gather your possibilities and achieve your highest potential. This blend harmonizes several grounding, calming, inspiring and empowering essential oils into one easy-to-use blend. Biochemist R. W. Moncrieff wrote that ylang ylang "soothes and inhibits anger born of frustration," removing roadblocks and opening new vistas. The uplifting fragrance of jasmine spurs creativity while the lavender (in Gathering) clears the thought processes.

Ingredients:

Australian Blue uplifts and inspires, while also grounding and stabilizing.

Gathering collects our emotional and spiritual thoughts and helps overcome the bombardment of chaotic energy that alters our focus and takes us off our path toward higher achievements.

Jasmine Absolute (*Jasminum officinale*) is exhilarating to the mind and emotions, helping to unlock past blocks. It also alleviates frigidity and hopelessness

Ylang Ylang (*Cananga odorata*) increases relaxation; balances male and female energies. It also restores confidence and equilibrium.

Application:

Dilute 1 part EO to 1 part vegetable oil.

Diffuse, directly inhale, or add 2-4 drops to bath water. Apply 2-4 drops on edge of ears, wrists, neck, or temples. Put 2 drops on a wet cloth and put in clothes dryer. Put 4-8 drops on cotton ball and locate on vents.

Possible skin sensitivity.

Hope

Hope is essential in order to go forward in life. Hopelessness can cause a loss of vision of goals and dreams. This blend helps to reconnect with a feeling of strength and grounding, restoring hope for tomorrow. It helps overcome suicidal depression.

Ingredients:

Melissa *(Melissa officinalis)* brings out gentleness. It is calming and balancing to the emotions, affecting the limbic part of the brain, the emotional center of memories. It removes emotional blocks and instills a positive outlook on life.

Spruce *(Picea mariana)* opens and releases emotional blocks, creating a feeling of balance and grounding. Traditionally, it was believed to possess the frequency of prosperity.

Juniper *(Juniperus osteosperma* and *J. scopulorum)* elevates spiritual awareness and creates feelings of love and peace.

Myrrh *(Commiphora myrrha)* is referenced throughout the Old and New Testaments constituting a part of a holy anointing formula given Moses (Exodus 30:22-27). It has one of the highest levels of sesquiterpenes, a class of compounds that can stimulate the hypothalamus, pituitary, and amygdala, the control center for emotions and hormone release in the brain. It also possesses the frequency of wealth according to legends.

Carrier Oil: Sweet Almond

Application:

Diffuse, directly inhale, or add 2-4 drops to bath water. Put 4-8 drops on cotton ball and locate on vents.

For topical use, apply 2-4 drops on edge of ears, wrists, neck, temples, over heart, or chakra/Vita Flex points.

For aromatic use directly inhale as needed or diffuse/humidify for 30-35 minutes daily.

Possible skin sensitivity.

Humility

Having humility and forgiveness helps us to heal ourselves and our earth (Chronicles 7:14). Humility is an integral ingredient in obtaining forgiveness and needed for a closer relationship with God. Through the frequency and fragrance of this blend, you may arrive at a place where healing can begin.

Ingredients:

Frankincense (Boswellia carteri) is considered a holy anointing oil in the Middle East and has been used in religious ceremonies for thousands of years. Stimulates the limbic part of the brain, elevating the mind and helping to overcome stress and despair.

Rose *(Rosa damascena)* possesses the highest frequency of the oils. It creates a sense of balance, harmony, and well-being and elevates the mind.

Rosewood *(Aniba rosaeodora)* is high in linalool, which has a relaxing, empowering effect. It is very grounding and strengthening.

Ylang Ylang *(Cananga odorata)* increases relaxation; balances male and female energies. It also restores confidence and equilibrium.

Geranium *(Pelargonium graveolens)* helps release negative memories, thereby opening and elevating the mind.

Melissa *(Melissa officinalis)* anciently used for nervous disorders, it brings out gentleness. It is calming and balancing to the emotions, affecting the limbic part of the brain, the emotional center of memories. It also relieves anxiety and depression.

Spikenard *(Nardostachys jatamansi)* was highly prized at the time of Christ and was used by Mary of Bethany to anoint the feet of Jesus. It stimulates the limbic part of the brain, tapping emotional memories. It can be relaxing and help with nervous tension.

Myrrh *(Commiphora myrrha)* is referenced throughout the Bible and was part of a holy anointing formula given Moses (Exodus 30:22-27). It is high in sesquiterpenes, a class of compounds that can stimulate the hypothalamus, pituitary, and amygdala, the control center for emotions and hormone release in the brain.

Neroli *(Citrus sinensis)* was used by the ancient Egyptians for healing the mind, body, and spirit. It is stabilizing and strengthening to the emotions, promoting peace, confidence, and awareness. It brings everything into focus. It is used for depression and anxiety.

Carrier Oil: Organic Sesame *(Sesamum indicum)* Seed Oil

Application:

Diffuse, directly inhale, or add 2-4 drops to bath water. Apply 1 to 2 drops over heart, on neck, forehead, or temples. Put 2 drops on a wet cloth and put in clothes dryer. Put 4-8 drops on cotton ball and locate on vents.

ImmuPower

Strengthens immunity and DNA repair in the cells. It is strongly antiseptic and anti-infectious.

Ingredients:

Cistus *(Cistus ladanifer),* enhances immunity and immune cell regeneration. It is anti-infectious, antiviral, and antibacterial.

Frankincense *(Boswellia carteri)* stimulates the hypothalamus and pituitary to amplify immunity.

Oregano *(Origanum compactum)* is one of the most powerful antimicrobial essential oils. Laboratory research at Weber State University showed it to have a 99 percent kill rate against *in vitro* colonies of *Streptococcus pneumoniae*, a microorganism responsible for many kinds of lung and throat infections. Oregano is antiviral, antibacterial, antifungal, and antiparasitic.

Idaho Tansy *(Tanacetum vulgare)* is antiviral, anti-infectious, antibacterial, and fights cold, flu and infections. According to E. Joseph Montagna's *Herbal Desk Reference*, tansy tones the entire body.

Cumin *(Cuminum cyminum)* amplifies immunity and DNA repair. It is antiseptic, antibacterial, and anti-inflammatory.

Clove *(Syzygium aromaticum)* is one of the most powerful antioxidants of all essential oils. Prevents cellular DNA damage. It is also strongly anti-microbial and antiseptic, antiviral, anti-inflammatory, and antifungal.

Hyssop *(Hyssopus officinalis)* has anti-inflammatory and antiviral properties and is also antiparasitic, mucolytic, a decongestant, and is anti-infectious.

Ravensara *(Ravensara aromatica)* is referred to by the people of Madagascar as the oil that heals. It is antiseptic, anti-infectious, antiviral, antibacterial, and antifungal.

Mountain Savory *(Satureja montana)* is immune stimulating, antiviral, antibacterial, antifungal, and antiparasitic. It is excellent for HIV, Herpes, etc., and back ailments (lumbago, scoliosis, etc.).

Application:
Possible skin sensitivity.

Diffuse/humidify, directly inhale, or add 2-4 drops to bath water. Apply around navel, chest, temples, wrists, under nose, or foot Vita Flex points. Use with Raindrop Technique. Dilute 1:15 with vegetable oils for body massage. Put 4-8 drops on cotton ball and locate on vents.

For topical use, dilute 1 drop of ImmuPower with 4 drops of V-6 or olive oil, then apply to affected area as needed.

For aromatic use diffuse up to 30 minutes three times daily.

Alternate with Thieves and Exodus II. To enhance effects add rosewood, melissa, oregano, clove, cistus, frankincense, or mountain savory.

Caution: Test on small area of skin on the underside of arm after diluting for sensitivity. Not intended for children under the age of 6 without the advice of a health professional.

Inner Child

When children are abused, they become disconnected from their inner child, or identity, which causes confusion. This fractures personality and creates problems in the early- to mid- adult years, often mislabeled as a mid-life crisis. This fragrance stimulates memory response and help one reconnect with the inner-self or identity. This is one of the first steps to finding emotional balance.

Ingredients:

Orange *(Citrus sinensis)* is elevating to the mind and body and brings joy and peace. A 1995 Mie University study documented the ability of citrus fragrances to combat depression and bring about a deep sense of security.

Tangerine *(Citrus reticulata)* contains esters and aldehydes that are sedating and calming, helping with anxiety and nervousness.

Jasmine *(Jasminum officinale)* is stimulating to the mind and improves concentration. It is also an antidepressant and uplifts while relieving indifference and listlessness.

Ylang Ylang *(Cananga odorata)* increases relaxation; balances male and female energies. It also restores confidence and equilibrium. Combats anger, low self esteem, and filters out negative energy.

Sandalwood *(Santalum album)* is high in sesquiterpene compounds which stimulate the pineal gland and the limbic region of the brain, the center of emotions and memory. Used traditionally in yoga and meditation. May help remove negative programming in the mind/body/spirit.

Spruce *(Picea mariana)* opens and releases emotional blocks, fostering a sense of balance and grounding. Traditionally, it was believed to possess the frequency of prosperity.

Lemongrass *(Cymbopogon flexuosus)* increases blood circulation and uplifts the spirit. It also promotes awareness and purification.

Neroli *(Citrus sinensis)* was used by the ancient Egyptians for healing the mind, body, and spirit. It is stabilizing and strengthening to the emotions, promoting peace, confidence, and awareness. It uplifts the spirit, encourages true joy, and helps with insomnia.

Application:

Dilute 1 part EO to 1 part vegetable oil.

Diffuse, directly inhale, or add 2-4 drops to bath water. Apply 1 to 2 drops on edge of ears, wrists, neck, or temples. Dilute 1:15 with vegetable oil for body massage. Add 2 drops to a wet cloth and put in clothes dryer. Put 4-8 drops on cotton ball and locate on vents.

Possible sun sensitivity.

Inspiration

Creates a feeling of being wrapped in a cocoon of spiritual quietness. These oils were traditionally used by the Native Americans to enhance spirituality, prayer and inner awareness. Inspiration brings us closer to our spiritual connection.

Ingredients:

Frankincense *(Boswellia carteri)* stimulates the limbic part of the brain, elevating the mind and helping to overcome stress and despair. It is used in European medicine to combat depression.

Frankincense contains sesquiterpenes which stimulate the limbic system of the brain (the center of memory and emotions) and the hypothalamus, pineal and pituitary glands. The hypothalamus is the master gland of the human body, producing many vital hormones including thyroid and growth hormone.

Cedarwood *(Cedrus atlantica)* is high in sesquiterpenes, which can stimulate the limbic part of the brain, the center of emotions and memory. It stimulates the pineal gland, which releases melatonin, thereby improving thoughts, cognition, and memory. Cedarwood is also very grounding and centering.

Spruce *(Picea mariana)* opens and releases emotional blocks, fostering a sense of balance and grounding. Traditionally, it was believed to possess the frequency of prosperity.

Rosewood *(Aniba rosaeodora)* is high in linalool, which has a relaxing, empowering effect. It is very grounding and strengthening.

Sandalwood *(Santalum album)* is high in sesquiterpene compounds which stimulate the pineal gland and the limbic region of the brain, the center of emotions and memory. Used traditionally in yoga and meditation. May help remove negative programming from the cells.

Myrtle *(Myrtus communis)* is energizing, inspiring, elevating, and euphoric.

Mugwort *(Artemisia vulgaris)* Avoid during pregnancy. Has been used historically under pillows to produce vivid dreams.

Application:

Possible skin sensitivity.

Diffuse, directly inhale, or add 2-4 drops to bath water. Apply 1 to 2 drops on edge of ears, wrists, neck, temples, forehead, crown of head, bottom of feet, or along spine. Add 2 drops to a wet cloth and put in clothes dryer. Put 4-8 drops on cotton ball and locate on vents.

Into the Future

Helps one leave the past behind in order to progress with vision and excitement. So many times we find ourselves settling for mediocrity and sacrificing our own potential and success because of fear of the unknown and the future. This blend inspires determination and a pioneering spirit and creates a strong emotional feeling of being able to reach one's potential.

Ingredients:

Frankincense (*Boswellia carteri*) is considered a holy anointing oil in the Middle East and has been used in religious ceremonies for thousands of years. It stimulates the limbic part of the brain, which elevates the mind, helping to overcome stress and despair. It is used in European medicine to combat depression.

Clary Sage (*Salvia sclarea*) enhances circulation and hormonal balance.

Jasmine (*Jasminum officinale*) is exhilarating to the mind and emotions, unlocking past blocks. It also alleviates nervous exhaustion, depression, and listlessness.

Juniper (*Juniperus osteosperma* and *J. scopulorum*) elevates spiritual awareness and creates feelings of love and peace.

White Fir (*Abies concolor*) creates a feeling of grounding, anchoring, and empowerment.

Orange (*Citrus sinensis*) is elevating to the mind and body and brings joy and peace. A 1995 Mie University study documented the ability of citrus fragrances to combat depression and bring about a deep sense of security.

Cedarwood (*Cedrus atlantica*) is high in sesquiterpenes, which can stimulate the limbic part of the brain, the center of emotions and memory. It stimulates the pineal gland, which releases melatonin, thereby improving thoughts, cognition, and memory.

Ylang Ylang (*Cananga odorata*) increases relaxation; balances male and female energies. It also restores confidence and equilibrium.

Idaho Tansy (*Tanacetum vulgare*) is antiviral, anti-infectious, antibacterial, and fights colds, flu, and infections. According to E. Joseph Montagna's PDR on herbal formulas, tansy helps skin problems, strengthen the kidneys, heart, joints, digestive system.

White Lotus (*Nymphaea lotus*) is calming and relaxing. Helps move forward overcoming self-defeating thoughts. It uplifts and brings deep peace and comfort.

Carrier Oil: Sweet almond (*Prunus dulcis*) oil

Application:

Diffuse, directly inhale, or add 2-4 drops to bath water. Apply 1 to 2 drops on edge of ears, over heart, on wrists, neck, or temples. Dilute 1:15 with vegetable oil for body massage. Put 4-8 drops on cotton ball and locate on vents.

Possible sun/skin sensitivity.

Joy

Produces a magnetic energy to bring joy to the heart, mind, and soul. It inspires romance and helps overcome deep seated grief and depression.

Ingredients:

Rose (*Rosa damascena*) has the highest frequency among essential oils. It creates a sense of balance, harmony, and well-being and elevates the mind. It creates a magnetic energy that attracts pure love and brings joy to the heart.

Bergamot (*Citrus bergamia*) balances hormones, calms emotions, and relieves anxiety, stress, and tension.

Mandarin (*Citrus reticulata*) has hypnotic properties and combats insomnia, stress and irritability.

Ylang Ylang (*Cananga odorata*) increases relaxation; balances male and female energies. It also restores confidence and equilibrium.

Lemon (*Citrus limon*) is stimulating and invigorating, promoting a deep sense of well-being. A 1995 Mie University study found that citrus fragrances boosted immunity, induced relaxation, and reduced depression.

Geranium (*Pelargonium graveolens*) stimulates the nerves and helps release negative memories so that joy can be attained.

Jasmine (*Jasminum officinale*) exudes an exquisite fragrance that revitalizes spirits. Brings feelings of love, support, and joy. Used to combat sorrow, depression, and nervous exhaustion.

Palmarosa (*Cymbopogon martinii*) it is stimulating and revitalizing, enhancing both the nervous and cardiovascular system. It also brings about a feeling of security.

Roman Chamomile *(Chamaemelum nobile)* combats restlessness, tension, insomnia. It purges toxins from liver where anger is stored. It also opens mental blocks.

Rosewood *(Aniba rosaeodora)* is high in linalool, which has a relaxing, empowering effect. Gives a feeling of being grounded, stable, and strong.

Application:

Dilute 1 part EO to 1 part vegetable oil.

Diffuse/humidify, directly inhale, or add 2-4 drops to bath water. Apply over heart, thymus, temples, and wrists. May also be used on lower back, abdomen, and on the heart and brain Vita Flex points. Dilute 1:15 with vegetable oil for a full-body massage. Put 2 drops on a wet cloth and put in clothes dryer. Put 4-8 drops on cotton ball and locate on vents.

Possible sun/skin sensitivity.

Juva Cleanse

The liver is the body's largest internal organ and major detoxifier for the body. Even the toxins in the air we breathe are filtered by the liver, including chemicals from aerosol cleaners, paint, bug sprays, etc. But, even filters need cleaning. The essential oils of ledum, celery seed, and helichrysum have long been known for their liver cleansing properties. JuvaCleanse was clinically tested in 2003 for removing mercury from body tissues.

A 2003 study conducted by Roger Lewis MD at the Young Life Research Clinic in Provo, Utah evaluated the efficacy of helichrysum, ledum, and celery seed in treating cases of advanced Hepatitis C. In one case a 20 year old male diagnosed with Hepatitis C had a viral count of 13,200. After taking two capsules (approx. 750 mg each) of a blend of helichrysum, ledum, and celery seed (JuvaCleanse) per day for one month with no other intervention, the patients viral count dropped more than 80 percent to 2,580.

Ingredients:

Helichrysum *(Helichrysum italicum)* regenerates tissue and improves circulation. It stimulates liver cell function and removes plaque from the veins and arteries.

Celery Seed *(Apium graveolens)* is a powerful liver cleanser and protectorant. It has been used against hepatitis.

Ledum *(Ledum groenlandicum)* shown in clinical studies to protect the liver and increase bile flow. Used with many liver dysfunctions, including hepatitis and fatty liver.

Application:

Apply over liver or on foot Vita Flex points for the liver and kidneys. Use with Raindrop Technique.

As a dietary supplement, dilute 50:50 and put in a size 0 capsule. Take twice/day.

JuvaFlex

Supports liver and lymphatic detoxification. Anger and hate are stored in the liver, creating toxicity and leading to sickness and disease. JuvaFlex helps break addictions to coffee, alcohol, drugs, and tobacco.

Ingredients:

Geranium *(Pelargonium graveolens)* improves bile flow from the liver. It is antispasmodic and improves liver, pancreas, and kidneys function.

Rosemary *(Rosmarinus officinalis)* is antiseptic and antimicrobial. It balances the endocrine system. It is liver protecting, helps combat hepatitis and other infectious diseases.

Roman Chamomile *(Chamaemelum nobile)* is anti-inflammatory and expels toxins from the liver. Strengthens liver function.

Fennel *(Foeniculum vulgare)* is antiseptic and stimulating to the circulatory system. Increases bile flow and hepatocyte function.

Helichrysum *(Helichrysum italicum)* regenerates tissue and improves circulation. It stimulates liver cell function and removes plaque from the veins and arteries.

Blue Tansy *(Tanacetum annuum)* helps cleanse the liver and lymphatic system. It is anti-inflammatory.

Carrier Oil: Organic sesame *(Sesamum indicum)* seed oil

Application:

Apply over liver area, foot Vita Flex points, raindrop-style along spine, or use in compress.

Lady Sclareol

Designed to be worn as an exquisite fragrance, this blend is also rich in phytoestrogens. It enhances the feminine nature by improving mood and raising estrogen levels. May provide relief for PMS symptoms.

Ingredients:

Rosewood *(Aniba rosaeodora)* is high in linalool, which has a relaxing empowering effect. It is very grounding and strengthening.

Vetiver *(Vetiveria zizanioides)* is psychologically grounding and stabilizing. It has been shown to help with concentration and coping with stress and insomnia.

Geranium *(Pelargonium graveolens)* helps release negative memories, opening and elevating the mind. It has been used for centuries for skin care. It revitalizes tissue and nerves and has relaxant, anti-inflammatory, anti-infectious effects.

Orange *(Citrus sinensis)* is elevating to the mind and body. A 1995 Mie University study documented the ability of citrus fragrances to combat depression and bring about a deep sense of security.

Clary Sage *(Salvia sclarea)* balances the hormones. It contains natural sclareol, a phytoestrogen that mimics estrogen function. It helps with menstrual cramps, PMS, and circulatory problems.

Ylang Ylang *(Cananga odorata)* balances male and female energies, increases relaxation and restores confidence and equilibrium. Helps bring out our gentle nature.

Sandalwood *(Santalum album)* is high in sesquiterpenes, which stimulate the pineal gland and the limbic region of the brain, the center of our emotions. Used traditionally in yoga and meditation.

Spanish Sage *(Salvia lavandulifolia)* is high in limonene which prevents DNA damage.

Jasmine *(Jasminum officinale)* is used for muscle spasms, frigidity, depression, and nervous exhaustion. It is stimulating to the mind and improves concentration.

Application:

For topical or aromatic use as a perfume, apply 2-4 drops to Vita Flex points on the ankles or at the clavicle notch. May be applied to the abdomen for relieve of premenstrual discomfort.

Longevity

Contains the highest antioxidant and DNA-protecting essential oils. When taken as a dietary supplement, Longevity promotes longevity and prevents premature aging. (See Longevity Oil Softgels in the Supplement section).

ORAC: 1,511,025μTE/L

Ingredients:

Clove *(Syzygium aromaticum)* has the highest known antioxidant power as measured by ORAC (oxygen radical absorbent capacity), a test developed by USDA researchers at Tufts University. It is anticoagulant and one of the most antimicrobial and antiseptic of all essential oils. Prevents cellular DNA damage.

Thyme *(Thymus vulgaris)* has been shown in studies to dramatically boost glutathione levels in the heart, liver, and brain. It also prevents lipid peroxidation or degradation of the fats found in many vital organs. The oxidation of fats in the body is directly linked to accelerated aging.

Orange *(Citrus aurantium)* contains over 90 percent d-limonene, one of the most powerful anticancerous compounds studied in recent years, the subject of over 50 peer-reviewed research papers published in leading medical journals throughout the world.

Frankincense *(Boswellia carteri)* has been shown in research at Ponce University to combat cellular mutations and combat chemotherapy-resistant cancers.

Application:

Dilute 1 part EO to 4 parts vegetable oil.

For dietary, topical, or aromatic use. If used as a dietary supplement, put one drop in a capsule or in 4 fl. oz. of liquid (e.g. goat/rice milk, etc.)

As a dietary supplement, dilute 20:80 and put in a size 00 capsule. Take twice/day.

Possible sun/skin sensitivity.

M-Grain

Relieves pain from both headaches and severe migraine headaches. It is anti-inflammatory and antispasmodic.

Ingredients:

Marjoram *(Origanum majorana)* is anti-inflammatory and is used to treat sore and aching muscles. It relieves muscle spasms and migraine headaches and calms nerves.

Lavender *(Lavandula angustifolia)* is anti-inflammatory and antispasmodic. High in aldehydes and esters, it combats insomnia, stress, and nervous tension. Extremely relaxing and grounding.

Peppermint *(Mentha piperita)* has powerful pain-blocking, anti-inflammatory, and anti-spasmodic properties. A 1994 double-blind, placebo-controlled, randomized cross-over study at the University of Kiel in Germany found that peppermint oil had a significant analgesic effect, effectively blocking headache pain (Gobel et al., 1994).

Basil *(Ocimum basilicum)* combats muscle spasms and inflammation. It is relaxing to both striated and smooth muscles (involuntary muscles such as the heart and digestive system).

Roman Chamomile *(Chamaemelum nobile)* is a strong anti-inflammatory with antispasmodic effects. Helps with insomnia, restlessness, and tension.

Helichrysum *(Helichrysum italicum)* is a powerful anaesthetic and analgesic. It quenches pain and inflammation and reduces muscle spasms.

Application:
Dilute 1 part EO to 1 part vegetable oil. Possible skin sensitivity.

Diffuse, directly inhale, or add 2-4 drops to bath water. Apply on brain stem, forehead, crown, shoulders, back of neck, temples, and foot Vita Flex points. Put 4-8 drops on cotton ball and locate on vents.

Magnify Your Purpose

Stimulates the endocrine system and creates energy flow to the right hemisphere of the brain, activating creativity, motivation, and focus. This helps bring about commitment to purpose, magnifying your desire, and pure intentions until they become reality.

Ingredients:

Sandalwood *(Santalum album)* is high in sesquiterpene compounds which stimulate the pineal gland and the limbic region of the brain, the center of emotions and memory. Used traditionally in yoga and meditation. May help remove negative programming in the cells.

Nutmeg *(Myristica fragrans)* supports the adrenal glands for increased energy. It is powerfully stimulating and energizing.

Patchouli *(Pogostemon cablin)* is strongly grounding and centering. Very high sesquiter-penes that stimulate the limbic center of the brain. It reestablishes mental and emotional equilibrium and energizes the mind. Relaxes the mind to discard jealousies, obsessions, and insecurities.

Rosewood *(Aniba rosaeodora)* is high in linalool, which has a relaxing, empowering effect. It is very grounding and strengthening.

Cinnamon Bark *(Cinnamomum verum)* is the oil of wealth from the Orient and part of the formula the Lord gave Moses (Exodus 30:22-27). It has a frequency that attracts wealth and abundance. It has been used traditionally to release malice or spite.

Ginger *(Zingiber officinale)* is energizing and uplifting.

Sage *(Salvia officinalis)* strengthens the vital centers. It has been used for purification, healing and to dispel negative emotions.

Application:
Dilute 1 part EO to 1 part vegetable oil. Possible skin sensitivity.

Diffuse/humidify, directly inhale, or add 2-4 drops to bath water. Apply on heart, solar plexus, thymus, temples, ears, or wrists. Put 4-8 drops on cotton ball and locate on vents. Add 2 drops to a wet cloth and put in clothes dryer.

Melrose

A strong topical antiseptic that cleans and disinfects cuts, scrapes, burns, rashes, and bruised tissue. It helps regenerate damaged tissue and reduces inflammation. When diffused it dispels odors.

Ingredients:

Melaleuca *(Melaleuca alternifolia)* also known as tea tree, is antiseptic, antibacterial, antifungal, antiparasitic, anti-inflammatory.

Naouli *(Melaleuca quinquenervia)* is anti-infectious, antiparasitic, and antibacterial.

Rosemary *(Rosmarinus officinalis* CT cineol*)* is antiseptic, antifungal, and antimicrobial.

Clove *(Syzygium aromaticum)* is one of the most antimicrobial and antiseptic of all essential oils. It is antifungal, antiviral, anti-infectious, and antibacterial.

Application:

Dilute 1 part EO to 1 part vegetable oil. Possible skin sensitivity.

Diffuse/humidify, directly inhale, or add 2-4 drops to bath water. Apply to broken skin, cuts, scrapes, burns, rashes, and infection. Follow with rose ointment to keep wound and oils sealed in. Put 1 to 2 drops on a piece of cotton and place in the ear for earaches.

Mister

Helps to decongest the prostate and promote greater male hormonal balance.

Ingredients:

Blue Yarrow *(Achillea millefolium)* is a prostate decongestant and hormone balancer. It is anti-inflammatory.

Sage *(Salvia officinalis)* has been used in Europe for hair loss. It strengthens vital centers, relieves depression, and mental fatigue.

Myrtle *(Myrtus communis)* helps normalize hormonal imbalances of the thyroid and sex glands. Stimulates and balances functions of the prostate.

Fennel *(Foeniculum vulgare)* has hormone-like activity and is stimulating to the circulatory, cardiovascular and respiratory systems.

Lavender *(Lavandula angustifolia)* is antispasmodic, hypotensive, anti-inflammatory, anti-infectious, and an anticoagulant. It is very relaxing, grounding, and combats depression

Peppermint *(Mentha piperita)* strengthens the liver and glandular function.

Carrier Oil: Organic sesame seed oil

Application:

Diffuse, directly inhale, or add 2-4 drops to bath water. Apply to ankle Vita Flex points, lower pelvis, or areas of concern. Use in hot compress. Dilute 1:15 with vegetable oil for body massage.

Motivation

Stimulates feelings of action and accomplishment, providing positive energy to help overcome feelings of fear and procrastination.

Ingredients:

Roman Chamomile *(Chamaemelum nobile)* combats restlessness, tension, insomnia. It purges toxins from liver where anger is stored.

Spruce *(Picea mariana)* helps to open and release emotional blocks, creating a feeling of balance and grounding.

Ylang Ylang *(Cananga odorata)* increases relaxation; balances male and female energies. It also restores confidence and equilibrium.

Lavender *(Lavandula angustifolia)* has been documented to improve concentration and mental acuity. Researchers at the University of Miami School of Medicine in Florida reported that patients felt less depressed, performing math computations faster and more accurately following inhalation of lavender oil (Diego et al., 1998). It combats nervous tension, depression, and listlessness.

Application:

Diffuse, directly inhale, or add 2-4 drops to bath water. Apply on feet (big toe), chest, nape of the neck, behind ears, wrists, or around navel. Put 4-8 drops on cotton ball and locate on vents.

PanAway

Reduces pain and inflammation, increases circulation, and accelerates healing. Relieves swelling and discomfort from arthritis, sprains, muscle spasms and cramps, bumps, and bruises.

Ingredients:

Helichrysum *(Helichrysum italicum)* is a powerful anaesthetic and analgesic. It quenches pain and inflammation and reduces muscle spasms.

Wintergreen *(Gaultheria procumbens)* is strongly anti-inflammatory and antispasmodic. It is analgesic and reduces all types of pain.

Clove *(Syzygium aromaticum)* is used in the dental industry to numb gum and kill pain. It is one of the most antimicrobial and antiseptic of all essential oils.

Peppermint *(Mentha piperita)* has powerful pain-blocking, anti-inflammatory, and antispasmodic properties. A 1994 double-blind, placebo-controlled, randomized cross-over study at the University of Kiel in Germany found that peppermint oil had a significant analgesic effect (Gobel et al., 1994).

Application:
Dilute 1 part EO to 1 part vegetable oil.
Possible skin sensitivity.

Diffuse/humidify, directly inhale, or add 2-4 drops to bath water. Apply on location or on temples, back of neck, forehead. Use as a compress or Raindrop style along spine.

Use Relieve It for deep tissue pain. Add helichrysum to enhance effect of PanAway. For bone pain use Wintergreen. All can be diluted with Ortho Ease Massage Oil.

Peace & Calming

Promotes relaxation and a deep sense of peace and emotional well-being, helping to dampen tensions and uplift spirits. When massaged on the bottom of the feet, it can be a wonderful prelude to a peaceful night's rest. It may calm overactive and hard-to-manage children. Reduces depression, anxiety, stress, and insomnia.

Ingredients:

Blue Tansy *(Tanacetum annuum)* Helps cleanse the liver and lymphatic system. Emotionally, it combats anger and negative emotions.

Patchouli *(Pogostemon cablin)* is strongly grounding and centering. Very high sesquiterpenes that stimulate the limbic center of the brain. It reestablishes mental and emotional equilibrium and energizes the mind. Helps clarify thoughts.

Tangerine *(Citrus reticulata)* contains esters and aldehydes that are sedating and calming, helping with anxiety and nervousness.

Orange *(Citrus sinensis)* is elevating to the mind and body and brings joy and peace. A 1995 Mie University study documented the ability of citrus fragrances to combat depression and bring about a deep sense of security.

Ylang Ylang *(Cananga odorata)* increases relaxation; balances male and female energies. It also restores confidence and equilibrium.

Application:
Possible sun/skin sensitivity.

Diffuse, directly inhale, or add 2-4 drops to bath water. Apply to wrists, edge of ears, or foot Vitaflex points. Dilute 1:15 with vegetable oil for body massage. Put 4-8 drops on cotton ball and locate on vents.

Combine with Lavender (for insomnia) and German chamomile (for calming).

Present Time

An empowering fragrance that creates a feeling of being in the moment. Disease develops when we live in the past and with regret. Being in present time is key to progressing and moving forward.

Ingredients:

Neroli *(Citrus sinensis)* was used by the ancient Egyptians for healing the mind, body, and spirit. It is stabilizing and strengthening to the emotions, promoting peace, confidence, and awareness. It brings everything into focus. Alleviates anxiety, depression, and insomnia.

Ylang Ylang *(Cananga odorata)* increases relaxation; balances male and female energies. It also restores confidence and equilibrium.

Spruce *(Picea mariana)* opens and releases emotional blocks, fostering a sense of balance and grounding.

Carrier Oil: Almond

Application:
Diffuse, directly inhale, or add 2-4 drops to bath water. Apply to sternum and thymus area, neck and forehead.

Purification

Cleanses and disinfects the air and neutralizes mildew, cigarette smoke, and disagreeable odors. Disinfects and cleanses cuts, scrapes and bites from spiders, bees, hornet, and wasps.

Ingredients:

Citronella *(Cymbopogon nardus)* is antiseptic, antibacterial, antispasmodic, anti-inflammatory, insecticidal, and insect-repelling.

Lemongrass *(Cymbopogon flexuosus)* has strong antifungal properties. Tends to be purifying and antibacterial.

Lavandin *(Lavandula* x *hybrida)* is antifungal, antibacterial, a strong antiseptic, and a tissue regenerator.

Rosemary *(Rosmarinus officinalis* CT cineol*)* is antiseptic, antifungal, and antimicrobial and may be beneficial for skin conditions and dandruff. It helps fight candida and is anti-infectious.

Melaleuca *(Melaleuca alternifolia)* also known as tea tree, is antibacterial, antifungal, anti-parasitic, antiseptic, and anti-inflammatory.

Myrtle *(Myrtus communis)* is antibacterial and may support immune function in fighting colds, flus, and other infectious disease.

Application:
Dilute 1 part EO to 1 part vegetable oil. Possible skin sensitivity.

Diffuse 15 to 30 minutes every 3 to 4 hours. Directly inhale, or add 2-4 drops to bath water. Apply on location to cuts, sores, bruise, or wound. Put 4-8 drops on cotton ball and locate on vents. Add 2 drops to a wet cloth and put in clothes dryer.

R.C.

Gives relief from colds, bronchitis, sore throats, sinusitis, coughs and respiratory congestion. Decongests sinus passages, combats lung infections, and relieves allergy symptoms.

Ingredients:

Eucalyptus globulus has shown to be a powerful antimicrobial and germ-killer. It is expectorant, mucolytic, antibacterial, antifungal, antiviral, and antiseptic. It reduces infections in the throat and lungs, such as rhinopharyngitis, laryngitis, flu, sinusitis, bronchitis, pneumonia.

Eucalyptus radiata is anti-infectious, antibacterial, antiviral, an expectorant, and anti-inflammatory. It has strong action against bronchitis and sinusitis.

Eucalyptus citriodora decongests and disinfects the sinuses and lungs. It is anti-inflammatory, anti-infectious, and antispasmodic.

Myrtle *(Myrtus communis)* supports the respiratory system and helps treat chronic coughs and tuberculosis. It is suitable to use for coughs and chest complaints with children. Sinus decongestant and alleviates throat infections.

Pine *(Pinus sylvestris)* opens and disinfects the respiratory system, particularly the bronchial tract. It has been used since the time of Hippocrates to support respiratory function and fight infection. According to Daniel Pénoël, MD, pine is one of the best oils for bronchitis and pneumonia.

Spruce *(Picea mariana)* helps the respiratory and nervous systems. It is anti-infectious, antiseptic, and anti-inflammatory.

Marjoram *(Origanum majorana)* supports the respiratory system and reduces spasms. It is anti-infectious, antibacterial, and antiseptic.

Lavender *(Lavandula angustifolia)* is antispasmodic, hypotensive, anti-inflammatory, and antiseptic. It is relaxing and grounding.

Cypress *(Cupressus sempervirens)* promotes blood circulation and lymph flow. It is anti-infectious, antibacterial, antimicrobial, mucolytic, antiseptic, refreshing, and relaxing.

Peppermint *(Mentha piperita)* is a powerful nasal and lung decongestant with antiseptic properties. It opens nasal passages, reduces cough, improves airflow to the lungs, and kills airborne bacteria, fungi and viruses. A 1994 double-blind, placebo-controlled, randomized cross-over study at the University of Kiel in Germany found that peppermint oil exerted a significant analgesic effect (Gobel et al., 1994).

Application:

Dilute 1 part EO to 1 part vegetable oil.
Possible skin sensitivity.

Diffuse/humidify, directly inhale, apply on chest, neck, throat, or over sinus area. Use as a hot compress or with Raindrop Technique. Dilute 1:15 with vegetable oil for body massage. Put 4-8 drops on cotton ball and locate on vents.

TO COMBAT SINUS/LUNG CONGESTION: Add R.C., Raven or Wintergreen to bowl of hot, steaming water. Place a towel over your head and water/oil mixture and inhale the steam. Combine with Raven and Thieves (alternating morning and night) to enhance effects.

Raven

Treats respiratory disease and infections such as tuberculosis, influenza, and pneumonia. It is highly antiviral and antiseptic.

Ingredients:

Ravensara *(Ravensara aromatica)* is referred to by the people of Madagascar as the oil that heals. It is antiseptic, anti-infectious, antiviral, antibacterial, antifungal, and expectorant. It has been used to treat influenza, sinusitis, bronchitis, and herpes.

Eucalyptus radiata may have a profound antiviral effect upon the respiratory system. It may also help reduce inflammation of the nasal mucous membrane.

Peppermint *(Mentha piperita)* is a powerful anti-inflammatory and antiseptic for the respiratory system. It is used to treat bronchitis and pneumonia. High in menthol and menthone, it helps suppress coughs and clears lung and nasal congestion.

Wintergreen *(Gaultheria procumbens)* is strongly anti-inflammatory and antispasmodic. It is analgesic and reduces pain. Helps increase respiratory capacity.

Lemon *(Citrus limon)* increases microcirculation and promotes immunity.

Application:

Dilute 1 part EO to 1 part vegetable oil.
Possible sun/skin sensitivity.

Diffuse/humidify, directly inhale, or add 2-4 drops to bath water. Apply to throat and lung area and foot Vita Flex points. Use as hot compress over lungs or with Raindrop Technique. To use in suppository dilute with vegetable oil 1:10 and retain during the night.

Release

Helps release anger and memory trauma from the liver in order to create emotional well-being. Letting go of negative emotions and frustration enables one to progress in a positive way.

Ingredients:

Ylang Ylang *(Cananga odorata)* increases relaxation; balances male and female energies. It also restores confidence and equilibrium.

Lavandin *(Lavandula* x *hybrida)* is antifungal, antibacterial, a strong antiseptic, and a tissue regenerator.

Geranium *(Pelargonium graveolens)* stimulates nerves and assists in balancing hormones. Its aromatic influence helps release negative memories, thereby opening and elevating the mind.

Sandalwood *(Santalum album)* is high in sesquiterpene compounds which stimulate the pineal gland and the limbic region of the brain, the center of emotions and memory. Used traditionally in yoga and meditation. May help remove negative programming in the cells.

Blue Tansy *(Tanacetum annuum)* helps cleanse the liver and lymphatic system. Emotionally, it combats anger and negative emotions and promotes a feeling of self-control.

Carrier Oil: Organic olive *(Olea europea)* oil

Application:

Diffuse, directly inhale, or add 2-4 drops to bath water. Apply over liver or anywhere trauma has occurred, or as a compress. Massage on bottom of feet and behind ears. Dilute 1:15 with vegetable oil for body massage. Put 4-8 drops on cotton ball and locate on vents.

Relieve It

High in anti-inflammatory compounds that relieve deep tissue pain and muscle soreness.

Ingredients:

Spruce *(Picea mariana)* is anti-infectious, antiseptic, and anti-inflammatory.

Pepper, Black *(Piper nigrum)* is anti-inflammatory and combats deep tissue pain. It has been traditionally used to treat arthritis.

Peppermint *(Mentha piperita)* has powerful pain-blocking, anti-inflammatory, and antispasmodic properties. A 1994 double-blind, placebo-controlled, randomized cross-over study at the University of Kiel in Germany found that peppermint oil had a significant analgesic effect (Gobel et al., 1994).

Hyssop *(Hyssopus officinalis)* is anti-inflammatory and anti-infectious.

Application:

Dilute 1 part EO to 1 part vegetable oil. Possible skin sensitivity.

Apply on location to relieve pain. Use as cold or hot compress.

RutaVaLa

Promotes the relaxation of body and mind, counters stressed nerves and revitalizes passion.

Ingredients:

Lavender *(Lavandula angustifolia)* has been shown in endless research to calm and relax physical and mental tension. Its unique sedative properties add even more relaxation power to the RutaVala blend.

Valerian *(Valeriana officinalis)* well-known for its sedative and relaxation properties, valerian is used both as an herb and as an essential oil to promote mental balance and as a sleep aid.

Ruta *(Ruta graveolens)* is harvested and distilled in Ecuador. It is sometimes referred to as Rue. Its use dates back to biblical times, as an herb to be tithed. It is antiseptic and was one of the oils used in the original Vinegar of Four Thieves during the Black Plague

Application:

This product is for aromatic use only. Diffuse or inhale 1-2 drops every hour or as needed.

Sacred Mountain

Instills strength, empowerment, grounding, and protection with the sacred feeling of the mountains.

Ingredients:

Spruce *(Picea mariana)* opens and releases emotional blocks, fostering a sense of balance and grounding. Traditionally, it was believed to possess the frequency of prosperity.

Idaho Balsam Fir *(Abies balsamea)* has been researched for its ability to kill airborne germs and bacteria. As a conifer oil, it creates a feeling of grounding, anchoring, and empowerment.

Cedarwood *(Cedrus atlantica)* is high in sesquiterpenes, which stimulate the limbic part of the brain, the center of emotions and memory. It stimulates the pineal gland, which releases melatonin, thereby improving thoughts, cognition, and memory. Cedarwood is very stabilizing and grounding.

Ylang Ylang *(Cananga odorata)* increases relaxation; balances male and female energies. It also restores confidence and equilibrium.

Application:

Dilute 1 part EO to 1 part vegetable oil. Possible skin sensitivity.

Diffuse, directly inhale, or add 2-4 drops to bath water. Apply to crown of head, back of neck, behind ears, on thymus and wrists. Dilute 1:15 with vegetable oil for body massage. Put 4-8 drops on cotton ball and locate on vents. Add 2 drops to a wet cloth and put in clothes dryer.

SARA

Enables one to relax into a mental state to facilitate the release of the trauma of Sexual And/or Ritual Abuse. SARA also helps unlock other traumatic experiences such as physical and emotional abuse.

Ingredients:

Geranium *(Pelargonium graveolens)* helps release negative memories, thereby opening and elevating the mind.

Lavender *(Lavandula angustifolia)* is relaxing and grounding. University of Miami researchers found that inhalation of lavender oil increased beta waves in the brain, suggesting heightened relaxation. It also reduced depression and improved cognitive performance (Diego et al., 1998). A 2001 Osaka Kyoiku University study found that lavender reduced mental stress and increased alertness (Motomura et al., 2001). High in aldehydes and esters, it helps overcome insomnia, stress, and nervous tension.

Rose *(Rosa damascena)* possesses the highest frequency of all essential oils, creating balance, harmony, and well-being as it elevates the mind. Brings joy to the heart.

Blue Tansy *(Tanacetum annuum)* helps cleanse the liver and calm the lymphatic system, helping one to overcome anger and negative emotions, promoting a feeling of self-control. Its primary constituents are limonene and sesquiterpenes.

Orange *(Citrus sinensis)* is elevating to the mind and body and brings joy and peace. A 1995 Mie University study documented the ability of citrus fragrances to combat depression and bring about a deep sense of security.

Cedarwood *(Cedrus atlantica)* is high in sesquiterpenes, which stimulate the limbic part of the brain, the center of emotions and memory. It stimulates the pineal gland, which releases melatonin, thereby improving thoughts, cognition, and memory. Cedarwood is very stabilizing and grounding.

Ylang Ylang *(Cananga odorata)* increases relaxation; balances male and female energies. It also restores confidence and equilibrium.

White Lotus *(Nymphaea lotus)* helps overcome self-defeating thoughts. It may also help release negative trauma and bring one a sense of comfort and ease.

Carrier Oil: Almond *(Prunus dulcis)*

Application:
Possible sun sensitivity.

Apply over energy centers and areas of abuse, on navel, lower abdomen, temples, nose, and foot Vita Flex points.

SclarEssence

Balances hormones naturally using essential oil phytoestrogens. Has been shown to increase estrogen levels. Combines the soothing effects of peppermint with the balancing power of fennel and clary sage and the calming action of Spanish lavender for an extraordinary dietary supplement.

Ingredients:

Clary Sage *(Salvia sclaria)* balances the hormones. It contains natural sclareol, a phytoestrogen that mimics estrogen function. It helps with menstrual cramps, PMS, and circulatory problems.

Peppermint *(Mentha piperita)* strengthens the liver and glandular function.

Spanish Sage *(Salvia lavandulifolia)* is high in limonene which prevents DNA damage.

Fennel *(Foeniculum vulgare)* is antiseptic and stimulating to the gastrointestinal system. It is antispasmodic so it may provide relief from cramps. It also has estrogen-like properties and helps balance hormones.

Application:
Put 1-10 drops in a 00 capsule mixed with a pure vegetable oil (V6). Ingest 1 capsule daily as needed. Do not use in conjunction with any other hormone products.

Sensation

Profoundly romantic, refreshing, and arousing. It amplifies excitement of experiencing new heights of self-expression and awareness.

Sensation is also nourishing and hydrating for the skin and is beneficial for many skin problems.

Ingredients:

Ylang Ylang (*Cananga odorata*) increases relaxation; balances male and female energies. It also restores confidence and equilibrium. Brings out our more gentle nature.

Rosewood (*Aniba rosaeodora*) is antiseptic, antifungal, and nourishing to the skin. It enhances skin elasticity. It is very grounding and strengthening.

Jasmine (*Jasminum officinale*) is beneficial for dry, oily, irritated, or sensitive skin. Combats muscle spasms, frigidity, depression, listlessness, and brings joy and harmony to the heart.

Application:

Possible skin sensitivity.

Diffuse or add 2-4 drops to bath water. Apply on location, neck or wrists. Uses as a compress over abdomen. Dilute 1:15 with vegetable oil for body massage. Put 4-8 drops on cotton ball and locate on vents. Add 2 drops to a wet cloth and put in clothes dryer.

Surrender

Helps one surrender aggression and a controlling attitude. Stress and tension are released quickly when we surrender our own will.

Ingredients:

Lavender (*Lavandula angustifolia*) has sedative and calming properties. It helps overcome nervous tension, depression, and chaotic energy.

Roman Chamomile (*Chamaemelum nobile*) combats restlessness, tension, insomnia. It purges toxins from liver where anger is stored. It also opens mental blocks.

German Chamomile (*Matricaria recutita*) has an electrical frequency that promotes peace and harmony creating a feeling of security.

Angelica (*Angelica archangelica*) helps to calm emotions and brings memories back to the point of origin before trauma or anger was experienced, helping us to let go of negative feelings.

Mountain Savory (*Satureja montana*) is stimulating and energizing.

Lemon (*Citrus limon*) is stimulating and invigorating, promoting a deep sense of well-being. A 1995 Mie University study found that citrus fragrances boosted immunity, induced relaxation, and reduced depression. Very calming and reassuring to many individuals.

Spruce (*Picea mariana*) opens and releases emotional blocks, creating a feeling of balance and grounding. Traditionally, it was believed to possess the frequency of prosperity.

Application:

Possible sun/skin sensitivity.

Diffuse, directly inhale, or add 2-4 drops to bath water. Apply on location, or on forehead, solar plexus, along ear rim, chest and nape of neck. Dilute 1:15 with vegetable oil for body massage. Put 4-8 drops on cotton ball and locate on vents.

3 Wise Men

Opens the subconscious mind through pineal stimulation to release deep-seated trauma. Engenders a sense of grounding and uplifting through emotional releasing and elevated spiritual consciousness.

Ingredients:

Sandalwood (*Santalum album*) is high in sesquiterpene compounds which stimulate the pineal gland and the limbic region of the brain, the center of emotions and memory. Used traditionally in yoga and meditation.

Juniper (*Juniperus osteosperma* and *J. scopulorum*) elevates spiritual awareness creating feelings of love and peace.

Frankincense (*Boswellia carteri*) is considered a holy anointing oil in the Middle East and has been used in religious ceremonies for thousands of years. It stimulates the limbic part of the brain, which elevates the mind.

Myrrh *(Commiphora myrrha)* is referenced throughout the Bible, constituting a part of a holy anointing formula given to Moses (Exodus 30:22-27). It has one of the highest levels of sesquiterpenes, a class of compounds that stimulate the hypothalamus, pituitary, and amygdala, the control center for emotions and hormone release in the brain.

Spruce *(Picea mariana)* opens and releases emotional blocks, creating a feeling of balance and grounding. Traditionally, it was believed to possess the frequency of prosperity.

Carrier Oil: Almond *(Prunus dulcis)*

Application:

Diffuse, directly inhale, or add 2-4 drops to bath water. Add 2 drops on crown of head, behind ears, over eyebrows, on chest, over thymus, and at back of neck. Dilute 1:15 with vegetable oil for body massage. Put 4-8 drops on cotton ball and locate on vents. Add 2 drops to a wet cloth and put in clothes dryer.

Thieves

A blend of highly antiviral, antiseptic, antibacterial, anti-infectious essential oils. Thieves was created from research of a group of 15th-century thieves who rubbed oils on themselves to avoid contracting the plague while they robbed the bodies of the dead and dying. When apprehended, these thieves disclosed the formula of herbs, spices, and oils they used to protect themselves in exchange for more lenient punishment.

Studies conducted at Weber State University (Ogden, UT) during 1997 demonstrated its killing power against airborne microorganisms. One analysis showed a 90 percent reduction in the number of gram positive *Micrococcus luteus* organisms after diffusing for 12 minutes. After 20 minutes of diffusing, the kill-rate jumped to 99.3 percent. Another study against the gram negative *Pseudomonas aeruginosa* showed a kill rate of 99.96 percent after just 12 minutes of diffusion.

Ingredients:

Clove *(Syzygium aromaticum)* is one of the most antimicrobial and antiseptic of all essential oils. It is antifungal, antiviral, anti-infectious.

Lemon *(Citrus limon)* has antiseptic-like properties and contains compounds that amplify immunity. It promotes circulation, leukocyte formation, and lymphatic function.

Cinnamon Bark *(Cinnamomum verum)* is one of the most powerful antiseptics known. It is strongly antibacterial, antiviral, and antifungal.

Eucalyptus *(Eucalyptus radiata)* is anti-infectious, antibacterial, antiviral, and anti-inflammatory.

Rosemary *(Rosmarinus officinalis* CT cineol*)* is antiseptic and antimicrobial. It is high in cineol— a key ingredient in antiseptic drugs.

Application:

Dilute 1 part EO to 4 parts vegetable oil.

Possible sun/skin sensitivity.

Diffuse for 15 minutes every 3 to 4 hours. Apply neat to bottom of feet. Dilute 1:15 in vegetable oil and massage over thymus. For headaches put 1 drop on tongue and push against roof of mouth.

Dilute 1:15 with vegetable oil for body massage. Put 4-8 drops on cotton ball and locate on vents. Add 2 drops to a wet cloth and put in clothes dryer.

Tranquil Roll-on

This proprietary blend of lavender, cedarwood and Roman chamomile essential oils, packaged in a roll-on applicator provides convenient and portable relaxation and stress relief. All three of these oils have been well-documented as effective in reducing restlessness, decreasing anxiety and inducing calm to mind and body. Their combined effect is uplifting as well as calming and can be useful in promoting sleep as well as reducing stress.

Ingredients:

Lavender *(Lavandula angustifolia)* is used in the traditional medicine of many cultures as a calmative. One of the most versatile of the essential oils, lavender can be applied topically or used for aromatherapy to contribute to overall relaxation.

Cedarwood *(Cedrus atlantica)* has an extremely high level of sesquiterpenes, which can act directly on the limbic system in the brain to induce relaxation and calm. Like other conifer oils, cedarwood provides a feeling of 'grounding' that contributes to relaxation. It can also be applied topically or inhaled aromatically.

Roman Chamomile *(Chamomaelum nobilis)* has traditionally been used to calm and soothe small children. It combats restlessness, tension and insomnia

Fractionated and Virgin Coconut Oils
(Cocos nucifera)

Application:

Apply liberally to temples, neck or wrists as needed.

Transformation

Repressed trauma and tragedy from the past may be out of sight, but they are definitely not out of mind. Memories are imprinted in our cells for better or worse. Stored negative emotions need to be replaced with joy, hope and courage. Transformation blend radiates with the purifying oils of lemon and peppermint, along with the revitalizing power of sesquiterpenes from sandalwood and frankincense. Balsam fir anchors new mental programming.

Reaching into the deepest recesses of memory, Transformation empowers and upholds the changes you want to make in your belief system. Positive, uplifting beliefs are foundational for the transformation of behavior.

Ingredients:

Lemon *(Citrus limon)* is an antiseptic oil that is rich in limonene, which has been extensively studied for its ability to combat tumor growth in over 50 clinical studies. It increases microcirculation, which may improve vision.

Peppermint *(Mentha piperita)* Dr. William N. Dember of the University of Cincinnati found that inhaling peppermint oil increased mental accuracy by 28 percent. Stimulating, energizing, and empowering.

Sandalwood *(Santalum album)* is high in sesquiterpenes, which stimulate the pineal gland and the limbic region of the brain, the center of

our emotions. Used traditionally in yoga and meditation. May help remove negative programming in the cells.

Clary Sage *(Salvia sclarea)* balances the hormones. It contains natural sclareol, a phytoestrogen that mimics estrogen function.

Frankincense *(Boswellia carteri)* stimulates the limbic part of the brain, which elevates the mind, helping to overcome stress and despair. It is used in European medicine to combat depression.

Idaho Balsam Fir *(Abies balsamea)* has been researched for its ability to kill airborne germs and bacteria. As a confer oil, it creates a feeling of grounding, anchoring and empowerment.

Rosemary *(Rosmarinus officinalis* CT cineol) helps overcome mental fatigue, stimulating memory and opens the conscious mind. University of Miami scientists found that inhaling rosemary boosted alertness, eased anxiety and amplified analytic and mental ability.

Cardamom *(Elettaria cardamomum)* is uplifting, refreshing and invigorating. It may be beneficial for clearing confusion. In a study done by Dember, et al., 1995, cardamom was found to enhance performance accuracy.

Application:

Diffuse for most effective use. May also be applied topically on appropriate Vita Flex points.

Trauma Life

Releases buried emotional trauma (ie., accidents, death of loved ones, assault, abuse). It combats stress and uproots traumas that cause insomnia, anger, restlessness, and a weakened immune response.

Ingredients:

Valerian *(Valeriana officinalis)* is calming, relaxing, grounding, and emotionally balancing. Clinically researched for its tranquilizing properties. German health authorities have pronounced valerian to be an effective treatment for restlessness and sleep disturbances resulting from nervous conditions. It helps minimize shock, anxiety, and the stress that accompanies traumatic situations.

Lavender *(Lavandula angustifolia)* is relaxant and helps overcome insomnia and anxiety. It combats nervous anxiety, depression, and chaotic energy.

Frankincense *(Boswellia carteri)* elevates the mind and helps overcome stress and despair. It stimulates the limbic region of the brain, the center of emotions. In ancient times, frankincense was known for its anointing and healing powers.

Sandalwood *(Santalum album)* is high in sesquiterpene compounds which stimulate the pineal gland and the limbic region of the brain, the center of emotions and memory. Used traditionally in yoga and meditation. May help remove negative programming in the cells.

Rose *(Rosa damascena)* has the highest frequency among essential oils. It creates a sense of balance, harmony, and well-being and elevates the mind. It creates a magnetic energy that attracts love and brings joy to the heart.

Helichrysum *(Helichrysum italicum)* improves circulation and helps release feelings of anger promoting forgiveness.

Spruce *(Picea mariana)* opens and releases emotional blocks, fostering a sense of balance and grounding.

Geranium *(Pelargonium graveolens)* stimulates the nerves and helps release negative memories.

Davana *(Artemisia pallens)* is high in sesquiterpenes which help overcome anxiety.

Citrus hystrix has aldehydes and esters that are calming and sedating.

Application:
Possible sun/skin sensitivity.

Diffuse, directly inhale, or add 2-4 drops to bath water. Apply to bottom of feet, chest, forehead, nape of neck, behind ears, and along spine raindrop-style. Dilute 1:15 with vegetable oil for body massage. Put 4-8 drops on cotton ball and locate on vents. Add 2 drops to a wet cloth and put in clothes dryer.

Valor

Balances energies to instill courage, confidence, and self-esteem. It helps the body self-correct its balance and alignment.

Ingredients:

Rosewood *(Aniba rosaeodora)* is anti-infectious, antibacterial, antifungal, and antispasmodic. It is very grounding and strengthening.

Blue Tansy *(Tanacetum annuum)* helps cleanse the liver and lymphatic system helping one to overcome anger and negative emotions promoting a feeling of self-control.

Frankincense *(Boswellia carteri)* is considered a holy anointing oil in the Middle East and has been used in religious ceremonies for thousands of years. Stimulates the limbic part of the brain, elevating the mind and helping to overcome stress and despair. It is used in European medicine to combat depression.

Spruce *(Picea mariana)* opens and releases emotional blocks, fostering a sense of balance and grounding. Traditionally, it was believed to possess the frequency of prosperity.

Carrier Oil: Sweet Almond *(Prunus dulcis)*

Application:
Diffuse, directly inhale, or add 2-4 drops to bath water. Apply 4 to 6 wrists, chest, and base of neck, bottom of feet, or along spine in raindrop technique. When using a series of oils, apply Valor first and wait 5 to 10 minutes before applying other oils. Dilute 1:15 with vegetable oil for body massage.

Valor Roll-on

Ingredients:

Spruce *(Picea mariana)* helps open and release emotional blocks, brining about a feeling of balance and grounding.

Rosewood *(Aniba rosaeodora)* is high in linalool, which has a relaxing, empowering and uplifting effect. It is also very grounding and strengthening.

Frankincense *(Boswellia carteri)* is high in sesquiterpenes which have a stimulating effect on the limbic system, elevating the mind and helping to replace feelings of sadness and despair with courage and determination.

Blue Tansy *(Tanacetum annuum)* cleanses and calms the lymph system and the liver, helping to overcome anger and negative emotions, and promoting a feeling of self-control.

Fractionated and Virgin Coconut Oils
(Cocos nucifera)

Application:
Apply generously to feet, writs or back of the neck. Can be worn as a fragrance.

White Angelica

Increases the aura around the body to bring a delicate sense of strength and protection, creating a feeling of wholeness in the realm of one's own spirituality. Its frequency neutralizes negative energy and gives a feeling of protection and security.

Ingredients:

Ylang Ylang *(Cananga odorata)* increases relaxation; balances male and female energies. It also restores confidence and equilibrium.

Rose *(Rosa damascena)* has the highest frequency among essential oils. It creates a sense of balance, harmony, and well-being and elevates the mind. It creates a magnetic energy that attracts love and brings joy to the heart.

Melissa *(Melissa officinalis)* brings out gentleness. It is calming and balancing to the emotions, affecting the limbic part of the brain, the emotional center of memories. Used anciently to treat nervous disorders and many different ailments of the heart.

Sandalwood *(Santalum album)* is high in sesquiterpene compounds which stimulate the pineal gland and the limbic region of the brain, the center of emotions and memory. Used traditionally in yoga and meditation.

Geranium *(Pelargonium graveolens)* stimulates the nerves and helps release negative memories thereby opening and elevating the mind.

Spruce *(Picea mariana)* opens and releases emotional blocks, fostering a sense of balance and grounding. Traditionally, it was believed to possess the frequency of prosperity.

Myrrh *(Commiphora myrrha)* is referenced throughout the Old and New Testaments, constituting a part of a holy anointing formula given to Moses (Exodus 30:22-27). It has one of the highest levels of sesquiterpenes, a class of compounds that stimulate the hypothalamus, pituitary, and amygdala, the control center for emotions and hormone release in the brain.

Hyssop *(Hyssopus officinalis)* is strongly balancing for emotions. Helps stimulate creativity and meditation

Bergamot *(Citrus bergamia)* is simultaneously uplifting and calming, with a unique ability to relieve anxiety, stress, and tension.

Rosewood *(Aniba rosaeodora)* is soothing and nourishing to the skin, enhancing elasticity. It is high in linalool, which has a relaxing, empowering effect. It is very grounding and strengthening.

Carrier Oil: Sweet Almond *(Prunus dulcis)*

Application:
Diffuse, directly inhale, or add 2-4 drops to bath water. Apply to shoulders, along spine, on crown of head, on wrists, behind ears, base of neck, or foot Vitaflex points. Dilute 1:15 with vegetable oil for body massage. Put 4-8 drops on cotton ball and locate on vents. Add 2 drops to a wet cloth and put in clothes dryer.

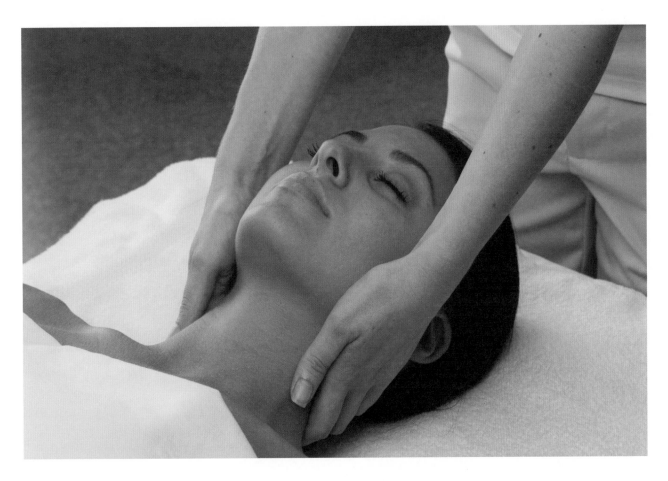

Massage and therapeutic touch have long been part of both physical and emotional healing. When essential oils are combined with massage, the benefits are numerous. Massage improves circulation, lymphatic drainage, and aids in the elimination of tissue wastes. The oils bring peace and tranquility as well as keen mental awareness. Massage opens and increases the flow of energy, balancing the entire nervous system and helping to release physical and emotional disharmony. The unrefined carrier vegetable oils are rich in fat-soluble nutrients and essential fatty acids.

Cel-Lite Magic

Cel-Lite Magic enhances circulation and helps to provide nutrients to reduce fat and cellulite.

Vegetable Oils:

Coconut Oil (fractionated) is distilled from pure coconut oil. It is colorless, odorless, never goes rancid, and is easily washed out from fabrics.

Grape Seed Oil is light-textured, odorless, and nourishing to the skin.

Olive Oil is rich in cell-protecting phyto-nutrients and antioxidants like squalene.

Wheatgerm Oil is rich in lecithin, vitamin E, and B vitamins. Protects skin from free radical damage. Moisturizing and noncomedogenic.

Almond Oil is high in vitamin E and phytonutrients. Highly nourishing to the skin, it protects cell membranes from oxidative damage.

Essential Oils:

Cedarwood (*Cedrus atlantica*) historically used for its calming, purifying properties; highly beneficial for skin.

Cypress (*Cupressus sempervirens*) increases circulation. Reduces edema and water retention, and improves lymphatic drainage.

Juniper (*Juniperus osteosperma* and *J. scopulorum*) detoxifies and cleanses.

Grapefruit (*Citrus paradisi*) is a disinfectant with unique fat-dissolving properties.

Clary Sage (*Salvia sclarea*) supports cells and hormonal balance. It contains natural phytoestrogens.

Pepper (*Piper nigrum*) is anti-inflammatory and can be stimulating, increases circulation, combats soreness and pain in deep muscles.

Directions: Apply on location. Can be used in massage or added to bath water.

Dragon Time Massage Oil

Dragon Time combines essential oils that have been researched in Europe for their balancing effects on hormones.

Vegetable Oils:

Coconut Oil (fractionated) is distilled from pure coconut oil. It is colorless, odorless, never goes rancid, and is easily washed out from fabrics.

Grape Seed Oil is light-textured, odorless, and nourishing to the skin.

Almond Oil is high in vitamin E and phytonutrients. Highly nourishing to the skin, it protects cell membranes from oxidative damage.

Olive Oil is rich in cell-protecting phyto-nutrients and antioxidants like squalene.

Wheatgerm Oil is rich in lecithin, vitamin E, and B vitamins. Protects skin from free radical damage. Moisturizing and noncomedogenic.

Essential Oils:

Blue Yarrow (*Achillea millefolium*) balances hormones and reduces inflammation

Clary Sage (*Salvia sclarea*) supports cells and hormonal balance. It contains natural phytoestrogens. Helps with PMS, menstrual cramps, and circulation.

Fennel (*Foeniculum vulgare*) has estrogren-like action; stimulating to circulatory system.

Lavender (*Lavandula angustifolia*) is highly regarded for the skin. Excellent for burns and for cleansing cuts, bruises, and skin irritations. It is uniquely calming and relaxing. It helps overcome depression and nervous anxiety.

Jasmine (*Jasminum officinale*) is beneficial for dry, oily, irritated, or sensitive skin. It can also be uplifting and stimulating. It combats depression, nervous exhaustion, and dischord.

Sage (*Salvia officinalis*) has estrogen-like activity and used for treating many types of skin conditions. Strengthens the vital centers.

Ylang Ylang (*Cananga odorata*)—may be extremely effective in calming and bringing about a sense of relaxation.

Ortho Ease Massage Oil

An anti-inflammatory and pain-killing complex of vegetable and essential oils. Ideal for strained, swollen, or torn muscles and ligaments.. Also combats insect bites, dermatitis, and itching.

Vegetable Oils:

Coconut Oil (fractionated) is distilled from pure coconut oil. It is colorless, odorless, never goes rancid, and is easily washed out from fabrics.

Wheatgerm Oil is rich in lecithin, vitamin E, and B vitamins. Protects skin from free radical damage. Moisturizing and noncomedogenic.

Grape Seed Oil is light-textured, odorless, and nourishing to the skin.

Almond Oil is high in vitamin E and phytonutrients. Highly nourishing to the skin, it protects cell membranes from oxidative damage.

Olive Oil is rich in cell-protecting phytonutrients and antioxidants like squalene.

Essential Oils:

Wintergreen (*Gaultheria procumbens*) contains a cortisone-like compound that combats pain from sore bones, muscles, and joints.

Juniper (*Juniperus osteosperma* and *J. scopulorum*) detoxifies and cleanses.

Marjoram (*Origanum majorana*) reduces pain and inflammation in sore muscles; antiseptic.

Red Thyme (*Thymus vulgaris*) is powerfully antiviral, antimicrobial, and antibacterial. It is also rubefacient or warming to the skin.

Vetiver (*Vetiveria zizanioides*) is an anti-inflammatory that soothes joint and muscle pain.

Peppermint (*Mentha piperita*) cooling and invigorating, it blocks pain and itching. (Gobel et al., 1996). Antifungal and antibacterial.

Eucalyptus globulus is antibacterial and anti-fungal.

Eucalyptus radiata stimulates circulation.

Lemongrass (*Cymbopogon flexuosus*) has powerful antifungal properties that were documented in the journal *Phytotherapy Research*.

Ortho Sport

An anti-inflammatory and pain-killing complex of vegetable and essential oils. Ideal for strained, swollen, or torn muscles and ligaments. It has a higher phenol content than Ortho Ease and produces a greater warming sensation.

Vegetable Oils:

Coconut Oil (fractionated) is distilled from pure coconut oil. It is colorless, odorless, never goes rancid, and is easily washed out from fabrics.

Wheatgerm Oil is rich in lecithin, vitamin E, and B vitamins. Protects skin from free radical damage. Moisturizing and noncomedogenic.

Grape Seed Oil is light-textured, odorless, and nourishing to the skin.

Olive Oil is rich in cell-protecting phytonutrients and antioxidants like squalene.

Almond Oil is high in vitamin E and phytonutrients. Highly nourishing to the skin, it protects cell membranes from oxidative damage.

Essential Oils:

Wintergreen (*Gaultheria procumbens*) contains a cortisone-like compound that combats pain from sore bones, muscles, and joints.

Oregano (*Origanum vulgare*) is high in carvacrol, a potent anti-inflammatory.

Red Thyme (*Thymus vulgaris*) is powerfully antiviral, antimicrobial, and antibacterial. It is also rubefacient or warming to the skin.

Peppermint (*Mentha piperita*) cooling and invigorating, it blocks pain and itching. (Gobel et al., 1996). Antifungal and antibacterial.

Eucalyptus globulus is a powerful antimicrobial agent, rich in eucalyptol (a key ingredient in many antiseptic mouth rinses). It also repels insects. Can be cooling on the skin.

Lemongrass (*Cymbopogon flexuosus*) has pain-killing and antifungal actions.

Vetiver (*Vetiveria zizanioides*) is an anti-inflammatory that soothes joint and muscle pain.

Elemi (*Canarium luzonicum*) used in Europe for hundreds of years in salves for skin and celebrated healing ointments. Elemi belongs to the same botanical family as frankincense and myrrh. Antiseptic and antimicrobial, it is widely regarded today for soothing sore muscles, protecting skin, and stimulating nerves.

Relaxation Massage Oil

Promotes relaxation and eases tension.

Vegetable Oils:

Coconut Oil (fractionated) is distilled from pure coconut oil. It is colorless, odorless, never goes rancid, and is easily washed out from fabrics.

Grape Seed Oil is light-textured, odorless, and nourishing to the skin.

Almond Oil is high in vitamin E and phytonutrients. Highly nourishing to the skin, it protects cell membranes from oxidative damage.

Wheatgerm Oil is rich in lecithin, vitamin E, and B vitamins. Protects skin from free radical damage. Moisturizing and noncomedogenic.

Olive Oil is rich in cell-protecting phyto-nutrients and antioxidants like squalene.

Essential Oils:

Tangerine (*Citrus nobilis*) is soothing for anxiety and nervousness.

Rosewood (*Aniba rosaeodora*) is soothing and nourishing to the skin. Weber State University has documented its antibacterial action.

Spearmint (*Mentha spicata*) oil helps support the respiratory and nervous systems. Its hormone-like activity may help open and release emotional blocks and bring about a feeling of balance.

Peppermint (*Mentha piperita*) cooling and invigorating, it blocks pain and itching. (Gobel et al., 1996). Antifungal and antibacterial.

Ylang ylang (*Cananga odorata*) is calming and brings about a sense of relaxation.

Lavender (*Lavandula angustifolia*) is highly regarded for the skin. Excellent for burns and for cleansing cuts, bruises, and skin irritations, it is uniquely calming and relaxing.

Sensation Massage Oil

Inspires the senses and promotes feelings of youthfulness and passion. Leaves skin feeling silky and youthful

INGREDIENTS:

Grape Seed Oil—light-textured and odorless, it is nourishing to the skin and is an excellent carrier for essential oils

Sweet Almond Oil—reduces friction and promotes smooth application during massage

Wheatgerm Oil—a rich and lush-textured oil high in lecithin, vitamin E, and B vitamins

Vitamin E—protects skin and cell membranes against oxidative damage

ESSENTIAL OILS:

Rosewood (*Aniba rosaeodora*) is soothing and nourishing to the skin. It has been researched at Weber State University for its inhibition rate against gram positive and gram negative bacterial growth.

Ylang Ylang (*Cananga odorata*) is extremely effective in calming and bringing about a sense of relaxation

Jasmine Absolute (*Jasminum officinale*) is beneficial for dry, oily, irritated, or sensitive skin. It can also be uplifting and stimulating in ties of hopelessness and nervous exhaustion.

V-6 Enhanced Vegetable Oil Complex

A complex of nourishing, antioxidant vegetable oils that is colorless and odorless. It is the ideal carrier for essential oils. It is non-staining to almost all materials and has a long shelf-life.

Vegetable Oils:

Coconut Oil (fractionated) is distilled from pure coconut oil. It is colorless, odorless, never goes rancid, and is easily washed out from fabrics.

Olive Oil is rich in cell-protecting phytonutrients and antioxidants like squalene.

Sesame Seed Oil contains powerful phyto-nutrients and is nourishing to the skin.

Almond Oil is high in vitamin E and phytonutrients. Highly nourishing to the skin, it protects cell membranes from oxidative damage.

Sunflower Seed Oil is compatible with the skin's natural oils and sebum.

Wheatgerm Oil is rich in lecithin, vitamin E, and B vitamins. Protects skin from free radical damage. Moisturizing and noncomedogenic.

Grape Seed Oil is light-textured, odorless, and nourishing to the skin.

SECTION 4

CHAPTER 9

Ningxia Wolfberry

OVERVIEW AND HISTORY

Chinese Olympic swimmer Wu Yanyan had a secret. A secret only her coach and a few selected confidants knew about

In 1997 she stunned the world when she leapt from outside the world's top 50 rankings to set new world records in the 200-meter and 400-meter swimming competitions. So amazing was Wu Yanyan's jump in performance at the National Games in Shanghai that critics were attributing it to the fact that she, like many of her fellow Chinese swimmers, was doping with dehydrotestosterone (DHT). But in truth, Wu Yanyan had been tested for drugs over 10 times in the previous 12 months and showed no evidence of any illegal hormones.

As further evidence, Wu pointed out she had ranked in the top 15 swimmers from 1993 to 1996 and was indisputably clean of drugs even as seven fellow Chinese swimmers tested positive for drug use during the 1994 Asian Games in Hiroshima.

So what was the secret of Wu Yanyan's sudden world-beating performance? The Ningxia Wolfberry.

According Wu Yanyan, "We Chinese have traditional medicinal herbs which help us recover quickly. This is something you people in the West don't understand." Her coach, Wu Jicai, a year or two before, had started her on a broth of Chinese wolfberry and walnuts. And the results exceeded even her most optimistic projections. [1,2]

Geography and Botany

Native to the Ningxia Hui Autonomous Region of northern China, Lycium barbarum L. is a small red medicinal berry that is known as Fructus lycii or wolfberry in the West and Di gu zi, Kei Tze and Gou qi zi (Goji) throughout Asia.

Only 10 Chinese Lycium species exist in China. Of these, 7 species, 3 varieties, and 35 cultivars are found in Northern China. The most highly esteemed for its medicinal and healing properties is *Lycium barbarum L*. The rest are considered inferior or second-rate.

Lycium barbarum L is grown only in a small area of northern China near the Yellow River: the Ningxia Hui Autonomous Region and the Xinjiang Uygur Autonomous Region.

Olympic Athletes' Secret Weapon

- Chinese wolfberry has been declared a "national treasure" by the China State Scientific and Technological Commission.
- Ma Junren, coach of many world record holding distance runners, uses wolfberries to help runners achieve greatness.
- Wu Jicai, coach of Olympic swimmers, uses wolfberries as his "secret weapon".

Ningxia Hui Autonomous Region

Location: North West China near Inner Mongolia.

Size: The size of the state of Texas.

Elevation: 1000 meters above sea level, with many farms surrounding the plateau along the Yellow River.

Population: 1.78 million people, mostly Muslim. The Ningxia people have almost 30 times the number of 100-year-olds (centenarians) as the rest of China.

Climate: A semi-arid climate featuring hot summers (up to 92 F) and cold winters (down to -5 F).

Diet: The Muslims of Yongning County eat mutton or beef once a week, rice, fresh vegetables, pancakes, green tea, red jujubes, raisins, and wolfberries on a daily basis.

Lycium chinense Miller, a closely related but nevertheless distinct species of wolfberry, is slightly inferior to the Ningxia wolfberry in both nutrient content and bioactive properties. It is grown in Ningxia, Gansu, Hebei, Nei Monggol, Qinghai, Shanxi, and other locations in Northern China.[3]

In 2001 and 2002 Young Living compared antioxidant values of the Ningxia wolfberry with the other Chinese wolfberries. While they both ranked well above any known nutrient, the *Lycium chinense* had a significantly lower ORAC score (202 µmTE/g) than did the *Lycium barbarum* (303 µmTE/g).

Why is the Wolfberry Unknown in the West?

Both *Lycium barbarum L.* and *Lycium chinense* Miller have been used as a dietary staple for thousands of years in Northern China where people are known for their longevity.

For most of their long history, the Ningxia people of the west elbow plateau of the Yellow

River have been relatively isolated from the rest of civilization. Nestled in a silt-water valley in Zhongning County in northern China, they have been protected for centuries by deserts and mountains and the enormous landmass of central China, which has shielded them from outside influences and cultures.

Wolfberry legends and records of ancient Chinese medicine reach back 5,000 years. The great folklore healer Shen Nung may have included wolfberry in the world's first pharmacopoeia printed about 475 B.C. A physician's handbook, Ben Zao Gen Mo, written during the Ming Dynasty documents ancient use of wolfberry.

The Ningxia wolfberry has been included in a number of Chinese herbal pharmacopoeias and is still prescribed for patients with deficiency of the liver (yin) and kidney (yin), diabetes, and vision problems.

The wolfberry remained unknown to the West because China kept its borders closed to foreigners for thousands of years. The Great Wall of China symbolizes that isolation, and it is for that reason that Beijing is known as The Forbidden City.

The Ningxia wolfberry has long been regarded as a national treasure by the native Chinese and for

Wolfberry Facts

The Ningxia wolfberry, *Lycium barbarum L.* is a member of the solanaceae family (nightshade). This botanical group includes a variety of other plants and foods including potatoes, tomatoes, peppers (Capsicum species), eggplant, paprika, and tobacco.

There are over 80 different *Lycium* species worldwide. In the United States, a distant species of Lycium known as "matrimony vine" is sprinkled throughout the Midwest.

Only 10 *Lycium* species exist in China. These include 7 species, 3 varieties, and 35 cultivars that are found throughout Northern China. The most highly esteemed for its medicinal and healing properties is *Lycium barbarum L.* and *Lycium Chinense Miller*. The rest are considered inferior or second-rate.

Only three species of *Lycium* berry are listed in World Economic Plants, the most authoritative source for herbs and plants traded in world commerce:
- *Lycium barbarum L.* (syn: Lycium halimifolium Mill. or Lycium vulgare)
- *Lycium chinense* Miller.
- *Lycium ferocissimum* Miers.

that reason has been used by Olympic coaches as their "secret weapon" to achieve gold-medal results.

Only the *barbarum* and *chinense* species of the wolfberry have thus far been studied for their therapeutic effects.

Siltwater Secrets

The Yellow River flood plain where the Ningxia wolfberry crop is concentrated derives its water from the Himalayan mountains. As the water flows through the mountain snowpack and lower Himalayan foothills, it becomes charged with an unprecedented assortment of minerals and organic nutrients. By the time it reaches the Ningxia province of Northern China it is a mineral-rich, superfertile siltwater, the likes of which is found nowhere else on earth.

In addition, studies on the plants grown in the region show an usually low level of lead and other heavy metals commonly found in many industrialized areas of the world.

The Ningxia region is called "China's herbal medicine valley" and wolfberries originating from the local farms are often accompanied by a "Green Certificate"—the equivalent of the USDA's organic certification. And the proof of the wolfberry's lack of heavy chemical treatments was verified when the whole dried wolfberry powder passed the FDA pesticide screen when Young Living first imported large-scale quantities in 1996.

The Myth of the "Tibetan" Wolfberry

Some marketers claim wolfberries originated in Tibet and have even concocted botanical names that combine unrelated plant species. In fact, no wolfberries are commercially grown in or near Tibet. In actual visits throughout the Himalayan foothills of Pakistan and China, we conducted dozens of interviews concerning the native diets and commonly grown botanical species and no one had ever heard of a "Tibetan" wolfberry. The only wolfberries available came from in or around Zhongning County in Northern China. Moreover, Tibetan materia medicas make no mention of lycium berries.

Wolfberries are native to slightly arid temperate regions and cannot grow over 5,500 feet in elevation. This is because a high altitude would create an early frost that stifles the buds needed to reproduce. Averaging over 12,000 feet in elevation from sea level, Tibet is not conducive to wolfberry cultivation on any scale. It may be possible that some distant but related Lycium species have adapted to the high altitude, but these scarce specimens would be very different from the commercially-cultivated Ningxia species and would not be feasible to harvest.

The wolfberry is so famous for its healing properties, that a two-week Chinese festival is centered around the wolfberry.*

BIOACTIVE BONANZA

In the mid 1980's when biochemists at the Ningxia Institute of Nutrition analyzed the Ningxia wolfberry (which is called Goji berry by native Chinese and *Lycium barbarum L.* by botanists), they found that it was a virtual vitamin capsule in the form of a fruit. Over 15 percent protein by weight, the wolfberry contains over 21 essential minerals, 18 amino acids, and substantial amounts of chromium. Levels of vitamins such as thiamin (vitamin B1), niacin (vitamin B3), and vitamin C were extraordinarily high.

To confirm these results, we commissioned an independant lab in the United States to run another

---

* The only two-week festival in the world that celebrates wolfberries is in China not Tibet. Moreover, the word "goji" is not Tibetan but Chinese. Other spurious reports allege that the wolfberry is connected to the Dalai Lama.

Vitamin A (iu) in 100 grams of Food[1]

Ningxia Wolfberries, dried [2]	12,600	Mangos, raw	3,894
Carrots, raw	12,035	Cantaloupe, raw	3,224
Turnip greens, frozen	7,975	Broccoli, florets, raw	3,000
Apricots, dried	7,240	Peaches, raw	535
Spinach, raw	6,720	Papayas, raw	284
kale, frozen	6,354	Kelp, raw	120
Peppers, red, raw	5,700	Strawberries, raw	25

1. U.S. Department of Agriculture, Agricultural Research Service. 2004. USDA National Nutrient Database for Standard Reference, Release 17.
2. Preliminary data from dried fruit of Ningxia wolfberry (Lycium barbarum) stored 1-3 years. Analysis performed by Eurofins Scientific, Petaluma, CA
3. Haytowitz DB, et al. USDA's National Food and Nutrient Analysis Program: Comparison of Old and New Carotenoid Values. Beltsville Human Nutrition Research Center, ARS, USDA, Beltsville, MD.

Vitamin C (mg) in 100 grams of Food[1]

Ningxia Wolfberries, dried[2]	148	Orange juice, raw	50
Parsley, raw	133	Cauliflower, raw	46
Kiwi fruit,, raw	98	Lemon juice, raw	46
Papayas, raw	62	Strawberries, frozen	41
Strawberries, raw	57	Tangerines, raw	31
Oranges, raw	53	Turnip greens, frozen	22
Lemons, raw	53	Pineapple, raw	15

1. U.S. Department of Agriculture, Agricultural Research Service. 2004. USDA National Nutrient Database for Standard Reference, Release 17.
2. Preliminary data from dried fruit of Ningxia wolfberry (Lycium barbarum) stored 1-3 years. Analysis performed by Industrial Labs, Denver, CO

Key Wolfberry Nutrients Compared with 14 other Foods[1]

	Cal[3]	Mg[4]	K[5]	Protein	Fiber	Vit B1	Vit B3	Vit C[6]
Ningxia Wolfberry, dried[2]	110	130	1600	16%	21.0%	27.00	88.00	148
Brown rice, raw	23	143	223	8%	3%	0.40	5.09	0
Walnuts, raw, English	98	158	441	15%	7%	0.34	1.13	1
Oats, raw	54	177	429	17%	11%	0.76	0.96	0
Figs, dried	162	68	680	3%	10%	0.09	0.62	1
Oranges, raw	40	10	181	1%	2%	0.09	0.03	53
Cottage cheese 1%	61	5	86	12%	0%	0.02	0.13	0
Beef Sirloin 1/4" fat, raw	7	22	341	21%	0%	0.07	6.56	0
Broccoli, raw	47	21	316	3%	3%	0.07	0.64	89
Raisins seeded	28	30	825	2%	7%	0.11	1.11	5
Whole egg raw	53	12	134	13%	0%	0.07	0.07	0
Yogurt plain, low fat	183	17	234	5%	0%	0.04	0.11	1
Barley raw	29	79	280	10%	16%	0.19	4.60	0
Dandelion Greens, raw	187	36	397	3%	3%	0.19	0.81	35
Strawberries, raw	16	13	153	1%	2%	0.02	0.39	58

1. All data per 100 grams. Source: U.S. Department of Agriculture, Agricultural Research Service. 2004. USDA National Nutrient Database for Standard Reference, Release 17. Nutrient Data Laboratory
2. Preliminary data from dried fruit of Ningxia wolfberry (Lycium barbarum) stored 1-3 years. Industrial Labs, Denver, CO
3. Cal = Calcium
4. Mg = Magnesium
5. K=Potassium

analysis. The results showed that Ningxia Wolfberries contained:

> 67 times the thiamin (vitamin B1) of brown rice
> 2 times the niacin (vitamin B3) of baker's yeast
> 3 times the vitamin C of raw oranges
> 5 times the calcium of raw cauliflower
> 2 times the beta carotene of raw spinach

> The fruits of *Lycium barbarum* have been used for thousands of years in traditional Chinese medicine and cuisine since *L. barbarum* is believed to be beneficial to the eyes, liver and kidney.
>
> —Man-Shan Yu et al., Laboratory of Neurodegenerative Diseases, University of Hong Kong.[4]

Highest Known Source in Vitamins B1 and B3

The Ningxia wolfberry is the richest known whole food source of natural vitamin B1 or thiamin. Thiamin is essential for proper energy production, carbohydrate metabolism, and thyroid function. Thiamin deficiencies can result in impaired carbohydrate burning and a decline in the energy hormone thyrotropin. The wolfberry also has 100 times the niacin (vitamin B3) as oat bran. Over two decades of research document the ability of niacin to support the heart.

Triple the Vitamin C of Raw Oranges

Just 100 grams of dried Ningxia wolfberries contain well over double the recommended daily allowance of vitamin C (ascorbic acid). The value of vitamin C for health has been well documented, with extensive research documenting its antioxidant and immune-enhancing properties.

Minerals: Key to Long Life

Minerals truly are the "Cinderellas" of the nutrition world because vitamins cannot be utilized by the body nor be assimilated without the aid of minerals. Moreover, the human body cannot manufacture a single mineral (unlike vitamins, some of which the body can manufacture on its own).

Minerals perform countless pivotal functions in the human body. Not only are they crucial to the electrolyte balance of our cells, which forms the foundation of health, but they also play essential roles in nerve conduction, muscle contraction, heart action, blood clotting, protein metabolism, bone and teeth formation, and enzyme activation. Every process of the body is dependent on minerals.

Minerals also constitute central components of some of the most powerful antioxidant compounds in the human body. The mineral zinc is instrumental in the formation of superoxide dismutase (SOD), a key enzymatic antioxidant that declines with age. SOD is responsible for deactivating the most prevalent and dangerous free radical in the body: superoxide.

Ningxia Wolfberries contain significant amounts of:

Calcium—Important for building bones; shown to help reduce body fat and lower the risk of some cancers.

Chromium (trivalent)—part of the Glucose Tolerance Factor, it enhances insulin sensitivity and makes it easier for glucose to enter the cell.

Magnesium—Reduces the risk of diabetes and cardiovascular disease; treats depression and headaches.

Potassium—Lowers blood pressure and is associated with improved longevity

Copper, Zinc, and **Manganese**—Essential for collagen development and blood vessel health; superoxide dismutase (SOD), one of the most vital antioxidant enzymes in the body. The most important of these processes are cellular respiration, cellular utilization of oxygen, DNA and RNA reproduction, maintenance of cell membrane integrity, and sequestration of free radicals.[5]

Balancing Minerals

Minerals must be properly balanced. For example, excess dietary calcium or copper can result in a zinc deficiency and poor immunity. Conversely zinc consumption in excess of 300 mg per day not only suppresses immunity but also contributes to copper depletion and anemia.[6]

Both the mineral *profile* and mineral *balance* of the Ningxia wolfberry is without equal in the plant kingdom, with magnesium to calcium ratios at almost 1:1, zinc to copper ratios at 2:1 and potassium to magnesium ratios at 8:1.

THIAMINE and NIACIN (mg) in 100g Food[1]

FOOD	Vitamin B-1	Vitamin B-3
Ningxia Wolfberry, dried[2]	27.00	88.00
Baker's Yeast	2.36	39.75
Oat bran	1.17	0.93
Sesame seeds	0.72	4.68
Pecans	0.66	1.17
Tomatoes, sun dried	0.53	9.05
Buckwheat, flour	0.42	6.15
Walnuts	0.34	1.13
Almonds	0.24	3.93
Salmon	0.22	6.67
Pinto beans	0.19	0.32
Barley, raw	0.19	4.60
Dandelion greens	0.13	0.51
Raisins	0.11	0.77
Oranges, raw	0.09	0.28
Spinach raw	0.08	0.72
Alfalfa seeds	0.08	0.48
Broccoli, raw	0.07	0.64
Egg, raw	0.07	1.44
Carrots, raw	0.07	0.98
Asparagus	0.07	1.04
Mangos, raw	0.06	0.58
Cauliflower, raw	0.06	0.53
Prunes, dried	0.05	1.88
Yogurt, plain skim	0.05	0.12
Turkey w/giblets boiled	0.03	7.00
Strawberries, raw	0.02	0.39

1. U.S. Department of Agriculture, Agricultural Research Service. 2004. USDA National Nutrient Database for Standard Reference, Release 17.
2. Preliminary data from dried fruit of Ningxia wolfberry (Lycium barbarum) stored 1-3 years. Analysis performed by Industrial Labs, Denver, CO

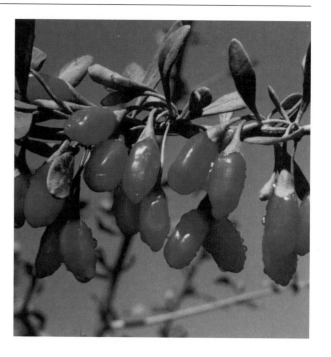

Potassium and Magnesium

Wolfberries are also rich in potassium and magnesium. A three-ounce serving of dried fruit contains nearly 1600 mg of potassium—which is quadruple the amount found in 3 oz. of fresh bananas, which is looked upon by many as a high-potassium food.

Potassium is the single most important mineral to human health and longevity, being essential for normal electrolyte and pH balance within the cell. When excess sodium begins to accumulate in conjunction with a potassium deficit, this can result in hypertension (high blood pressure) and high blood sugar, both of which can lead to lowered GABA production and exert a dampening effect on the hypothalamus and pituitary glands. This can directly contribute to subnormal growth hormone levels as we age.[7-9]

Calcium in 100 grams of Food[1]

Ningxia Wolfberry, dried[2]	110	Oat, bran, raw	59
Spinach, raw	100	Cabbage, red, raw	51
Walnuts, English	99	Raisins, seedless	49
Okra, frozen	96	Broccoli, raw	48
Kale	72	Brussels sprouts	36
Navy Beans	70	Cauliflower, raw	22
Cottage Cheese	61	Rice, brown, long-grain	10

1. U.S. Department of Agriculture, Agricultural Research Service. 2004. USDA National Nutrient Database for Standard Reference, Release 17.
2. Preliminary data from dried fruit of Ningxia wolfberry (Lycium barbarum) stored 1-3 years. Analysis performed by Industrial Labs, Denver, CO

Nutrients in 100 grams of Ningxia Wolfberry[1]		
Nutrient	Amount	RDA
Protein	15.6%	31.2
L-arginine	920 mg	
Fiber	21 g	84%
Fat	0.45 g	
Sugar	42 g	
Vitamin A	12,600 iu	250%
Vitamin B-1	27 mg	1800%
Vitamin B-3	88 mg	440%
Vita B-5	1.2 mg	12%
Vitamin C	148 mg	246%
Biotin	28 mcg	9%
Calcium	110 mg	11%
Chromium	79 mg	65%
Copper	1.1 mg	55%
Iron	11 mg	61%
Magnesium	130 mg	325%
Manganese	1.3 mg	65%
Potassium	1,600 mg	102%
Zinc	1.8 mg	12%

1. Preliminary data from dried fruit of Ningxia wolfberry (*Lycium barbarum*) stored 1-3 years

Our potassium deficit becomes more lopsided as we grow older and the kidneys become less and less able to effectively retain potassium and excrete sodium from the body. Researchers have estimated kidney function declines by up to 75% between age 30 and 80. [10,11]

A multi-year longitudinal study on aging clearly demonstrated that declining potassium levels are closely linked with signs of aging. Conducted over a period of nearly two decades, researchers followed 650 subjects and found that between age 40 and 60, potassium levels in the body dropped by over 13 percent. [12]

This decline in potassium levels coincides closely with the decline in GABA and growth hormone levels, suggesting that declining GABA, growth hormone, and potassium levels may be linked.

"Potassium alone or in combination with magnesium produced a significant reduction in systolic and diastolic blood pressures."

—*Patki et al., British Medical Journal*

"Increases in dietary potassium benefits several disease states. These include the treatment of hypertension, stroke prevention, arrhythmia prevention, and treatment of congestive heart failure."

—Steven Coco, Yale University School of Medicine

POTASSIUM (mg) in 100 grams of Food[1]			
Ningxia Wolfberry, dried[2]	1600	Lima beans	411
Apricots, dried	1377	Wheat flour, whole	405
Sunflower seed kernels	850	Kidney Beans, red	402
Raisins	751	Bananas, raw	395
Almonds	726	Prunes, dried	333
Figs, dried	713	Brussels sprouts, frozen	325
Dates, natural, dry	653	Broccoli, raw	325
Buckwheat flour, whole	576	Barley, pearled, raw	280
Oat bran, raw	565	Dandelion greens	232
Spinach, raw	556	Strawberries, raw	166
Walnuts, English	440		

1. U.S. Department of Agriculture, Agricultural Research Service. 2004. USDA National Nutrient Database for Standard Reference, Release 17.
2. Preliminary data from dried fruit of Ningxia wolfberry (*Lycium barbarum*) stored 1-3 years. Analysis performed by Industrial Labs, Denver, CO

Amino Acids in 100 grams Ningxia Wolfberry[1]			
Alanine	720 mg	Lysine	390 mg
Arginine	930 mg	Methionine	148 mg
Aspartate	2,100 mg	Phenylalanine	380 mg
Glutamine	1,400 mg	Proline	1.030 mg
Glycine	430 mg	Serine	640 mg
Histidine	270 mg	Threonine	460 mg
Isoleucine	350 mg	Tyrosine	160 mg
Leucine	630 mg	Valine	1040 mg

1. Preliminary data from dried fruit of Ningxia wolfberry (Lycium barbarum) stored 1-3 years. Analysis performed by Industrial Labs, Denver, CO.

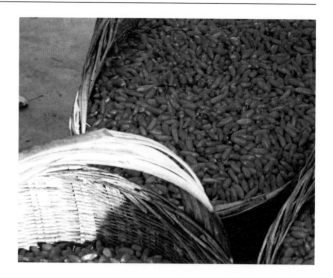

Increasing your intake of potassium can potentially slow the age-related decline of GABA and growth hormone. The Ningxia wolfberry is the highest-known, whole food source of whole food potassium.

High Protein Powerhouse

With a total of 15.6% protein by weight, the Ningxia wolfberry has more protein than bee pollen. It is rich in the amino acids L-arginine and L-glutamine. Wolfberry contains 1.4% of the branched chain amino acid L-leucine as well as significant amounts of tyrosine which is a key building block for dopamine production. Dopamine is an essential neurotransmitter in the brain that decreases with age.

While the Recommended Daily Allowance for protein is 63 grams for men and 50 grams a day for women. Tufts University researchers showed that a mild protein deficiency can contribute to muscle wasting in older people. According to Dr. Carmen Sceppa, "We randomly chose to study two-thirds of the RDA and found it is not enough; it still contributes to muscle loss."

Experts estimate that the average person loses about six to seven pounds of muscle with every decade of life after age 30, and that the rate of protein loss accelerates after age 45. Age-related muscle loss is known as sarcopenia.[13]

Canada's Population Health Research Institute recently found that people who ate the most protein (greater than 17.4% of dietary calories) had the slimmest waists and lowest waist to hip ratios (WHR). Those with the most abdominal fat consumed the least protein (less than 16% of dietary calories) and had over double the risk of diabetes and heart disease mortality.[14,15]

L-Arginine (grams) per 100 grams of Food[1]			
Halibut	1.60	Oatmeal bread	0.40
Egg yolk, raw	1.10	Tomatoes, sun dried	0.34
Buckwheat, flour	0.94	Broccoli raw	0.19
Ningxia Wolfberry, dried[2]	0.93	Yogurt, plain, skim milk	0.17
Shiitake mushroom	0.65	Spinach raw	0.16
Bulgur, dry	0.58	Asparagus frozen	0.14
Cottage Cheese, 1% fat	0.57	Dates, dried	0.14
Pinto beans	0.50	Cauliflower, raw	0.10
Barley, raw	0.50	Figs, dried	0.08
Raisins seedless	0.41	Apricots dried	0.07

1. U.S. Department of Agriculture, Agricultural Research Service. 2004. USDA National Nutrient Database for Standard Reference, Release 17.
2. Preliminary data from dried fruit of Ningxia wolfberry (Lycium barbarum) stored 1-3 years. Analysis performed by Industrial Labs, Denver, CO

Arginine

The Ningxia wolfberry contains almost 1% of the amino acid L-arginine by weight—more than many other food. L-arginine has been shown to have numerous biological effects, ranging from reducing blood pressure, stimulating growth hormone, and improving circulation to combat diabeties and boosting immunity.

Glycemic Index* of Selected Foods	
	Glycemic Index
Glucose	100
Brown Rice	66
Millet	72
Buckwheat	54
Ningxia Wolfberry	29

* Measures the speed with which a food raises blood sugar levels. The higher the fiber content of the food, the slower its effect on blood sugar levels.

Fiber: The Staff of Life?

With over 21% fiber by weight, the Ningix wolfberry has more fiber than oat bran and double the fiber of buckwheat. In fact, the Ningxia wolfberry has one of the highest percentages of fiber of any whole food.

High intake of fiber is directly correlated with:

- **Lower risk of cancer.** Fiber speeds up the intestinal flow, minimizing exposure to harmful substances. This is especially important if animal products are consumed.

- **Better control of blood sugar levels.** High fiber foods have low glycemic indexes and can help balance and lower blood sugar levels. High blood sugar can damage arteries, lead to cardiovascular disease, macular degeneration, hypertension, and kidney failure.

- **Lower risk of heart disease.** Fiber and minerals are required for the proper metabolism of fats and elimination of excess cholesterol.

Plant fiber has been repeatedly shown to be very effective in controlling blood sugar levels in diabetics. In one study, 20 diabetic men were switched from a high-fat, western-type diet to a high-fiber diet. In less than 17 days, 55 percent of these men were able to discontinue insulin injections, and the majority of the rest drastically reduced their insulin dosages. Even more noteworthy, along with the drop in blood sugar levels, the men experienced a concomitant plunge in average cholesterol levels—from 208 to 147.

The Ningxia wolfberry is also rich in soluble fiber, which is highly efficient in removing triglycerides and cholesterol from the blood and lowering the risk of heart disease. Numerous studies have linked a high intake of soluble fiber with lowered blood pressure and improved cardiovascular health. [16-21]

Cholesterol is one of the few compounds in the body that cannot be broken down into smaller components and excreted (in contrast, sugars, amino acids, and fatty acids are all converted into

Fiber (grams) in 100 grams of Food[1]			
Ningxia wolfberry dried[2]	21.0	Oatmeal Bread	4.0
Barley, raw	15.6	Raisins	3.7
Oat bran, raw	15.4	Turnip greens	3.5
Tomatoes, sun dried	12.3	Rice, brown long-grain raw	3.5
Almonds	11.8	Carrots, raw	2.8
Buckwheat flour	10.0	Cauliflower, raw	2.5
Apricots, dried	7.3	Brussels sprouts	2.6
Pinto Beans	9.0	Broccoli, raw	2.6
Dates, dried	8.0	Apples, raw, with skin	2.4
Raspberries, raw	6.8	Oranges, raw,	2.4
Prunes, dried	7.1	Strawberries, raw	2.0
Walnuts	6.7	Spinach, raw	2.2
Wild rice, raw	6.2	Turnips	2.0

1. U.S. Department of Agriculture, Agricultural Research Service. 2004. USDA National Nutrient Database for Standard Reference, Release 17.
2. Preliminary data from dried fruit of Ningxia wolfberry (Lycium barbarum) stored 1-3 years. Analysis performed by Industrial Labs, Denver, CO

Other Bioactive Components of Ningxia Wolfberry

Acyclic diterpene glycosides[1]	Monomenthyl succinate [2]
Alpha carotene [7,8]	Monoterpene glycosides [2]
Betaine [5,10]	P-coumaric acid [5]
Beta-D-Glucopyranosyl ascorbate [3]	Polyphenols [14]
Beta sitosterol [5]	Polysaccharides [6,11]
Beta cryptoxanthin [7,8]	Pyrroles
Cerebrosides [9]	Scopoletin [5,12]
Cyclic peptides [1]	Taurine [15]
Daucosterol [5]	Vanillic acid [12]
Ellagic Acid [14]	Withanolides [13]
Lutein [7,8]	Zeaxanthin dipalmitate [4,7,8]

1. Yahara S, et al., Cyclic peptides, acyclic diterpene glycosides and other compounds from Lycium chinense Mill. Chem Pharm Bull (Tokyo). 1993 Apr;41(4):703-9.
2. Hiserodt RD, et al. Identification of monomenthyl succinate, monomenthyl glutarate, and dimenthyl glutarate in nature by high performance liquid chromatography-tandem mass spectrometry. J Agric Food Chem. 2004 Jun 2;52(11):3536-41.
3. Toyoda-Ono Y et al., 2-O-(beta-D-Glucopyranosyl)ascorbic acid, a novel ascorbic acid analogue isolated from Lycium fruit. J Agric Food Chem. 2004 Apr 7;52(7):2092-6.
4. Weller P, Breithaupt DE. Identification and quantification of zeaxanthin esters in plants using liquid chromatography-mass spectrometry. J Agric Food Chem. 2003 Nov 19;51(24):7044-9.
5. Xie C et al., Studies on chemical constituents in fruit of Lycium barbarum L.. Zhongguo Zhong Yao Za Zhi. 2001 May;26(5):323-4.
6. Huang LJ, Tian GY, Ji GZ. Structure elucidation of glycan of glycoconjugate LbGp3 isolated from the fruit of Lycium barbarum L. J Asian Nat Prod Res. 1999;1(4):259-67.
7. Li Z, Peng G, Zhang S. Separation and determination of carotenoids in Fructus lycii by isocratic non-aqueous reversed-phase liquid chromatography. Se Pu. 1998 Jul;16(4):341-3.
8. Analysis by Eurofins Scientific, Pelalum, CA.
9. Kim SY, et al., LCC, a cerebroside from Lycium chinense, protects primary cultured rat hepatocytes exposed to galactosamine. Phytother Res. 2000 Sep;14(6):448-51.
10. Shin YG, et al.,Determination of betaine in Lycium chinense fruits by liquid chromatography-electrospray ionization mass spectrometry. J Chromatogr A. 1999 Oct 1;857(1-2):331-5.
11. Peng X, Tian G. Structural characterization of the glycan part of glycoconjugate LbGp2 from Lycium barbarum L. Carbohydr Res. 2001 Mar 9;331(1):95-9.
12. Hansel R, Huang JT. Lycium chinense, III: isolation of scopoletin and vanillic acid. Arch Pharm (Weinheim). 1977 Jan;310(1):38-40.
13. Hansel R, Huang JT, Rosenberg D. Two withanolides from Lycium chinense. Arch Pharm (Weinheim). 1975 Aug;308(8):653-4.
14. Brunswick Laboratories, Wareham, MA. 2005
15. Xie H, Zhang S. Determination of taurine in Lycium barbarum L. by high performance liquid chromatography with OPA-urea pre-column derivatization. Se Pu. 1997 Jan;15(1):54-6.

water, carbon dioxide, and ammonia for elimination). The only mechanism by which cholesterol can be flushed from the body is through bile acids. However, if feces lack sufficient fiber, cholesterol is not sufficiently excreted, forcing the remainder to be recirculated in the gall bladder.

More than Vitamins, Minerals, and Amino Acids

The Ningxia wolfberry is more than just a whole food multivitamin; it also contains a virtual cornucopia of exotic and unique phytonutrients that have been shown to protect the liver, eyes, heart and cellular DNA from age-related deterioration and disease.

It also contains powerful immune-boosting compounds known as lycium polysaccharides, a distant relative of the unusual long-chain sugars found in *Echinacea purpurea*, maitake mushrooms, and other immune-building herbs.

Carotenoids

The Ningxia wolfberry is rich in a broad spectrum of carotene-like substances known as carotenoids. Beta carotene is only one member of this family of nutrients. So far more than half a dozen have been studied for their powerful therapeutic effects and over 18 different carotenoids have been identified in human blood. [22]

Carotenoid (Xanthophyll) Content of Ningxia Wolfberry*

Alpha carotene	101 μg
Beta carotene	23 μg
Lutein	2.1 μg
Zeaxanthin	278 μg
Beta-cryptoxanthin	32 μg

*Preliminary data from dried fruit of Ningxia wolfberry (Lycium barbarum) stored 1-3 years. Analysis by Eurofins Scientific, Petaluma, CA.

Even though some of these carotenoids have no vitamin A activity, they have far greater health benefits than ordinary beta carotene. In many studies they have been shown to have far more pronounced anti-cancer and cell-protective activity than ordinary beta carotene.

Hoyoku Nashino, PhD, a Molecular Biologist at the Kyoto Prefectural University of Medicine in Japan, underscored that it is the complete carotenoid complex, not just isolated beta carotene, which exerts cancer protective properties. "Various carotenoids which co-exist with beta-carotene in vegetables and fruits," emphasized Dr. Nashino, "have anti-carcinogenic activity. And some of them, such as alpha-carotene, showed higher potency than beta-carotene to suppress experimental carcinogenesis."[23]

Zeaxanthin and **lutein** have been shown to protect against skin cancer and protect the eyes against such diseases as age-related macular degeneration, the most common cause of blindness in older people.

Beta-cryptoxanthin has been shown to inhibit cancer. It has also been researched for stimulating bone growth and linked to an 18% reduced incidence of glaucoma in a Harvard study.[24-30]

"Although smoking is the strongest risk factor for lung cancer," stated Harvard epidemiologist Satu Männistö, PhD, "greater intake of foods high in beta-cryptoxanthin, such as citrus fruit, may modestly lower the risk."[31]

Männistö's colleagues at USC agree. According to Jian-Min Yuan, PhD, a researcher at the University of Southern California Keck School of Medicine in Los Angeles, "High prediagnostic serum beta-cryptoxanthin levels have been found to be associated with reduced risk of lung cancer."[32]

The wolfberry also contains zeaxanthin, which is a pigment concentrated in the eye. Lower levels of zeaxanthin are linked to age-related blindness. German scientists have identified a special type of highly bioavailable zeaxanthin in Ningxia wolfberry known as zeaxanthin dipalmitate. "Dried wolfberries (*Lycium barbarum*) proved to be valuable zeaxanthin ester sources," states Peter Weller, a biochemist at Hohenheim University in Stuttgart, Germany. Zeaxanthin dipalmitate has been shown to not only protect against eye diseases but also defend against liver damage.[33,34]

Ellagic Acid and Polyphenols

According to a July, 2001, analysis at Brunswick Labs, the Ningxia wolfberry contains 86 mg of ellagic acid and 1309 mg of phenolics per 100 grams, one of the highest of any food yet tested. The anti-cancer and detoxifying properties of ellagic acid are well researched.

Cerebrosides and Pyrroles

In 1998, Korean researchers discovered special compounds in wolfberries that afford powerful protection for the most important organ in the human body: the liver. Known as pyrroles and cerobrosides, these nutrients have been shown to protect the liver against chemical-induced and hepatitis damage.[35-37]

Polysaccharides

The Ningxia wolfberry ranks highest in its content of a unique protein-sugar complex known as a lycium polysaccharide. Also known as a

---

Lycium Polysaccharide: A Challenge to Isolate

In 1992 researchers in China identified the structure of this protein-sugar polysaccharide. A very large molecule with an atomic weight 88,000 daltons (88kD (kilodaltons), this polysaccharide complex is 250 times heavier than an atom of gold and 2750 times larger than an atom of oxygen. Scientists have found that 30% of this polysaccharide is protein and 70% is a long-chain complex sugar linked by a variety of different chemical bonds.

This large molecule has an intricate structure that makes it very challenging to study. This is because it readily breaks into a huge number of random smaller fragments when subjected to intense heat or light.

This makes creating a uniform extract of the polysaccharide from the wolfberry outlandishly difficult. In fact, one researcher in China attempted to base his doctoral thesis on the polysaccharide, but gave up after he encountered formidable difficulties in identifying a unique spectrum of breakdown products from the polysaccharide. He found that a difference of only one or two degrees Celsius resulted in a very different spectra of polysaccharide fragments.

Currently only one manufacturer in China has developed the expertise to obtain a consistant, low-temperature water extraction of the polysaccharide from the Ningxia wolfberry.

glycoconjugate, this low-glycemic polysaccharide is only found in *Lycium barbarum* and in lesser amounts in *Lycium chinense*.

During the last 15 years, a number of studies have documented the cardioprotective, anti-cancerous and immune-stimulating properties of the wolfberry polysaccharide.[38-40]

The polysaccharide may also lower blood sugar levels, reduce glycated hemoglobin, and protect the pancreas according to studies at the College of Public Health at Wuhan University and elsewhere.[41]

All Sugars Are Not Equal

The dried wolfberries used extensively by the Ningxia people have been shown to have one of the lowest glycemic indexes of any food. A glycemic index measures the impact on blood sugar levels two hours after ingestion. The lower the glycemic index, the lower the rise in blood sugar levels.

At first glance it would seem counter-intuitive that a dried berry with little water would have such a modest impact on serum blood sugar. But recent clinical studies have found that the dried berry has a glycemic index of only 29, which is two-thirds lower than glucose and 50% less than white bread or boiled potatoes.

The consumption of low glycemic foods is very important for minimizing the insidious degenerative damage generated by long-term elevated blood sugar levels, which are strenuous to the heart, kidneys, pancreas and circulatory system. Over time, the injury can become cumulative and shave years off of life.

Sugars found in Ningxia wolfberry	
Arabinose	0%
Galactose	4.3%
Rhamnose	1.03%
Xylose	13.3%
Mannose	14.8%
Glucose	62.7%
Huang L, et al.,. Isolation, purification and physico-chemical properties of immunoactive constituents from the fruit of Lycium barbarum L. Yao Xue Xue Bao. 1998 Jul;33(7):512-6.	

Synergy: 1 + 1 = 3

Ultimately it may be the synergy of all of these nutrients that is responsible for the Ningxia wolfberry's ability to support so many different functions of the body. According to Cornell University biochemist, Riu Liu, PhD, "The additive and synergistic effects of phytochemicals in fruits and vegetables are responsible for these potent antioxidant and anti-cancer activities. This explains why no single antioxidant can replace the combination of natural phytochemicals in fruits and vegetables to achieve the health benefits."[42]

AN ASTOUNDING ANTIOXIDANT

Oxidative stress to the body has been linked to diseases ranging from cancer to heart disease. Oxidative damage can also vastly accelerate the cellular destruction that occurs with diabetes.

This is why preserving the antioxidant status in the body is of enormous concern. The simplest way to maximize antioxidant levels is to follow a diet high in antioxidant foods.

Wolfberry Polysaccharide Blocks Free Radical Damage by Increasing SOD

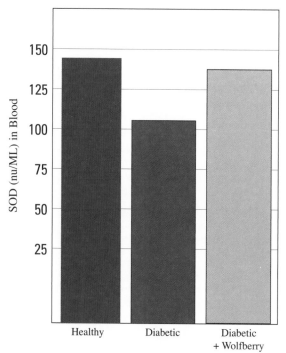

Clinical Studies

A recent study published in June 2006 found that the consuming Ningxia wolfberry polysaccharies was able to almost completely reverse the DNA and oxidative damage caused by diabetes. Researchers at the School of Public Health in Fudan Univeristy in Shanghai found that feeding animals just 10 mg per day of the Wolfberry polysaccharide (the human

Top Antioxidant Foods

	ORAC[2] (umTE/g)
Ningxia wolfberry, dried[3]	303
Chinese wolfberry, dried	202
Acai	184
Black Raspberry	164
Pomegranate	105
Ningxia wolfberry, fresh[4]	95
Prune	57
Blackberry	51
Boysenberry	35
Blueberry	32
Plum	28
Red Raspberry	27
Strawberry	26
Orange	24
Cherry	21
Raisin	21
Garlic	19
Kale	18
Raspberry	16
Apple	14
Peach	13
Spinach	12
Red Grape	11
Brussels Sprouts	9
Alfalfa Spouts	9
Broccoli florets	9
Kiwi	9
Beet	8
Onion	4
Cauliflower	4
Mango	3
Cabbage	3
Banana	3
Apple	3
Tomato	2
Carrot	2

1. All foods are fresh unless otherwise noted with "dried."
2. Oxygen Radical Absorbance Capacity
3. Data from dried fruit stored 1-3 years. Analysis performed by Brunswick Labs, Wareham, MA
4. Analysis performed by Brunswick Labs, Wareham, MA

ORAC and Tufts University

According to a test known as ORAC (Oxygen Radical Absorbance Capacity) developed by USDA researchers at Tufts University, the Ningxia wolfberries are the highest known antioxidant food, possessing an unmatched ability to absorb injurious free radicals that attack the body.

Developed by Dr. Guohoa Cao at the USDA Human Nutrition Research Center on Aging at Tufts University, the ORAC test is one of the most sensitive and reliable methods for assessing the ability of antioxidants to absorb oxygen radicals. It is the only test to combine both time and degree of inhibition of free radicals.[44-45]

equivalent is about 2600 mg) resulted in dramatic drops in the markers of tissue and blood damage caused by free radicals.[43]

Some of the most delicate cells of the body are the reproductive cells, which are extremely vulnerable to oxidative damage. Even small amounts of DNA damage to progenitor cells can result in birth defects and death in the offspring.

Researchers at the University of Hong Kong tested the ability of Lycium barbarum polysaccharides to protect male reproductive cells from heat stress. Some of the most sensitive cells to heat are sperm-making cells in the male scrotum. One cohort of a large group of randomly selected male rats were assigned to have their testicles submerged in hot water (43C) for 15 minutes--sufficient to cause significant oxidative damage to the DNA-loaded cells. Then other groups of animals were assigned different daily dosages of wolfberry for 14 days: 10, 50, 100, and 200 mg per kilo of body weight). Following the treatment, cells were analyzed for SOD levels and cellular damage using an MDA test. In addition, testosterone levels in the serum was also measured along with other hormones such as leutinizing hormone (LH) and follicle-stimulating hormone (FSH).

Results? Wolfberry was most effective at the lowest dosage, suggesting that very little is required to trigger meaningful health-protective effects.

Amazingly, even in heat-stressed animals, testosterone levels actually soared past the levels of the normal, unstressed animals. Similarly both LH and FSH rebounded past levels of those healthy subjects.

	SOD	MDA	Testosterone	LH	FSH
Normal Animals	302	0.78	24.35	11.09	4.19
Heat-stressed only	206	2.78	16.09	8.71	2.92
Heat-stresssed plus 10 mg/kg per day	387	1.11	27.05	12.60	4.71

On an antioxidant level, levels of MDA, a marker of tissue damage, dropped in all of the wolfberry-treated subjects. SOD, an enzyme that deactivates damaging superoxide free radicals in the blood, also increased in the treated animals.[46]

New Test Measures Antioxidant Levels of Common Foods

In 1994, a Tufts University scientist working for U.S. Department of Agriculture developed a powerful new method of assaying the antioxidant activity of common foods. Using a vitamin E analogue known as Trolox, Dr. Guohoa Cao created the Oxygen Radical Absorbance Capacity assay (ORAC) which could measure a food's free-radical fighting capacity. It was the first test to quantify both duration and degree of antioxidant activity.[47]

The ORAC assay is currently the most sensitive and reliable method commonly used for calculating a food's antioxidant potential against the peroxyl free radical, the second most common in the human body.

Wolfberry Analyzed by USDA Antioxidant Test

In October of 2000, Young Living Essential Oils researcher Marc Schreuder contacted a colleague at Ohio State University to locate a laboratory that could perform an ORAC assay on the Ningxia wolfberry. Marc was told that the only lab in the world currently using the Tufts University-developed ORAC protocol was Brunswick Laboratories in Wareham, Massachusetts.

By November Marc had submitted a sample of the dried Ningxia wolfberry to Dr. Wang at Brunswick for ORAC antioxidant analysis.

The results were astonishing. According to the ORAC results, dried Ningxia wolfberries had five times the antioxidant power of prunes, 10 times the antioxidant power of oranges, 12 times the antioxidant power of raisins, and 55 times the

Lifespan of SOD deficient mice vs. normal mice

antioxidant power of cauliflower. In fact, according to the published ORAC data, the dried Ningxia wolfberry had the highest known ORAC score for any whole food (303 µmTE/g).

As the most powerful antioxidant, the Ningxia wolfberry can aggressively block the free radical damage that leads to cellular mutation and cancer.

Antioxidants protect the body by blunting the damaging effects of free radicals produced during the burning of foods for energy, immune responses, and chemicals in the environment.

The most common free radicals in the body are created from oxygen. When oxidized, the normal oxygen in the air we breathe forms four different oxygen free radicals and two nitrogen free radicals all of which damage cell membranes and disrupt the DNA, the delicate cellular command center.

Over time, free-radical damage to the tissues and organs accumulates and the pace of cellular mutations accelerates, eventually reaching a point where the body cannot repair or dispose of damaged cells fast enough. This results in premature aging and cancer.

The Four Deadliest Free Radicals

Superoxide (O^{2-})

Superoxide is the most common free-radical in the body and the mother of many other free radicals, including hydroxyl and hydrogen peroxide radicals. A paired oxygen molecule that is burdened with an extra electron, superoxide attacks cell membranes, mitochondria, and chromosomes, thus destroying or mutating the cell. Superoxide is inactivated by superoxide dismutase (SOD) as well as by the antioxidants found in several types of berries.

Hydrogen Peroxide (H^{2}O^2)

Hydrogen peroxide is created when superoxide is deactivated. Less reactive than superoxide, it is eliminated by antioxidants, such as catalase (which works in water) or glutathione peroxidase (which works in fat). Hydrogen peroxide can damage the DNA inside the cell, which can lead to mutations and cancer. It can also oxidize the fats and promote atherosclerosis.

Hydroxyl Radical (HO$^-$)

The most reactive and toxic of all free radicals to protein, hydroxyl groups are created when hydrogen peroxide is not completely deactivated. Because of its reactivity, it can lead to a cascade of oxidative damage, causing a chain reaction of free-radical creation. Certain minerals like iron, cadmium, or mercury can stimulate hydrogen peroxide creation.

Singlet Oxygen (1O^2)

Oxygen almost always occurs in a paired state (O^2). When it is split apart, two highly reactive singlet oxygen molecules are formed. Excess singlet oxygen is implicated in several age-related diseases, including cataracts, macular degeneration, and arthritis.

ORAC and the Peroxyl Radical

The ORAC test developed at Tufts University measures one kind of free radical, the peroxyl (hydrogen peroxide) free radical. This is the second most common in the body. Since the advent of ORAC, Brunswick Labs also has developed additional tests to measure hydroxyl free radicals (HORAC) and peroxynitrite free radicals (NORAC). Recently, MIT-trained researchers succeeded in developing a new test that measures superoxide-scavenging activity: S-ORAC. Superoxide is the most prevalent and damaging free radical in the body and is responsible for generating other types of free radicals as well, such as hydrogen peroxide and hydroxyl radicals. Some have even dubbed superoxide the Mother of All Free Radicals. Some researchers believe that the S-ORAC test will ultimately replace the ORAC test as the test measures the total antioxidant activity.

Superoxide vs Life Expectancy

A January 2005 Stanford University study found that animals with the lowest levels of SOD, and therefore the weakest ability to scavenge superoxide free radicals, lived over 35% shorter lives than controls. A critical enzyme in the body known as superoxide dismutase (SOD) is essential to mopping up and deactivating superoxide. When this enzyme is deficient life expectancy drops dramatically and the rate of liver cancer soars.[48]

Ningxia wolfberry vs Superoxide

One of the earliest studies on the power of wolfberry to neutralize superoxide radicals was conducted in China in 1982. Fifty persons aged 64-80 were given 50 grams of wolfberries for 10 days. When their blood was evaluated, it showed that levels of the free-radical enzymatic antioxidant SOD (superoxide dismutase) leaped by 48%. In addition, lipid peroxides dropped by 65%.[49]

A study published in December 2004 by Kaohsiung Medical University in Taiwan indicates that the Ningxia wolfberry may indeed have strong superoxide-neutralizing activity.

Researchers found that depending on its concentration, a water extract of wolfberry scavenged from 28.8% to 82.2% superoxide radicals. The concentrations of wolfberry that inhibited 50% of the

> Animals with longer life spans appear to have higher levels of SOD to detoxify the free radical called superoxide.
>
> —Leonard Hayflick, Ph.D.

superoxide activity were tiny, ranging from 0.77 to 2.55 parts per million. In percentage this works out to be 0.000077% to 0.00025%. The minute concentrations used are indicative of the Ningxia wolfberry's exceptional superoxide neutralizing power.[50]

Stopping the Buildup of Rancid Fat in Your Tissues

One of the hallmarks of old age is the accumulation of oxidized or rancid fat in the body. Scientists measure this oxidative damage by checking for levels of malondialdehyde (MDA), a breakdown product from these oxidized fats.

Each of the 3 trillion cells of the human body has a cell membrane composed primarily of fats that is susceptible to oxidative damage. The cell also contains miniature furnaces or power plants (mitochondria) that are also housed in a membrane made of fat.

The most important part of the cell is its mitochondrial oxygen-burning furnace. As carbohydrates and oxygen are combusted here, free radical "sparks" shoot off that can damage the cell. Some of this damage occurs to the fats (lipids) that form the outer structure of both the mitochondria and the cell itself. When these fats become oxidized or "rancid," malondialdehyde (MDA) starts to build up. The more of these "lipid peroxides" and MDA that form, the more brittle the cell membrane becomes and the poorer the cell functions until eventually it self-destructs.

Protecting these fats from oxidative damage (or rancidity) is crucial for slowing down the damage that occurs with aging and keeping the machinery humming normally.

Another finding of the Kaohsiung Medical University study was that the Ningxia wolfberry extract possessed the strongest inhibition of all of medicines tested on reducing MDA levels in the livers of rats.

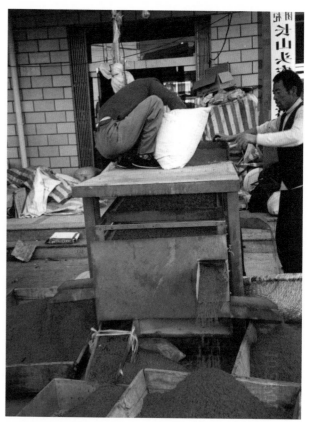

Grading and sorting the wolfberry harvest

An earlier study at the Department of Nutrition and Food Hygiene at the Ningxia Medical College had similarly found that Ningxia flavonoids prevented free radical damage to liver cells and red blood cells. In particular, the flavonoids lowered liver levels of MDA and prevented oxidation of fats in the red blood cells and the liver mitochondria. Amazingly the fluidity of the mitochondrial membrane was restored to a more youthful level.

What is notable about this study is that small concentrations of Ningxia wolfberry (between 0.025 and 2.0 mg/ml) were sufficient to produce significant effects.[51]

Reversing Aging in Animal Studies

Other studies have confirmed that Ningxia wolfberry has strong activity against the superoxide radical. A 2003 investigation by the Chinese Academy of Science tested the ability of Ningxia wolfberry polysaccharide (LBP) to reverse the effects of aging in three-month female mice who were dosed with a chemical that vastly accelerates the aging process, D-galactose.[52]

D-galactose was used because it mimics the type of damage typically seen in the elderly and diabetics.

To measure the animals' ability to resist aging, lead researcher Hong-Bin Deng used a number of tests, including an immunological assay, a memory test, and an AGE (advanced glycosylated end products) test. He also assayed serum levels of superoxide dismutase (SOD), which is the most important free-radical deactivator due to its function of quenching deadly superoxide radicals.

Hong-Bin Deng found that the wolfberry polysaccharide restored SOD levels in aging animals to that of more youthful levels. The polysaccharide also blunted the damaging effects of D-galactose on mental function and AGE levels in the tissues. In short, the wolfberry appeared to reverse aging in animals subjected to a chemical that hastened the onset of old age.

Ningxia wolfberry vs High Altitude Stress

A related study at the Faculty of Preventive Medicine at Ningxia Medicine College in Yinchuan tested SOD and catalase activity in a group of 56 mice who were subjected to oxidative stress caused by lack of oxygen. These "hypoxic" conditions were similar to what you would find at high altitudes. In a subgroup fed Ningxia wolfberry, both SOD and catalase activity jumped significantly compared with the control group.

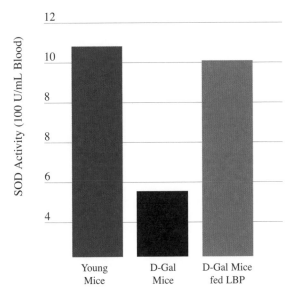

Wolfberry Polysaccharide stops SOD declines caused by accelerated aging

SOD Activity (100 U/mL Blood)

Young Mice — D-Gal Mice — D-Gal Mice fed LBP

Clinical Reports: Wolfberry vs Free Radicals

- Effect of Lycium barbarum polysaccharide on the improvement of antioxidant ability and DNA damage in NIDDM rats.--Wu H et al., 2006.

- Lycium barbarum polysaccharides: Protective effects against heat-induced damage of rat testes and H(2)O(2)-induced DNA damage in mouse testicular cells and beneficial effect on sexual behavior and reproductive function of hemicastrated rats.--Luo Q, et al., 2006

- Antioxidant activities of some common ingredients of traditional chinese medicine, Angelica sinensis, Lycium barbarum and Poria cocos. —Wu SJ, Ng LT, Lin CC. 2004

- Effect of wolfberry fruit and epimedium on DNA synthesis of the aging-youth 2BS fusion cells. —Wu BY et al., 2003

- Inhibiting effects of Achyranthes bidentata polysaccharide and Lycium barbarum polysaccharide on nonenzyme glycation in D-galactose induced mouse aging model. —Deng HB, et al., 2003

- Protective effect of Fructus Lycii polysaccharides against time and hyperthermia-induced damage in cultured seminiferous epithelium. —Wang Y et al., 2002

- Effect of lycium barbarum L on defending free radicals of mice caused by hypoxia. —Li G, et al., 2002

- The protective effects of total flavonoids from Lycium Barbarum L. on lipid peroxidation of liver mitochondria and red blood cell in rats. —Huang Y et al., 1999

- Scavenging effect of total flavonoids of lycium barbarum L on active oxygen radicals and inhibitory effects on heat output from L1210 cells. —Huang Y, et al., 1998

The simultaneous elevation of both these antioxidant enzymes is important because the two depend on each other to maximize their effectiveness. While SOD deactivates superoxide free radicals, catalase mops up hydrogen peroxide free radicals. The combination of the two working together is vital because SOD actually produces hydrogen peroxide as a byproduct of defusing superoxide. Catalase is one of the few enzymes capable of neutralizing hydrogen peroxide.[53]

Ningxia Wolfberry Extends Cell Life 21%

Gerontologists at the Department of Cell Biology and Genetics at Peking University discovered that including a vanishingly small amount of wolfberry (0.025%) in the culture medium could extend the number of times human lung cells could divide from 49 times to 61 times. Each time a cell divides, the chance of error creeps in, as well as the cumulative burden of oxidative damage. Using wolfberry in the nutrient broth, researchers effectively increased the lifespan of the lung tissue by 22%.[54]

An October 2002 study at the Department of Histology and Embryology at the Ningxia Medical College in Yinchuan tested the ability of Ningxia wolfberry to help sperm-producing cells resist damage from excess cold (hyperthermic conditions) and ultraviolet sunlight radiation. According to lead researcher, Wang, "We found that fructus lycii polysaccharide (FLPS) is a potent inhibitor of both of these reactions. Together, these results demonstrate the protective effect of FLPS on time and hyperthermia induced testicular degeneration in vitro."

This study is significant not only because of its implications for increased fertility (yes, it is true that Ningxia wolfberry extracts have been used for centuries to boost reproductive success), but the real significance of this study pertains to the antioxidant protection that Ningxia wolfberry affords to cells that are most vulnerable to oxidative damage: testicle cells. Reproductive cells are very easily damaged by cold stresses and UV radiation, so the ability of Ningxia wolfberry to effectively defend against these types of attacks shows the true measure of the berry's antioxidant potential.[55]

IMPROVING IMMUNITY

With a centuries-old tradition of stimulating vital energy, the Ningxia wolfberry has been shown in recent years to hold enormous promise as a non-inflammatory immune stimulant. It has been found to contain a number of powerful bioactive components that can elevate natural killer cell activity, interleukin-2, phagocytosis, and lymphocyte activation.

The best studied of these immunoactive compounds is a complex and high-molecular-weight glycoprotein known as the wolfberry polysaccharide or Lycium barbarum polysaccharide (LBP).[56]

Researchers have also identified a number of other carotenoids found in Ningxia wolfberry that can amplify immunity.

Healthy Immunity and Anti-aging

During the past two decades, a number of clinical studies have shown a direct link between cancer, accelerated aging, and poor immune function. In particular, a key weapon in our nonspecific immunity called a "natural killer" cell is very adept at automatically destroying suspicious looking cancer cells without requiring "education" in the immune glands of the body (ie, thymus). [57-68]

A 2002 study at the University of Milan documented a direct link between stress and inflammation and lowered natural killer cell activity and poorer outcomes in cancer cases.[69]

An earlier study published in the *International Journal of Cancer* showed that animals with higher levels of NK(Natural Killer) activity were able to suppress metastatic cancer growth by up to 7-fold in comparison with normal mice.[70]

Researchers at the Mount Sinai Medical Center in New York also showed a link between low immunity (natural killer cell activity) and poor outcomes in cancer survival. After analyzing the survival data from 102 colorectal cancer patients, Tartter and Steinberg found that having a preoperative low NK cell function triggered a frightening jump in the danger of cancer recurrence.[71] Similarly a 2002 Chiba University study

Cumulative incidence rates of cancer by cytotoxic activity of peripheral-blood lymphocytes among men and women
Categorised by tertiles. Men—low: ≤42%; medium: 43–58%; high: >58%. Women—low: 34%; medium: 35–51%; high: >51%.

on 140 patients with colorectal cancer found that lowered NK cell activity was linked to a 50% risk of cancer colonization and spread compared to patients with normal or better NK cell function. Lead researcher Keiji Koda, MD, stated, that "the patient's own anticancer immunity, as well as the potent malignancy of the tumor, may play a role in the development of recurrence following curative surgery... preoperative natural killer (NK) cell activity was the only [variable] associated with distant metastasis following curative surgery for colorectal cancer." [72]

Carotenoids and Immunity

During the past five years, food scientists working for the state government in Germany have identified a number of carotenoids that can stimulate immunity without provoking inflammation that can worsen the symptoms of arthritis. Chief among these is beta cryptoxanthin, but other carotenoids have also been identified, include alpha carotene and lutein. As one of the richest sources of all carotenes, the Ningxia wolfberry can afford significant immune boosting potential. [73-75]

Early Research: 75% Jump in Immune Cells

The State Scientific and Technological Commission in China was the first organization to embark on systematic reviews of the pharmacological

---

Understanding Immunity

There are two types of Immunity:

Innate Immunity, the first line of defense, is fast-acting and general, recognizing certain cell-surface patterns that warn of diseased or damaged cells.

- NK cells
- Macrophages, neutrophils

Specific Immunity is acquired through exposure to certain disease-causing microorganisms. It is slow-acting and targeted. There are two types of specific immunity:

1. Cell-mediated (for invaded cells)

- Creates special T-cells for each pathogen. They remember each invader.
- T lymphocytes of T-Cells mature in the thymus and recognize specific diseases.

2. Humoral-mediated (for yet-to-be invaded cells)

- B-Cells are responsible for humoral immunity and are generated from the bone marrow.
- B cells are created for each kind of pathogen. While they are very efficient at neutralizing pathogens that have not invaded the cells, they can trigger proinflammatory cytokines that can damage tissues and organs over time.

---

action of Ningxia wolfberries. During a two year period from July 1982 to January 1984, a multicenter investigation was initiated to examine the bioactive properties of the berries. Scientists from a number of different organizations were involved, including researchers from Suzhou Medical College, Shanghai First Medical College, and Ningxia Institute of Drug Inspection.

A second, longer clinical experiment on the Ningxia wolfberry was conducted by Ningxia Medical College from October 1982 to May 1985. Researchers concluded that the wolfberry "increased greatly the number of human white cells, lymphocyte transformation rate and phagocytosis." [76]

In a 1988 report published by the State Scientific and Technological Commission of China, scientists reported the immune-enhancing effects of wolfberries on a group of 50 human volunteers. After consuming 50 grams of wolfberries for 10 days, the test subjects showed a 700 point increase in white blood cell counts, a 10% jump in lymphocyte transformation rates, and 75% leap in immunoglobulin A (IgA).

The significance of this should not be overlooked because a decline in IgA is an important biomarker of aging, which suggests that Ningxia wolfberry nutrients work to retarding the aging process.

Immune Boosting Lycium Polysaccharides

The first wolfberry polysaccharide was identified in 1994 when Chinese biochemists extracted an unusual protein-carbohydrate complex (also known as a glycoprotein, glycoconjugate, or sugar-protein) from the wolfberry. Dubbing it "Lycium barbarum polysaccharide," researchers began learning that this low-glycemic long-chain molecule could be responsible for many of the wolfberry's strong immune boosting, anti-cancer, and cardiovascular protective benefits.

This original wolfberry polysaccharide is a very large sugar-protein complex (atomic weight of about 88,000 daltons or 88 kD) that occurs only in the Chinese and Ningxia wolfberries. The richest known food source of this compound is the Ningxia variety of wolfberry, *Lycium barbarum L.*

In 1998 researchers at the Shanghai Institute of Organic Chemistry in China identified three other wolfberry polysaccharides with high molecular weights (92,500, 210,480, and 23,700 daltons) that also have strong immunological activity. Chemical analyses of these polysaccharides revealed a protein content of 6.4%, 14.4%, and 91.4% respectively. The protein arm of the molecule had over 18 different amino acids, while the sugar linkage was composed of galactose, rhamnose, xylose, mannose, and glucose.[77]

Clinical Studies

The Ningxia wolfberry's immune-boosting effect seems to be combined with an anti-inflammatory effect. This means that the immune-supporting action of Ningxia wolfberry is less likely to trigger worsening of arthritis or other autoimmune diseases that are inflammatory in nature.[78]

- A 2003 Institute of Medicinal Biotechnology study at the Peking Union Medical College in Beijing, China, found that Ningxia wolfberry polysaccharide stimulated production of interleukin-2, an non-inflammatory part of immunity that protects against cancer cells and microbial invasion.[79]

- A March 2003 study published in the *European Journal of Pharmacology* showed *in vitro* data that Ningxia wolfberry polysaccharide dramatically expanded output of interleukin-2 and tumor necrosis factor alpha from specialized human immune cells known as peripheral mononuclear cells (PMC). The surges in both interleukin-2 and tumor necrosis factor alpha hit a peak after four to twelve hours and remained well above baseline for 24 hours.[80]

- A Guangdong College of Pharmacy study in China in 1999 documented the ability of Ningxia wolfberry to block the immune-suppressing action of hydrocortisone on rat spleen cells.[81]

- An August 2001 study by the State Key Laboratory of Bio-Organic Chemistry in Shanghai showed that the Ningxia wolfberry polysaccharide had an unusual combination of "good immunoactivity and antioxidative activity." The polysaccharide markedly spurred phagocyte immune cell activity and promoted lymphocyte upregulation.[82]

- A 2004 study at the Huazhong University of Science and Technology in Wuhan, China, documented the ability of wolfberry polysaccharide to enhance the proliferation of lymphocyte immune cells in the spleen.[83]

- A 1999 Hubei Medical University study in China found that wolfberry polysaccharides "showed a remarkable effect on immunological enhancement" in mice.[84]

- A 2004 Huazhong University of Science and Technology study found that mice treated with 10 mg/kg of wolfberry polysaccharide for 10 days showed improved macrophage phagocytosis, spleen lymphocyte proliferation, cytotoxic T lymphocyte (CTL) activity, and interleukin-2 (IL-2) expression. Polysaccharide-fed animals could also resist the growth of transplanted cancer tumor cells (sarcoma S180).[85]

Protein and Immunity

With 15.6% protein, the wolfberry is an ample source of amino acids to sustain both innate and acquired immune function. Protein is a vital building block of white blood cells and antibodies which are some of the most prolifically reproducing cells in the body.

A healthy thymus gland is vital for optimum cell-mediated immunity since it acts as a training camp to physically condition and train SWAT teams of T-lymphocytes to recognize and wipe out disease-causing infections or growth-crazed cancer cells. Autopsies of protein-deficient children have revealed a shrunken, nonfunctional thymus gland. For this reason doctors refer to the thymus gland as a "barometer of nutrition," because a chronic lack of protein shrinks the thymus gland, thereby impairing immune response.

Zinc and Immunity

The Ningxia wolfberry is a rich vegetarian source of zinc, a mineral critical for healthy immunity. The dried berry has five times as much zinc as Brussels sprouts and more zinc than raw eggs.[86]

Zinc plays an essential role in the production of natural killer cells, IgG, gamma interferon, and tumor necrosis factor alpha. Zinc also enhances the microbe-killing activity of macrophages and increases levels of CD4 cytotoxic lymphocytes while lowering levels of CD8 immune-suppressing lymphocytes.[87]

According to Lothar Rink, an immunologist at the University of Lubeck School of Medicine in Germany, "the important role of zinc as an essential trace element for immune function has already been well established." He cited over 100 studies in support of this.[88]

A graphic example of how damaging a zinc deficiency can be to immunity and longevity is cited by Ananda Prasad, a Wayne State University immunologist. Victims suffering acrodermatitis enteropathica (also known as Brandt Syndrome or Danbolt-Cross Syndrome) have a genetic flaw that blocks their ability to absorb zinc from the diet. Unless treated with supplemental zinc, the disease is fatal, with victims usually succumbing to infection.[89-91]

"With careful management, however," notes Anne Walling MD, a physician at the University of Kansas, Wichita, "patients with this previously fatal disorder should enjoy a normal life and have a normal life-span." One of best interventions, is zinc supplementation.[92]

Zinc deficiencies have been shown in both animal and human models to produce a variety of immune deficits including: T-lymphocyte depletion in the spleen and lymph nodes, impaired antibody response, shrinking of the thymus gland, and lower populations of cells associated with both humoral and cell-mediated immunity.

Even more disconcerting is the fact that zinc deficiencies become more pronounced with advancing age as stomach acid declines.

ZINC (mg) in 100 grams of Food[1]			
Baker's Yeast	6.43	Lima Beans	0.95
Beef, top sirloin	5.85	Alfalfa seeds sprouted	0.91
Oat bran, raw	3.11	Bamboo Shoots	0.65
Rice, brown, raw	2.02	Asparagus frozen	0.56
Ningxia Wolfberry, dried[2]	1.80	Kidney Beans	0.55
Turkey, light meat, raw	1.62	Oatmeal	0.49
Wild rice, cooked	1.34	Brussels sprouts	0.36
Ricotta Cheese	1.34	Dates, dry	0.29
Egg, whole, raw	1.10	Raisins	0.27
Navy Beans	1.06	Kale	0.24

1. U.S. Department of Agriculture, Agricultural Research Service. 2004. USDA National Nutrient Database for Standard Reference, Release 17.
2. Preliminary data from dried fruit of Ningxia wolfberry (Lycium barbarum) stored 1-3 years. Analysis performed by Industrial Labs, Denver, CO

A Wayne State University study discovered that among a group of 180 randomly selected elderly subjects, the mean dietary intake of zinc was only 9 mg per day, which is 40% less than the recommended dietary allowance of 15 mg per day set by the Food and Nutrition Board. Moreover, over 30% of this group had depleted levels of zinc in two types of immune cells, granulocytes and lymphocytes which correlated with depleted interleukin-1 (IL-1) production. Following zinc supplementation in a selected group, IL-1 jumped and lymphocyte activity surged.[93-95]

A September 2004 Case Western Reserve University review strongly indicates that zinc is effective for treating the common cold caused by the rhinovirus. "Clinical trial data support the value of zinc in reducing the duration and severity of symptoms of the common cold when administered within 24 hours of symptoms," states Hulisz in the *Journal of the American Pharmaceutical Association*.[96]

A 1999 Johns Hopkins clinical trial showed how effective a modest amount of zinc could be on malaria-infected children living in an endemic area of Papua New Guinea.

A group of 274 preschool children aged 6 to 60 months were given 10 mg elemental zinc for 6 days a week for 46 weeks. After tabulating data, researchers found that zinc supplementation resulted in a 38% reduction in episodes of parasite overload (parasite counts greater than 9200 parasites/microl) and a 69% reduction in severe parasite overload (parasitemia greater than 100,000/microl).[97]

Wolfberry and Intestinal Flora

The high polysaccharide and fiber content of the Ningxia wolfberry can promote the growth of beneficial bacteria in the gastrointestinal system. Diets high in protective vegetable fibers such as those in the wolfberry result in higher levels of health-giving *Lactobacilli* cultures and reduced populations of damaging cultures like *Clostridium perfringens*.

Seventh Day Adventists, whose religion restricts them from eating animal products, have been shown to have higher populations of beneficial bacteria and lower counts of pathogenic bacteria compared to non-vegetarians on a conventional American diet.[98]

Beneficial bacteria may block cancer by producing short chain fatty acids in the colon, which acidify the terrain. This reduced pH in the colon is strongly associated with lower colon cancer risk.[99,100]

How Arginine in Wolfberry Boosts Immunity

The wolfberry's rich payload of arginine is yet another reason for its immune-boosting properties. A semi-essential amino acid, L-arginine is considered an important nutrient for healthy immunity. For that reason many hospitals add it to enteral and parenteral tube feedings for burn and trauma patients.

A large number of clinical studies show that supplemental L-arginine boosts non-inflammatory components of immunity such as gamma interferon and natural killer (NK) cells. NK cells are very powerful immune cells that can detect virally infected or mutated (cancerous) cells and tag them for destruction. NK cells also stimulate the production of cytokines such as gamma interferon which can enhance the body's defenses against numerous types of pathogenic microorganisms.[101,102]

L-arginine's ability to ramp up non-inflammatory immunity may be due to its production of nitric oxide. L-arginine may also exert its immune-enhancing effects as a precursor to tetrapeptide tuftsin.[103]

A 1999 study on burn patients at the West China University of Medical Sciences in Sichuan, China, tested the benefits of 15 grams of L-arginine supplementation on partial-thickness burn patients. Using a randomized controlled format, this clinical trial found that L-arginine markedly boosted natural killer cell activity and IL-2 production.

"It suggests that," stated lead researcher Yuen Cen, a staff member of the hospital's Department of Burn and Plastic Surgery, "exogenous arginine supplementation is beneficial for recovery of cellular immunity function and protein anabolism in partial-thickness burned patients."[104]

A 1998 study at the Osaka University Medical School in Japan, tested the effect of oral L-Arginine on NK cell function in 21 healthy individuals.

Ningxia Wolfberries are sun-dried for 2-3 weeks prior to sale.

Researchers found that L-arginine indeed boosted NK cell activity, although this effect was not seen in patients suffering from Chronic Fatigue Syndrome (CFS). This may be due to the fact that CFS sufferers have a shortcircuit in their arginine- and NO (nitric oxide)-mediated NK cell activation.[105]

Synergy of Arginine and Glutamine

L-arginine's stimulation of healthy immunity may be amplified when combined with another amino acid found in the Ningxia wolfberry: L-glutamine.

A medical group at Shanghai Medical University in China researched the use of an arginine and glutamine solution for tube feeding in gastrointestinal cancer patients, where adequate nutrition and amplified immunity is of life-or-death importance. In this double-blind clinical trial, 48 patients were randomized into a control group with a standard diet and a treatment group supplemented with arginine and glutamine. The study lasted 8 days.

Tolerance of both diets was excellent, according to the researchers, but with big differences in immune and inflammatory responses between the two groups. Patients who received these two amino acids showed greater immunity and less inflammation than the control group. The supplemented group had much higher levels of nitric oxide, total lymphocytes, T lymphocytes, T-helper cells, and NK cells. They also exhibited lower levels of C-reactive protein, a marker for inflammation and heart disease.[106]

REFERENCES

1. Cockerill, Ian. Great Fall of China, 1/11/98, Sportsweek, Sunday Age

2. SPORT, The Age, 12/05/97

3. Hitchcock, CL 1932. A monographic study of the genus Lycium of the Western Hemisphere Ann. Missouri Bot. Gard. 19: 179-374.

4. Yu MS, Ho YS, So KF, Yuen WH, Chang RC. Cytoprotective effects of Lycium barbarum against reducing stress on endoplasmic reticulum. Int J Mol Med. 2006 Jun;17(6):1157-61.

5. Chan et al., Clinical Lab Medicine, 1998

6. McKenna AA et al. Zinc balance in adolescent females consuming a low- or high-calcium diet. Am J Clin Nutr. 1997 May;65(5):1460-4

7. Ichida T, et al., Age-related decrease of gamma-aminobutyric acid (GABA) release in brain of spontaneously hypertensive rats. Life Sci. 1996;58(3):209-15.

8. Patki, P. S., et al. "Efficacy of Potassium and Magnesium in Essential Hypertension: A Double-Blind, Placebo-Controlled Crossover Study." British Medical Journal 301: 521-3 (1990).

9. MacGregor GA, et al., Moderate potassium supplementation in essential hypertension. Lancet. 1982 Sep 11;2(8298):567-70.

10. Anderson, J. "Hypolipidemic Effects of High-carbohydrate, High-fiber Diets. Metabolism 29:551-558 (1980).

11. Meyer DK, Conzelmann U, Schultheiss K. Effects of somatostatin-14 on the in vitro release of [3H]GABA from slices of rat caudatoputamen. Neuroscience. 1989;28(1):61-8.

12. Flynn, M., G. B. Nolph, A. Baker, et al. "Total Body Potassium in Aging Humans: A Longitudinal Study." American Journal of Clinical Nutrition 50: 713-17 (1989).

13. Castaneda C, Resistance training to reduce the malnutrition-inflammation complex syndrome of chronic kidney disease. Am J Kidney Dis. 2004 Apr;43(4):607-16.

14. Merchant AT et al. Protein intake is inversely associated with abdominal obesity in a multi-ethnic population. J Nutr. 2005 May;135(5):1196-201.

15. Bales CW, Ritchie CS. Sarcopenia, weight loss, and nutritional frailty in the elderly. Annu Rev Nutr. 2002;22:309-23. Epub 2002 Jan 4.

16. Brown L., et al. "Cholesterol-lowering Effects of Dietary Fiber: A Meta-analysis." American Journal of Clinical Nutrition: 30-42 (1999).

17. Romero A. L, et al. "Cookies Enriched with Psyllium or Oat Bran Lower Plasma LDL Cholesterol in Normal and Hypercholesterolemic Men from Northern Mexico." Journal of American College of Nutrition: 601-8 (1998).

18. Buhman K. K., et al. "Dietary Psyllium Increases Fecal Bile Acid Excretion, Total Steroid Excretion and Bile Acid Biosynthesis in Rats." Journal of Nutrition: 1199-203 (1998).

19. Mekki N., et al. "Effects of Lowering Fat and Increasing Dietary Fiber on Fasting and Postprandial Plasma Lipids in Hypercholesterolemic Subjects Consuming a Mixed Mediterranean-Western Diet." American Journal of Clinical Nutrition: 1443-51 (1997).

20. Ullrich, I.H. "Evaluation of a High-fiber Diet in Hyperlipidemia: A Review." Journal of the American College of Nutrition: 19-25 (1987).

21. Venter C. S., et al. "Soluble-fibre Concentrate Lowers Plasminogen Activator Inhibitor-1 in Baboons (Papio ursinus)." British Journal of Nutrition (1997): 625-37.

22. Khachik F et al., Separation and identification of carotenoids and their oxidation products in the extracts of human plasma. Anal Chem. 1992 Sep 15;64(18):2111-22.

23. Nishino H, Cancer prevention by natural carotenoids. Biofactors. 2000;13(1-4):89-94.

24. Noguchi S et al. Effects of oxygenated carotenoid beta-cryptoxanthin on morphological differentiation and apoptosis in Neuro2a neuroblastoma cells. Biosci Biotechnol Biochem. 2003 Nov;67(11):2467-9.

25. Donaldson MS. Nutrition and cancer: A review of the evidence for an anti-cancer diet. Nutr J. 2004 Oct 20;3(1):19.

26. Nomura AM, Lee J, Stemmermann GN, Franke AA. Serum vitamins and the subsequent risk of bladder cancer. J Urol. 2003 Oct;170(4 Pt 1):1146-50.

27. Uchiyama S, Yamaguchi M. beta-Cryptoxanthin stimulates cell proliferation and transcriptional activity in osteoblastic MC3T3-E1 cells. Int J Mol Med. 2005 Apr;15(4):675-81.

28. Yamaguchi M, Uchiyama S. beta-Cryptoxanthin stimulates bone formation and inhibits bone resorption in tissue culture in vitro. Mol Cell Biochem. 2004 Mar;258(1-2):137-44.

29. Uchiyama S, Sumida T, Yamaguchi M. Oral administration of beta-cryptoxanthin induces anabolic effects on bone components in the femoral tissues of rats in vivo. Biol Pharm Bull. 2004 Feb;27(2):232-5.

30. Kang JH et al. Antioxidant intake and primary open-angle glaucoma: a prospective study. Am J Epidemiol. 2003 Aug 15;158(4):337-46.

31. Mannisto S et al. Dietary carotenoids and risk of lung cancer in a pooled analysis of seven cohort studies. Cancer Epidemiol Biomarkers Prev. 2004 Jan;13(1):40-8.

32. Yuan JM et al. Dietary cryptoxanthin and reduced risk of lung cancer: the Singapore Chinese Health Study. Cancer Epidemiol Biomarkers Prev. 2003 Sep;12(9):890-8.

33. Weller P, Breithaupt DE. Identification and quantification of zeaxanthin esters in plants using liquid chromatography-mass spectrometry. J Agric Food Chem. 2003 Nov 19;51(24):7044-9.

34. Kim HP et al., Zeaxanthin dipalmitate from Lycium chinense has hepatoprotective activity. Res Commun Mol Pathol Pharmacol. 1997 Sep;97(3):301-14.

35. Kim SY, et al., New antihepatotoxic cerebroside from Lycium chinense fruits. J Nat Prod. 1997 Mar;60(3):274-

36. Chin YW, et al., Hepatoprotective pyrrole derivatives of Lycium chinense fruits. Bioorg Med Chem Lett. 2003 Jan 6;13(1):79-81.

37. Kim HP, et al., Zeaxanthin dipalmitate from Lycium chinense fruit reduces experimentally induced hepatic fibrosis in rats. Biol Pharm Bull. 2002 Mar;25(3):390-2.

38. Gan L, Zhang SH, Liu Q, Xu HB. A polysaccharide-protein complex from Lycium barbarum upregulates cytokine expression in human peripheral blood mononuclear cells. Eur J Pharmacol. 2003 Jun 27;471(3):217-22.

39. Jia YX et al., The effect of lycium barbarum polysaccharide on vascular tension in two-kidney, one clip model of hypertension. Sheng Li Xue Bao. 1998 Jun;50(3):309-14.

40. Hu Q, et al., A study on the anti-cancer effect of ningxia wolfberry. J Tradit Chin Med. 1989 Jun;9(2):117-24.

41. Luo Q, Cai Y, Yan J, Sun M, Corke H. Hypoglycemic and hypolipidemic effects and antioxidant activity of fruit extracts from Lycium barbarum. Life Sci. 2004 Nov 26;76(2):137-49.

42. Liu RH. Health benefits of fruit and vegetables are from additive and synergistic combinations of phytochemicals. Am J Clin Nutr. 2003 Sep;78(3 Suppl):517S-520S

43. Wu H, Guo H, Zhao R. Effect of Lycium barbarum polysaccharide on the improvement of antioxidant ability and DNA damage in NIDDM rats. Yakugaku Zasshi. 2006 May;126(5):365-71

44. Ibid.

45. Prior RL and Cao G Analysis of botanicals and dietary supplements for antioxidant capacity: J AOAC Int. 2000 Jul-Aug;83(4):950-6.

46. Luo Q, Li Z, Huang X, Yan J, Zhang S, Cai YZ. Lycium barbarum polysaccharides: Protective effects against heat-induced damage of rat testes and H(2)O(2)-induced DNA damage in mouse testicular cells and beneficial effect on sexual behavior and reproductive function of hemicastrated rats. Life Sci. 2006 Mar 6.

47. Cao G, et al. Automated assay of oxygen radical absorbance capacity with the COBAS FARA II. Clin Chem. 1995 Dec;41(12 Pt 1):1738-44.

48. Elchuri S, Oberley TD, Qi W, Eisenstein RS, Jackson Roberts L, Van Remmen H, Epstein CJ, Huang TT. CuZnSOD deficiency leads to persistent and widespread oxidative damage and hepatocarcinogenesis later in life. Oncogene. 2005 Jan 13;24(3):367-80.

49. 2 Li Xueru et al., Clinical Experiment on Lycium, Bulletin on Achievements in Scientific and Technological Research, Serial 84, No. 4, 1988.

50. Wu SJ, Ng LT, Lin CC. Antioxidant activities of some common ingredients of traditional chinese medicine, Angelica sinensis, Lycium barbarum and Poria cocos. Phytother Res. 2004 Dec;18(12):1008-12.

51. Huang Y, Lu J, Shen Y, Lu J. The protective effects of total flavonoids from Lycium Barbarum L. on lipid peroxidation of liver mitochondria and red blood cell in rats. Wei Sheng Yan Jiu. 1999 Mar 30;28(2):115-6.

52. Deng HB et al., Inhibiting effects of Achyranthes bidentata polysaccharide and Lycium barbarum polysaccharide on nonenzyme glycation in D-galactose induced mouse aging model. Biomed Environ Sci. 2003 Sep;16(3):267-75.

53. Li G, Yang J, Ren B, Wang Z. Effect of lycium barbarum L on defending free radicals of mice caused by hypoxia. Wei Sheng Yan Jiu. 2002 Feb;31(1):30-1.

54. Wu BY, Zou JH, Meng SC. Effect of wolfberry fruit and epimedium on DNA synthesis of the aging-youth 2BS fusion cells. Zhongguo Zhong Xi Yi Jie He Za Zhi. 2003 Dec;23(12):926-8.

55. Wang Y, et al., Protective effect of Fructus Lycii polysaccharides against time and hyperthermia-induced damage in cultured seminiferous epithelium. J Ethnopharmacol. 2002 Oct;82(2-3):169-75.

56. Xiao PG, Xing ST, Wang LW. Immunological aspects of Chinese medicinal plants as antiaging drugs. J Ethnopharmacol. 1993 Mar;38(2-3):167-75.

57. Currier NL, Miller SC. Echinacea purpurea and melatonin augment natural-killer cells in leukemic mice and prolong life span. J Altern Complement Med. 2001 Jun;7(3):241-51.

58. Fujisawa T, Yamaguchi Y. Autologous tumor killing activity as a prognostic factor in primary resected nonsmall cell carcinoma of the lung. Cancer. 1997 Feb 1;79(3):474-81.

59. Hanna N. The role of natural killer cells in the control of tumor growth and metastasis. Biochim Biophys Acta. 1985;780(3):213-26.

60. Wu J, Lanier LL. Natural killer cells and cancer. Adv Cancer Res. 2003;90:127-56.

61. Herberman RB, Ortaldo JR. Natural killer cells: their roles in defenses against disease. Science. 1981 Oct 2;214(4516):24-30.

62. Oliver RT, Tobias J, Gallagher C. Prebiopsy neo-adjuvant endocrine therapy for breast cancer to prevent post-surgery trauma-induced growth factor and immune-suppression mediated tumour progression. Eur J Cancer. 1996 Mar;32A(3):396-7.

63. Page GG, Ben Eliyahu S, Liebeskind JC. The role of LGL/NK cells in surgery-induced promotion of metastasis and its attenuation by morphine. Brain Behav Immun. 1994 Sep;8(3):241-50.

64. Levy SM, Herberman RB, Maluish AM, et al. Prognostic risk assessment in primary breast cancer by behavioral and immunological parameters. Health Psychol. 1985;4(2):99-113.

65. Page GG, Ben Eliyahu S, Taylor AN. The development of sexual dimorphism in natural killer cell activity and resistance to tumor metastasis in the Fischer 344 rat. J Neuroimmunol. 1995 Dec;63(1):69-77.

66. Schantz SP, Brown BW, Lira E, et al. Evidence for the role of natural immunity in the control of metastatic spread of head and neck cancer. Cancer Immunol Immunother. 1987;25(2):141-8.

67. Tjalma WA, Winter-Roach BA, Rowlands P, et al. Port-site recurrence following laparoscopic surgery in cervical cancer. Int J Gynecol Cancer. 2001 Sep;11(5):409-12.

68. Wiltrout RH, Herberman RB, Zhang SR, et al. Role of organ-associated NK cells in decreased formation of experimental metastases in lung and liver. J Immunol. 1985 Jun;134(6):4267-75.

69. Gaspani L, Bianchi M, Limiroli E, et al. The analgesic drug tramadol prevents the effect of surgery on natural killer cell activity and metastatic colonization in rats. J Neuroimmunol. 2002 Aug;129(1-2):18-24.

70. Gorelik E, Wiltrout RH, Okumura K, et al. Role of NK cells in the control of metastatic spread and growth of tumor cells in mice. Int J Cancer. 1982 Jul 15;30(1):107-12.

71. Tartter PI, Steinberg B, Barron DM, et al. The prognostic significance of natural killer cytotoxicity in patients with colorectal cancer. Arch Surg. 1987 Nov;122(11):1264-8.

72. Koda K, Saito N, Takiguchi N, et al. Preoperative natural killer cell activity: correlation with distant metastases in curatively research colorectal carcinomas. Int Surg. 1997 Apr;82(2):190-3.

73. Watzl B, Bub A, Briviba K, Rechkemmer G. Supplementation of a low-carotenoid diet with tomato or carrot juice modulates immune functions in healthy men. Ann Nutr Metab. 2003;47(6):255-61.

74. Watzl B, Bub A, Blockhaus M, Herbert BM, Luhrmann PM, Neuhauser-Berthold M, Rechkemmer G. Prolonged tomato juice consumption has no effect on cell-mediated immunity of well-nourished elderly men and women. J Nutr. 2000 Jul;130(7):1719-23.

75. Watzl B, Bub A, Brandstetter BR, Rechkemmer G. Modulation of human T-lymphocyte functions by the consumption of carotenoid-rich vegetables. Br J Nutr. 1999 Nov;82(5):383-9.

76. Li Xueru et al., Clinical Experiment on Lycium, Bulletin on Achievements in Scientific and Technological Research, Serial 84, No. 4, 1988.

77. Huang L, Lin Y, Tian G, Ji G. Isolation, purification and physico-chemical properties of immunoactive constituents from the fruit of Lycium barbarum L. Yao Xue Xue Bao. 1998 Jul;33(7):512-6.

78. Xu Y, He L, Xu L, Liu Y. Advances in immunopharmacological study of Lycium barbarum L. Zhong Yao Cai. 2000 May;23(5):295-8.

79. Deng HB et al., Inhibiting effects of Achyranthes bidentata polysaccharide and Lycium barbarum polysaccharide on nonenzyme glycation in D-galactose induced mouse aging model. Biomed Environ Sci. 2003 Sep;16(3):267-75.

80. Gan L, Zhang SH, Liu Q, Xu HB. A polysaccharide-protein complex from Lycium barbarum upregulates cytokine expression in human peripheral blood mononuclear cells. Eur J Pharmacol. 2003 Jun 27;471(3):217-22.

81. Lu X, Xian X, Lu W, Wu X, Gu H. The regulation of Lycium barbarum on apoptosis of rat spleen in vitro. Zhong Yao Cai. 1999 May;22(5):250-1.

82. Peng XM, Wang ZF, Tian GY. Physico-chemical properties and activity of glycoconjugate LbGp2 from Lycium barbarum L. Yao Xue Xue Bao. 2001 Aug;36(8):599-602.

83. Du G, Liu L, Fang J. Experimental study on the enhancement of murine splenic lymphocyte proliferation by Lycium barbarum glycopeptide. J Huazhong Univ Sci Technolog Med Sci. 2004;24(5):518-20, 527.

84. Luo Q, Yan J, Zhang S. Effects of pure and crude Lycium barbarum polysaccharides on immunopharmacology. Zhong Yao Cai. 1999 May;22(5):246-9.

85. Gan L et al., Immunomodulation and anti-tumor activity by a polysaccharide-protein complex from Lycium barbarum. Int Immunopharmacol. 2004 Apr;4(4):563-9.

86. U.S. Department of Agriculture, Agricultural Research Service. 2001. USDA Nutrient Database for Standard Reference, Release 16. Nutrient Data Laboratory Home Page, http://www.nal.usda.gov/fnic/foodcomp

87. Shankar AH, Prasad AS. Zinc and immune function: the biological basis of altered resistance to infection. Am J Clin Nutr. 1998 Aug;68(2 Suppl):447S-463S.

88. Rink L, Kirchner H. Zinc-altered immune function and cytokine production. J Nutr. 2000 May;130(5S Suppl):1407S-11S.

89. Chandra RK. Acrodermatitis enteropathica: zinc levels and cell-mediated immunity. Pediatrics.1980 Nov;66(5):789-91.

90. Janaki VR, et al. Acrodermatitis enteropathica. J Indian Med Assoc 1981;76:43-4.

91. Moynahan EJ. Acrodermatitis enteropathica: a lethal inherited human zinc-deficiency disorder. Lancet 1974;2(7877):399-400.

92. Anne Walling, MD. Acrodermatitis enteropathica. 1989, American Academy of Family Physicians

93. Prasad AS et al. Zinc deficiency in elderly patients. Nutrition. 1993 May-Jun;9(3):218-24.

94. Shankar AH, Prasad AS. Zinc and immune function: the biological basis of altered resistance to infection. Am J Clin Nutr. 1998 Aug;68(2 Suppl):447S-463S.

95. Prasad AS, Dardenne M, et al. Serum thymulin and zinc deficiency in humans.Trans Assoc Am Physicians. 1987;100:222-31.

96. Hulisz D. Efficacy of zinc against common cold viruses: an overview. J Am Pharm Assoc (Wash DC). 2004 Sep-Oct;44(5):594-603.

97. Shankar AH et a., Zinc and immune function: the biological basis of altered resistance to infection. Am J Clin Nutr. 1998 Aug;68(2 Suppl):447S-463S.

98. Finegold SM et al., Fecal microbial flora in Seventh Day Adventist populations and control subjects. Am J Clin Nutr 1977;30:1781–1792.

99. Goldin BR, Gorbach SL. The effect of milk and lactobacillus feeding on human intestinal bacterial enzyme activity. Am J Clin Nutr 1984;39:756–761.

100. Aso Y, Akazan H. Prophylactic effect of a Lactobacillus casei preparation on the recurrence of superficial bladder cancer. BLP Study Group. Urol Int 1992;49:125–129.

101. Bogdan C, Rollinghoff M, Diefenbach A. The role of nitric oxide in innate immunity. Immunol Rev. 2000 Feb;173:17-26.

102. Jyothi MD, Khar A. Induction of nitric oxide production by natural killer cells: its role in tumor cell death. Nitric Oxide. 1999 Oct;3(5):409-18.

103. Cifone MG et al., Interleukin-2-activated rat natural killer cells express inducible nitric oxide synthase that contributes to cytotoxic function and interferon-gamma production. Blood. 1999 Jun 1;93(11):3876-84.

104. Cen Y, Luo XS, Liu XX. Effect of L-arginine supplementation on partial-thickness burned patients. Zhongguo Xiu Fu Chong Jian Wai Ke Za Zhi. 1999 Jul;13(4):227-31.

105. Ogawa M et al., Decreased nitric oxide-mediated natural killer cell activation in chronic fatigue syndrome. Eur J Clin Invest. 1998 Nov;28(11):937-43.

106. Wu GH, Zhang YW, Wu ZH. Modulation of postoperative immune and inflammatory response by immune-enhancing enteral diet in gastrointestinal cancer patients. World J Gastroenterol. 2001 Jun;7(3):357-62.

CHAPTER 10

Dietary Supplements with Essential Oils

Young Living has an outstanding line of wellness tools that afford an unparalleled opportunity—to people of all ages—to improve mind, body, and spirit. Indeed, Young Living's line of dietary supplements provides one of the most potent and effective tools available to support health and wellness.

Many of these supplements contain herbs, nutrients and therapeutic-grade essential oils. The oils in these supplements are formulated using a unique process pioneered by D. Gary Young. The essential oils mixed in these supplements act as catalysts to help deliver nutrients through the cell membranes while assisting in the removal of cellular wastes.

It is important to remember that these supplements are usually dissolved and assimilated by the body within a couple of hours. Therefore, spacing them throughout the day will provide better assimilation and nutrient value than consuming a handful all at once.

Because of their purity and quality, YL's supplements have a strength and efficacy unequalled in the marketplace. Because of this, we recommend that you choose and use only those products best suited to your metabolism, need, and physiological make-up. This would mean limiting the simultaneous ingestion of YL supplements to no more than four at once. For example, if you are on a cleansing program, use only those products designed to facilitate the cleansing and avoid using other products concomitantly that are suited for building or balancing body systems until after the cleansing is completed. Similarly, if you are looking to support cardiovascular function, limit your use to the products best designed to accomplish this, while avoiding excess simultaneous intake of unrelated supplements.

When using supplements, a general guideline is to discontinue use for at least one or two days a week to allow the body to regain homeostasis and permit its natural recuperative powers to engage.

PRODUCTS

AlkaLime

This specially designed alkaline mineral powder contains an array of high-alkaline salts and other yeast and fungus fighting elements, such as citric acid and essential oils. Its precisely balanced, acid-neutralizing mineral formulation helps preserve the body's proper pH balance—the cornerstone of health. By boosting blood alkalinity, yeast and fungus are deprived of the acidic terrain they require to flourish. The effectiveness of other essential oils is enhanced when the body's blood and tissues are alkaline.

AlkaLime may help reduce the following signs of acid-based yeast and fungus dominance:

- fatigue/low energy
- unexplained aches and pains
- overweight conditions
- low resistance to illness
- allergies
- headaches
- irritability/mood swings
- indigestion
- colitis/ulcers
- diarrhea/constipation
- urinary tract infections
- rectal/vaginal itch
- Candida

INGREDIENTS:

Calcium carbonate provides calcium, which is needed for healthy bones.

Potassium bicarbonate added for electrolyte balance.

Magnesium citrate – a crucial co-factor for collagen creation..

Magnesium supports healthy intestinal flora, the first-line defense against fungus overgrowth.

Sodium bicarbonate used for electrolyte and pH balance.

Natural lemon-lime flavoring.

Sea salts have trace minerals that regulate pH.

Citric acid is added to help cleanse the digestive system.

ESSENTIAL OILS:

Lemon (*Citrus limon*) prevents cellular mutation and enhances DNA repair (Reddy et al., 1998). Also helps digestive system retain alkalinity.

Lime (*Citrus aurantiifolia*) decongests the lymphatic system.

Caution: Not recommended for sodium-restricted diets or for individuals with high blood pressure.

Directions: Stir one teaspoon into eight oz. of distilled or purified water and drink immediately. Mix only with water. To aid in alkalizing connective tissue, AlkaLime may be taken 1-3 times per day one hour before meals or before eating. As an antacid, AlkaLime may be taken as needed. Otherwise, an ideal time to take AlkaLime would be prior to bedtime.

Companion Products: Essentialzyme, Mineral Essence, Di-Gize, MultiGreens, peppermint, Purification, spearmint, Thieves.

Agave (*A tequilana*)

(See BLUE AGAVE NECTAR, ORGANIC)

Balance Complete

Vanilla Cream Meal Replacement

This unique meal replacement, formulated with superfood nutrients, is both a powerful nutritive energizer and a cleanser. It is comprised of 3 key components:

1 A premium New Zealand whey blend made from milk that is certified hormone-free, antibiotic-free and pesticide-free, providing top quality protein for tissue building and weight control

2 A proprietary fiber blend, called V-Fiber, which provides the optimal viscosity to improve toxin and fat elimination, curb food cravings and support colon health.

3 An improved, proprietary enzyme pack to improve digestibility and minimize the gas and bloating common with many protein powders.

4 A long list of powerful phytonutrients providing natural vitamins, minerals and other nutrients from natural food sources, to build energy, strength and immunity.

INGREDIENTS:

Proprietary V-Fiber™ Blend (larch polysaccharides, Ningxia wolfberry (*Lycium barbarum*) fruit, brown rice bran, guar gum, konjac root, xanthan gum, chicory root fiber extract (FOS), and sodium alginate); whey protein concentrate; nonfat dry milk; medium-chain triglycerides; natural vanilla flavor; fructose; lecithin; calcium (as tricalcium phosphate); phosphorus; Proprietary Enzyme complex (lactase, lipase, bromelain, papain, and amylase); xylitol; magnesium oxide; barley grass; neohesperidin derivative (flavor from natural citrus); cinnamon bark; mixed carotenoids (vitamin A); lo han kuo extract; cream flavor; barley grass juice; aloe vera; vitamin C (ascorbic acid); mixed tocopherols (vitamin E); vitamin B3 (niacinamide); zinc oxide; selenium (as selenomethionine); beta-carotene; molybdenum citrate; vitamin B5 (pantothenic acid from calcium pantothenate); vitamin B6 (pyridoxine HCl); chromium amino nicotinate; vitamin B1 (thiamine HCl); vitamin B2 (riboflavin); vitamin D3 (cholecalciferol); vitamin B12 (methylcobalimin); folic acid; orange (*Citrus sinensis*) rind essential oil, biotin; and iodine (as potassium iodide)

NUTRITION FACTS:

Total Calories	190	9.5%
Calories From Fat 56		%DV
Total Fat	6 g	9%
Saturated Fat	2.78 g	14%
Cholesterol	26.3 mg	9%
Sodium	112.6 mg	5%
Potassium	369.3 mg	11%
Protein	11.5 g	23%

Total Carbohydrate . . . . 26 g 4%
Dietary Fiber . . . . 11 g 44%
Soluble Fiber . . . . 8.75 g
Insoluble Fiber . . . . 2.27 g
Sugars . . . . 10.56 g

Vitamin A	28%	Vitamin C	28%
Vitamin D	28%	Vitamin E	28%
Thiamin	28%	Riboflavin	28%
Niacin	30%	Calcium	41%
Iron	2%	Vitamin B6	28%
Folate	33%	Vitamin B12	35%
Biotin	29%	Pantothenic Acid	24%
Phosphorus	26%	Iodine	28%
Magnesium	37%	Zinc	28%
Selenium	31%	Chromium	29%
Molybdenum	18%		

Directions: Add two scoops of Balance Complete™ to 8 oz. cold water. May be mixed with rice, almond, or other milk. Shake, stir, or blend until smooth. For added flavor, add fruit or essential oils.

USAGE During the 5-Day Nutritive Cleanse™, replace all three daily meals with Balance Complete and follow recommended schedule. As part of a low calorie diet, replace two daily meals with Balance Complete.

Companion Products: Ningxia Red, Omega Blue, Longevity, GTrue Source, Life 5 and Digest + Cleanse.

Be-Fit

A high-powered formula for enhancing strength and endurance, promoting muscle formation, and supporting immunity.

INGREDIENTS:

Ningxia Wolfberry fruit/seed powder contains over 15 percent protein by weight. It is rich in amino acids for supporting muscle integrity.

HMB (Beta-hydroxy beta-methylbutyrate) is the best documented nutrient for increasing muscle mass.

Eleuthero root (formerly referred to as Siberian ginseng) strengthens the adrenal glands, increases glycogen which is used for energy, normalizes blood pressure, and increases endurance.

Ginkgo biloba leaf extract improves energy, memory, and mood, due to its ability to enhance cerebral and peripheral circulation. (standardized to 24% ginkoflavoneglycosides, 6% terpenes)

L-arginine is an amino acid that promotes circulation in the small capillaries of our tissues, allowing greater nutrient absorption and cellular metabolism.

L-lysine works to enhance the benefits of the amino acid L-leucine found in wolfberry powder.

Creatine monohydrate is a naturally occurring compound of three amino acids, providing high-energy fuel for muscles. It helps increase muscle mass as well as muscle contraction for improved intensity and endurance.

Cayenne pepper (*Capsicum annuum*) **fruit** dilates blood vessels to improve circulation, stamina, and energy.

ESSENTIAL OILS:

Nutmeg (*Myristica fragrans*) is used for its adrenal cortex-like activity, which helps support the adrenal glands for increased energy. It is also anti-inflammatory.

Lemongrass (*Cymbopogon flexuosus*) regenerates connective tissue and ligaments. It also improves circulation in muscles.

Rosemary (*Rosmarinus officinalis*) helps overcome mental fatigue. Has a cooling effect on muscles.

Wintergreen (*Gaultheria procumbens*) has a cortisone-like action for pain relief due to its high concentration of methyl salicylate. Used to increase respiratory capacity.

Directions: Take 2 capsules three times daily.

Companion Products: True Source Multivitamins, Power Meal, Protein Complete Gelatin Caps, Ultra Young+, Wolfberry Crisp Bars.

Blue Agave Nectar, Organic

The ultimate low-glycemic sweetener, Blue Agave nectar is harvested from organic *Agave tequilana* plants. The hearts (heads) of the agaves are chopped, ground, and pressed for their juices. The result is a viscous, honey-like fluid that has a color and shelf stability similar to honey.

- A sugar alternative with a low glycemic index of 11 (it has minimal impact on blood sugar levels). This makes it a sweetener of choice for diabetics, hypoglycemics, or others who cannot tolerate sucrose or choose not to use artificial sweeteners.

- Blue Agave is about 50 percent sweeter and has fewer calories per teaspoon than sucrose (table sugar).

- Records show that the ancient Meso-Americans used this plant as food as well as externally and internally for injuries and illnesses. Known as the Mexican Tree of Life and Abundance.

Directions: In recipes, substitute an amount of blue agave nectar equal to 1/2 to 3/4 of the amount of sugar called for in the recipe. You may also need to reduce the amount of liquid, just as you would for honey. Can be used in most recipes, on bread, in teas, desserts, sauces, etc.

Companion Products: Stevia

BLM (Bones, Ligaments, and Muscles) Capsules

A high-powered arthritis treatment that includes essential oils and a special collagen complex for building bones, ligaments and muscles. The exclusive collagen and hyaluronic acid blend strengthens and rebuilds damaged joints and cartilage as it combats arthritis inflammation and pain.

INGREDIENTS:

Glucosamine Sulfate is a proteoglycan with over 30 years of double-blind placebo-controlled studies on its ability to rebuild damaged cartilage and reduce arthritis symptoms. Derived from shellfish.

Collagen – Type II is the raw material from which joints are built. It contains the most proteoglycans of any cartilage source. Contains cartilage matrix glycoprotein which reduces oxidative damage to joints. It also reduces inflammation by acting on lymphoid tissue in the digestive system. Derived from avian cartilage.

Rice flour

MSM—Methysulfonylmethane is an exceptionally bioavailable source of sulfur that restores flexibility to cell membranes and slows the breakdown of cartilage.

Potassium (7%)

Manganese Citrate is a crucial cofactor in collagen creation.

ESSENTIAL OILS:

Idaho Balsam Fir (*Abies balsamea*) is a powerful inflammatory essential oil which reduces swelling and pain in joints

Wintergreen (*Gaultheria procumbens*) contains methyl salicylate, which has been used for decades for its anti-inflammatory and pain-relieving properties. Listed in the United States Pharmacopeia for combating muscle and joint pain.

Clove (*Syzygium aromaticum*) has been shown to have anti-inflammatory and antioxidant effects.

Directions: Take 1 gelatin capsule three times a day if you weigh less than 120 lbs.

Take 1 capsule four times a day if you weigh between 120 and 200 lbs.

Take 1 capsule five times a day if you weigh over 200 lbs.

Allow 4-8 weeks of daily use before expecting noticeable results

Companion Products: Acceptance, Aroma Siez, clove, Idaho balsam fir, Joy, MegaCal or SuperCal, nutmeg, PanAway, peppermint, Release, Sulfurzyme, and Wintergreen

BLM (Bones, Ligaments, and Muscles) Powder

Same powerful arthritis formula as found in BLM capsules with the addition of bacteria-fighting xylitol as a bone strengthener.

INGREDIENTS:

Glucosamine Sulfate is a proteoglycan with over 30 years of double-blind placebo-controlled studies on its ability to rebuild damaged cartilage and reduce arthritis symptoms. Derived from shellfish.

Collagen – Type II is the raw material from which joints are built. It contains the most proteoglycans of any cartilage source. Contains cartilage matrix glycoprotein which reduces oxidative damage to joints. It also reduces inflammation by acting on lymphoid tissue in the digestive system. Derived from avian cartilage.

Xylitol a non-caloric, anti-bacterial sweetener

Rice bran

MSM – Methysulfonylmethane is an exceptionally bioavailable source of sulfur that restores flexibility to cell membranes and slows the breakdown of cartilage.

Manganese Citrate is a crucial cofactor in collagen creation.

Potassium (7%)

ESSENTIAL OILS:

Clove *(Syzygium aromaticum)* has been shown to have anti-inflammatory and antioxidant effects.

Peppermint *(Mentha piperita)* is known for its ability to relieve pain and inflammation.

Idaho Balsam Fir *(Abies balsamea)* is a powerful inflammatory essential oil which reduces swelling and pain in joints.

Wintergreen *(Gaultheria procumbens)* contains methyl salicylate, which has been used for decades for its anti-inflammatory and pain-relieving properties. Listed in the United States Pharmacopeia for combating muscle and joint pain.

Directions: If you weigh less than 120 lbs., take 1/4 tsp. 3 times daily. If you weigh 120-200 lbs., take 1/4 tsp. 4 times daily. If you weigh more than 200 lbs., take 1/4 tsp. 5 times daily. Allow 4-8 weeks of daily use before expecting noticeable results.

Companion Products: Acceptance, Aroma Siez, clove, Idaho balsam fir, Joy, MegaCal or SuperCal, nutmeg, PanAway, peppermint, Release, Sulfurzyme, and Wintergreen

Bodygize

Bodygize is a high-powered nutritional drink mix fortified with vitamins, minerals, amino acids, and pure therapeutic-grade essential oils. It helps balance the body at its ideal weight and promotes muscle formation. It contains whey solids that have been studied for their effects against breast and ovarian cancer. It is designed as a high-powered meal alternative. Over 30-percent protein by weight, Bodygize contains a complete vitamin and amino acid profile.

INGREDIENTS:

Non-fat dry milk supplies organic calcium and high quality protein.

Ultrafiltered Microfiltered Whey is the best source of high quality protein, with the highest Protein Efficiency Ratio and Protein Digestibility Corrected Amino Acid Score. It is rich in alpha-lactalbumin, beat lactoglobulin, immunoglobulins, lactoferrin, lactoperoxidase, calcium and magnesium. Ultrafiltered whey is far superior to the denatured protein found in ion exchange whey which is very high in sodium and low in calcium, potassium, and magnesium. Ion exchange whey is also devoid of glycomicropeptides, lactoperoxidase, and lactoferrin.

Fructose is a low-glycemic sweetener having minimal impact on blood sugar levels.

Potassium citrate + chloride + iodide prevents heart disease, strokes, and high blood pressure.

Vanilla Bean *(Vanilla planifolia)* **Extract** from Madagascar vanilla beans.

Lecithin is a key phospholipid essential for cell membrane integrity and healthy liver function.

Xanthan/Guar gum is a natural stabilizer.

Sodium chloride for electrolyte balance.

Magnesium citrate is crucial for proper enzyme function, muscle contractions, and heart rhythm. It reduces blood pressure, prevents arteriosclerosis, and improves insulin action.

Vitamin C (ascorbic acid) helps the body manufacture collagen for connective tissue, cartilage, tendons, etc., and is used for proper immune function. It is also an antioxidant.

Vitamin E (mixed tocopherols) protects against cardiovascular disease and is beneficial for acne, allergies, and wound healing. Also beneficial for heart functions and healthy blood, joints, and eyes.

Vitamin A (palmitate) is an important antioxidant.

Calcium pantothenate (**vitamin B5**) is needed for the prevention of depression and tinnitus.

Niacinamide (**vitamin B3**) is essential for the production of energy, regulates blood sugar, and reduces cholesterol.

Zinc citrate is crucial for proper immune function and is needed for proper action of many hormones, including insulin and growth hormone. It helps improve wound healing.

Copper is necessary for proper red blood cell formation and immune function.

Vitamin D helps with the absorption of calcium and has many anticancer properties.

Vitamin B6 supports immune function and protects the heart and blood vessels. It inhibits skin cancer growth and helps prevent kidney stones and PMS symptoms. Vitamin B6 requires folic acid and magnesium to maximize its effects.

Riboflavin (vitamin B2) is crucial in the production of cellular energy, helps regenerate the liver, and prevents cellular mutations.

Thiamin HCI (vitamin B1) is essential for energy production, carbohydrate metabolism, and nerve cell function.

Vitamin B12 (cyanocobalamin) is critical for red blood cell formation and proper immune and nerve function. Works with vitamin B6 to prevent heart disease. Vegetarians often lack adequate B12.

Folic acid plays an important role in cardiovascular health.

Biotin helps convert fats and amino acids into energy. It promotes healthy nails and hair and combats yeast and fungus overgrowth.

Lutein

Lycopene

Selenium (as selenomethionine)

Manganese citrate – a crucial co-factor in collagen creation.

Silica

ESSENTIAL OILS:

Lime (*Citrus aurantiifolia*) prevents cellular mutation and enhances DNA repair. It also decongests the lymphatic system.

Tangerine (*Citrus reticulata*) is an anticoagulant that increases blood flow and circulation. It is also a digestive aid.

Orange (*Citrus sinensis*) prevents cellular mutation and enhances DNA repair (Reddy et al., 1998). It is very high in limonene, a supernutrient that has been studied extensively for its ability to prevent cellular mutations and reverse cancer. Over 50 peer-reviewed research papers have investigated limonene against a variety of cancers including breast, lung, and colon.

Lemon (*Citrus limon*) prevents cellular mutation and enhances DNA repair. Full of limonene. See LEMON in Single Oils section

Cypress (*Cupressus sempervirens*) improves circulation and blood flow. Enables lymphatic drainage, reduces edema, and water retention.

Grapefruit (*Citrus paradisi*) prevents DNA and cellular mutation. Also has unique fat-dissolving properties.

Mandarin (*Citrus reticulata*) is antifungal, antispasmotic, and promotes digestion.

Directions: Add one scoop to 1 cup of purified water, juice, rice milk, soy milk, or low-fat milk. For a smooth consistency, mix in blender for 30 seconds. Ice cubes may be added to thicken like a shake. Bodygize works with all juices. It is a predigested protein and may be taken anytime. For optimum results, take with True Source Multivitamins and Thyromin.

Allergen Warning: Contains non-fat dry milk

Companion Products: Be-Fit, Longevity Softgels, MultiGreen, nutmeg, Power Meal, Thyromin, and Wolfberry Crisp Bars

Tips for Getting the Most from Bodygize

1. **For fast weight reduction:** Enjoy Bodygize as a meal alternative for breakfast and dinner. Eat a sensible, low-fat, well-balanced lunch, which should include vegetables, fruits, and whole grains. As with any weight balancing program, fats, sugars, and high-caloric foods should be omitted from your diet. Raw organic vegetables and fruits are excellent snacks.

2. **For weight gain:** Enjoy Bodygize mixed with whole milk or apple juice. Add a banana or a pear and drink after each meal.

3. **For good health and weight maintenance:** After you have achieved your ideal weight, enjoy a Bodygize shake as a meal alternative

daily, possibly for breakfast. Bodygize may also be used as a filling and nutritious snack. Drink plenty of distilled or purified water.

Note: Anyone who is pregnant, nursing, under a doctor's care, or wants to lose more than 50 pounds or more than 20 percent of his/her body weight, should consult a physician before starting this or any other weight management program.

Carbozyme®

Designed to relieve bloating, cramping, gas, intestinal problems, intestinal distress, and combat Candida and yeast overgrowth, Carbozyme is an advanced starch and sugar digesting vegetarian enzyme complex that contains pure amylase and pure therapeutic-grade essential oils. Clinical studies in 2002 using two capsules twice a day of Carbozyme, eliminated the need for insulin in diabetic patients.

INGREDIENTS:

Amylase (alpha) is a powerful starch digesting enzyme prevents starch fermentation in the digestive system.

Bee pollen is rich in natural enzymes and coenzymes.

Trace Mineral Complex: Rice Bran, Rosebud extract

ESSENTIAL OILS:

Thieves is a powerful antiseptic and antifungal blend of therapeutic grade essential oils.

Cinnamon is researched for its ability to aid in digesting sugars

Eucalyptus radiata

Clove (*Syzygium aromaticum*) has been shown to have anti-inflammatory and antioxidant effects.

Lemon (*Citrus limon*) decreases platelet stickiness and improves blood.

Rosemary (*Rosmarinus officinalis*) is antiparasitic and balances the endocrine system.

Directions: Take 1 capsule three times daily or as needed just before meals containing carbohydrates.

Allergen Warning: Product contains bee pollen

Warning: Do not give this product to children under 12 years of age except under the supervision of a doctor. If symptoms persist, discontinue use and consult your physician.

Companion Products: Balance Complete, JuvaTone, Stevia Extract, Thieves

CardiaCare

Nutritionally strengthens and supports the heart and cardiovascular system.

INGREDIENTS:

Rhododendron caucasicum root extract (minimum 50% polyphenols, 5% taxifolins) contains phenylpropanoids that have been shown in clinical studies to increase the efficiency of the cardiovascular system.

Ningxia Wolfberry (*Lycium barbarum*) **fruit/berry powder** contains the amino acids that are vital to supporting cardiovascular function.

Magnesium (as magnesium citrate) is crucial for proper enzyme function, muscle contractions and heart rhythm. It reduces blood pressure, prevents arteriosclerosis, and improves insulin action.

Hawthorn (*Crateagus laevigata*) **berry** has been used for decades in European cardiac medicine. Active constituents in the berries dilate coronary blood vessels, thereby increasing blood circulation in the heart.

Coenzyme Q10 (CoQ10) is used by every cell in the body to convert food to energy. Heart cells require more CoQ10 than any other cell.

Vitamin E (as d-alpha tocopheryl succinate) prevents oxidative damage to low-density lipoproteins (LDLs), a primary cause of clogged coronary arteries and heart disease.

ESSENTIAL OILS:

Helichrysum (*Helichrysum italicum*) helps regulate cholesterol, stimulates liver function, and helps reduce blood stickiness.

Lemon (*Citrus limon*) promotes leukocyte formation and increases immune function.

Marjoram (*Origanum majorana*) provides support for smooth muscles of the heart, relieves spasms, and may work as a diuretic.

Ylang Ylang (*Cananga odorata*) has been used traditionally to support healthy heart functions, including regulating heartbeat.

Directions: Take three gelatin capsules two times daily.

Companion Products: Abundance, Aroma Life, Forgiveness, HRT, Joy, Longevity Softgels, and Mineral Essence

Chelex Tincture

Chelex contains herbs that have been traditionally used to chelate and neutralize heavy metals and and disarm free radicals. Excellent for boosting the immune system.

INGREDIENTS:

Extracts:

Astragalus is used as a diuretic, a vasodilator, and respiratory infection treatment. This herb reputedly has immune-stimulating effects and increases energy.

Garlic (*Allium satiuum*) was demonstrated by Louis Pasteur to have antibacterial properties in 1858. Albert Schweitzer used garlic to treat amoebic dysentery. Later, researchers found that garlic can protect against heart disease and cancer. Garlic juice halts the growth of more than 60 types of fungi and 20 types of bacteria.

Sarsaparilla contains saponins, steroid-like molecules that neutralize endotoxins (poisons secreted by fungi and bacteria in the human body) that contribute to many kinds of disease.

Eleuthero root (formerly referred to as Siberian ginseng) strengthens the adrenal glands, enhances immune function, normalizes blood pressure, improves mental alertness, and promotes hormonal balance.

Red Clover is a heavy metal detoxifier. It is used to treat asthma, bronchitis, skin ailments, ulcers, and arthritis. Used in some cultures to prevent recurrence of cancer.

Royal jelly is the substance fed to queen bees that allows them to live thirty to forty times longer than worker bees. It is very rich in amino acids, minerals, and vitamins B5 and B6. It stimulates the adrenal glands to increase energy.

Rosebud extract

ESSENTIAL OILS:

Rosemary (*Rosmarinus officinalis*) is a natural detoxifier, is antiparasitic and balances the endocrine system.

Roman chamomile (*Chamaemelum nobile*) promotes bile flow and strengthens liver function.

Eucalyptus (*Eucalyptus globulus*) is a powerful antimicrobial agent, rich in eucalyptol (a key ingredient in many antiseptic mouth rinses).

Helichrysum (*Helichrysum italicum*) has been studied by European researchers for regenerating tissue and improving circulation. This oil has also been studied for its natural chelating action.

Pure grain alcohol

Directions: Take 3 ml three times daily in distilled water or as needed. Shake well before using. Refrigerate after opening.

Companion Products: Comfortone, ICP, Immuflo, Juva Cleanse, JuvaFlex, Detoxzyme, Essential-zyme, and Polyzyme

ComforTone®

A high-powered herbal laxative complex of bentonite, apple pectin, and herbal extracts that may relieve constipation, enhance colon and digestive functions, and dispel parasites and toxins.

ComforTone can help eliminate parasites from the body, break up encrustations along the colon wall, and relax intestinal spasms. If you experience nausea when using ComforTone, use Digest & Cleanse Softgels, Di-Gize or peppermint (diluted if necessary); if you experience constipation, increase your water intake and avoid using ICP. Take MegaCal or Mineral Essence daily to soften stools. If you have a history of chronic constipation, do not start ICP and ComforTone at the same time. First use ComforTone until the system is open, and then follow with ICP. Drink ten glasses of water per day.

INGREDIENTS:

Licorice (*Glycyrrhiza glabra*) **root extract** cleanses the blood and supports the liver, the most important organ for cleansing.

Psyllium (*Plantago ovata*) **seed** is a soft fiber that helps relieve abdominal pain, constipation, diarrhea, and protects against flatulence and nausea.

Apple pectin helps with enzyme production and supports proper digestive function.

Bentonite is an intestinal cleansing agent.

Fennel (*Foeniculum vulgare*) **seed** is antiparasitic, antimicrobial, antispasmotic, is a digestive aid, helps regulate intestinal flora, and increases gastric secretions.

Garlic (*Allium sativum*) **bulb** is antifungal, antiparasitic, antiviral, an immune stimulant, works as a digestive aid, and is a catalyst for the oils. Garlic juice halts the growth of more than 60 types of fungi and 20 types of bacteria.

Barberry (*Berberis vulgare*) **bark**

German chamomile (*Matricaria reticulita*) **flower extract** is antimicrobial, anti-inflammatory, limits the parasympathetic nervous system in its production of mucus, and relaxes spasms in the colon wall.

Echinacea (*E. purpurea*) **root** is antimicrobial, antiparasitic, lowers bowel transit time, absorbs toxins in the colon, and stimulates the immune system.

Ginger (*Zingiber officinale*) **root** is anti-inflammatory, antispasmodic, helps lower cholesterol, and cleanses the colon.

Rosebud extract

Cascara sagrada (*frangula purshiana*) works as an herbal laxative and as a liver cleanser.

Burdock (*Arctium lappa*) **root** lowers bowel transit time, balances intestinal flora, and absorbs toxins from the bowels.

Diatomaceous earth is an excellent intestinal cleansing agent as it absorbs mercury, E-coli, viruses, pesticide residue, and undigested proteins.

Cayenne pepper (*Capsicum annuum*) **fruit** is stimulating to circulation.

ESSENTIAL OILS:

Rosemary (*Rosmarinus officinalis*) is antiparasitic and balances the endocrine system. It is also antifungal, antibacterial, antiparasitic and helps cleanse the liver.

German chamomile (*Matricaria recutita*) helps prevent acne, rashes, and eczema. It also improves bile flow from the liver.

Tarragon (*Artemisia dracunculus*) has been used to reduce intestinal spasms, sluggish digestion, and fermentation.

Peppermint (*Mentha piperita*) reduces candida, nausea, and vomiting. Also reduces inflammation and eases intestinal cramps.

Ginger (*Zingiber officinale*) combats indigestion, diarrhea, loss of appetite, and congestion.

Anise (*Pimpinella anisum*) helps prevent flatulence, colon spasms, and indigestion.

Mugwort (*Artemisia vulgaris*) has been used traditionally to calm nerves. It is a gastrointestinal regulator and used for muscle spasms.

Tangerine (*Citrus reticulata*) is cleansing and purifying to the digestive system.

Fennel (*Foeniculum vulgare*) is antiseptic and antiparasitic. Improves digestion and pancreatic functions.

Directions: Start with 2-5 gelatin capsules first thing in the morning, and 2-5 capsules just before bed. Drink eight to ten eight-ounce glasses of purified or distilled water per day for best results. If you get cramps, lower the dosage or skip one day and resume the following. After starting ComforTone do not stop completely. Take at least one in the morning and one in the evening. For maximum results, take with JuvaTone and Essentialzyme one hour after taking ComforTone. ComforTone may be taken every day without becoming addictive.

Companion Products: Chelex, ICP, JuvaTone, Essentialzyme, ParaFree Softgels, DiGize, JuvaFlex, Juva Cleanse, Purification, and Thieves

Safety Data: ComforTone may be taken during pregnancy, as long as you do not get diarrhea. Diarrhea might cause cramping, which could induce labor.

CortiStop® - Women's

Designed to counter rising cortisol levels in women.

INGREDIENTS:

Pregnenolone is the precursor hormone from which all other hormones are created. It is an important precursor for the body's production of progesterone which blocks cortisol receptors.

Black Cohosh (*Actaea racemosa*) root extract has natural estrogen-like effects that counteract higher cortisol levels.

L-a-lysophosphatidalcholine

L-a-phosphatidylcholine

DHEA (*Dioscorea villosa*) is derived from wild yam and is an important hormone precursor for progesterone.

Magnesium stearate

ESSENTIAL OILS:

Fleabane (*Conyza canadensis*) reduces cortisol levels and promotes hormone balance.

Peppermint (*Mentha piperita*) is a hormone balancer, and has a cooling, refreshing effect.

Frankincense (*Boswellia carteri*) hormone balancer.

Fennel (*Foeniculum vulgare*) has estrogen-like activity that combats excess cortisol.

Clary Sage (*Salvia sclarea*) increases estrogen balance and blunts the effects of excess cortisol.

Also contains: Magnesium stearate silica, and gelatin

Directions: Take one capsule in the morning before breakfast. If desired, for extra benefits, take another capsule before bedtime. Use daily for 8 weeks. Discontinue for 2-4 weeks before resuming.

Caution: For adult use only. If pregnant or under a doctor's care, consult a physician before using.

Companion Products: Dragon Time, Endoflex, Prenolone Cream, Prenolone+ Cream, and Progessence Cream

Detoxzyme

A vegetable enzyme complex designed to promote detoxification of the body. Combines essential oils with enzymes designed to digest starches, sugars, proteins, and fats. This formula is structured with trace minerals that help the body detoxify itself, reducing cholesterol and triglycerides. It helps in opening the gallbladder duct and cleansing the liver, preventing candida and yeast overgrowth, and promoting general detoxification.

The formula facilitates optimal absorption of nutrients from foods and supplements, delays the aging process, and maintains optimal energy levels. It also helps to regulate the pH level and reduce acidification and parasite colonization and infestation.

Detoxzyme also contains phytase, an enzyme essential for people eating vegetarian diets. Phytase is crucial for unlocking the mineral content of many grains, nuts, seeds, and other foods which contain high levels of essential minerals that are unavailable to the human body because they are bound up in insoluble indigestible phytate complexes. Up to 90% of the magnesium, potassium, and zinc in foods like barley, cashews, walnuts, and rice is irreversibly tied up by phytic acid and cannot be absorbed by the digestive system. Thus the phytase in Detoxzyme results in a a huge boost in mineral absorption from diets high in nuts, seeds, and whole grains.

The benefits of essential minerals to human health cannot be overemphasized. Magnesium is crucial for blood pressure regulation and antioxidant production, zinc is critical for normal immune function, and potassium is vital for blood pressure and water balance and is found inside of every cell in the body.

INGREDIENTS:

Amylase (alpha) is a powerful starch digesting enzyme prevents starch fermentation in the digestive system.

Glucoamylase

Alpha-galactosidase

Invertase

Lactase

Cellulase

Protease – great health benefits in polyzyme.

Bromelain is a natural enzyme and carbohydrate digester.

Lipase is a fat-dissolving enzyme vital for proper absorption of Vitamin D, E, and A.

Phytase – also contains vegetable cellulose.

Cumin seed has been used for centuries in the Middle East to help promote digestion and stimulate enzyme activity.

Rice bran

Silica

ESSENTIAL OILS:

Cumin (*Cuminum cyminum*) has been shown to be a great digestive aid that is also antiparasitic anti-inflammatory, and antiviral.

Anise (*Pimpinella anisum*) is antiparasitic and promotes digestion and protein breakdown.

Fennel (*Foeniculum vulgare*) is antiseptic and antiparasitic and improves digestive and pancreatic functions.

Directions: Take 2-3 capsules three times daily, between meals.

Companion Products: ComforTone, JuvaTone, Di-Gize, JuvaFlex, and Juva Cleanse

Digest + Cleanse Softgels

Soothes bowel upset and improves digestion with clinically proven and time-tested essential oils. Enteric coated to release essential oils in the intestine, preserving their efficacy and significantly improving absorption.

ESSENTIAL OILS:

Peppermint leaf (*Mentha piperita*) — clinically researched to soothe and calm the digestive tract while promoting perstalsis. Kills bacteria, yeasts, fungi and mold.

Caraway seed (*Carum carvi*) — enhances digestion and sooths bowel spasms

Lemon peel (*citrus limon*) — traditional remedy for stimulating digestion and reducing acidity

Ginger root (*Zingiber officinale*) — improves digestion and helps reduce gas and intestinal fermentation. Has antispasmodic and antiseptic properties

Fennel seed (*foeniculum vulgare*) — a gastrointestinal stimulant that helps eliminate flatulence and nausea

Anise seed (*Pimpinella anisum*) — creates an unfriendly environment for parasites.

Also Contains:

Virgin coconut oil, fractionated coconut oil, gelatin, glycerin, aqueous coating solution (oleic acid, sodiuim alginate, MCFAs, ethylcellulose, stearic acid)

EndoGize

A daily supplement expressly formulated to support and maintain a healthy and balanced endocrine system in women.

INGREDIENTS:

Vitamin B6 (pyridoxine HCl) must be obtained from the diet because humans cannot synthesize it. Vitamin B6 plays a vital role in the function of approximately 100 enzymes that catalyze essential chemical reactions in the human body

Zinc (zinc aspartate) is an essential trace element for all forms of life. Nearly 100 different enzymes depend on zinc for their ability to catalyze vital chemical reactions. Zinc has also been shown to enhance immune system function.

Ashwaganda root (*Withanaia somenifera*) is a small evergreen tree—a member of the pepper family—that grows in India and is widely used in Auyervedic medicine. It is said to boost physical performance, stimulate sexual capacity and enhance reproductive function in both men and women.

Muira puama root (*Ptychopetalum olacoides*)

L-arginine is used by the body to make nitric oxide, which reduces blood vessel stiffness, increases blood flow, and improves blood vessel function.

Epimedium leaf (*Epimedium grandiflorum*), also known by its common name of Horny Goat Weed, one of the most valued tonics of Chinese herbalism. In China it is especially used for supporting healthy sexual activity.

***Tribulus terrestris* fruit** has long been a constituent in tonics in Indian ayurveda practice. Independent studies suggest that Tribulus terrestris extract slightly increases hormone levels, though leaving them in the normal range.

Phosphatidylcholine makes cholesterol more soluble and less able to cause hardening of the arteries.

Lecithin (soy) in several studies has been shown to have significant effects on lowering cholesterol and triglycerides, while increasing HDL ("good cholesterol") levels in the blood

Eurycoma longifolia root extract comes from a small flowering evergreen that grows in Malaysia. It has been shown to have anti-cancer properties as well as hormone enhancing properties. The *British Journal of Sports Medicine* published a study in 2003, which showed that *Eurycoma longifolia* caused increased muscle strength and size when compared to a placebo.

Black Pepper *(Piper nigrum)* fruit extract increases the body's ability to absorb and use nutrients

Amylase 5000 FCC is an enzyme that breaks starch down into sugar.

Validase AFP protease is the digestive enzyme needed to break down proteins

Cellulase 4000 is an enzyme that breaks down cellulose

Glucoamylase is a digestive enzyme that breaks starches down into sugar

DHEA is the most abundant hormone made by the adrenal glands. Once it enters the bloodstream, DHEA travels throughout the body and is converted into female hormones, known as estrogens, and male hormones, known as androgens.

ESSENTIAL OILS:

Ginger *(Zingiber officinale)* has been traditionally used to combat nausea and promote gastrointestinal well-being.

Myrrh *(Commiphora myrrha)* has high levels of sesquiterpenes, a class of compounds that can stimulate the limbic system in the brain which controls emotions and hormone release.

Cassia *(Cinnamomum cassia)* is anti-infectious, antibacterial and anticoagulant.

Clary Sage *(Salvia sclarea)* is known as a hormone balancer. It contains natural sclareol, a phytoestrogen that mimics estrogen function. It helps with menstrual cramps, PMS, and circulatory problems.

Canadian Fleabane *(Conyza canadensis)* stimulates production of growth hormone and is a tonic for the liver and pancreas.

Essentialzyme

A high-quality enzyme complex that may improve and aid digestion and the elimination of toxic waste from the body. Essentialzyme was formulated to help supply enzymes to those who have difficulty digesting or assimilating food. Essentialzyme helps reestablish proper enzyme balance in the digestive system and throughout the body and helps improve intestinal flora. It may also help retard the aging process.

Enzyme supplementation is particularly important for people suffering chronic pancreatitis, cystic fibrosis, or in any condition where the pancreas duct or common bile duct is blocked, thereby preventing enzymes from reaching the intestine.

INGREDIENTS:

Pancrelipase a powerful complex of fat, protein, and starch-dissolving enzymes derived from pork.

Trypsin is an animal product that has amino acid precursor action, helps with carbohydrate conversion, and food/nutrient assimilation.

Carrot root powder has the second highest concentration of natural enzymes in vegetables.

Alfalfa sprouts are a source of natural amylase.

Pancreatin 4X is a protein-digesting enzyme complex that has been used to treat cancer. It is a natural full-spectrum enzyme complex containing proteases, amylases, and lipases.

Papain is a vegetable enzyme derived from unripe papayas and an excellent carbohydrate digester.

Bromelain is a proteolytic enzyme from pineapple stems, and is a natural enzyme and carbohydrate digester.

Betaine HCl helps digest protein.

Cumin seed has been used for centuries in the Middle East to help promote digestion and stimulate enzyme activity.

Magnesium stearate

Di-Calcium phosphate

Stearic acid

Thymus leaf

ESSENTIAL OILS:

Tarragon (*Artemisia dracunculus*) is antiviral, antibacterial, and anti-inflammatory. It also helps prevent fermentation in the intestinal tract.

Peppermint (*Mentha piperita*) improves digestion and intestinal health.

Anise (*Pimpinella anisum*) improves digestion and intestinal health. Also known to ease intestinal cramps and inflammation.

Fennel (*Foeniculum vulgare*) has been used for centuries for proper digestion.

Clove (*Syzygium aromaticum*) is beneficial for its antibacterial, antiviral, antifungal, anti-infectious, and antiparasitic properties.

Directions: Take 3 tablets, three times daily prior to or with meal. Take Essentialzyme with meals, especially high-protein meals, after 3 p.m., as it will help lessen the burden on the digestive system.

Companion Products: Polyzyme, Carbozyme, and DiGize

Estro

Estro is an herbal tincture containing plant-derived phytoestrogens, such as black cohosh, which are widely used in Europe as a safe alternative to synthetic estrogen. Phytoestrogens have been researched for their ability to support the body during PMS without many of the side effects associated with estrogen-replacement therapies. Contains the therapeutic-grade essential oil of clary sage (*Salvia sclarea*), which contains natural sclareol, a plant-based estrogen. Start with one dropper two to three times daily. Increase as needed to as much as eight droppers daily. Estro may take as long as four weeks to reach maximum effectiveness.

INGREDIENTS:

Black Cohosh extract—approved by the German Commission E for combating PMS sysmptoms. Its constituents have been found to mimic those of estrogen.

Blue Cohosh extract—the main ingredient brewed in a tea used by Native American women to relieve menstrual and labor cramping, now recommended by modern herbalists to induce menstruation and as a uterine stimulant and antispasmodic.

Royal Jelly extrct—a secretion produced by worker bees, upon which all bee larvae feed during the first three days of life. Because queen larvae continue to feed on this substance (and live thirty to forty times longer), various herbalists claim that royal jelly is especially effective in halting or controlling the aging process, nourishing the skin, and erasing facial blemishes and wrinkles.

ESSENTIAL OILS:

Fennel (*Foeniculum vulgare*)—is antiseptic and stimulating to the circulatory and respiratory systems.

Lavender (*Lavandula angustifolia*)—is calming, relaxing, and balancing, both physically and emotionally.

Clary Sage (*Salvia sclarea*)—is a source of natural estrogen.

Exodus

Exodus is the ultimate supercharged antioxidant containing a biblical blend of essential oils and other nutritional herbs to provide important support for the immune system.

INGREDIENTS:

Uncaria tomentosa (Cat's Claw, Una de Gato) contains alkaloids including mitraphylline that substantially amplify immunity.

Amino acid complex of alanine, cystine, arginine, glycine, lycine, threonine, and thorine is used as the building block of the enzymes, proteins, and cells of our natural defenses.

Yucca (*Yucca schidigeria*) cleanses the blood.

Echinacea (*Echinacea purpurea*) is one of the best-studied immune boosters. It increases the number and activity of white blood cells, T-cells, and natural interferon.

Vitamin A is a powerful antioxidant essential for proper immunity.

Grape seed extract is one of the strongest known antioxidants.

Trace minerals has complex proven immune-stimulating properties.

Pantothenic acid boosts the formation of antibodies.

ESSENTIAL OILS:

Frankincense (*Boswellia carteri*) was historically used for its healing properties. It has antitumoral and immune-stimulating properties.

Hyssop (*Hyssopus officinalis*) has been recognized for thousands of years for its anti-inflammatory, anti-infectious, and antiparasitic properties. It helps discharge toxins and mucus.

Bay laurel (*Laurus nobilis*) has antiseptic and antimicrobial properties.

Spikenard (*Nardostachys jatamansi*) is highly regarded in India as a medicinal herb. It is used as an immune stimulant.

Myrrh (*Commiphora myrrha*) is anti-infectious and antitumoral, enhancing the immune system.

Directions: Take 3 capsules, 2 to 3 times daily.

Companion Products: ImmuPro, ImmuneTune, Super C Chewable, Exodus II, and Thieves

FemiGen

This is a formula with herbs and amino acids, to help balance the reproductive system from the developmental years all the way through menopause. FemiGen acts as a natural estrogen and helps balance the hormones.

INGREDIENTS:

Damiana has been described as a blood purifier, an expectorant, and is used as a diuretic.

Epimedium has been used to help detoxify kidneys and help eliminate lower back pain and frequent urination.

Dong Quai has estrogenic qualities and increases blood flow to the reproductive organs of the female system. It has also been used as a menstrual balancer.

Muira puama (potency wood) has been used for treatment of frigidity, menstrual cramps, impotency, and PMS

Wild yam root contains compounds that are similar in structure to steroids. It is good for muscle spasms and contains anti-inflammatory compounds.

Also contains:

American ginseng, licorice root, black cohosh, cramp bark, squaw vine, magnesium, L-carnitine, dimethylglycine, L-phenylalanine, L-cystine, L-cysteine, and L-tryptophan.

HRT

HRT tincture combines concentrated extracts of some of the best-studied herbs for improving heart function, including hawthorn berry, garlic, and cayenne. Hawthorn berry's role in supporting the heart has been gaining increasing notice among both authors and physicians. According to Varro Tyler, Ph.D., one of the most highly esteemed herbalists in the U.S., "Studies are urgently needed for [an herb] as potentially valuable as this one."

INGREDIENTS:

Hawthorn (*Crateagus laevigata*) **berries** have been used since the time of Dioscorides in the first century A.D. They are one of the best studied herbs to support the heart, protecting against heart muscle weakness, angina, and mild arrhythmia. J. L. Rodale published an entire book on the subject, *The Hawthorn Berry for the Heart*.

Garlic protects against heart disease and cancer. Garlic juice halts the growth of more than 60 types of fungi and 20 types of bacteria.

Lobelia protects and stimulates the heart muscle.

Cayenne pepper (*Capsicum annuum*) **fruit** possesses fibrinolytic activity (able to break down blood clots) and stimulates circulation.

Royal jelly is a substance fed to queen bees that allows them to live thirty to forty times longer than worker bees. It is very rich in amino acids, minerals, and vitamins B5 and B6. It stimulates the adrenal glands to increase energy.

blackberry fruit extract is a powerful antioxidant.

ESSENTIAL OILS:

Lemon (*Citrus limon*) promotes leukocyte formation and increases immune function.

Rosewood (*Aniba rosaeodora*) has been researched at Weber State University for its antibacterial antimicrobial action.

Ylang ylang (*Cananga odorata*) is traditionally used to support heart healthy function and circulation.

Cypress (*Cupressus sempervirens*) is an oil most used for the circulatory system. Increases lymphatic drainage and strengthens the entire vascular system.

Pure grain alcohol

Directions: Take 1 to 3 droppers three times daily in distilled water or as needed.

Companion Products: Cardiacare, Super Cal, and Longevity Softgels

ICP

ICP Multiple Fiber Beverage is a unique source of fiber and bulk for the diet, which helps speed the transit time of waste matter through the intestinal tract. Psyllium, oat bran, flax, and rice bran are specifically balanced in ICP to eliminate allergy symptoms that many people experience when taking psyllium alone. Essential oils enhance ICP's flavor and may help dispel gas and pain. This formula is unsurpassed as an aid in enhancing normal bowel function.

INGREDIENTS:

Psyllium *(Plantago ovata)* **seed powder** expands when mixed with water and is smooth and filling, not abrasive, to the intestinal walls. It is a soft fiber that helps relieve abdominal pain, constipation, diarrhea, and protects against nausea.

Plant Cellulose is a toxin-absorbing fiber.

Aloe vera leaf extract is a natural laxative and lubricant that relaxes the colon.

Rice bran is an outstanding source of soluble and semisoluble fiber.

Oat bran *(Avena sativa)* binds up fat so it does not enter the blood stream. It is also high in immune-supporting beta-glucans.

Guar gum has been used in expanding and cleansing the colon.

Flax seed is an excellent cleanser for intestinal walls and the digestive system. It is also a rich source of fiber, lignans, and omega-3 fats.

Protease 3.0, 4.5, 6.0 are protein digesting enzymes designed to work in a broad range of pH conditions. Acid stable proteases are essential for amino acid creation in the acid environment of the stomach while alkaline proteases are more effective in the large intestine. This combination of proteases is scientifically formulated to maximize protein digestion and amino acid formation.

Phytase is an enzyme essential for people eating vegetarian diets. Phytase is crucial for unlocking the mineral content of many grains, nuts, seeds, and other foods which contain high levels of essential minerals that are unavailable to the human body because they are bound up in insoluble indigestible phytate complexes. Up to 90% of the magnesium, potassium, and zinc in foods like barley, cashews, walnuts, and rice is locked up by phytic acid and cannot be absorbed by the digestive system, unless phytase is present.

Yucca *(Yucca schidigeria)* helps break up obstructions in the digestive system and contains enzymes for digestion.

Fennel seed stimulates the gastrointestinal mucous membrane, which in turn stimulates the pancreas to secrete digestive enzymes to dissolve undigested proteins. It is antiparasitic.

Pepsin is an enzyme to aid digestion.

Peptidase promotes the formation and absorption of amino acids in the digestive system.

ESSENTIAL OILS:

Fennel (*Foeniculum vulgare*) is antibacterial and antiparasitical. Helps digestive and pancreatic functions. Increases gastric secretions

Tarragon (*Artemisia dracunculus*) is anti-infectious, antispasmodic, and antiviral. It prevents fermentation in the intestinal tract.

Ginger (*Zingiber officinale*) improves digestion and combats parasites.

Lemongrass (*Cymbopogon flexuosus*) is antifungal and promotes digestion. It is also anti-inflammatory, anti-parasitic, and antibacterial.

Rosemary (*Rosmarinus officinalis*) reduces indigestion and helps regulate cholesterol. It is also antifungal, antiparasitic, antibacterial and helps cleanse the liver.

Anise (*Pimpinella anisum*) helps colon spasms and indigestion.

Directions: Take five times a week for maintenance (1/2 cup water, 1/2 cup apple juice, and one heaping teaspoon of ICP). Take more often for cleansing (Start with one heaping teaspoon, 2 to three times a day with carrot or other vegetable juices. Increase to three teaspoons, three times a day.) ICP dilutes better in warm water. Drink immediately as this product tends to thicken quickly when added to liquid.

For best results, take ComforTone first, then ICP, morning and night. ICP absorbs toxins and can build and improve peristalsis, the wave-like movement of the intestinal walls.

Companion Products: ComforTone, Digest & Cleanse Softgels, JuvaTone, ParaFree Softgels, DiGize, JuvaFlex, Purification, and Thieves

ImmuneTune

ImmuneTune is a super antioxidant complex that supports the immune system and fights free radicals. The curcuminoid blend in this product has been found to be 60 percent stronger in antioxidant activity than pine bark or grape seed extract. However, synergy is the key to obtaining maximum effect. Through combining curcuminoids with grapeseed extract, its antioxidant power is almost doubled.

INGREDIENTS:

Curcuminoids (from curcumin and turmeric) are potent antioxidants and immune supporters. They are also anti-inflammatory.

Grape seed extract is one of the strongest natural antioxidants known.

Magnesium is essential for healthy immunity.

Potassium is critical for immune health.

Calcium pantothenate may serve as protection against high blood pressure and colon cancer.

Alpha lipoic acid is one of the most powerful known antioxidants. It is the only antioxidant

that is both oil and water soluble. It has been used to treat diabetes, heart, and liver disease.

Chromium nicotinate improves insulin sensitivity and blood sugar metabolism.

Selenium has been extensively researched for its anticancer and antioxidant properties.

Echinacea increases white blood cell count and stimulates the immune system.

Ginger extract has been used to treat indigestion, flatulence, diarrhea, and stomach ache.

Yucca (*Yucca schidigeria*) is an excellent antioxidant that supports the liver and gall bladder.

ESSENTIAL OILS:

Orange (*Citrus sinensis*) contains limonene, a powerful antioxidant.

Pine (*Pinus sylvestris*) helps prevent respiratory infection and bronchitis.

White Fir (*Abies concolor*) has also been used for different types of respiratory infections and bronchitis.

Cistus (*Cistus ladanifer*) has been used to improve immune function, and enhance immune cell regeneration.

Pantothenic acid boosts the formation of antibodies.

Ravensara (*Ravensara aromatica*), known as the "oil that heals," may help support the immune system. It is antiviral, antibacterial, and antifungal.

Lemon (*Citrus limon*) promotes leukocyte formation and increases immune function.

Directions: For slow metabolism, take 2 to 3 capsules daily. For fast metabolism, take 3 to 6 capsules daily. It is best taken on an empty stomach. For stomach sensitivity, take with meals.

Companion Products: Exodus, ImmuPro, ParaFree Softgels, Super C Chewable, Exodus II, ImmuPower, DiGize, and Thieves

ImmuPro

ImmuPro chewable is packed with some of the most powerful immune stimulants known, including wolfberry polysaccharide and beta glucan (a polysaccharide from reishi, maitake, and *Agaricus blazei* mushrooms). Numerous studies have documented the ability of these botanicals to reverse cancer and stimulate both cell-mediated and humoral immunity, dramatically boosting levels of macrophages, neutrophiles, phagocytes, B-cells, T-cells, natural killer cells, interleukins, and interferons. Contains a complex of the potent immune-boosting minerals zinc, copper, and selenium. Also contains melatonin, one of the most powerful immune stimulants known, shown to clinically reverse tumor growth. Melatonin levels steadily decrease with age and are a factor that contributes to accelerated aging.

INGREDIENTS:

Wolfberry *(Lycium barbarum)* **polysaccharide** used in China for centuries, has been shown to be one of the most powerful supporters of immune function.

Organic reishi, maitake, and *Agaricus blazei* **mushrooms** are the highest known sources of a rich variety of beta glucans, potent immune-stimulating polysaccharides which have been documented by numerous studies as having significant immune-boosting effects.

Strawberry powder

Orange oil *(Citrus sinensis)* contains over 90 percent d-limonene, one of the most powerful anticancer as compounds studied in recent years. A potent antioxidant.

Fructose is a low-glycemic sweetener having minimal impact on blood sugar levels.

Calcium is key for bone health and prevents high blood pressure

Zinc Citrate is a superb, bioavailable source of zinc, a mineral crucial to normal immune function.

Copper chelate (rice protein) an essential mineral which should always be combined with zinc at the correct ratio. This is due to the fact that copper and zinc compete for absorption in the intestines. Excess of either zinc or copper can create a mineral deficiency that can result in immune suppression instead of immune activation.

Selenomethionine is essential for normal immunity, activating T-lymphocytes, interleukins, interferons, and NK cells.

Lemonene (from *Citrus aurantium)*

Melatonin is one the most powerful known immune stimulants, boosting both cell-mediated and humoral immunity. It has been documented as an immune treatment for tumors.

Arabinogalactin 100

Coconut oil

Silicia

Directions: Take 1 tablet before retiring. If under stress take 2 to 4 tablets before retiring or as needed.

Companion Products: Exodus, ImmuneTune, Thieves, and Longevity Oil Blend or Softgels

Inner Defense Softgels

Containing antibacterial, antifungal, and antiviral essential oils, Inner Defense is designed to eliminate the maximum spectrum of pathogenic organisms, reduce the risk of infectious disease, and act as an antioxidant. A specially formulated blend of high-powered aldehydes and phenolics, Inner Defense essential oil formula is encapsulated in an uncoated fast-release vegetarian soft gel to provide immediate and maximum effects. For best results, use Life 5™ probiotic 8 hours after use.

ESSENTIAL OILS:

Enhanced Thieves Blend: A proprietary blend of clove, cinnamon, rosemary, eucalyptus radiata, lemon oil, and citronella that have been university-tested for the ability to kill bacteria, fungi, and parasites.

Oregano *(Origanum compactum)* is rich in carvacrol and is one of the most powerful purifying and antiseptic essential oils known to science. High in DNA-repair activity, oregano provides antioxidant protection as it cleans the body of pathogens.

Thyme *(Thymus vulgaris)* is rich in thymol and is very antiseptic with extremely penetrating anti-parasitic effects. Used in German herbal medicine to combat respiratory infections, thyme has a powerful sanitizing effect inside the body.

Directions: 1-2 capsules twice a day to help eliminate bacterial and viral infections. Do not take more than 10 capsules per day. For best results, use Life 5™ probiotic 8 hours after use.

Companion Products: Life 5, Super C, Omega Blue, Balance Complete, Ningxia Red, Dried wolfberries, NutriVida multivitamins, ImmuPro, Thieves antiseptic Spray, FreshEssence Plus Mouthwash

Juva Cleanse

See Essential Oil Blend information in Chapter 7

JuvaFlex

See Essential Oil Blend information in Chapter 7

JuvaPower/JuvaSpice

A whole food high antioxidant vegetable powder complex that is a rich source of acid-binding foods and high in liver-protecting nutrients like tocotrienols, xanthophylls, and tocopherols. It is also rich in antimutagenic sulphoraphane and squalene.

INGREDIENTS:

Rice Bran *(Oryza Sativa)*: Stabilized, nonchemically treated. Contains gamma-oryzanol, tocotrienols, tocopherols, squalene, ferulic acid, IP6 (inositol hexaphosphate) and Gamma-oryzanol, a triterpene alcohol that is more effective than vitamin E in stopping oxidation of cholesterol. In studies at the Louisiana State University in Baton Rouge, researchers concluded that gamma-oryzanol "had activities higher than that of any of the 4 vitamin E components. Gamma-oryzanol may be a more important antioxidant of rice bran in the reduction of cholesterol oxidation than vitamin E."[1]

Rice bran is considered one of the best sources of squalene, an antimutagen and anti-cancer agent also found in olive oil and shark liver oil. [2,3]

Ferulic acid is also found in rice bran and acts as an antioxidative, hypotensive polyphenol that reduces blood pressure.[4]

Spinach powder *(Spinacea oleracea)* One of the highest known antioxidant foods (1,260 ORAC units/100g), rich in mixed carotenoids (ie., lutein, zeaxanthin), 9-cis-beta-carotene, flavonoids, and p-coumaric acid derivatives. "Neoxanthin from spinach significantly reduced cell viability to 10.9% for PC-3, 15% for DU 145 (prostate cell cancer lines)." E Kotake-Nara E, Hokkaido University.

Tomato flake *(Lycospersicon esculentum)* High in antimutagens lycopene, kaempferol, and chlorogenic acid.

Beet root powder *(Beta vulgaris)* High-pigment red phenotypes have been shown to have the best liver-protecting properties, according to M. Wettasinghe, University of Wisconsin at Madison.

Flax seed bran *(Linum usitatissimum)* high in lignans, which prevent cellular mutations according to over 50 peer-reviewed clinical studies. The lignans in flax seed also protect the liver against over burden of toxins, according to recent university research (Rakuno Gakuen University, Ebetsu, Japan).[5]

Oat bran *(Avena sativa)* high in immune-supporting beta glucans. It also binds up fat and helps flush it out of the body.

Peppermint leaf *(Mentha piperita)*: studied for its ability to combat cellular mutation. Promotes healthy digestive functions and anti-inflammatory.

Broccoli floret powder *(Brassica oleracea ssp. cymosa)* high in sulphoraphane, protective against cellular mutations; 890 TE/100g According to Cornell University scientists, "Broccoli possessed the highest total phenolic content, followed by spinach, yellow onion, red pepper, carrot, cabbage, potato." Y. Chu, Cornell University.

Cucumber powder *(Cucumis sativus)* 100 grams has 5,160 iu Vit. A, 312 mcg folate, 3,456 mg Vit. K

L-taurine Essential for bile acid formation and liver protection.

Dill Leaf *(Anethum graveolens)* excellent cleansing herb for the liver.

---

1. Z. Xu et al., *J Agric Food Chem.* 2001.

2. TJ Smith, University of South Carolina (*Expert Opin Investig Drugs.* 2000)

3. HL Newmark, Rockefeller University, New York (*Ann N Y Acad Sci.* 1999)

4. Suzuki A et al., "Short- and long-term effects of ferulic acid on blood pressure in spontaneously hypertensive rats." *Am J Hypertens.* 2002 Apr;15(4 Pt 1):351-7.

5. Endoh D et al., Rakuno Gakuen University, Ebetsu, Japan.

Barley sprout powder *(Hordeum vulgare L.)*

Ginger root powder *(Zingiber officinale Rosc.)*

Aloe vera *(Aloe barbadensis)* **leaf extract** is a natural laxative and lubricant that relaxes the colon.

Slippery elm, inner bark, *(Ulmus fulva)*

Psyllium seed husk *(Plantago ovata)*, a key colon cleanser. A healthy liver requires a healthy colon. It protects against nausea, diarrhea, constipation, and is cleansing on the intestinal walls.

Anise (Pimpinella anisum) seed and EO.

Fennel (Foeniculum vulgare) seed and EO.

Potassium cloride (JuvaSpice only)

Real Salt mined from Redmond, Utah (Juva-Spice only)

Cayenne Pepper *(Capsium Annum)* **fruit** (JuvaSpice only) Stimulates circulation and supports healthy heart functions.

Directions: Sprinkle 1 tablespoon on food or add to purified drinking water.

Companion Products: JuvaTone, Juva Cleanse, and JuvaFlex

JuvaTone

JuvaTone is a special herbal complex designed to support the liver. The liver is one of the most important organs of the body. It purifies the blood and is a key to converting carbohydrates to energy. An overtaxed liver may affect our energy, digestion, and skin. Fats and bile within the liver can easily become oversaturated with oil-soluble toxins, synthetic chemicals, and heavy metals. As toxins build, the liver becomes taxed and stressed, resulting in aggravating skin conditions, rashes, fatigue, headaches, muscle pain, digestive disturbances, pallor, dizziness, irritability, mood swings, and mental confusion. The liver also plays a major role in helping the body detoxify. The final products of digestion are transported through the portal vein from the colon to the liver to be cleansed.

INGREDIENTS:

Calcium is key for bone health and prevents high blood pressure

Choline bitartrate has been used in the treatment of many liver disorders, including elevated cholesterol levels, viral hepatitis, and cirrhosis.

Inositol helps the liver rid itself of fat and bile.

Beet root powder is a source of enzymes that protects the liver.

L-cysteine promotes the production of glutathione, one of the most powerful antioxidants and vital for protecting the liver.

Plant cellulose is a toxin-absorbing fiber.

Bee propolis supports liver detoxification.

Dl-methionine is one of the most powerful antioxidants in the body, and especially important to protect the liver.

Oregon grape root *(Berberis aquifolium)* contains berberine, which has been studied as a liver protectant and for its effects against hepatitis.

Dandelion root is used for disturbances in bile flow and liver disorders.

Other INGREDIENTS: Alfalfa sprouts, echinacea root, parsley *(Petroselinum crispum)* herb has been used to purify the urinary tract, sodium copper chlorophyllin in herbal extracts, magnesium stearate, di-calcium phosphate, silica, stearic acid.

ESSENTIAL OILS:

Geranium *(Pelargonium graveolens)* has been used for centuries as a liver cleanser and to regenerate tissue and nerves.

German chamomile *(Matricaria recutita)* improves bile flow from the liver.

Rosemary *(Rosmarinus officinalis)* supports the liver and combats cirrhosis. Helps combat hepatitis and other infectious diseases.

Lemon *(Citrus limon)* promotes leukocyte formation and increases immune function.

Blue tansy *(Tanacetum annuum)* is anti-inflammatory and is used for hypertension and arthritis. It is also exceptional for cleansing the liver and lymphatic system.

Myrtle *(Myrtus communis)* helps break up mucus and stimulate the thyroid. It stimulates the liver and alleviates skin disorders (psoriasis, acne, etc.).

Directions: For slow metabolism, take 2 tablets, three times daily. Increase as needed up to 4 tablets, four times daily. For fast metabolism, take 3 tablets, three times daily and increase to 4 tablets, four times daily or as needed. Best taken between meals. Tablets may be chewed, broken, or swallowed whole. For optimum results, use with ComforTone, one hour apart.

Companion Products: ComforTone, ICP, Essential-zyme, ParaFree Softgels, Di-Gize, Forgiveness, JuvaFlex, Release, Surrender, and Juva Cleanse

K & B Tincture

K & B tincture contains extracts of herbs that promote kidney and bladder health.

INGREDIENTS:

Juniper berries—long used by Greek, Arabic, and Native American peoples as a kidney stimulant to encourage cleansing and increased filtration.

Parsley is used to purify the urinary tract.

Uva Ursi a mild diuretic, astringent, and urinary tract infection remedy.

Dandelion root—traditionally used to treat edema and digestive, gallbladder, and liver disorders.

Royal jelly is a substance fed to queen bees that allows them to live thirty to forty times longer than worker bees. It is very rich in amino acids, minerals, and vitamins B5 and B6.

ESSENTIAL OILS:

Clove (*Syzygium aromaticum*) is one of the most antimicrobial and antiseptic essential oils.

Juniper (*Juniperus osteosperma* and *J. scopulorum*) is a strong diuretic. It is also excellent for cleansing and detoxifying

Sage (*Salvia officinalis*) strengthens the vital centers and supports metabolism.

Fennel (*Foeniculum vulgare*) is antiseptic to the digestive tract. Supports digestion.

Geranium (*Pelargonium graveolens*) opens the bile duct. It has also been used for centuries to regenerate tissue and nerves.

Roman chamomile (*Chamaemelum nobile*) promotes the flow of bile to and from the liver, a key aspect of cleansing and detoxification.

Pure grain alcohol

Directions: Take 1 to 3 droppers three times daily in distilled water or as needed.

Companion Products: Juniper, Essentialzyme, Detoxzyme, JuvaTone, Juva Cleanse, and JuvaFlex

Life 5™ High-potency Probiotic

A blend of the most resilient probiotics studied with proven ability to colonize the gut and promote immunity, infection-resistance, and vitamin sysnthesis. Includes two new super-strains that improve colonization up to 10 times because they have the best adhesion of any probiotic known: *Lactobacillus rhamnosus* (HN001-HOWARU) and *Bifidobacterium lactis* (HN019-HOWARU). It also contains superstrains of *B. bifidus*, *L. acidophilus* and *S. thermophilus*. Also within each capsule is a special prebiotic mix developed especially for these blends, consisting of a proprietary complex of calcium, lactoferrin, and other synergistic to provide unmatched enhancement of culture growth and implantation inside the body.

INGREDIENTS:

Streptococcus thermophilus (ST-21) 200 billion active cultures/gram (Danisco) 0.5 billion per serving

Lactobacillus rhamnosus (HN001-HOWARU) 450 billion/gram (Danisco) 5 billion per serving

Lactobacillus acidophilus (LA-14) 150 billion/gram (Danisco) 1.5 billion per serving

Bifidobacterium Lactis (HN019-HOWARU) 300 billion/gram (Danisco) 3 billion per serving

Bifidobacterium bifidum (BB-01) 450 billion/gram (Danisco) 0.5 billion per serving.

Directions: 2-5 capsules daily, as needed for intestinal health and comfort and to strengthen immunity.

Companion Products:
ICP/Comfortone/Essentialzyme, Balance Complete, Longevity Softgels, Detoxzyme, DiGize, peppermint, ginger.

Longevity Softgels

A potent, proprietary blend of fat-soluble antioxidants, Longevity softgels are as essential as a multivitamin and should be taken daily to prevent the damaging effects of our modern lifestyle. One of the most powerful antioxidant supplements available, with an ORAC score of 150,000, this formula provides 700 times the antioxidant power of carrots.

ESSENTIAL OILS:

Thyme leaf *(Thymus vulgaris)* — preserves fats from degradation in the brain, heart, liver and kidneys, while raising total antioxidant levels, including glutathione and superoxide dismutase.

Orange peel *(Citrus sinensis)* — contains 90% limonene documented in over 50 studies for its antimutagenic (DNA-protecting), antitumoral, anticancerous attributes

Clove bud *(syzygium aromaticum)* — reduces the stickiness of blood cells and decreases joint pain and swelling. Dr. Nagashima of the Nihon University in Japan found eugenol (the active ingredient in clove oil) inhibited the destruction of the fatty outer layer of human red blood cells.

Frankincense gum *(Boswellia carterii)* — supports normal cell regeneration and healthy immune function.

Also Contains:

Coconut oil, fractionated coconut oil, gelatin, glycerin, enteric coating solution (oleic acid, sodium alginate, MCFAs, ethylcellulose, stearic acid), mixed tocopherols

MegaCal

A high-powered calcium and essential mineral complex with a 1:1 calcium to magnesium ratio. Contains over 650 mg of elemental magnesium and calcium per serving along with key quantities of zinc, manganese, and copper, balanced to scientific ratios to avoid mineral interactions and competition. Calcium and magnesium are necessary not only for healthy bones and teeth, but also for proper heart and blood function and to keep nerve and muscles working properly.

INGREDIENTS:

Calcium: Calcium Lactate Pentahydrate, Calcium Glycerophosphate, Calcium Carbonate, Calcium Ascorbate

Magnesium: Magnesium Citrate, Magnesium Sulfate, Magnesium Carbonate

Zinc Gluconate

Copper Gluconate

Manganese Sulfate

Xylitol, as an anti-bacterial agent and bone strengthener

Lemon *(Citrus Limon)* essential oil, which prevents DNA mutation and enhances cellular repair.

Fractionated Coconut Oil, which is anti-fungal and can help prevent or eliminate candida infections.

Directions: Take 1 tablespoon daily, at least 1 hour after a meal.

Companion Products: BLM capsules or powder, and Prenolone

Mineral Essence

A balanced organic, ionic mineral complex with more than 60 different minerals. Without minerals, vitamins cannot be properly assimilated or absorbed by the body. Mineral Essence has a natural electrolyte balance, helping to prevent disease and premature aging. Minerals are also necessary for proper immune and metabolism functions.

Mineral essence also includes essential oils to enhance bioavailability. To demonstrate this, a group of volunteers consumed a teaspoon of liquid trace minerals without essential oils. Each volunteer experienced diarrhea within 24 hours. Following a washout period of several days, the same volunteers were given double the dosage of the same liquid trace minerals blended with essential oils. None experienced diarrhea.

INGREDIENTS:

Purified water is needed to dilute the minerals for liquifying this blend.

Honey is an emulsifier and natural sweetener.

Royal Jelly is a substance fed to queen bees that allows them to live thirty to forty times longer than worker bees. It is very rich in amino acids, minerals, and vitamins B5 and B6. It stimulates the adrenal glands to increase energy.

Trace mineral complex includes beryllium, bismuth, boron, bromine, calcium, carbon, cesium, chloride, chromium, copper, gallium, germanium, gold, hafnium, indium, iodine, iron, lithium, lutecium, manganese, magnesium, molybdenum, euroGen, nickel, niobium, nitrogen, phosphorus, potassium, rubidium, scandium, selenium, silica, silver, sodium, strontium, sulfur, tantalum, thallium, tin, titanium, tungsten, vanadium, yttrium, zinc, and zirconium.

ESSENTIAL OILS:

Lemon (*Citrus limon*) promotes leukocyte formation and increases immune function.

Cinnamon bark (*Cinnamomum verum*) is anti-infectious, antibacterial, antiviral, antifungal, antiparasitic and anticoagulant.

Peppermint (*Mentha piperita*) promotes healthy digestion and mineral absorption.

Directions: Take 5 droppers morning and evening or as needed for a mineral supplement.

Companion Products: True Source Multivitamins, MightyVites, MightyMist, Sulfurzyme Caps or Powder, and Super Cal

MultiGreens

A natural, sustainable energy source with (1) bioactive sea vegetables that increase vitality, (2) nutrient-dense bee pollen, (3) a purifying essential oil blend to increase assimilation, and (4) an excellent source of choline, critical for energy production.

Clinical experience has shown that before putting essential oils in the MultiGreens formula, there was 42% blood absorption in 24 hours. After adding the essential oils to the formula, blood absorption increased to 64% in 30 minutes and 86% in 1 hour. The conclusion was that the cells were now receiving nutrients that they had previously not been able to assimilate.

INGREDIENTS:

Spirulina—a source of chlorophyll, a magnesium rich pigment that has been linked to improved energy and metabolism. Spirulina has been used as a tonic, purifier, and detoxifier. It targets the immune systems, liver, kidneys, blood, intestinal flora and cardiovascular systems.

Barley Grass juice concentrate—a powerful, cleansing antioxidant that is rich in vital minerals

Bee Pollen—high in protein and low in fat and sodium, it is loaded with vitamins and minerals, including potassium, calcium, magnesium, zinc, manganese, copper and B vitamins

Choline bitartrate—has been used in the treatment of Alzheimer's disease. It is essential for liver health

Pacific kelp (*Laminaria digitata*)—contains nutrients to prevent thyroid hormone deficiency and estrogen imbalance

Alfalfa leaf (*Medicago sativa*)—high in chlorophyll and minerals

Eleuthero root (*Eleutherococcus senticosus*)—boosts energy and reduces stress. Can also boost lymphocyte formation which strengthens the immune system

Amino Acid Complex, containing:

L-Arginine—promotes circulation in the small capillaries of our tissues, improving nutrient delivery and cellular metabolism

L-Cysteine—supports healthy liver function and healthy hair

L-Tyrosine—supports the formation of neurotransmitters, such as dopamine and serotonin

ESSENTIAL OILS:

Rosemary (*Rosmarinus officinalis CT cineol*) balances the endocrine system and prevents candida.

Lemon (*Citrus limon*) prevents cellular mutation and enhances DNA repair.

Lemongrass (*Cymbopogon flexuosus*) is anti-parasitic, antifungal and supports good digestion.

Melissa *(Melissa officinalis)* is anti-inflammatory and energizing.

Directions: Take 3 capsules, three times daily.

Companion Products: Juva Power, Omega Blue, Protein Complete, Power Meal, Thyromin, Wolfberry Crisp Bars, and En-R-Gee

NingXia Red (Juice)

This is the highest antioxidant liquid dietary supplement from whole food sources. Rich in ellagic acid, polyphenols, flavonoids, vitamins, and minerals.

INGREDIENTS:

Ningxia wolfberry *(Lycium barbarum)* juice is one of the highest known antioxidant nutrients. It is rich in polysaccharides that have been studied for their ability to combat cancer and strengthen the immune system. It is rich in polyphenols, carotenoids, magnesium, potassium, and vitamin C.

Blueberry Juice (from concentrate) is one of the highest antioxidant foods according to ORAC research developed by USDA researchers at Tufts University. Animal studies at Tufts University have shown that blueberry extracts can reverse many of the signs of aging.

Grape pomace seed/stem extract

Vitamin C (ascorbic acid) helps preserve color and increase shelf life.

Raspberry Juice (from concentrate) is rich in ellagic acid, a vital anti-aging nutrient which provides powerful protection against cell mutation.

Pomegranate *(Punica grangium)* **Juice** (from concentrate) is an extremely high antioxidant nutrient that has been shown to prevent heart disease in clinical studies.[6,7,8]

Apricot Juice (from concentrate) contains high concentrations of carotinoids, a class of high-powered antioxidants that includes beta carotene (provitamin A). Apricots are also rich in rutin, which strengthens blood vessels.

Organic Blue Agave Nectar is an extremely low-glycemic sweetener from the desert cactus *Agave tequilana*.

Potassium sorbate (preservative)

Sodium benzoate (preservative)

Blueberry Flavor

ESSENTIAL OILS:

Orange *(Citrus sinensis)* is very high in limonene, a supernutrient that has been studied extensively for its ability to prevent cellular mutations and reverse cancer. Over 50 peer-reviewed research papers have investigated limonene against a variety of cancers, including breast, lung, and colon.

Lemon *(Citrus limon)* promotes leukocyte formation and increases immune function.

Directions: Drink at least one ounce once a day. To maximize benefits, drink at least one hour before meals.

Companion Products: Wolfberry Crisp Bar, and Longevity

Ningxia Wolfberries, whole, dried (*Lycium barbarum*)

The Ningxia wolfberry is the earth's most powerful antioxidant fruit. It is rich in polysaccharides, with more vitamin C than oranges, more beta-carotene than carrots, and more calcium than broccoli.

Directions: Chew at least one teaspoonful daily.

Companion Products: NingXia Red

Omega Blue Softgels

These softgels provide a clinically proven dose of Omega-3 (EPA + DHA) fatty acids blended with a proprietary Omega Enhance essential oil blend, to synergize and protect the Omega 3 ingredients. Research shows nutrients in Omega Blue are important to support heart, eye, brain, and joint health.

6. "Pomegranate juice consumption inhibits serum angiotensin converting enzyme and reduces systolic blood pressure" Pomegranate 2000 Israel Aviram, Dornfeld Atherosclerosis

7. "Pomegranate juice consumption reduces oxidative stress, atherogenic modifications to LDL, and platelet aggregation: Studies in humans and in atherosclerotic apolipoprotein E-deficient mice 1,2 Pomegranate, Free Radical, Heart Disease 1999 Israel Aviram, Dornfeld, Rosenblat, Volkova, Kaplan, Coleman, Hayek, Presser, Fuhrman *American Journal of Clinical Nutrition*

8. "Pomegranate juice supplementation to atherosclerotic mice reduces macrophage lipid peroxidation, cellular cholesterol accumulation and development of artherosclerosis" Pomegranate, 2001 Israel, Kaplan, Hayek, Raz, Coleman, Dornfeld, Vaya, Aviram, *Journal of Nutrition*

The fish oil used in Omega Blue is harvested from small fish grown wild in pristine waters and then gently refined to insure it is completely free of heavy metals, PCBs and dioxins, yet still maintains natural Omega-3 ratios.

Omega Blue softgels are enteric coated so they release their contents in the intestines without being compromised by stomach acid. This yields up to three times the absorption rate of Omega 3s and eliminates the risk of 'fishy' aftertaste.

INGREDIENTS:

Fish oil (sardine, anchovy, mackerel)—the source of the vital Omega 3 fatty acids

Rice bran oil

ESSENTIAL OILS:

Omega Enhance Essential Oil Blend, containing:

Lemongrass *(Cymbopogon flexuosus)* —enhances Omega Blue's cardiovascular protection by helping to maintain normal, healthy levels of cholesterol.

Myrrh *(Commiphora myrrha)* — a powerful antioxidant, this oil protects the stability of the Omega 3 fatty acids and prevents unhealthy inflammation.

Clove bud *(Syzygium aromaticum)* — has the highest antioxidant levels of any essential oil and enhances Omega 3 nutritive support.

German chamomile *(Matricaria recutata)* — an anti-inflammatory nutrient that helps the body respond properly to inflammation challenges.

Also Contains:

Gelatin, glycerin, enteric coating solution (oleic acid, sodiuim alginate, MCFAs, ethylcellulose, stearic acid)

ParaFree Softgels

An advanced blend of some of the strongest essential oils that have been studied for their antiparasitic properties.

INGREDIENTS:

Organic sesame *(Sesamum indicum)* **seed oil**

Organic olive *(Olea europea)* **oil**

Glycerin

ESSENTIAL OILS:

Cumin *(Cuminum cyminum)* has been shown to be antiparasitic and antiviral. It supports immune function.

Anise *(Pimpinella anisum)* is antiparasitic and promotes digestion and protein breakdown.

Fennel *(Foeniculum vulgare)* is antiseptic and antiparasitic and improves digestive and pancreatic functions.

Bay laurel *(Laurus nobilis)* is antiseptic, anti-bacterial, antiparasitic, and antiviral. It is also a diuretic, fungicidal, and digestive aid.

Vetiver *(Vetiveria officinalis)* is antiseptic, anti-spasmodic, anti-inflammatory, and immune-supporting.

Nutmeg *(Myristica fragrans)* supports adrenal glands, is antibacterial and anti-inflammatory, and stimulates immune function. It has also been used to reduce diarrhea. It is also antiviral, anti-parasitic, and antifungal.

Tea Tree *(Melaleuca alternifolia)* is antifungal, antiparasitic, and antibacterial.

Clove *(Syzygium aromaticum)* has potent anti-parasitic, antibacterial, and antifungal properties.

Idaho tansy *(Tanacetum vulgare)* is one of the most potent worm-expelling essential oils.

Thyme *(Thymus vulgaris)* is one of the strongest antibacterial, antifungal, and antiviral essential oils.

Companion Products: ComforTone, ICP, JuvaTone, Juva Cleanse, Thieves, ImmuPower, Detoxzyme, Polyzyme, Essentialzyme

Directions: Liquid: Take 2 to 4 droppers, three times daily for 21 consecutive days.

Gelcaps: Take 2 to 5 gelcaps, two to three times a day for 21 consecutive days out of each month.

Repeat for three cycles or as needed. Use ParaFree Softgels with ComforTone and ICP for cleansing. The ICP will help break up plaque along the intestinal walls.

Note: Use in moderation during pregnancy, possibly 2 capsules daily. If diarrhea occurs, discontinue. A good parasite cleanse is recommended before conception. Consult your health care provider before starting a cleansing program.

PD 80/20

PD 80/20 is a dietary supplement designed to provide natural hormone support for the body. As hormone levels decline with age, maintaining adequate hormone reserves becomes vital for sustaining health and preventing premature aging.

INGREDIENTS:

Pregnenolone is the precursor hormone from which all other hormones are created. It is an important precursor for the body's production of progesterone which blocks cortisol receptors.

DHEA (*Dioscorea villosa*) is derived from wild yam and is an important hormone precursor for progesterone.

Rice flour

Companion Products: Essentialzyme, Sulfurzyme (capsules or powder), MultiGreens, Progessence, Prenolone, and Prenolone+

Companion Oils: Clary sage, fennel, and Dragon Time

Directions: Start with 1 capsule a day, then increase to 2 capsules a day as needed.

Polyzyme

The enzyme complexes in Polyzyme are used medically as powerful anti-inflammatories that combat arthritis, irritable bowel syndrome, fibromyalgia, ALS, and food allergies.

By promoting complete digestion of proteins, Polyzyme increases the production of key amino acids from food proteins. Amino acids are absolutely vital for healthy immunity and health and form the building blocks of hormone creation, tissue repair, and muscle formation. By promoting complete digestion, Polyzyme prevents putrefaction in the intestines that can lead to allergies, liver stress, and toxic blood.

INGREDIENTS:

Protease 3.0, 4.5, 6.0 are protein digesting enzymes designed to work in a broad range of pH conditions. Acid stable proteases are essential for amino acid creation in the acid environment of the stomach while alkaline proteases are more effective in the large intestine. This combination of proteases is scientifically formulated to maximize protein digestion and amino acid formation.

Phytase is an enzyme essential for people eating vegetarian diets. Phytase is crucial for unlocking the mineral content of many grains, nuts, seeds, and other foods which contain high levels of essential minerals that are unavailable to the human body because they are bound up in insoluble indigestible phytate complexes. Up to 90% of the magnesium, potassium, and zinc in foods like barley, cashews, walnuts, and rice is locked up by phytic acid and cannot be absorbed by the digestive system, unless phytase is present.

Lipase is a fat-dissolving enzyme vital for proper absorption of Vitamin D, E, and A.

Bromelain is a proteolytic enzyme from pineapple stems.

Papain is a plant enzyme from unripe papayas with a broad spectrum of digesting activity.

Peptidase promotes the creation and absorption of amino acids in the digestive system.

Rice bran is rich in ferulic acid and vitamin E.

Silica

Vegetable cellulose

ESSENTIAL OILS:

Anise (*Pimpinella anisum*) promotes digestion and helps eliminate parasites.

Peppermint (*Mentha piperita*) is a powerful promoter of digestion and peristalsis in the intestines. It is highly antifungal, combating candida, nausea, and vomiting.

Rosemary (*Rosmarinus officinalis* CT cineol) is highly antiseptic, with a broad-spectrum of antiparasitic and antifungal activity that prevents fermentation and yeast/fungal overgrowth in the intestines.

Directions: Take 1 capsule three times daily or as needed just before meals with proteins.

Companion Products: Power Meal, Protein Complete, Wolfberry Crisp Bar, and DiGize

Power Meal

A delicious, satisfying, rice-based meal replacement that also contains Ningxia wolfberries, Power Meal is rich in calcium and delivers an impressive 20 grams of protein per serving plus a complete vitamin, mineral, and enzyme profile. Benefits include:

- Builds lean muscle mass
- Antioxidants that strengthen immunity
- Supports bone health
- Amino acids that enhance digestive activity

Whole-grain, brown rice protein is one of the very best sources of protein available. Rich in selenium, manganese, and phenolics, brown rice contains powerful antioxidants that work in multiple ways to boost the immune system. A great alternative to whey or soy protein, brown rice protein is:

- Dairy-free
- Allergen-free
- Easily absorbed in the body
- Loaded with amino acids

Whether used as a meal alternative or snack, Power Meal can serve as an axcellent weight management tool. Free of fats and synthetic ingredients, Power Meal provides the building blocks the body required for regeneration and energy. A new flavor pack dramatically improves the flavor.

INGREDIENTS:

Rice protein concentrate is high in branched chain amino acids required for building muscles.

Ningxia wolfberry (*Lycium barbarum*) has 18 amino acids, 21 trace minerals, beta carotene, and vitamins B1, B2, B6, and E. It is an excellent whole food and has many functions in the body.

Rice Bran (*Oryza Sativa*): Stabilized, nonchemically treated. Contains gamma-oryzanol, tocotrienols, tocopherols, squalene, ferulic acid, IP6 (inositol hexaphosphate) and Gamma-oryzanol, a triterpene alcohol that is more effective than vitamin E in stopping oxidation of cholesterol. In studies at the Louisiana State University in Baton Rouge, researchers concluded that gamma-oryzanol "had activities higher than that of any of the 4 vitamin E components. Gamma-oryzanol may be a more important

antioxidant of rice bran in the reduction of cholesterol oxidation than vitamin E."

Rice bran is considered one of the best sources of squalene, an antimutagen and anti-cancer agent also found in olive oil and shark liver oil.

Ferulic acid is also found in rice bran and acts as an antioxidative, hypotensive polyphenol that reduces blood pressure.

Ginkgo biloba extract increases energy, improves memory and is excellent for cerebral circulation, oxygenation, and blood flow.

Guar gum promotes healthy colon function.

Calcium carbonate is needed for healthy bones, teeth and joints.

Soy Lecithin (food for the brain) is excellent for liver disorders and helps to balance cholesterol

Choline bitartrate has been used in the treatment of many liver disorders (including elevated cholesterol levels), Alzheimer's disease, viral hepatitis, and cirrhosis.

Magnesium (Magnesium oxide) is crucial for proper enzyme function, muscle contractions and heart rhythm. It reduces blood pressure, prevents arteriosclerosis, and improves insulin action.

MSM supports healthy hair, skin, liver, and immune function.

Betaine HCl promotes protein digestion.

Proteolytic Enzyme Blend containing lipase, protease, phytase and peptidase.

Kelp (*Laminaria digitata*) contains iodine, which is necessary to prevent goiters.

PABA (para amino benzoic acid) assists healthy bacteria in producing folic acid and helps form red blood cells.

Zinc (Zinc lactate) is crucial for immunity, cell growth, wound healing, and proper action of many hormones, including insulin and growth hormone.

Mixed Carotenoid Complex including lycopene, lutein, zeaxanthin, beta carotene and astaxanthin

Copper is necessary for proper red blood cell and immune function.

Medium Chain Triglycerides are more quickly and easily metabolized in the liver than most other fats. Animal and human studies have shown that the fast rate of oxidation of MCTs leads to greater energy expenditure with the potential for less body weight gain. MCTs have also been shown to control appetite better than other fats.

Xanthan gum is a stabilizer and emulsifier that serves as a natural substitute for gluten

Lo Han Kuo extract is a natural sweetener used in Chinese medicine for a wide variety of purposes from regulating digestion to reducing stress but is also widely used to control hunger cravings.

Talin is a high molecular weight protein that aids in immune system function

Manganese *(Manganese gluconate)*

Vitamin A (beta carotene) is a highly pigmented fat soluble compound found in many fruits, grains and vegetables. It is essential in the body for healthy bones, a healthy reproductive system, and good vision.

Vitamin C (Ascorbic acid) is vital for healthy immunity and blood vessel integrity. It fights free-radical damage and premature aging.

Vitamin E *(mixed tocopherols)* protects the heart and blood and combats free-radical oxidative damage.

Vitamin D3 *(Cholecalciferols)* stimulates the absorption of calcium and exerts many anticancerous properties, especially against breast and colon cancer.

Chicory Root Fiber, a primary source of FOS (Fructooligosaccharides) is one of the best-documented natural nutrients for promoting the growth of *lactobacilli* and bifidobacteria, the linchpin of sound health. FOS has also been clinically studied for its ability to increase magnesium and calcium absorption, lower blood glucose, cholesterol, and LDL levels, and to inhibit production of the reductase enzymes that can contribute to cancer. Because FOS may increase magnesium absorption, it may also lead to lowered blood pressure and better cardiovascular health.

Alpha lipoic acid is one of the most powerful known antioxidants. It is the only antioxidant that is both oil and water soluble. It has been used to treat diabetes, heart disease, and liver disease.

Selenium has been extensively researched for its anticancer and antioxidant properties.

Vitamin B1 (Thiamin) is essential for energy production, carbohydrate metabolism, and nerve cell function.

Vitamin B2 (Riboflavin) is important in the production of energy, regenerating glutathione and preventing cancer.

Vitamin B3 (Niacin) converts carbohydrates into energy. At least 4.4 mg is needed for every 1,000 calories consumed to avoid deficiency diseases.

Vitamin B5 (Panthoneic acid)

Vitamin B6 (Pyridoxine HCl) protects the heart and blood vessels. Prevents cellular mutations. Requires folic acid. Vitamin B12, and magnesium to be assimilated.

Vitamin B12 (Methylcobalamin) is critical for red blood cell formation and proper immune and nerve function. Works with vitamin B6 to prevent heart disease. Vegetarians are often deficient in Vitamin B12.

Chromium improves insulin sensitivity and blood sugar metabolism.

Folic acid plays an important role in cardiovascular health and helps prevent neural tube defects.

Biotin helps convert fats and amino acids into energy. It promotes healthy nails and hair and combats yeast and fungus overgrowth.

Also includes the following flavorings, spices and sweetener: Natural vanilla flavor, natural orange flavor, cinnamon, ginger, white pepper, clove, nutmeg, fennel, cardamom, neohesperidin derivative (flavor from natural citrus), and fructose

ESSENTIAL OILS:

Grapefruit *(Citrus paradisi)* prevents DNA and cellular mutation.

Orange *(Citrus sinensis)* contains the powerful antioxidant limonene, is anti-inflammatory, antispasmodic, and anticoagulant.

Lemon (*Citrus limon*) prevents cellular mutation and enhances DNA repair.

Anise (*Pimpinella anisum*) promotes digestion and helps eliminate parasites.

Fennel (*Foeniculum vulgare*) is antiparasitic, antimicrobial, antispasmodic, helps regulate intestinal flora, is a digestive aid, and increases gastric secretions.

Nutmeg (*Myristica fragrans*) helps support the adrenal glands for increased energy.

NUTRITION FACTS:

Per Serving (2 level scoops/52g):

Calories 187 Calories from Fat 30   %DV

Total Fat . . . . .3.32 g 5%		
Saturated Fat . . . . .1.1 g 6%		
Unsaturated Fat . . . . . .2.2 g 6%		
Trans Fat . . . . .0 g 0%		
Sodium . . . . .51.1 mg 2%		
Potassium . . . . .149.8 mg 4%		
Total Carbohydrates . . . .24.2 g 8%		
Total Fiber . . . . .7.1 g 28%		
Soluble Fiber. . . . . . .3.8 g		
Insoluble Fiber . . . . .3.2 g		
Sugars . . . . .8.9 g . . . .**		
Protein . . . . .20.6 g 41%		

Vitamin A . . . 35%	Vitamin C 48%
Vitamin D . . . 33%	Vitamin E 33%
Thiamin 117%	Riboflavin 30%
Niacin 58%	Vitamin B6 . . . . 33%
Folic Acid . . . 35%	Vitamin B12 . . . 33%
Biotin 33%	Calcium 38%
Iron 9%	Pantothenic Acid 33%
Phosphorus . . 35%	Magnesium 37%
Zinc. 32%	Selenium 47%
Copper 34%	Manganese 154%
Chromium. . . 28%	Choline 37%

Directions: Take 2 scoops in water or rice milk as a meal alternative or as needed for energy and endurance.

Companion Products: Wolfberry Crisp, WheyFit, ThermaBurn.

ProGen

ProGen is an all-vegetable and herbal support for the prostate and male glandular system. Saw palmetto is one of the most widely used herbs to combat prostate enlargement, which affects most men over 45. *Pygeum africanum* prevents prostate atrophy and malfunction.

INGREDIENTS:

Natural Extracts:

Saw Palmetto (*Serenoa repens*) reduces an enlarged prostate and relieves the inflammation and pain of benign prostatic hypertrophy.

Wild Yam (*Dioscorea villosa*) is antispasmodic and supports the reproductive organs.

Pygeum africanum is used to prevent prostate atrophy and malfunction.

Blessed Thistle (*Cnicus benedictus*) has been tested in laboratory studies for its properties against infections, cancer, and inflammation with promising results.

Marshmallow root (*Althaea officinalis*) is an expectorant that has been used on bruises, muscle aches, sprains, burns, and inflammations.

Eleuthero (*Eleutherococcus senticosus*) (formerly called Siberian ginseng) strengthens the adrenal glands and promotes hormonal balance

Organic sesame seed (*Sesamum indicum*) is an aid to digestion, stimulates blood circulation, and benefits the nervous system. With its vitamin E content, it also benefits the heart and nervous system.

Minerals and Amino Acids:

Zinc is one of the most important minerals for prostate health. It helps restore sexual potency.

Alpha glutaric acid plays an important role in amino acid metabolism. It is the precursor of glutamic acid, which contributes to brain energy supply.

L-glutathione is a sulfur-bearing liver antioxidant

L-carnitine may have cardioprotective effects, and it may have a triglyceride-lowering effect in some as well as help to elevate HDL-cholesterol levels. L-carnitine also has antioxidant properties. supports prostate health

L-arginine has been shown to help alleviate problems associated with erectile dysfunction

L-alanine is involved in sugar and acid metabolism, increases immunity, and provides energy for muscle tissue, brain, and the central nervous system.

Dimethylglycine is excellent for heart muscle support

ESSENTIAL OILS:

Sage *(Salvia officinalis)* has estrogen-like properties and may help balance hormones

Fennel *(Foeniculum vulgare)* also has hormone balancing properties

Lavender *(Lavandula angustifolia)* is calming and toning

Myrtle *(Myrtus communis)* helps fight inflammation associated with prostate swelling

Yarrow *(Achillea millefolium)* is supportive of the nervous system and prostate gland

Peppermint *(Mentha piperita)* is anti-inflammatory and helps decongest prostate and urinary tract

Directions: Take 2 capsules two times daily.

Companion Products: Be-Fit, Balance Complete, True Source Multivitamins, Omega Blue, Power Meal, Protein Complete, and Valor

Pure Protein Complete

High in bioactive protein, low in carbs, fat and calories, Pure Protein Complete is the perfect anytime protein boost. Each serving provides a whopping 20 grams of top quality, New Zealand whey protein, certified to be free of hormones, pesticides, and antibiotics. It is also blended with complimentary vitamins, minerals and enzymes to insure a delicious, satisfying protein drink. It has no artificial sweeteners and a very low glycemic index. Pure Protein Complete can be used to help support a weight loss program, while it sustains energy, curbs appetite, enhances enzyme activity and builds lean muscle mass.

INGREDIENTS:

Pure Protein Complete Proprietary Protein Blend (Whey protein concentrate, sweet whey, milk protein concentrate, nonfat dry milk, whey protein isolate), Proprietary Carbohydrate Matrix (chicory root fiber extract [FOS], natural vanilla flavor, fructose, guar gum, xanthan gum, xylitol, cellulose, lo han kuo extract Stevia *[S. rebaudiana]* leaf extract), Lecithin, Proporietary Enzyme Complex (lactase, papain, bromelain, amylase, lipase, bioperine), Magnesium Oxide, Tri-calcium phosphate, Mixed carotenoids, Vitamin C (ascorbic acid), Potassium citrate, Vitamin E (natural mixed tocopherols), Zinc gluconate, Vitamin B3 (Niacin), Beta Carotene, Vitamin B5 (calcium pantothenate), Neohesperidin derivative (flavor from natural citrus), Vitamin B6 (pyridoxine HCl), Vitamin B2 (riboflavin), Vitamin B1 (Thiamine HCl), Orange (Citrus sinensis) rind, Chromium nicotinate, Vitamin D3 (cholecalciferol), Vitamin B12 (methylcobalamin), Folic acid, Biotin, Potassium iodide, Sodium Selenite

Rehemogen Tincture

Rehemogen tincture contains herbs that were used by Chief Sundance and other Native Americans to cleanse, purify, disinfect and build the blood.

INGREDIENTS:

Red clover blossom prevents cellular mutations and builds blood.

Chaparral used by Native American healers as an internal disinfectant and to treat tuberculosis.

Licorice *(Glycyrrhiza glabra)* **root extract** traditionally used to to combat circulatory dysfunction and liver disorders.

Oregon grape root *(Berberis aquifolium)* contains berberine, a powerful liver protectant.

Peach Tree bark

Poke *(Phytolacca americana)* **root**

Sarsaparilla *(Phytolacca americana)* **root** contains saponins, steroid-like molecules that neutralize endotoxins (poisons secreted by fungi and bacteria in the human body), that contribute to many kinds of disease.

Cascara sagrada (*Caseara sagrada*) is used to support the liver, pancreas, gallbladder, and stomach.

Burdock root is eaten as a vegetable in Japan to cleanse the blood.

Royal jelly is the substance fed to queen bees that allows them to live thirty to forty times longer than worker bees. It is very rich in amino acids, minerals, and vitamins B5 and B6. It stimulates the adrenal glands to increase energy.

ESSENTIAL OILS:

Rosemary (*Rosmarinus officinalis*) is liver-protecting and helps combat fatigue. It is anti-bacterial, antiparasitic, and antifungal.

Thyme (*Thymus vulgaris*) is highly antimicrobial and antiseptic.

Melaleuca (*Melaleuca alternifolia*)–also known as tea tree, is antimicrobial and antiseptic.

Roman chamomile (*Chamaemelum nobile*)—promotes the flow of bile to and from the liver, a key part of cleansing and detoxification.

Pure grain alcohol

Also contains: Buckthorn bark, stillingia, and prickly ash bark.

Directions: Mix 1 to 3 droppers, three times daily in distilled water or as needed.

Companion Products: Essentialzyme, Polyzyme, Detoxzyme, and Di-Gize

Stevia Extract

Stevia extract is a super-sweet, low-calorie dietary supplement that helps regulate blood sugar and supports the pancreas. It is valuable for anyone with diabetes and hypoglycemia.

It is a first-rate aid to weight loss and weight management because it contains no calories. In addition, research indicates that it significantly increases glucose tolerance and inhibits glucose absorption. People who ingest stevia daily often report a decrease in their desire for sweets and fatty foods. It may also improve digestion and gastro-intestinal function, soothe upset stomachs, and help speed recovery from minor illnesses.

Stevia also inhibits the growth of some bacteria and infectious organisms, including those that cause tooth decay and gum disease. Many individuals using stevia have reported a lower incidence of colds and flu. Many who have used stevia as a mouthwash have experienced a significant decrease in gum disease.

When topically applied, stevia softens the skin and smooths out wrinkles while healing various skin blemishes, acne, seborrhea, dermatitis, and eczema. When used on cuts and wounds, stevia promotes rapid healing without scarring.

INGREDIENTS:

Stevia leaf extract—intensely sweet with a mild, licorice-like aftertaste.

Directions: Use as a supplemental sweetener.

Companion Products: Blue Agave Nectar

Sulfurzyme Powder and Capsules

Sulfurzyme is a unique combination of methyl-sulfonylmethane (MSM), the protein-building compound found in breast milk, fresh fruits and vegetables, and Ningxia wolfberry (*Lycium barbarum*). Together, they create a new concept in balancing the immune system and supporting almost every major function of the body. Of particular importance is the ability of MSM to equalize water pressure inside of the cells—a considerable benefit for those plagued with bursitis, arthritis, and tendonitis.

Ningxia wolfberry supplies nutrients to enhance the proper assimilation and metabolism of sulfur.

INGREDIENTS:

MSM (Methylsulfonymethane) is a special organic sulfur that combats autoimmune diseases including arthritis, asthma, lupus, and scleroderma. MSM is critical to proper skin, hair, and liver health. MSM is the subject of a bestselling book, *The Miracle of MSM, The Natural Solution for Pain*, authored by UCLA neuropsychiatrist Ronald Lawrence M.D., Ph.D., and Stanley Jacob, M.D.

Ningxia wolfberry (*Lycium barbarum*) **fruit** contains minerals and coenzymes to support sulfur metabolism.

OTHER INGREDIENTS::

Fructooligosaccharides (FOS) are one of the best-documented natural nutrients for promoting the growth of *lactobacilli* and bifidobacteria, the linchpin of sound health. FOS has also been clinically studied for its ability to increase magnesium and calcium absorption, lower blood glucose, cholesterol, and LDL levels, and to inhibit production of the reductase enzymes that can contribute to cancer. Because FOS may increase magnesium absorption, it may also lead to lowered blood pressure and better cardiovascular health.

In addition, FOS also has another benefit - it has a naturally sweet taste.

Sterioside (*Stevia rebaudiana*)

Directions:

CAPS: Take 2 capsules two times daily one hour before or after meals.

POWDER: Take 1/2 teaspoon with distilled water two times daily one hour before or after meals

Companion Products: BLM, Super Cal, Essential-zyme, Ortho Ease, PanAway, and Mega Cal

Super B

Super B is a comprehensive source of the B vitamins essential for good health, including, thiamine (vitamin B1), riboflavin (vitamin B2), niacin (vitamin B3), pyridoxine (vitamin B6), vitamin B12, biotin, folic acid, and PABA. It also includes minerals that aid the assimilation and metabolism of B vitamins.

B vitamins are particularly important during times of stress when reserves are depleted. Although research has shown that megadoses of B vitamins are not healthy, it has been known that the diets of many Americans do not provide the recommended amount of B vitamins essential for normal functions of immune response.

When many B vitamins are combined at once in the stomach, it can cause a fermentation resulting in stomach upset. To avoid this, Super B uses a synergistic suspension isolation process to isolate the various vitamins so they are released at different times.

INGREDIENTS:

Folic acid protects heart, blood vessels, and prevents heart disease. It requires Vitamins B6 an B12 to be assimilated.

Thiamin (vitamin B1) required for carbohydrate metabolism, and nerve cell function.

Riboflavin (vitamin B2) is crucial in the production of cellular energy, helps regenerate the liver, and prevents cellular mutations.

Niacin is essential for turning carbohydrates into energy. It lowers cholesterol and helps regulate blood sugar. At least 4.4 mg are needed for every 1,000 calories consumed to avoid pellagra.

Vitamin B6 (pyridoxine) supports immune function and protects the heart and blood vessels. It inhibits skin cancer growth, helps prevent kidney stones, and alleviates PMS symptoms. Vitamin B6 requires folic acid and magnesium to maximize its effects.

Vitamin B12 (cyanocobalamin) is critical for red blood cell formation and proper immune and nerve function. Works with vitamin B6 to prevent heart disease. Vegetarians often lack adequate B12.

Biotin helps convert fats and amino acids into energy. It promotes healthy nails and hair and combats yeast and fungus overgrowth.

Magnesium oxide is crucial for proper enzyme function, insulin action, muscle contractions and heart rhythm. It reduces high blood pressure.

PABA (para amino benzoic acid) assists healthy bacteria in producing folic acid. It also helps the bones form red blood cells.

Zinc is crucial for immunity, cell growth, wound healing, and proper action of many hormones, including insulin and growth hormone.

Selenium has been extensively researched for its anticancer and antioxidant properties.

Plant Cellulose is a toxin-absorbing fiber.

Di-calcium phoshate

Stearic acid

COMPARISON OF YOUNG LIVING'S CALCIUM SUPPLEMENTS

	MegaCal	SuperCal
Calcium per Serving	618 mg	242 mg
Percent of RDI of Calcium	61%	24%
Type of calcium	Lactate, Carbonate, Glycerophosphate Ascorbate	Citrate
Source of Calcium	High purity precipitated	High purity precipitated
Calcium:Magnesium Ratio	1:1	3:1
Other minerals	Potassium, Zinc, Copper, Manganese	Potassium Zinc, Boron
Additional nutrients	Xylitol, vitamin C	
Benefits	Fights osteoporosis, alleviates muscle cramps; supports normal thyroid function	Fights osteoporosis, joint support, improves metabolism; supports normal thyroid function
Designed for	Diets high in dairy products	Vegetarians, diets restricted in calories or high in carbonated beverages
Directions	Take 1 tbsp. 1 hour after meals	Take 1-2 capsules between meals
Other info	Time-released mineral complex	

Directions: Take 1/2 to 1 tablet daily, preferably with meals. If taken on an empty stomach, one may experience a niacin flush, a normal reaction which may last up to an hour.

Companion Products: Super C Chewable, Super Cal, and Longevity Softgels

Super C

Physical stress, alcohol, smoking, and using certain medications may lower the blood levels of this essential vitamin. When citrus fruits are not readily available, diets may not contain enough vitamin C. Super C is properly balanced with rutin, biotin, bioflavonoids, and trace minerals to work synergistically, balancing the electrolytes and increasing the absorption rate of vitamin C. Without bioflavonoids, vitamin C has a hard time getting inside cells; and without proper electrolyte balance and trace minerals, it will not stay there for long.

INGREDIENTS:

Vitamin C is an antioxidant essential for the creation of collagen, connective tissue, cartilage, tendons, and vital for immunity. It also helps blood vessel integrity and prevents premature aging.

Citrus bioflavonoids dramatically enhance vitamin C activity and act as potent antioxidants.

Manganese sulfate is needed for blood sugar control, energy metabolism, and proper thyroid function.

Rutin helps prevent capillary fragility, preventing easy bruising, swelling, and nosebleeds.

Calcium carbonate and phosphate is needed for healthy bones, teeth, and joints.

Cayenne pepper (*Capiscum annum*) is excellent as a general stimulant and stamina booster.

Zinc is crucial for immunity, cell growth, wound healing, and proper action of many hormones, including insulin and growth hormone.

Potassium chloride is required for proper electrolyte balance and to prevent high blood pressure.

Plant Cellulose is a toxin-absorbing fiber.

Di-calcium phosphate

ESSENTIAL OILS:

Orange (*Citrus sinensis*) contains the powerful antioxidant limonene. Also a great natural flavoring. Rich in limonene which prevents DNA and cellular mutation.

Tangerine (*Citrus reticulata*) is an anticoagulant and helps decongest the lymphatic system.

Lemon (*Citrus limon*) promotes leukocyte formation and increases lymphatic function.

Grapefruit (*Citrus paradisi*) prevents DNA and cellular mutation.

Lemongrass (*Cymbopogon flexuosus*) is antiparasitic, antifungal, and promotes digestion.

Directions: For reinforcing immune strength, 2 tablets daily. For maintenance, one tablet daily. Best taken before meals.

Companion Products: Exodus, ImmuPro, Immune-Tune, MultiGreens, Citrus Fresh, Exodus II, and ImmuPower

Super C Chewable

The only vitamin C chewable vitamin in the world to combine citrus essential oils, citrus bioflavonoids, and whole-food natural vitamin C in one tablet.

According to Dr. Victor Herbert, professor of medicine at the Mount Sinai School of Medicine in New York, synthetic vitamin C as a supplement "is not an antioxidant. It's a redox agent--an antioxidant in some circumstances and a pro-oxidant in others." In other words, synthetic ascorbic acid can actually be a free-radical in some cases. Only natural vitamin C that occurs naturally in foods has no oxidizing effects.

Scientists are also discovering that Vitamin C needs be combined with citrus bioflavonoids to fully unlock its therapeutic effects. Bioflavonoids are known to have a vitamin P-type action that improves microcirculatory and blood vessel integrity.

INGREDIENTS:

Acerola cherry (*Malphighia glabra*) is one of the highest natural sources of vitamin C.

Citrus bioflavonoid (*Citrus limon*) enhances vitamin C activity. It is extremely high in antioxidants and flavonoids.

Fructose is a low-glycemic sweetener having minimal impact on blood sugar levels.

ESSENTIAL OIL:

Orange (*Citrus sinensis*) is rich in limonene, which prevents DNA and cellular mutation. It is also a great natural flavoring.

Also contains: palm oil, silica, stearic acid, sugar cane (as a lubricant).

Directions: Take 2 to 4 tablets between meals. If under stress take 4 to 8 tablets during the day.

Companion Products: Exodus, Power Meal, ImmuPro, ImmuneTune, MultiGreens, Citrus Fresh, Exodus II, ImmuPower, and NingXia Red

Super Cal

A high-powered calcium, potassium, and magnesium complex. Restores proper electrolyte and hormonal balance, and improves muscle and bone development.

INGREDIENTS:

Calcium citrate is essential for healthy bones and teeth. Calcium citrate is one of the best absorbed calciums available.

Magnesium works with calcium to build bones.

Potassium chloride is vital for improving bone density and to prevent strokes and high blood pressure.

Manganese is a crucial co-factor in collagen production.

Boron increase calcium absorption and utilization.

Zinc citrate enhances calcium absorption and is crucial for proper hormone activity and growth hormone production

Stearic acid

ESSENTIAL OILS:

Wintergreen (*Gaultheria procumbens*) contains methyl salicylate which relieves bone, joint, and muscle pain. Also anti-inflammatory and anti-spasmotic.

Marjoram (*Origanum majorana*) supports muscles and nerves.

Lemongrass (*Cymbopogon flexuosus*) is used for ligament support. It is also anti-inflammatory and antibacterial.

Myrtle (*Myrtus communis*) supports muscles with its powerful antispasmotic activity and is antimutagenic.

Directions: Take 1 to 2 capsules before meals.

Companion Products: Ortho Sport, Ortho Ease, Sulfurzyme, Idaho Balsam Fir, Peppermint, Prenolone, Progessence, Regenolone, Wintergreen, and PanAway

ThermaBurn

A revolutionary appetite-suppressing, weight-control herbal complex with thermogenic essential oils. It is the only herbal, fat-reducing supplement to contain liver cleansers and defatters to increase metabolism and prevent oxidative damage from excess fat-burning.

INGREDIENTS:

Chromium polynicotinate acts as a "spark plug" for revving metabolism and carbohydrate burning.

Boron promotes calcium utilization.

Inositol hexaniacinate improves circulation and insulin action.

Dl-methionine protects the liver cells from oxidative damage due to increased metabolism.

Theobromine is a natural energizer that increases red blood cells. When combined with niacin, it boosts blood flow.

Glycerin

Hydroxycitric Acid

L-carnitine is an amino acid so powerful that an entire book was written discussing its fat-burning and energizing effects (*The Carnitine Miracle* by R. Crayhon, M.S.).

Garcinia cambogia increases metabolism and fat burning on a cellular level. It speeds the oxidation/burning of carbohydrates while suppressing fat synthesis (*Lowenstein, 1971; Sullivan et al., 1974; Rao et al., 1988*).

Guarana *(Paullina cupana)* **seed extract** is high in xanthines, which provide energizing and appetite-suppressing effects (Engels et al., *1999*).

Licorice *(Glycyrrhiza glabra)* **root extract** increases fat utilization and glycogen production in the liver.

Yerba mate leaf extract contains matein, which exerts a safe, energizing effect that combats fatigue. This herb has been used for centuries to increase endurance and promote health.

Chromium picolinate improves insulin sensitivity and blood sugar metabolism.

Rice flour

Silica

ESSENTIAL OILS:

Nutmeg (*Myristica fragrans*) helps support the adrenal glands for increased energy. It is also a stomach and liver protectant.

Spearmint (*Mentha spicata*) improves digestion, helps increase metabolism.

Peppermint (*Mentha piperita*) has the ability to directly affect the brain's satiety center, triggering a sense of fullness after meals.

Myrtle (*Myrtus communis*) helps increase and balance thyroid functions and is elevating.

Frankincense (*Boswellia carteri*) is a thermo-genic antioxidant.

Canadian fleabane (*Conyza candensis*) increases growth hormone production.

Directions: Take 1 to 2 capsules two hours before or after meals.

Companion Products: Thyromin, Power Meal, En-R-Gee, and Bodygize

ThermaMist Oral Spray

A revolutionary appetite-suppressing, weight-control herbal complex with thermogenic essential oils. It has a very high nutrient absorption rate due to its oral absorption method of delivery. It affords unmatched appetite and metabolism control.

INGREDIENTS:

Niacin (vitamin B3) is a critical coenzyme used in cellular reactions involved with energy metabolism.

Guarana leaf extract (*Paullina cupana*) is high in xanthines, which provide energizing and appetite-suppressing effects (Engels et al., *1999*).

Yerba mate leaf extract contains matein, which exerts a safe, energizing action that helps combat fatigue (Weiner, 1994) and enhance metabolism.

Yohimbe extract is an energizing herb grown in Africa.

Schizandra supports normal liver function and the breakdown of fats in the liver. It is also a superb antioxidant (Naggai et al., 1988; Zhao et.al., *1990*)

Garcinia cambogia increases metabolism and fat burning on a cellular level. It speeds the oxidation/burning of carbohydrates while suppressing fat synthesis (*Lowenstein, 1971; Sullivan et al., 1974; Rao et al., 1988*).

5-HTP (5-hydroxytryptophan) is known to help suppress the appetite and reduce hunger.

Stevia *(Stevia rebaudiana)* increases insulin efficiency.

Trace mineral complex

Chromium nicotinate helps burn fats, and enhances insulin utilization.

Grapefruit (*Citrus paradisi*) **extract** stimulates fat-burning and cellulite elimination.

Pure grain alcohol

Omega 3, 6, & 9 Complex

Phosphatidyl choline

Vegetable glycerin

ESSENTIAL OILS:

Peppermint (*Mentha piperita*) has the ability to directly affect the brain's satiety center, triggering a sense of fullness after meals.

Spearmint (*Mentha spicata*) has hormone-like properties that support the thyroid, helps increase metabolism, and improves digestion.

Directions: Spray 3 sprays into buccal cavity of the mouth 3 times a day or whenever "cravings" occur. Individual needs may vary.

Companion Products: Balance Complete Therma-Burn, Be-Fit, and Thyromin

Thyromin

This product was developed to nourish the thyroid, balance metabolism, and reduce fatigue. It contains a combination of specially selected glandular nutrients, herbs, amino acids, minerals, and essential oils. All of the oils are therapeutic-grade quality and are perfectly balanced to bring about the most beneficial and nutritional support to the thyroid.

INGREDIENTS:

Adrenal/pituitary extracts from bovine sources (Argentina) provide the building blocks to thyroid hormone synthesis.

Vitamin E (d-Alpha Tocopheryl Acetate and as d-alpha tocopheryl succinate) provides many health benefits including helping to prevent acne, AIDS, cancer, diabetes, cataracts, lupus, macular degeneration, myopathy, and works as a wonderful antioxidant.

Iodine (kelp) is a key component of the T3 and T4 thyroid hormones that are pivotal for increasing energy levels and metabolism. It also prevents goiters and stimulates the thyroid.

Potassium supports healthy thyroid function.

Carrageenan

CoQ10 is used by every cell in the body to convert food to energy.

Magnesium carbonate

Magnesium stearate

Parsley *(Petroselinum crispum)* **herb**

L-cysteine is an amino acid for thyroid health. It also promotes the production of glutathione, one of the most powerful antioxidants, which is vital for protection of the liver.

ESSENTIAL OILS:

Peppermint (*Mentha piperita*) supports digestion and pancreatic function.

Spearmint (*Mentha spicata*) has hormone-like properties that support the thyroid.

Myrtle (*Myrtus communis*) has been studied for normalizing hormonal imbalance of the thyroid and sexual organs. It is also antispasmotic and elevating.

Myrrh (*Commiphora myrrha*) is also a thyroid support.

Directions: Take 1 to 2 capsules daily, immediately before going to sleep.

Companion Products: MultiGreens, ThermaBurn, ThermaMist, En-R-Gee, and EndoFlex

True Source™ Daily Whole Food Multi-Nutrient

Multi-colored natural super vitamin supplement. Contains naturally occurring Vitamin C from oranges and other natural whole food extracts to help provide full vitamin supplementation.

This product is a set of 3 different capsules—one green, one yellow, one purple—prepacked into cellophane packs which come in a box, not a bottle. Green capsules contain broccoli powder, spirulina, chlorella and barley grass in a custom vitamin complex. Yellow capsules contain wolfberry powder, curcumin, olive leaf extract, and a natural tangerine citrus bioflavonoid complex in a full vitamin profile. Purple capsules contain grape extract and resveratrol to fight aging, in addition to a supercharged micronutrient mix.

INGREDIENTS and **POTENCIES** (for each of the 3 capsules):

Each capsule contains:		% daily value
Vitamin A (as alpha and beta carotene)	333.34 IU	6%
Vitamin C (as ascorbic acid) from oranges	20 mg	33%
Vitamin D (as cholecalciferol)	220 IU	55%
Vitamin E (as mixed tocopherols)	6.67 IU	22%
Vitamin K (as phytonadione)	50 mcg	62%
Thiamin (Vitamin B1 as mononitrate)	0.56 mg	37%
Riboflavin (Vitamin B2)	0.86 mg	50%
Niacin (as niacinamide) (Vitamin B3)	11.67 mg	58%
Vitamin B6 (as pyridoxine HCI)	2 mg	50%
Vitamin B6 (as pyridoxal -5-phosphate)	0.67 mg	33%
Folate (as folic acid)	233.34 mcg	58%
Vitamin B12 (as methylcobalamin)	3.34 mcg	55%
Biotin (as biotin yeast)	100 mcg	33%
Pantothenic acid (as calcium pantothenate) (vitamin B5)	2.67 mg	26%
Iodine (as potassium iodide)	55 mcg	37%
Magnesium (as magnesium oxide)	16.67 mg	4%
Zinc (from zinc yeast complex)	1.67 mg	11%
Selenium (from selenium yeast complex)	30 mcg	43%
Copper (from copper yeast complex)	0.134 mg	6%
Chromium (from chromium yeast complex)	6.67 mcg	5%
Choline (as c. bitartrate)	15.33 mg	2%

Green capsules contain:

Chlorella algae
Spirulina (Spirulina platensis) algae
Lecithin (soy)
Barley grass
Orange (Citrus sinensis) fruit
Tocotrienols (from natual palm oil)
Broccoli (Brassica oleracea) florets
MSM (methylsulfonylmethane)
Olive (Olea europaea) leaf extract
L-Leucine
Ningxia wolfberry (Lycium barbarum) fruit polysaccharides
Boron (as boron AAC)
Lutein (from marigold flowers)

Yellow capsules contain:

Broccoli (Brassica oleracea) florets
Lecithin (soy)
Barley grass
Citrus flavonoids (from tangerine extract)
Orange (Citrus sinensis) fruit
Tocotrienols (from natural palm oil)
Curcumin (Curcuma longa) root and rhizome extract
MSM (methylsulfonylmethane)
Olive (Olea europaea) leaf extract
Ningxia wolfberry (Lycium barbarum) fruit polysaccharides
L-Leucine
Boron (as boron AAC)
Lutein (from marigold flowers)

Purple capsules contain:

Resveratrol (from Polygonum cuspidatum)
Lecithin (soy)
Broccoli (Brassica oleracea) florets
Orange (Citrus sinensis) fruit
Pomegranate (40% ellagic acid)
Grape (Vitis vinifera) skin extract
Tocotrienols (from natural palm oil)
MSM (methylsulfonylmethane)
Olive (Olea europaea) leaf extract

Ningxia wolfberry (Lycium barbarum)
   fruit polysaccharides
L-Leucine
Boron (as boron AAC)
Lutein (from marigold flowers)

Other Ingredients:

Gelatin, maltodextrin, silica, coral calcium, rice flour, mannitol, alginate, arabic gum, pea starch, modified food starch, sucrose, sodium ascorbate, dextrin, soy bean oil, and glucose

Directions: Take one pack of 3 capsules—one green, one yellow and one purple—each morning for a full complement of vitamins, minerals, antioxidants and other valuable phytonutrients.

Companion Products: Omega Blue, Longevity softgels, Balance Complete, Life 5, Ningxia Red, Dried wolfberries

Ultra Young +

Ultra Young + is a revolutionary spray supplement that supports healthy pituitary and growth hormone secretion. It contain Vicia Faba, which contains L-dopa. In 1976 a National Insitute of Aging study found that administration of L-dopa to patients over 60 years of age resulted in an increase in growth hormone levels. A study conducted by Dr. George Cotzias showed that mice, fed small doses of L-dopa, lived twice as long as the control group not receiving L-dopa.

INGREDIENTS:

Vicia faba major contains unusually high concentrations of L-dopa, an amino acid that has been shown in several studies to restore the sensitivity of the hypothalamus, which can lead to dramatic increases in both GHRH and GH levels.

Ningxia wolfberry (*Lycium barbarum*) is rich in polysaccharides, which have potent immune-stimulating effects. These polysaccharides appear to be highly effective in raising levels of immunoglobulin A (IgA), an immune protein that steadily declines with age.

Grape (*Vitis vinifera*) **seed/skin extract** is

L-arginine is an amino acid that helps increase natural growth hormone production.

L-glutamine is an amino acid that has been researched for its hGH-promoting effects.

L-ornithine promotes muscle-building activity in the body by increasing levels of anabolic (growth-promoting) hormones such as insulin and growth hormone.

L-glycine is an amino acid used by the body to build proteins. It also promotes the health of the thymus gland, spleen, and bone marrow and balance white cell production.

L-Lysine is important for proper growth. It appears to help the body absorb and conserve calcium and it plays an important role in the formation of collagen, a substance important for bones and connective tissues including skin, tendon, and cartilage.

Pyroglutamate is believed to increase circulation in the brain and improve memory

GABA (Gamma-aminobutyric acid) is a nutrient that can amplify growth hormone production.

Ginko biloba extract increases energy, improves memory and is excellent for cerebral circulation, oxygenation and blood flow

MSM supports healthy hair, skin, liver, and immune function. It helps restore flexibility to cell membranes and slows the breakdown of cartilage.

Eleuthero (*Eleutherococcus senticosus*) root extract , formerly referred to as Siberian ginseng, strengthens adrenal glands, enhances immune function, normalizes blood pressure, improves mental alertness and promotes hormone balance.

Bee Pollen is high in protein and low in fat and sodium. It contains many minerals and vitamins, including potassium, calcium, magnesiuim, zinc, manganese, copper and B vitamins. It is a great source of concentrated energy.

Ginger (*Zingiber officinale*) root extract, in addition to its popularity as a stomach aid, has also been shown to improve circulation by relaxing muscles around blood vessels so blood can flow more easily.

Zinc (*Zinc proteinate*) plays a pivotal part in maintaining optimal pituitary function.

DHEA is a precursor to many human hormones, particularly estrogens and testosterone. It has been used to improve memory, physical performance and mood.

Vitamin B3 *(Niacin)* provides nutritional support for the hypothalamus and pituitary.

Vitamin B6 supports glandular and cognitive function.

Vitamin E *(d-alpha tocopheryl acetate)* protects the heart and blood and combats free-radical oxidative damage.

Selenium has been extensively researched for its anticancer and antioxidant properties.

Stevia *(Stevia rebaudiana)* is a natural super-sweet herbal supplement.

Inosine is an ingredient used in fitness supplements and has been shown to have neuroprotective properties

Octacosanol has been shown to have antiviral properties and may be support nerve health. It also has conferred enhanced physical endurance in some studies.

ESSENTIAL OILS:

Sandalwood *(Santalum album)* is high in sesquiterpenes, which stimulate the hypothalamus and pituitary glands.

Fleabane *(Conyza canadensis)* Stimulates liver and pancreas.

NUTRITION FACTS:

Per Serving (3 sprays 0.5ml):

Calories 187 Calories from Fat 30   %DV
Vitamin E . . . . 7 IU 25%
  (as d-alpha-tocopheryl acetate)
Niacin (vitamin B3) . . 1.5 mg 7.5%
Vitamin B6 . . . . .19 mg 9%
Zinc (as zinc proteinate) 2.5 mg 16%
Selenium . . . . 7 mcg 7%
  (as selenium yeast proteinate)

Companion Products: AD&E, Be-Fit, Essential Manna, JuvaTone, Mineral Essence, Power Meal, Sulfurzyme, Vitagreen, and Wolfberry Bars.

Companion Oil Blends: Abundance, En-R-Gee, EndoFlex, Envision, Joy, JuvaFlex, Live with Passion, Magnify Your Purpose, Release, and Valor.

Suggested Use: Spray Ultra Young directly inside cheeks and on the roof of the mouth. Avoid swallowing for one to two minutes. Spray upon waking, between meals, and just before retiring. Avoid spraying on the tongue because this reduces its effectiveness. It is best used one to two hours before or after meals, with no snacking in between because high blood sugar levels also reduce its effectiveness.

VitaGreen

(See MULTIGREENS)

Wolfberry Crisp

A convenient, whole food, low-glycemic, super-nutrient bar, containing 16 grams of protein. It is rich in antiooxidants and phytonutrients an does not signifiantly raise blood sugar levels. Can be used as a meal replacement. All natural and certified kosher.

INGREDIENTS:

Soy & Whey Protein Complex is an ideal source of balanced, quality protein

Organic blue agave *(Agave tequilana)* **nectar** is a very low glycemic index (39) organic cactus extract that is sweeter than sucrose.

Raw almond butter is high in monounsaturated fats, minerals (magnesium and potassium) and fiber.

Ningxia *(Lycium barbarum)* **wolfberry fruit** is the highest antioxidant food known, rich in alpha carotene, beta carotene, lutein, and zeaxanthin.

Raw pumpkin *(Curcubita pepo)* **seeds** are high in zinc, magnesium, calcium and phytosterols and sterolins. They also contain fatty acids that neutralize parasites. Pumpkin seeds must be eaten raw, since roasted or cooked seeds harbor altered fat that creates arterial plaque.

Raw cashews (*Anacardium occidentale*) have high levels of monounsaturated fatty acids and selenium, magnesium, and potassium.

Raw walnuts (*Juglans regia*) are very high in ALA (Alpha lipoic acid), an important Omega-3 fat crucial for human health. Of all the nuts, it has the second-best omega 3 to omega 6 ratio. According to a recent study at the Thomas Jefferson University in Philadelphia, PA, "walnuts, when consumed as part of a low fat, low-cholesterol diet, have a beneficial effect on serum cardiovascular risk factors."

Carob chips (unsweetened vegan)

Pure vanilla bean (*Vanilla planifolia*) **extract** is a pure extract of Madagascar vanilla beans.

Vanilla (*Vanilla planifolia*) **bean extract**

Natural banana flavoring is a natural flavoring that is completely free of propylene glycol.

Directions: Eat 1 bar a day, or as a meal alternative.

Companion Products: Balance Compete, NingXia Red, JuvaPower, Longevity Softgels, and Protein Complete

Wolfberries, Ningxia

(See NINGXIA WOLFBERRIES)

YL Manna

Looking for a healthy and delicious snack in between meals? Young Living's Manna bars are full of natural flavors and nutrient-rich whole foods like juicy apples, crunchy almonds, 7 whole grains, pumpkin and sesame seeds, and essential oils. Perfect for a convenient and nutritious snack at home, in the office, or on the go. Delivers 4 grams of fiber and contains prebiotic fibers. Available in two delicious flavors.

Apple-Cinnamon

INGREDIENTS:

Brown rice syrup; apple pieces; Ningxia wolfberry (*Lycium barbarum*) fruit; inulin; raw almonds; virgin coconut oil; rolled oats; wheat flakes; barley flakes; buckwheat; raw pumpkin seeds; raw walnuts; infused cranberries (cranberries and sunflower oil); brown rice crisp (brown rice flour, evaporated cane juice, sea salt, and malt extract); vegetable glycerin; coconut; amaranth; millet; blackstrap molasses; raw sesame seeds; evaporated cane juice; cinnamon powder, vanilla flavor, sea salt; soy lecithin; cinnamon (*Cinnamomum verum*) bark essential oil; and frankincense (*Boswellia carteri*) gum/resin essential oil.

Apricot

INGREDIENTS:

Brown rice syrup; apple pieces; apricots; Ningxia wolfberry (*Lycium barbarum*) fruit; inulin; raw almonds; virgin coconut oil; rolled oats; wheat flakes; barley flakes; buckwheat; raw pumpkin seeds; brown rice crisp (brown rice flour, evaporated cane juice, sea salt, and malt extract); vegetable glycerin, coconut; amaranth; millet; blackstrap molasses; raw sesame seeds; raw walnuts; natural apricot flavor; evaporated cane juice; sea salt; soy lecithin; frankincense (*Boswellia carteri*) gum/resin essential oil; and lemon (*Citrus limon*) rind essential oil.

CHAPTER 11

Topical Hormone Products

Declining Hormones Signal Old Age

As we age, critical hormone imbalances can contribute to accelerated aging and heighten risk of cancers and other chronic diseases. Hormone replacement therapy using natural hormones (not synthetic analogues or look-alikes) in a cream application for transdermal absorption may be the best solution for reducing risk of cancer and alleviating other chronic diseases such as osteoporosis, disturbed sleep, depression, and obesity. In the specific case of progesterone, Harvard University researcher, John R. Lee, MD, found that natural progesterone is "very well absorbed through the skin, 40 to 70 times more efficiently than if you take it by mouth."

Research also indicates that essential oils enhance the penetration of topical hormone into the blood. This means that topical hormone creams with essential oils are more effective than other creams without penetration enhancers.

Hormones that decline with age include, DHEA, melatonin, testosterone, and progesterone. Estrogens (estradiol) can also drop with age, although not as quickly as progesterone, which creates an estrogen dominant condition common in women over 40. Cortisol, sometimes referred to as the death hormone, increases with age, contributing to a number of age-related problems.

Insomnia, Immunity, and Cancer

Declines in melatonin are directly linked with lowered immunity, disturbed sleep cycles, and heightened cancer risk. Declines in DHEA are correlated with lower energy and central obesity.

CAUTION: Before commencing any regimen of natural progesterone, pregnenolone, or DHEA supplementation, you should have your hormone levels tested and evaluated by a health care professional or a reliable laboratory which specializes in saliva hormone tests. In an arena as complex as hormone therapy, it is critical that any deficiencies be correctly identified BEFORE supplementation is initiated.

ZRT Laboratories offers affordable, accurate at-home testing of the following hormones:

Progesterone	DHEA
Estradiol	Estrone
Estriol	Testosterone
Melatonin	

ZRT Labs can be contacted at:
PHONE: (503) 466-2445
WEBSITE: www.salivatest.com/index.html

Cortisol: The Death Hormone

Hormones that increase with age, such as cortisol can also contribute to many age-related chronic diseases such as high blood pressure, abdominal obesity and blood sugar imbalances. Lowering cortisol levels not only increases immunity but also increases insulin sensitivity and enhances fat metabolism.

Dangers of Synthetic Hormones

Recent research has discredited many of the supposed benefits of synthetic hormones such as conjugated (horse urine) estrogens and medroxyprogesterone acetate and other synthetic progestins. These patented synthetic imposters of human hormones are very different biochemically than the natural hormones found in plants and in the human body, and their effects can be hazardous to health. Long term use of these synthetic hormones has been linked with dramatically higher risks of heart disease, ovarian cancer, breast cancer, and osteoporosis. (Natural hormones cannot be patented.)

In contrast, the natural hormones found in the human body are some of the safest natural compounds to prevent heart disease and cancer. A good example of natural hormone safety is illustrated by progesterone. When a woman reaches the late stage of pregnancy, her levels of progesterone rise to over 300 times that of normal, and both mother and child thrive on this.

Osteoporosis and Prostate Cancer

Natural progesterone has been used to successfully treat osteoporosis, heart disease, and breast cancer in women. Research by Dr. John R. Lee, MD has shown that progesterone can be to used to effectively treat prostate cancer and Benign Prostate Hyperplasia (BPH) in men.

Lowering Cancer Risk Naturally

As women grow older and approach menopause (between age 35 and 45), they become increasingly susceptible to estrogen dominance, due to an increased frequency of ovulation and dramatically lowered production of progesterone. This shortage of progesterone can lead to osteoporosis, mood swings, depression, weight gain, and increased risk of breast, endometrial, cervical, and uterine cancers.

Premenopausal women can also suffer from an estrogen deficiency, which can markedly raise their risk of heart disease (which is one reason why women's risk of heart disease reaches the equivalents of men's after age 40). A simultaneous estrogen and progesterone deficiency is one of the most common and insidious conditions afflicting women over age 40 and can result in significant deleterious effects on both physical and mental health.

Transdermal hormone creams have revolutionized the way women can manage hormone control. Because natural progesterone, pregnenolone, and DHEA are readily absorbed through the skin and into the tissues, they are rapidly becoming the standard for convenient and economical hormone replacement therapy in the United States.

Usage Guide for Progessence, Prenolone, and Prenolone+

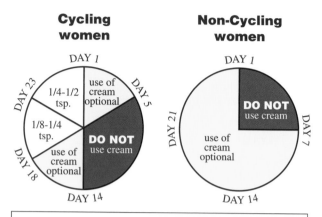

Hormone Content in mg (per ounce)			
	Pregnenolone	Progesterone	DHEA
Progessence	0	400	
Regenolone	1000	5	
NeuroGen	1000	5	100
Prenolone	1000	5	
Prenolone+	1000	5	250
PD80/20	640		160

A variety of transdermal hormone creams are available to target both progesterone, estrogen, and DHEA deficiencies among women. Women who are primarily progesterone deficient and estrogen dominant, primarily need progesterone supplementation. Women who are both estrogen and progesterone deficient, need both pregnenolone and progesterone hormones (the body converts pregnenolone into the needed amounts of estrogen).

Andropause: Menopause in Men

Declining testosterone and DHEA occurs in men over 40 and has the following symptoms:

Loss of sexual desire
Lower strength (shrinking muscles)
Reduced energy
Depression
Increased anxiety
Thinning hair
Wrinkles
Prostate Problems (restricted urine flow, sexual performance etc.)

To combat these symptoms, a cream containing DHEA and pregnenolone is a first line of defense treatment.

Essential Oils: Hormone Skin Penetration Enhancers

A number of clinical studies have shown that essential oils enhance by many times the ability of hormones and other medicines to penetrate the skin and enter the blood stream.

Studies conducted at Pisa University in 2002 found that essential oils (ie., cajeput, cardamom, melissa, myrtle, niaouli, orange oil) and essential oil components (1,8 cineole, alpha-pinene, alpha-terpineol, d-limonene) dramatically boosted estradiol hormone penetration through the skin and into the blood and tissues. Studies at the University of Bradford in the UK also found that essential oil compounds enhanced drug penetration by 13 times. A 1996 study at the China Pharmaceutical University in Nanjing similarly found a dramatic increase in drug absorption following eucalyptus and peppermint essential oils. [1,2,3]

PRODUCTS

ImmuPro

Boosts melatonin and T-lymphocyte immune cells. Designed for people who have interrupted or shortened sleep cycles, low immunity, or high risk of cancer.

ACTIVE INGREDIENTS:
4 mg/oz melatonin

Directions: Take 2-4 tablets before bed.

(See Supplement section for more information on this product)

NeuroGen

Nerve regeneration cream. Designed for people who suffer nerve degeneration (diabetics) or pain.

A topically applied pregnenolone cream that contains essential oils, hormones, and nutrients designed to stimulate nerve regeneration.

For more information on pregnenolone's ability to regenerate nerves, please consult: *Pregnenolone: A Radical New Approach to Health, Long Life, and Emotional Well-Being* by D. Gary Young.

ACTIVE INGREDIENTS:
1,000 mg/oz pregnenolone from soybeans
5 mg/oz natural progesterone from soybeans
100 mg/oz natural DHEA from wild yam

INGREDIENTS:

Natural Extracts

Aloe vera *(Aloe barbadensis)* leaf gel, English marigold *(Calendula officinalis),* Roman chamomile *(Anthemis nobilis)*, Rose hip *(Rosa canina)*, Green tea *(Camellia sinensis)*, St. Johns Wort *(Hypericum perforatum),* Grape seed *(Vinus vinifera),* Wolfberry Seed *(Lycium barbarum)* oil, Flaxseed *(Linum usitatissimum)* oil, Wheat germ *(Triticum vulgare)* oil, Allantoin—an extract of comfrey, Lecithin—an extract of soy, Red algae *(Gelidiella acerosa)*, Locust bean *(Ceratonia siliqua)* gum, Wild yam *(Dioscorea villosa)* root, Ginkgo biloba leaf, Eleuthero *(Eleutherococcus senticosus)* root, Kelp *(Macrocystis pyrifera)*, Black cohosh *(Cimicifuga racemosa)* root, Blue cohosh *(Caulophyllum thalictroides)* root

Nutrients and other active ingredients:
MSM (methylsulfonylmethane), Pregnenolone, Trace mineral complex, Retinyl palmitate (Vitamin A), Tocopheryl linoleate and acetate(Vitamin E), Ascorbic acid (Vitamin C), Progesterone (from soy)

Emollient/Moisturizing Cream Base:
Deionized water, Caprylic/capric triglyceride, Sorbitol, Shea (Butyrospermum parkii) butter, Glyceryl stearate, Sodium PCA, Stearic acid, Hydrolyzed wheat protein

Essential Oils:
Juniper *(Juniperus osteosperma/ Juniperus scopulorum),* Peppermint *(Mentha piperita),* Lemongrass *(Cybopogon flexuosus)*

Directions: Apply 1/8 to 1/4 tsp. on location 3 x day or as needed for nerve regeneration.

Companion Products: Sulfurzyme, BLM, PanAway, and Helichrysum

1. Abdullah D, Ping QN, Liu GJ. "Enhancing effect of essential oils on the penetration of 5-fluorouracil through rat skin." *Yao Xue Xue Bao*. 1996;31(3):214-21.

2. Monti D, et al., "Effect of different terpene-containing essential oils on permeation of estradiol through hairless mouse skin." *Int J Pharm*. 2002 Apr 26;237(1-2):209-14.

3. Cornwell PA, Barry BW. "Sesquiterpene components of volatile oils as skin penetration enhancers for the hydrophilic permeant 5-fluorouracil." *J Pharm Pharmacol*. 1994 Apr;46(4):261-9.

Prenolone Cream

Boosts ESTROGEN & PROGESTERONE levels. Designed for people who either have insufficient results with **Progessence** or have deficient levels of both estrogen and progesterone.

A topically applied pregnenolone cream that is designed as a broad-spectrum hormone supplement for men and women.

A powerful natural hormone cream that treats osteoporosis, depression, bloating, mood swings, weight gain, PMS, menstrual irregularity, cramps.

Pregnenolone is the precursor hormone from which the body creates all other sex and adrenal hormones, including progesterone, estradiol, estrone, estriol, testosterone, DHEA, and aldosterone.

For more information on pregnenolone's ability to regenerate nerves, please consult: *Pregnenolone: A Radical New Approach to Health, Long Life, and Emotional Well-Being* by D. Gary Young.

ACTIVE INGREDIENTS:

1000 mg/oz pregnenolone from soybeans
5 mg/oz natural progesterone from soybeans

INGREDIENTS:

Natural Extracts:

Aloe vera *(Aloe barbadensis)* leaf gel, English marigold *(Calendula officinalis),* Roman chamomile *(Anthemis nobilis)*, Rose hip *(Rosa canina)*, Green tea *(Camellia sinensis)*, St. Johns Wort *(Hypericum perforatum)*, Grape seed *(Vinus vinifera)*, Wolfberry Seed *(Lycium barbarum)* oil, Flaxseed *(Linum usitatissimum)* oil, Wheat germ *(Triticum vulgare)* oil, Allantoin— an extract of comfrey, Lecithin—an extract of soy, Red algae *(Gelidiella acerosa)*, Locust bean *(Ceratonia siliqua)* gum, Wild yam *(Dioscorea villosa)* root, Ginkgo biloba leaf , Eleuthero *(Eleutherococcus senticosus)* root, Kelp *(Macrocystis pyrifera)*, Black cohosh *(Cimicifuga racemosa)* root, Blue cohosh *(Caulophyllum thalictroides)* root

Nutrients and active ingredients:

MSM (methylsulfonylmethane), Pregnenolone, Trace Mineral complex, Retinyl palmitate (Vitamin A), Tocopheryl acetate (Vitamin E), Tocopheryl linoleate (Vitamin E), Progesterone (from soy), Ascorbic acid (Vitamin C)

Emollient/Moisturizing Cream Base:

Deionized water, Caprylic/capric triglyceride, Sorbitol, Shea (Butyrospermum parkii) butter, Glyceryl stearate, Sodium PCA, Stearic acid, Hydrolyzed wheat protein

Essential Oils:

Ylang ylang *(Cananga odorata)*, Clary sage *(Salvia sclarea)*, Geranium *(Pelargonium graveolens)*, Bergamot *(Citrus aurantium bergamia)*, Fennel *(Foeniculum vulgare)*, Sage *(Salvia officinalis)*, Yarrow *(Achillea millefolium)*

Directions: Massage 1/4 to 1/2 tsp. thoroughly into soft tissue areas of the body (arms, thighs, abdomen, neck etc.) until absorbed. Rotate sites of application daily. Individual needs may vary. Apply for three weeks out of the month (See chart on page 224).

Companion Products: Dragon Time, Mister, Sulfurzyme, and PD80/20

Prenolone +

Boosts ESTROGEN, PROGESTERONE, & DHEA levels. Designed for people who either have inadequate results with **Progessence** or **Prenolone**, or have deficient levels of estrogen, progesterone, and DHEA or testosterone.

Contains pure pregnenolone derived from soy. Also contains DHEA derived from wild yam. This triple hormone cream is designed for those who require a more rounded hormone balance or who have insufficient levels of testosterone or DHEA. For usage, instructions, and ingredients, see Prenolone.

For more information on pregnenolone's ability to regenerate nerves, please consult: *Pregnenolone: A Radical New Approach to Health, Long Life, and Emotional Well-Being* by D. Gary Young.

ACTIVE INGREDIENTS:

1000 mg/oz pregnenolone from soybeans
5 mg/oz natural progesterone from soybeans
250 mg/oz natural DHEA from wild yam

INGREDIENTS:

Natural Extracts:

Aloe vera *(Aloe barbadensis)* leaf gel, English marigold *(Calendula officinalis),* Roman chamomile *(Anthemis nobilis)*, Rose hip *(Rosa canina)*, Green tea *(Camellia sinensis)*, St. Johns

Wort *(Hypericum perforatum),* Grape seed *(Vinus vinifera),* Wolfberry Seed *(Lycium barbarum)* oil, Flaxseed *(Linum usitatissimum)* oil, Wheat germ *(Triticum vulgare)* oil, Allantoin—an extract of comfrey, Lecithin—an extract of soy, Red algae *(Gelidiella acerosa),* Locust bean *(Ceratonia siliqua)* gum, Wild yam *(Dioscorea villosa)* root, Ginkgo biloba leaf, Eleuthero *(Eleutherococcus senticosus)* root, Kelp *(Macrocystis pyrifera),* Black cohosh *(Cimicifuga racemosa)* root, Blue cohosh *(Caulophyllum thalictroides)* root

Nutrients and active ingredients:

MSM (methylsulfonylmethane), Pregnenolone Trace Mineral complex, Retinyl palmitate (Vitamin A), Tocopheryl acetate (Vitamin E), Tocopheryl linoleate (Vitamin E), Progesterone (from soy), Ascorbic acid (Vitamin C)

Emollient/Moisturizing Cream Base:

Deionized water, Caprylic/capric triglyceride Sorbitol, Shea (Butyrospermum parkii) butter, Glyceryl stearate, Sodium PCA, Stearic acid, Hydrolyzed wheat protein

Essential Oils:

Ylang ylang *(Cananga odorata),* Clary sage *(Salvia sclarea),* Geranium *(Pelargonium graveolens),* Bergamot *(Citrus aurantium bergamia),* Fennel *(Foeniculum vulgare),* Sage *(Salvia officinalis),* Yarrow *(Achillea millefolium)*

Progessence Cream

To combat ESTROGEN DOMINANCE and amplify progesterone levels. The first treatment of choice for women over 40.

Increased progesterone is very powerful anti-aging therapy for women over 40, and has been shown effective to reverse osteoporosis, depression, bloating, weight gain, PMS menstrual problems, and heightened risk of breast, cervical, ovarian, and uterine cancer and heart disease. For those who are deficient in both progesterone and estrogen, use **Prenolone**.

Progessence contains high levels of natural, soy-derived progesterone identical to that produced in the human body. It combats estrogen dominance, a condition common in women over 40 years of age. Symptoms of estrogen dominance include hot flashes, depression, bloating, weight gain, excessive bone loss, and increased risk of breast and endometrial cancer and heart disease.

John Lee, MD, discusses in detail the benefits of topically applied progesterone in his book, "What Your Doctor May Not Tell You About Menopause." According to Dr. Lee, progesterone can actually reverse bone loss in older women as well as reduce the need for hormone replacement in women lacking ovaries or not ovulating.

Studies have shown the skin application of progesterone creams results in far better absorption than hormones taken orally. Further studies have shown that combining hormones with essential oils further amplifies skin absorption into the blood stream.

ACTIVE INGREDIENTS:

400 mg/oz pure progesterone from soybeans.

INGREDIENTS:

Essential Oils:

Geranium *(Pelargonium graveolens),* Fennel *(Foeniculum vulgare),* Sage *(Salvia officinalis),* Yarrow *(Achillea millefolium)*

Natural Extracts:

Aloe vera *(Aloe barbadensis)* leaf gel, English marigold *(Calendula officinalis),* Roman chamomile *(Anthemis nobilis),* Rose hip *(Rosa canina),* Green tea *(Camellia sinensis),* St. Johns Wort *(Hypericum perforatum),* Grape seed *(Vinus vinifera),* Wolfberry Seed *(Lycium barbarum)* oil, Flaxseed *(Linum usitatissimum)* oil, Wheat germ *(Triticum vulgare)* oil, Allantoin—an extract of comfrey, Lecithin—an extract of soy, Red algae *(Gelidiella acerosa),* Locust bean *(Ceratonia siliqua)* gum, Wild yam *(Dioscorea villosa)* root, Ginkgo biloba leaf , Eleuthero *(Eleutherococcus senticosus)* root, Kelp *(Macrocystis pyrifera),* Black cohosh *(Cimicifuga racemosa)* root, Blue cohosh *(Caulophyllum thalictroides)* root

Nutrients and other active ingredients:

MSM (methylsulfonylmethane), Tocopheryl acetate and linoleate (Vitamin E), Retinyl palmitate (Vitamin A), Ascorbic acid (Vitamin C), Progesterone (from soy)

Emollient/Moisturizing Cream Base

Deionized water, Caprylic/capric triglyceride, Sorbitol, Shea (Butyrospermum parkii) butter, Glyceryl stearate, Sodium PCA, Stearic acid, Hydrolyzed wheat protein

Directions: Massage 1/4 to 1/2 tsp. thoroughly into soft tissue areas of the body (arms, thighs, abdomen, neck etc.) until absorbed. Rotate sites of application daily. Individual needs may vary. Apply for three weeks out of the month (See chart on page 224).

Companion Products: PD 80/20, and Dragon Time/Mister

Regenolone Cream

Muscle and join pain cream. Designed for people who suffer severe pain, inflammation, and stiffness from arthritis, rheumatism, or other muscle and joint conditions.

Contains pure pregnenolone derived from soy. Also includes MSM and essential oils to provide unmatched relief from arthritis pain, back pain, and other muscle and skeletal inflammation and pain.

For more information on pregnenolone's ability to regenerate nerves, please consult: *Pregnenolone: A Radical New Approach to Health, Long Life, and Emotional Well-Being* by D. Gary Young.

ACTIVE INGREDIENTS:

1,000 mg/oz pregnenolone from soy beans
5 mg/oz natural progesterone from soybeans

INGREDIENTS:

Essential Oils:

Wintergreen *(Gaultheria procumbens)*

Peppermint *(Mentha piperita)*

Douglas Fir *(Pseudotsuga menziesii)*

Oregano *(Origanum compactum)*

Natural Extracts:

Aloe vera *(Aloe barbadensis)* leaf gel, English marigold *(Calendula officinalis)*, Roman chamomile *(Anthemis nobilis)*, Rose hip *(Rosa canina)*, Green tea *(Camellia sinensis)*, St. Johns Wort *(Hypericum perforatum)*, Grape seed *(Vinus vinifera)*, Wolfberry Seed *(Lycium barbarum)* oil, Flaxseed *(Linum usitatissimum)* oil, Wheat germ *(Triticum vulgare)* oil, Allantoin— an extract of comfrey, Lecithin— an extract of soy, Red algae *(Gelidiella acerosa)*, Locust bean *(Ceratonia siliqua)* gum, Wild yam *(Dioscorea villosa)* root, Ginkgo biloba leaf , Eleuthero *(Eleutherococcus senticosus)* root, Kelp *(Macrocystis pyrifera)*,

Black cohosh *(Cimicifuga racemosa)* root, Blue cohosh *(Caulophyllum thalictroides)* root

Nutrients and other active ingredients:

MSM (Methylsulfonylmethane), Pregnenolone, Tocopheryl acetate and linoleate (Vitamin E), Trace minerals, Retinyl palmitate (Vitamin A), Progesterone (from soy), Ascorbic acid (Vitamin C)

Emollient/Moisturizing Cream Base:

Deionized water, Caprylic/capric triglyceride, Sorbitol, Shea *(Butyrospermum parkii)* butter, Glyceryl stearate, Sodium PCA, Stearic acid, Hydrolyzed wheat protein

Directions: Apply 1/8 to 1/4 tsp. on location 3 x day or as needed to combat pain associated with arthritis, sciatica, back pain, and carpal tunnel syndrome.

Companion Products: Sulfurzyme, BLM, OrthoEase, Lemon-Sandalwood Bar Soap, Peppermint-Cedarwood Bar Soap, Aroma Siez, and PanAway

OTHER HORMONAL BALANCING SOLUTIONS FOR WOMEN (See Chapter 10 for more detailed information on these products.)

CortiStop WOMEN

Contains progesterone and hormone precursors which slow cortisol production in women.

PD 80/20

Contains pregnenolone and DHEA in a capsule for ingestion. It is designed for people who do not benefit from hormone creams such as Progessence, Prenolone, or Prenolone+.

Each capsule contains 640 mg of pure pregnenolone from soy and 160 mg of pure DHEA from wild yam.

Essential Oils

Many women ages 40-plus have found that essential oils effectively combat PMS and menopause problems. Oils with estrogen-like activity include fennel, anise, clary sage, and sage.

Fennel, anise, and clary sage can be combined in equal proportions in a double 00 capsule and ingested 2 to 8 capsules per day to raise estrogen levels. Find an endocrinologist who will monitor your estrogen levels through blood testing every 30 days until you have reached the levels you want. Research at the Young Life Research Clinic has shown that ingestion of these oils in capsules up to 8 per day **does not** cause side effects or toxicity to the human body or liver.

The blends of Dragon Time, SclarEssence, Lady Sclareol and Transformation have been used with excellent results by many women to balance and normalize hormone levels.

HORMONAL BALANCING SOLUTIONS FOR MEN

(See Chapter 10 for more detailed information on these products.)

ProGen

Contains high-powered herbal extracts (i.e., saw palmetto, Pygeum africanum) that improve prostate function. It slows the body's production of DHT, a hormone that creates abnormal cell proliferation in the prostate. BPH (benign prostate hyperplasia), common in men over age 40, can eventually lead to prostate cancer, one of the most common forms of cancer in the United States. BPH symptoms include incontinence, restricted urine flow, and impotence.

Maintenance: Take 2-3 capsules, 2 times daily

Aggressive deterioration: 6 capsules, 3 times daily.

Mister

An essential oil blend that supports the male reproductive system. May be taken as a dietary supplement: 3-10 drops under tongue, 2-3 times daily. Take 10-20 drops in water or in a capsule, 2 times daily. Use no more than 7 days and then rest 4 days. Massage on Vita Flex points between scrotum and rectum.

According to Environmental Protection Agency (EPA) reports, 40 million Americans are exposed to levels of lead in water that exceed the EPA-proposed maximum contaminant allowances. Even at low levels, lead in water causes reduced birth weight, premature births, delayed mental development, and impaired mental abilities.

Scientists at the U.S. Public Health Service report that trihalomethanes (dangerous toxins made from chlorine) found in tap water have been linked to higher-than-normal rates of miscarriage and birth defects.[1]

Using information gathered from the EPA, the National Resources Defense Council (NRDC) reports that more than 45 million Americans drink tap water polluted with fecal matter, pesticides, toxic chemicals, radiation, and lead.

The inhalation of trihalomethanes (in a vapor form that occurs with hot water) while showering is more toxic than drinking chlorinated water. Buying drinking water does not protect consumers from inhaling vapors.

Reports from the EPA indicate that entities such as mining companies and electrical power plants release 7.8 billion pounds of toxic substances per year onto the land, into the water, and into the air, and the amount is increasing.

The NRDC reports that over 940,000 Americans are sickened by contaminated tap water annually. In addition, the council reports that contaminated tap water kills 900 people each year.

Whole House Water Filtration System Cartridges

CARTRIDGE 1: DUAL GRADIENT FILTER

The first contains a dual-gradient filter that has one layer wrapped around the other to provide finer filtration than is found in most other filters. In the second, water flows through a high-powered carbon briquette filter system not available through retail channels.

The dual-gradient cartridge has three times the dirt-holding capacity of similarly sized cartridges. It removes sediment (dirt, sand, grit, rust, etc.) from the water to extend the life of the charcoal filters. In addition, the inner layers reduce the levels of fine particles.

CARTRIDGE 2: CARBON BRIQUETTE

The superior carbon filter system contains a carbon-briquette cartridge of bonded powdered charcoal. The powdered consistency of the briquette allows for increased surface contact that results in maximum absorption of chlorine.

The 0.5 micron post filter greatly reduces bacteria, including giardia and cryptosporidium.

The carbon filter removes trihalomethanes, which might otherwise be consumed, absorbed through the skin, or inhaled during a shower. It also reduces lead, and removes pesticides, odors, and objectionable tastes.

CARTRIDGE 3 (optional): UV FILTER

A third UV filtration unit is available separately. It will kill all types of viruses, bacteria, and fungi.

---

1. Magnus, P., et al. "Water Chlorination and Birth Defects." *Epidemiology,* 10:513-517 (1999)

SECTION 5

Human skin is like a large sponge. It absorbs traces of almost everything that comes into contact with it—both harmful and beneficial. The skin is especially susceptible to exposure to organic solvents and petroleum-based chemicals. When some of these come into contact with the skin, they can be absorbed in far higher volumes than other types of substances.

This means that many questionable petrochemicals commonly found in personal care products, such as Sodium Laurel Sulphate (SLS), Triethanol amine (DEA), PEGs, and quarterniums can be absorbed into the skin. Over time, some of these chemicals may accumulate in the organs and tissues and result in mounting brain, nerve, and liver damage (Matthew et al., 1995).

A Troubling Trend

The most troubling indication that the synthetic chemicals in cosmetics and shampoos may be leaching into our bodies was provided by the government-funded Human Adipose Tissue Survey (Bock, 1996). According to this study, almost every person tested showed measurable levels of petroleum-based, carcinogenic chemicals, such as toluene, benzene, and styrene, in their fatty tissues.

This is why increasing numbers of health professionals are recommending personal care formulas that are completely natural and free of synthetic or petroleum-based ingredients. "To stay healthy, people have do more than just exercise and eat healthy," states Denver physician Terry Friedmann, M.D. "Consumer should also avoid personal care products that contain toxic synthetic ingredients that can penetrate the skin and accumulate in their tissues. In some cases, these products can have a greater impact on health than

either diet or exercise." AromaSilk skin care products contain wolfberry seed oil, a costly and unusual ingredient that makes important contributions to healthy skin (see box). Along with wolfberry seed oil, AromaSilk products contains MSM, an essential nutrient that has an unsurpassed ability to strengthen the skin. "MSM is absolutely dynamite for the skin," says international fashion model Teri Williams, who was a cover model for Vogue Magazine. "In my experience, it is the single most important nutrient to support healthy skin and hair."

Ronald Lawrence, M.D., Ph.D. agrees. "The importance of MSM for healthy skin and hair cannot be overemphasized. In my clinical practice, I have seen the difference that MSM makes. It is outstanding whether applied topically or taken as dietary supplement."

In addition to wolfberry seed oil and MSM, the AromaSilk skin products also contain therapeutic-grade essential oils that have a long history of use in skin care. Pure myrrh, sandalwood, geranium, rosewood, frankincense, and Roman chamomile essential oils have been used to preserve the health of the skin throughout recorded history.

AromaSilk also includes a proprietary blend of antioxidant herbal extracts, such as Ginkgo biloba, orange blossom, witch hazel, cucumber, horse chestnut, and aloe vera gel, as well as special blends of pure vegetable oils such as almond, jojoba, avocado, and rose hip seed oils.

"They feel fabulous on my skin," raves Kay Cansler, a former Director of Educational Diagnostics. "Without question, these are products for the new millennium. I've been using them for six months, and I can feel and see a huge difference. I am very, very impressed."

A.R.T. Day Activator

Age Refining Technology (A.R.T.) Day Activator cream combines the skin revitalizing power of essential oils with a proprietary anti-aging peptide complex that reduces the look of fine lines and wrinkles, diminishes age spots, evens skin tone and increases the elasticity and density of your skin. A.R.T. Day Activator delivers a noticeable difference—more youthful-looking skin.

Ingredients (all plant-derived):

Base: Deionized water, Pentylene glycol, Glycerine, Glycerol stearate, Cetearyl alcohol, and Capric/Caprylic triglycerides

Plant Extracts: Plankton, Meadowfoam seed oil, Shea butter, Aloe vera (*Aloe barbadensis*), Dipotassium Glycyrrhizate, Green tea (*Camellia oleifera*), *Chlorella vulgaris*, Lecithin, Grape Seed (*Vitis vinifera*), Algae (*Gellidield acerasa*), and Mugwort (*Artemisia vulgaris*)

Preservatives: Phenoxyethanol, Chloraphenecin, and Benzoic Acid

Stabilizers: Xanthan gum, Sodium stearoyl lactylate, Carbomer, Polysorbate 20, and Dimethicone

Nutrients: Tetrahexyldecyl ascorbate, Tocopheryl acetate (vitamin E), Squalane, Sodium hyaluronate, Retinyl palmitate (vitamin A), and Sodium PCA

Active Ingredients: Ningzia wolfberry seed oil (*Lycium barbarum*), German Chamomile EO (*Matricaria recutita*), Micrococcus lysate, Palmityl oligopeptide, Palmitoyl tetrapeptide-3, Sandalwood essential oil (*Santalum album*), and Frankincense essential oil (*Boswellia carteri*)

Directions: Apply in the morning after cleansing. Using fingertips, massage a generous amount (usually 2 to 4 pumps) of Day Activator over face and neck regions as needed. Suitable for all skin types. For maximum benefit, Day Activator should be used with A.R.T. Gentle Foaming Cleanser and A.R.T. Night Reconstructor Cream.

A.R.T. Gentle Foaming Cleanser

This unique foaming cleanser was designed to clean the skin by gently removing oil, dirt and makeup. Gentle Foaming Cleanser is formulated from naturally occurring sugars and contains ingredients that penetrate the epidermis to remove unwanted oils and impurities. This cleanser also includes a quarter of pure therapeutic-grade essential oils that were specifically selected for their skin-enhancing benefits.

Ingredients (all plant derived):

Base: Deionized Water, Sodium cocoyl glutamate, Sodium methyl cocoyl taurate, Sodium lauroamphoacetate, Decyl glucoside, and Glycerine

Plant Extracts:, Aloe vera (*Aloe barbadensis*), Melissa leaf (*Melissa officinalis*), Gingko leaf (*Gingko biloba*), Camellia oleifera leaf (*Camellia oleifera*), and Lavender (*Lavandula angustifolia*) extract

Preservatives: Chlorphenesin, Benzoic Acid, and Phenoxyethanol

Stabilizers: Citric acid, Sorbic acid, NaOH Solution, and Cetyl hydroxyethylcellulose

Nutrients: Tocopheryl acetate (vitamin E), and Retinyl palmitate (vitamin A)

Active Ingredients: Sandalwood essential oil (*Santalum album*), Frankincense essential oil (*Boswellia carteri), and* Lemon essential oil (*Citrus limon*)

Directions: Splash face with warm water. Dispense and lather a small amount of cleanser from pump. With wet hands, massage gently over face. Rise thoroughly. To be used twice daily for a refreshing cleanse in the morning and a thorough cleansing at night. Suitable for all skin types. For maximum benefit, immediately apply A.R.T. Day Activator after morning cleansing and A.R.T. Night Reconstructor after the evening cleansing.

A.R.T. Night Reconstructor

While you rest, your body is hard at work replacing and repairing cells. A.R.T. Night Reconstructor facial cream will also be working to keep your skin hydrated and nourished. This full-bodied cream uses an amazing endonuclease enzyme to support cell revitalization all through the night. This formula is also enriched with three skin-soothing essential oils, German chamomile, sandalwood, and frankincense.

Ingredients (all plant derived):

Base: Deionized Water, Pentylene glycol, Glycerine, Glycerol stearate, and Cetearyl alcohol

Plant Extracts: Meadowfoam Seed Oil, Shea Butter, Aloe vera *(Aloe barbadensis),* Dipotassium Glycyrrhizate, Green Tea *(Camellia oleifera)*, *Chlorella vulgaris,* Lecithin, Grape Seed *(Vitis vinifera),* Algae *(Gellidield acerasa),* and Mugwort *(Artemisia vulgaris)*

Preservatives: Phenoxyethanol, Chloraphenecin, and Benzoic Acid

Stabilizers: Xanthan gum, Sodium stearoyl lactylate, Carbomer, Polysorbate 20, and Dimethicone

Nutrients: Tetrahexyldecyl ascorbate, Tocopheryl acetate (vitamin E), Squalane, Sodium hyaluronate, Retinyl palmitate (vitamin A), and Sodium PCA

Active Ingredients:, Wolfberry oil *(Lycium barbarum)*, German Chamomile essential oil *(Matricaria recutita)*, Micrococcus lysate, Palmityl oligopeptide, Palmitoyl tetrapeptide-3, Sandalwood essential oil *(Santalum album)*, and Frankincense essential oil *(Boswellia carteri)*

Directions: Apply in the evening after cleansing. Using fingertips, massage in a generous amount (usually 2 to 4 pumps) of Night Reconstructor cream over face and neck regions as needed. For maximum results, Night Reconstructor should be used with A.R.T. Gentle Foaming Cleanser and A.R.T. Day Activator cream.

A.R.T. Purifying Toner

A necessary step in any comprehensive skin care regimen, Young Living's Purifying Toner helps support cleansing by removing unwanted oil, dirt and impurities that can accumulate on the skin. Designed to work in synergy with the other products in the A.R.T. Skin Care System, the Purifying Toner contains the essential oils of frankincense and Sandalwood for their ability to replenish and revitalize skin; lemon and peppermint to cleanse and energize, and Melissa and lavender to soothe and balance. This mild formula absorbs quickly and leaves skin feeling clean, smooth and soft. It minimizes oily shine and reduces the appearance of pores.

Ingredients (all plant derived)

Base: Deionized water, SD Alcohol 38B (denatured with clove oil), Pentylene glycol, Witch Hazel *(Hammamelis Virginiana)* distillate, and Glycerin

Plant Extracts: Grape Seed *(Vitis vinifera)* extract, Aloe Leaf *(Aloe Barbadensisi)* Juice, Melissa Leaf *(Melissa Officinalis)* Extract, Lavender *(Lavandula Angustifolia)* Extract, Tea-oil Leaf *(Camellia Oleifera)* Extract

Stabilizers: Polysorbate-20, Disodium EDTA, and Citric Acid

Nutrients: Retinyl palmitate (vitamin A), and Allantoin

Active Ingredients: Sandalwood *(Santalum album)* essential oil, Frankincense *(Boswellia carterii)* essential oil, Lemon *(Citrus limon)* peel oil.

Directions: Shake well. After cleansing, sweep Purifying Toner over face with a cotton ball. Can be used in the morning and again in the evening. For best results, apply the A.R.T. Day Activator or Night Reconstructor cream over the Purifying Toner.

Boswellia Wrinkle Creme

Ingredients: Calendula extract, Chamomile extract, Linoleic acid, Lecithin (soy), Rosebud extract, Orange *(Citrus aurantium dulcis)* blossom extract, St. John's wort *(Hypericum perferatum)* extract, Aloe vera, Kelp extract, *Ginkgo biloba* extract, Grape seed extract, ASC 111, Goat's cream, Glyceryl stearate, Capric/caprylic triglyceride, Shea butter, Wolfberry *(Lycium barbarum)* seed oil, Stearic acid, Stearyl alcohol, Sodium PCA, Sodium hyaluronate, Ningxia wolfberry *(Lycium barbarum)* seed oil, Allantoin, Panthenol, Retinyl palmitate (vitamin A), Tocopheryl acetate (vitamin E), Beta-sitosterol, Mannitol, MSM *(Methylsulfonylmethane)*, Dipalmitoy / Hydroxyproline, Phenoxyethanol, and Sodium ascorbate

Essential Oils: Frankincense, Sandalwood, Myrrh, Geranium, and Ylang ylang

Directions: Boswellia Wrinkle Creme is a collagen builder. Used daily, it will help minimize and prevent wrinkles. Put small amount in hand, emulsify, and apply to face and neck using upward strokes.

Companion Products: Sandalwood Moisture Cream, Orange Blossom Face Wash, and Wolfberry Eye Cream

Cinnamint Lip Balm

Is a natural lip balm enriched with essential oils and vitamins to soothe and prevent chapping.

Ingredients: Sweet almond oil, Pure bees wax *(Cera alba)*, MSM, Hemp seed oil, Sesame oil, Orange wax, Orange oil, Tocopherol acetate (vitamin E), Ascorbyl palmitate (vitamin A), Ascorbic acid (vitamin C), Citric acid, Ningxia wolfberry *(Lycium barbarum)* seed oil, Virgin coconut oil, Jojoba *(Simmondsia chinensis)* oil, and Rosehip *(Rosa rubiginnosa)* seed oil

Essential Oils: Peppermint, Spearmint, Cinnamon bark, and Orange

Directions: To soften and moisturize lips, apply Cinnamint Lip Balm as often as needed.

Clara Derm (spray)

Helps relieve a variety of skin irritations, burning and itching, particularly in sensitive female areas. Its gentle spray helps control rashes, candida, etc. Especially suited for the vaginal area before and after childbirth.

Ingredients:

Coconut oil (fractionated) base

Myrrh *(Commiphora myrrha)* has been used in the Middle East for many skin conditions, including rashes and chapped or cracked skin. It contains sesquiterpenes which stimulate the limbic system of the brain and the hypothalamus. The hypothalamus is the master gland of the human body, producing many vital hormones including thyroid and growth hormone.

Tea Tree *(Melaleuca alternifolia)* is a powerful anti-bacterial, antifungal and anti-inflammatory essential oil that has been successfully used to heal many skin conditions, including acne and sores. It is an excellent topical cleanser that promotes healing.

Lavender *(Lavandula angustifolia)* relieves muscles spasm/sprains/pains, headaches, inflammation, anxiety. It is excellent for skin problems such as psoriasis, and is known for its ability to heal burns and other injuries without scarring. Has been used to reduce stretch marks. It is hypotensive, anti-infectious, and anticoagulant.

Frankincense *(Boswellia carteri)* is considered a holy anointing oil in the Middle East. It stimulates the hypothalamus to amplify immunity. Research at Ponce University in Puerto Rico shows that it inhibits breast cancer and enhances DNA repair. In ancient times, it was well-known for its healing powers, and was reportedly used to treat every conceivable ill.

Roman chamomile *(Chamaemelum nobile)* is calming and relaxing and has been historically used to calm crying children. It is used in Europe for skin conditions including acne, dermatitis and eczema). Its calmative effects can help with restlessness, anxiety, depression and insomnia.

Helichrysum *(Helichrysum italicum)* improves circulation and reduces blood viscosity. It is anticoagulant, regulates cholesterol, stimulates liver cell function and reduces plaque deposits from veins and arteries.

Directions: Spray on affected area 1-3 times daily as needed.

Essential Beauty Serums

One of the most powerful benefits of essential oils can be felt in their effect on the skin. Essential oils' fine lipid structure enable them to penetrate deep into skin tissues, carrying many active ingredients that renew, balance and build skin health.

Three different skin serums are available, based on skin type. All the serums start with a wonderful skin conditioning base of coconut, avocado, jojoba, rosehip seed and wolfberry seed oils. Additional nutrients, tocopherol (Vitamin E) and lecithin, are added for further emollient and softening effect. Then, active essential oils are selected for each of the three skin types.

INGREDIENTS:

Vegetables Oils, Emollients and Nutrients found in all three serums:

Coconut *(Cocos nucifera)* Oil
Jojoba *(Simmondsia chinensis)* Oil
Avocado *(Persea gratissima)* Oil
Rosehip *(Rosa rubiginosa)* Seed Oil
Wolfberry *(Lycium barbarum)* Seed Oil
Lecithin
Tocopherol

Application Instructions (for all 3 serums):

Use with the A.R.T. Skin Care products as follows:
1. Thoroughly clean the skin with A.R.T. Gentle Foaming Cleanser
2. Sweep A.R.T. Purifying Toner over the face with a cotton ball
3. Spot apply desired Essential Beauty Serum to problem areas on the face and neck before applying moisturizer, sunblock or makeup. 3-5 drops of the serum can be added and mixed well to the A.R.T. Day Activator (morning) or Night Reconstructor (evening) creams when they are applied.

Essential Beauty Serum for Dry Skin

ESSENTIAL OILS:

Cedarwood *(Cedrus atlantica)* Bark—stimulates skin cells and follicles. Cedarwood is a non-drying oil that stimulates the lymph system and is also antibacterial. Often used to soften and moisturize the skin.

Blue Cypress *(Callitris intratropica)* Wood—Anti-inflammatory and anti-viral. This oil was historically used in embalming to preserve tissues.

Lavender *(Lavandula angustifolia)*—promotes tissue regeneration and has been found effective on a wide variety of skin conditions including acne, eczema, psoriasis, stretch marks and burns.

Myrrh *(Commiphora myrrha)*—The ancient Arabian and Egyptian cultures used myrrh for many skin conditions, including chapped and cracked skin and wrinkles.

Clove *(Syzygium aromaticum)* Bud—is a powerful antioxidant that is one of the most antimicrobial and antiseptic of all essential oils. Prevents cellular DNA damage.

Sandalwood *(Santalum album)*—a highly antiviral oil that has been used for centuries in Ayurvedic medicine for skin revitalization.

Essential Beauty Serum for Oily Skin

ESSENTIAL OILS:

Orange *(Citrius aurantium dulcis)*—stimulates circulation and contains over 90 percent d-limonene, one of the most powerful anticancer compounds studied in recent years

Spearmint *(Mentha spicata)*—Antiseptic and anti-inflammatory. Also believed to increase metabolism

Davana *(Artemisia pallens)*— Davana is regarded as being anti-infectious, soothing to rough skin, and stimulating to the endocrine system.

Pink Pepper *(Schinus molle)*—Distilled from the fruit of the Peruvian pepper tree, pink pepper oil is dominated by monoterpenes and sesquiterpenes.

Nutmeg *(Myristica fragrans)* Seed—a powerful anti-inflammatory and anticoagulant. Nutmeg stimulates circulation and increases production of growth hormone.

Essential Beauty Serum for Acne-Prone Skin

ESSENTIAL OILS:

Eucalyptus staigeriana—highly antiseptic and cleansing without the medicine-like aroma of other Eucalyptus oils

Tea Tree *(Melaleuca alternifolia)* Leaf—mild essential oil that is antibacterial, antiviral AND antifungal. It all-purpose characteristics make it excellent for fighting acne.

Cedarwood *(Cedrus atlantica)* Bark—stimulates skin cells and follicles. Cedarwood is a non-drying oil that stimulates the lymph system and is also antibacterial. Often used to soften and moisturize the skin.

Manuka *(Leptospermum scoparium)*—Highly anti-bacterial and anti-fungal. One of the most effective essential oils known for acne.

Thyme *(Thymus vulgaris)*—Highly antiseptic essential oil, has been researched extensively for its powerful antioxidant (anti-aging) effects on lipids.

Genesis Hand and Body Lotion

Ingredients: MSM (Methylsulfonylmethane), Glyceryl stearate, Stearic acid, Glycerin, Green tea *(Camellia oleifera),* Grape seed extract, Sodium hyaluronate, Sorbitol, Rosehip *(Rosa rubiginosa)* seed oil, Shea butter, Mango butter, Wheat germ oil, Kukui nut oil, Lecithin, Safflower oil *(Carthamus tinctorius)*, Apricot oil, Almond oil *(Prunus dulcis)*, Tocopheryl acetate (vitamin E), Retinyl palmitate (vitamin A), Jojoba oil *(Simmondsia chinensis)*, Sesame oil *(Sesamum indicum)*, Calendula extract *(Calendula officinalis)*, Chamomile extract, Orange blossom extract, St. John's wort *(Hypericum perforatum)* extract, Algae extract, Aloe vera gel, Ascorbic acid (vitamin C), and *Gingko biloba* extract

Essential Oils: Rosewood, Palmarosa, Geranium, Jasmine, Lemon, Roman chamomile, Bergamot, and Ylang ylang

LavaDerm Cooling Mist

The essential oil of lavender has been highly regarded as a burn treatment since cosmetic chemist René Gattefossé used the oil to heal severe burns suffered in a laboratory explosion. Lavender oil has both antiseptic properties and an ability to reduce to the formation of scar tissue.

This cooling mist assists the healing of most topical burns, ranging from sunburn to second-degree thermal burns. It contains a highly purified concentrate of aloe vera gel, freshly processed from the leaves of aloe barbadiensis.

Ingredients: Re-structured water, Aloe vera, and Trace mineral complex

Essential Oil: Lavender

Directions: Mist as often as needed to keep the skin cool and promote tissue regeneration.

Orange Blossom Facial Wash

Ingredients: MSM (Methylsulfonylmethane), Ningxia wolfberry *(Lycium barbarum)* seed oil, Decyl polyglucose, Mixed fruit acid complex, Hydrolyzed wheat protein, Citric acid, Calendula extract, Roman chamomile extract, Rosebud extract, Orange *(Citrus aurantium dulcis)* blossom extract, St. John's wort *(Hypericum perferatum)* extract, Algae extract, Aloe vera gel, Kelp extract, *Ginkgo biloba* extract, Grape seed extract, and Dimethyl lauramine oleate

Essential Oils: Lavender, Patchouli, Lemon, and Rosemary *(Rosmarinus officinalis)* verbenon

Directions: Use either morning or night to cleanse and exfoliate the skin.

Rose Ointment

Is a skin ointment that protects and nourishes the skin and is outstanding when applied over essential oils to lock in their benefits. Note: Not recommended for burns initially, but is very helpful to maintain, protect, and keep the the scab soft.

Ingredients: Lecithin, Lanolin, Pure Bees wax *(Cera alba)*, Mink oil, Sesame *(Sesamum indicum)* seed oil, Wheat germ oil, Rosehip *(Rosa rubiginosa)* seed oil, and Carrot seed oil

Essential Oils: Carrot seed, Tea Tree *(Melaleuca alternifolia)*, Myrrh, Palmarosa, Patchouli, Rose, and Rosewood

Directions: Apply directly to skin or over open wound following essential oil application.

Sandalwood Moisture Creme

Ingredients: Deionized water, Calendula extract, Roman chamomile extract, Rosebud extract, Orange blossom extract, St. John's wort *(Hypericum perforatum)* extract, Aloe vera gel, Kelp, *Ginkgo biloba* extract, Grape seed extract, Capric/caprylic triglyceride, Sorbitol, Shea butter, Goat's cream, Glyceryl stearate, Ningxia wolfberry *(Lycium barbarum)* seed oil, Rosehip *(Rosa rubiginosa)* seed oil, Sodium PCA, Algae extract, Stearic acid, Allantoin, Lecithin, Retinyl palmitate (vitamin A), Tocopheryl acetate (vitamin E), Ascorbic acid (vitamin C), Locust bean gum, Hydrolyzed wheat protein, Sodium hyaluronate, Tocopheryl linoleate, and MSM (Methylsulfonylmethane)

Essential Oils: Myrrh, Sandalwood, Rosewood, Lavender, and Rosemary *(Rosmarinus officinalis)* Verbenon

Directions: For best results, use after cleansing and toning the face and neck to promote younger, healthier skin. Put small amount in hand, emulsify, and apply to face and neck using upward strokes.

Satin Facial Scrub - Mint

A gentle exfoliating scrub designed for normal skin. It gently eliminates layers of dead skin cells with a revolutionary formula of jojoba beads and other natural ingredients.

This scrub can be used as a drying face mask to draw impurities from the skin.

Ingredients: Glycerin, Capric/caprylic triglyceride, MSM (Methylsulfonylmethane), Sorbitol, Glyceryl stearate, Carnuba wax, Bees wax, jojoba wax beads, Aloe vera gel, Stearic acid, Algae extract, Rosemary *(Rosmarinus officinalis)* extract, Roman chamomile extract, Tocopheryl acetate (vitamin E), Retinyl palmitate (Vitamin A), Sodium PCA, Shea butter, Grape seed extract, Titanium dioxide, Mango butter, Ascorbic acid (vitamin C), Sodium Hyaluronate, Tocopheryl Linoleate, Allantoin, Hydrolyzed wheat protein, and Hydrolyzed soy protein

Essential Oil: Peppermint

Directions: Apply warm water to the face to moisten skin. Apply scrub directly to the face and gently massage in a gentle circular motion, creating a lather. Rinse thoroughly and gently pat dry. Use four or five times weekly, depending on need.

Sensation Hand and Body Lotion

Leaves the skin soft and moist as it protects from harsh weather, chemicals, and dry air.

Ingredients: Glycerin, Glyceryl stearate, Dionized water, MSM (Methylsulfonylmethane), Grape seed extract, Green tea *(Camellia oleifera)*, Aloe vera, Rosehip *(Rosa rubiginosa)* seed oil, Mango butter, Wheat germ oil, Kukui nut oil, Lecithin, Safflower oil, Apricot oil, Shea butter, Almond oil, Tocopheryl acetate (vitamin E), Retinyl palmitate (vitamin A), Jojoba oil, Sesame *(Sesamum indicum)* oil, Calendula extract, Roman chamomile extract, Ascorbic acid (vitamin C), Orange blossom extract, St. John's wort extract, Rosewood, Sodium hyaluronate, Sorbitol, and Stearic acid

Essential Oils: Ylang ylang, Jasmine, and Rosewood

Directions: Apply directly to skin.

Wolfberry Eye Creme

Eases eye puffiness and dark circles, and promotes skin tightening. Can be used before bed and in the morning.

Ingredients: Aloe vera gel, capric/caprylic triglycerides, MSM (Methylsulfonylmethane), Sorbitol, Glycerin, Glyceryl stearate, Goat's cream, Avocado oil, Shea butter, Kukui nut oil, Rosehip *(Rosa rubiginosa)* seed oil, Ningxia wolfberry *(Lycium barbarum)* seed oil, Hydrocotyl extract, Coneflower extract, Sodium PCA, Lecithin, Dipalmitoyl hydroxyproline, Phenoxyethanol, Beta-sitosterol, Linoleic acid, Tocopherol, Sodium ascorbate, Mannitol, Almond oil, Jojoba oil, Mango butter, Sodium hyaluronate, Cucumber extract, Green tea extract, Tocopherol acetate, Tocopherol palmitate (vitamin E), Ascorbyl palmitate (vitamin A), Ascorbic acid (vitamin C), Citric acid, Soy protein, Wheat protein, Allantoin, Witch hazel extract, Horse chestnut extract.

Essential oils: Lavender, Rosewood, Roman Chamomile, Frankincense, and Geranium

Directions: Apply a tiny amount under eye area and on the eyelid before bed. Repeat in morning if needed.

Chinese Secret to Youthful Skin

For centuries, the Chinese living in Inner Mongolia have been using a very unusual vegetable oil with exceptional benefits for the skin: Wolfberry seed oil. This rare and expensive oil from Inner Mongolia is painstakingly extracted from the seeds of the Ningxia variety of the Lycium berry. Not only is the oil rich in vitamin E, linoleic, and linolenic acids, but it also has an unusual chemistry that makes it ideal for nourishing and hydrating the skin. "The wolfberry seed oil is one of the best oils for the skin," according to researcher Sue Chao. "It is sought after throughout Asia and has some very unusual regenerative properties, such as protecting aging skin and adding luster to skin."

242

CHAPTER 14

Hair Care

Three Secrets to Great Hair

1. Use the right product for the right hair type.

No hair care product—regardless of its quality—works for all types of hair at all times. Hair that is naturally curly requires different hair treatments than those that are permed. Similarly, Asian hair (which tends to consist of thicker and rounder hair follicles) needs different hair care than does African hair (which tends to be very fine and frizzy).

This is why the AromaSilk line of hair products is segmented into three different lines:

- The Lavender Volumizing line adds volume and fullness to hair. This collection includes a Scalp Wash, Nourishing Rinse, and Sealer that is specifically designed for long, flat, or dull hair.

- The Rosewood Moisturizing line moisturizes dry or damaged hair. This trio of scalp washes, nourishing rinses, and sealers contains essential oils and herbal extracts that helps defrizz and protect damaged, dry, or overprocessed hair. Naturally curly, thin, or oily hairs will benefit the most from this line.

- The Lemon-Sage Clarifying line prepares hair for perms or coloring. It contains essential oils and special herbal extracts that help remove buildup from chemicals, pollutants, and chlorine. Designed for all types of hair.

2. Use the right scalp washes and rinses.

First, the hair and scalp is cleansed with the Hair and Scalp Wash to open up the hair follicle and remove buildup, grease, and chemicals. After the hair follicle is cleansed and opened up, it is then nourished with the Nourishing Rinse. This allows nutrients to penetrate into the hair. It also protects the hair follicle from dirt and pollution, imparting shine, bounce, and vigor. It also locks in the nutrients.

3. Keep hair free of petrochemical residues

Avoid synthetic hair treatments and styling aids. These can damage hair over time, breaking the sulfur bonds that make hair lustrous and alive.

Lavender Volume Shampoo

Contains all natural ingredients for gently cleansing and volumizing fine hair. MSM provides sulfur to help build and strengthen hair. Fortified with vitamin complex, including panthenol, and vitamins A, C, and E. Contains essential oils for a beautiful fragrance.

Ingredients: Coconut oil, Olive oil, Decyl polyglucose, MSM (Methylsulfonylmethane), Deionized water, Meadow seed oil (dimethicone copolyol meadowfoamate), Vegetable soya protein, Vegetable wheat protein, Vegetable oat protein, Lemon *(Citrus limonum)* extract, Sugar maple *(Acer sacchrinum)* extract, Orange *(Citrus aurantium dulcis)* extract, Aloe vera *(Aloe barbadersis)* gel, Almond *(Prunus amygdalus dulcis)* glyceride, Soapwort *(Saponaria officinalis)* extract, Dimethyl lauranine cleate, Cetyl triethylmonium Dimethicone copolyol phthalate, Acetamide MEA, Dimethlcanol panthenol, Keratin, Linoleic acid, Hyaluronic acid, Sorbitol, wheat germ oil, Dimethiconol cysteine, Jojoba *(Simmondsia chinensis)* oil, Inositol, and Niacin

Essential Oils: Lavender, Clary Sage, Lemon, and Jasmine absolute

Instructions: Wet hair thoroughly. Apply small amount of Lavender Volume Hair & Scalp Wash. Massage thoroughly into hair and scalp. Rinse well. Repeat if desired.

Lavender Volume Conditioner

Conditions and volumizes fine hair with MSM, amino acids, and a multi-vitamin complex. Essential oils enhance and provide vital components for healthy hair.

Ingredients: Unsaponified Oils of Coconut and Olive, Shea Butter, Phytantriol, MSM, Guar Gum, Mineral Water, Glycerine, Panthenol, Sodium PCA, Aloe Vera Gel 10X, Silk Protein, MICA, Natural Vitamin E, Organic Blue Agave Nectar, Avocado, Keratin, Evening Primrose, Hawaiian White Ginger, Horsetail, Plankton (Bladderwrack), Spirulina, Sunflower, BOIS II, Hyaluronic Acid, Jojoba Oil, Mineral Complex, Lecithin, Benzyl Alcohol, Inositol, Vitamin B3, and Vitamin A

Essential Oils: Lavender, Geranium, Rosewood, Palmarosa, Roman Chamomile, Ylang Ylang, Rose, Lemon, Bergamot, Jasmine, Sandalwood, and Cedarwood

Instructions: Apply Lavender Volume Nourishing Rinse through the hair. Leave on hair for just a few seconds for light conditioning or for several minutes for deep conditioning. Rinse well.

Lemon Sage Clarifying Shampoo

Removes buildup of styling products, leaving hair feeling naturally clean and healthy. Contains herbal extracts, vitamins, and essential oils to enhance the hair.

Ingredients: Saponified Oils of Coconut and Olive, Decylpolyglucose, MSM (Methylsulfonylmethane), Mineral Water, Decylpolyglucose-Extra Glycerine, Soapwort, Guar Gum, MICA, Polysorbate, Silk protein, Aloe Vera Gel 10X, MSM-Extra, Sodium PCA, Organic Blue Agave Nectar, Panthenol, Whole Egg, Hyaluronic Acid, BOIS II, Avocado, Bee Balm, Hawaiian White Ginger, Jaborandi, Plankton (Bladderwrack), Quince, Rosemary, Spirulina, Sunflower Extract, Vitamin E, Jojoba Oil, Mineral Complex, Benzyl Alcohol, Retinyl Palmitate, Inositol, Vitamin B3, and Glycerin

Essential Oils: Peppermint, Lemon, Cedarwood

Instructions: Wet hair thoroughly. Apply small amount of Lemon-Sage Clarifying Hair & Scalp Wash. Massage thoroughly into hair and scalp. Rinse well. Repeat if desired.

Lemon Sage Conditioner

Conditions hair of all types without building up on hair. Herbal extracts, vitamins, and essential oils work together to improve hair condition.

Ingredients: Unsaponified base of Shea Butter, Phytantriol, MSM (Methylsulfonylmethane), Guar Gum, Glycerine, Mineral Water, Sodium PCA, Aloe Vera Gel 10X, Silk protein, MICA, Lecithin, Natural Vitamin E, Blue Agave Nectar, Whole Egg, Avocado, Hawaiian White Ginger, Jaborandi, Peony, Rosemary, Spirulina, Sunflower, Hyaluronic Acid, Panthenol, BOIS II, Mineral Complex, Benzyl Alcohol, Allantoin, Inositol, Vitamin B3, Vitamin A

Essential Oils: Peppermint, Lemon, and Cedarwood

Instructions: Apply Lemon-Sage Clarifying Nourishing Rinse to hair from roots to ends. Leave on hair for just a few seconds for light conditioning or for several minutes for deep conditioning. Rinse well.

Rosewood Moisturizing Shampoo

Contains natural ingredients to moisturize dry hair while gently cleansing. Contains herbal extracts, vitamins, and essential oils for nourishing the hair.

Ingredients: Saponified Oils of Coconut and Olive, Decylpolyglucose, Guar Gum, MSM (Methylsulfonylmethane), Mineral Water, Decylpolyglucose Extra, Guar Gum Extra, Glycerine, Blue Agave Nectar, MSM Extra, Sodium PCA, Silk protein, Polysorbate, MICA, Whole Egg, Natural Vitamin E, Aloe Vera Gel, Hyaluronic Acid, Phantenol, Jojoba Oil, Avocado, Evening Primrose, Irish Moss, Peony, Plankton (Bladderwrack), Quince, Slippery Elm, Spirulina, Sunflower, Yucca, Wheat Germ Oil, Mineral Complex, Benzyl Alcohol, Retinyl Palmitate, Allantoin, Inositol, and Vitamin B3

Essential Oils: Rosewood, Cedarwood, Orange, and Bergamot

Instructions: Wet hair thoroughly. Apply small amount of Rosewood Moisturizing Hair & Scalp Wash. Massage thoroughly into hair and scalp. Rinse well. Repeat if desired.

Rosewood Moisturizing Conditioner

Conditions and moisturizes dry hair with natural vegetable fatty acids, MSM, milk protein, vitamins, and essential oils.

Ingredients: Unsaponified Oils of Coconut and Olive, Shea Butter, Phytantriol, MSM (Methylsulfonylmethane), Guar Gum, Glycerine, Blue Agave Nextrar, Fractionated Coconut Oil, Sodium PCA, Aloe Vera Gel 10X, Silk protein, MICA, Mineral Water, Natural Vitamin E, Avocado, Evening Primrose, Irish Moss, Peony, Slippery Elm, Spirulina, Sunflower, Yugga, Vitamin E, Whole Egg, Hyaluronic Acid, Jojoba Oil, Panthenol, BOIS II, Mineral Complex, Benzyl Alcohol, Allantoin, Retinyl Palmitate, Inositol, and Vitamin A

Essential Oils: Rosewood, Cedarwood, Orange, and Bergamot

Instructions: Apply Rosewood Moisturizing Nourishing Rinse to hair from roots to ends. Leave on hair for a few seconds for light conditioning or for several minutes for deep conditioning. Rinse well.

SHOWER GELS

Bath & Shower Gel Base

Bath Gel Base is a dispersing agent to help unlock the full effects of your aromatherapy bath. Contains natural botanical ingredients for cleansing the pores. You may add single essential oils or blends to create your own fragrance or specific therapeutic action.

How to use: Add 5-10 drops of an essential oil or blend (depending on the strength of the oil) to 3 Tbsp. Bath Gel Base. Mix well before using.

Ingredients: Saponified Oils of Coconut and Olive, Jojoba, Vegetable gum, Guar Gum, Aloe vera, Rosemary extract, and Glycerin

Dragon Time Bath & Shower Gel

This bath and shower gel was blended for women's stressful time of the month. This custom-formulated blend of essential oils and vegetable oils is exceptionally balancing and uplifting, both physically and emotionally.

Ingredients: Saponified Oils of Coconut and Olive, Jojoba, Vegetable gum, Guar Gum, Aloe vera, Rosemary extract, and Glycerin

Essential Oils: Bergamot, Clary Sage, Geranium, Jasmine, Lemon, Palmarosa, Roman Chamomile, Rosewood, Lavender, Blue Tansy, Mandarin, Sage, Fennel, Marjoram, and Ylang ylang

Evening Peace Bath and Shower Gel

Evening Peace blends natural botanical ingredients with therapeutic-grade essential oils to relax tired, fatigued muscles and help dampen stress and tension.

Ingredients: Saponified Oils of Coconut and Olive, Jojoba, Vegetable gum, Guar Gum, Aloe vera, Rosemary extract, and Glycerin

Essential Oils: Bergamot, Roman Chamomile, Clary Sage, Geranium, Jasmine, Lemon, Palmarosa, Rosewood, Blue Tansy, Sandalwood, and Ylang ylang

Morning Start Bath & Shower Gel

Morning Start is an invigorating gel that combines uplifting, energizing essential oils to jumpstart your vigor and energy.

Ingredients: Saponified Oils of Coconut and Olive, Jojoba, Vegetable gum, Guar Gum, Aloe vera, Rosemary extract, and Glycerin

Essential Oils: Lemongrass, Rosemary, Juniper, and Peppermint

Sensation Bath & Shower Gel

Sensation contains an enchantingly fragrant mix of oils used by Cleopatra to enhance love and increase desire to be close to someone special.

Ingredients: Saponified Oils of Coconut and Olive, Jojoba, Vegetable gum, Guar Gum, Aloe vera, Rosemary extract, and Glycerin

Essential Oils: Rosewood, Ylang ylang, and Jasmine

SOAPS

The Body's Largest Organ: The Skin

With skin covering the approximately 20 square foot outside surface of the human body, it is the largest human organ and the first line of defense against harmful substances, infection, and dehydration. For adults, the skin is between 15 and 20 percent of total body weight.

Because of its large surface area, the skin can soak in many types of toxins and petrochemicals. This can result in cancer-causing compounds leaching into the body and accumulating in the fat.

Many people complain that commercial soaps make their skin feel dry and itchy, or worse. Trapped free alkali is the most common irritant in soap. Soap is made from oils (an acid) mixed with water and alkali (a base). Acids and bases neutralize each other to form a salt, in this case soap, with glycerine as a by-product. Oils that did not combine with the alkali are "free" which creates a "superfatted" soap. These mild soaps are exceptionally good for the skin, even though they have a reduced lather and shelf life. Alkali that is not neutralized by essential oils is "free alkali", which makes soap harsh and drying. The handcrafting process for natural soap removes the excess alkali that other soaps leave in.

Benefits of Handmade Natural Soaps

Handcrafted in small batches, natural bar soaps are not only pure, natural, and nontoxic; they are also good for the skin. Handmade soaps have a "hand-lotion-in-the-soap" effect created by the natural vegetable oils and waxes in the soap as well as an emulsion of water and glycerin formed when the soap was made. While the "hand-lotion-in-the-soap" effect may reduce lathering, this is what makes handmade soap extraordinarily mild and moisturizing for dry and sensitive skin.

Secret to Creating the Best Handmade Soap

The best handmade soaps are made exclusively with natural ingredients that are blended in small batches and poured into wooden block molds. The soap is then wire cut into bars, dried on oak frames, and aged for over four weeks in a humidity and temperature-controlled curing room. The extended curing process is usually time-consuming and expensive, but it effectively eliminates most of the free alkali from the bar soap, a major cause of dryness and irritation.

Handmade natural soap can be made from a number of vegetable ingredients, such as saponified oils of palm, coconut, and olive, as well as therapeutic-grade essential oils. Rosemary extract can also be used as a natural preservative.

The result is a soap that does more than just cleanse the skin. It can also act as a therapeutic skin treatment with powerful antioxidant and skin-protecting properties that can be used to treat eczema, psoriasis, dermatitis, pigmentation, inflammation, and more.

"Natural" Can be Unnatural

Unfortunately, the term "natural" can be used in very deceptive ways. If an ingredient is a five generation derivative of coconut meat, some will claim it to be natural, even if you can't pronounce the name of the ingredient.

The main ingredients in many mass-produced bar soaps are substances known as "sodium tallowate" and "potassium tallowate." These are the fatty remains of slaughtered cows, sheeps, and horses. Brains, fatty tissues, other unwanted parts of dead and sometimes diseased animals are collected into large vats and used to create "tallow." This tallow is shipped off to commercial soapmakers where it is processed into bar soaps.

Unfortunately, the U.S. Food & Drug Administration does not regulate the ingredients in soap. Some ingredients in mass-marketed soap including isopropyl alcohol, fragrances, DEA, FD&C colors, propylene glycol and triclosan have been proven harmful to human health. Isopropyl alcohol's drying effects can also remove protective oils and create microscopic cracks in the skin, which can trap and harbor bacteria and other pathogens. DEA (diethanolamine) is a hormone disrupting chemical known to form cancer-causing nitrates and nitrosamines. Dr. Samuel Epstein of the University of Illinois has found that repeated skin applications of DEA-based detergents resulted in a major increase in the incidence of liver and kidney cancers.

Regarding coal-tar derived FD&C colors, A Consumer's Dictionary of Cosmetic Ingredients states "many pigments cause skin sensitivity and irritation…and absorption (of certain colors) can cause depletion of oxygen in the body and death."

Instead of synthetic colors, German chamomile can be used. Rich in chamazuline, an intense blue pigment, chamomile actually has anti-inflammatory properties that accelerate skin healing. Moreover, other compounds in chamomile and other essential oils combine therapeutic action with delightful aromas. Peppermint oil imparts a delightful fresh fragrance to a soap while containing compounds such as menthol that act as pain-relievers and anti-inflammatory agents.

Sadly, many of the compounds in the commercial fragrances used in bath and body products are carcinogenic or otherwise toxic. The word "fragrance" on a soap label refer to over 4,000 ingredients, most of which are synthetic. Not only are fragrances potentially carcinogenic, according to Home Safe Home author Debra Lynn Ladd, "Clinical observation by medical doctors has shown that exposure to synthetic fragrances can affect the central nervous system, causing depression, hyperactivity, irritability, inability to cope and other behavioral changes." A surprising number of people experience a dry-skin reaction from many common synthetic fragrances.

AromaSilk Bar Soaps

Aromasilk soaps are created through a proprietary soap-making process derived from a sixteenth century Spanish recipe which was combined with modern technology and a propriety blend of ultra-pure ingredients.

Hand-poured and cured for almost a month. AromaSilk bar soaps are unlike any other soaps on earth. Mild and longlasting, the soaps are made with therapeutic-grade essential oils that are redefining natural skin therapy.

AromaSilk Bar Soaps—

- Contain less than 1% free alkali. The proprietary soap-making process used in AromaSilk bar soaps minimizes the presence of irritating skin-drying alkali salts.

- Use a moisturizing vegetable base that contains over 50% moisturizers.

- Include therapeutic-grade essential oils, many of which have been studied for their antiseptic, anti-inflammatory, and antifungal properties. These oils are added at the optimum moment of the soap-making process to preserve their beneficial compounds.

- Contain only the finest organic ingredients, including:

  - Saponified oils of palm, coconut, jojoba (*Simmondsia chinensis*) and olive
  - Organic oatmeal
  - Therapeutic-grade essential oils
  - Ningxia wolfberry (*Lycium barbarum*) seed oil
  - Liquid aloe vera extract
  - Rosemary extract (as an antioxidant)
  - Glycerin

Lavender-Rosewood Moisturizing Bar Soap

Excellent for toning and nourishing the skin.

Essential Oils: Lavender and rosewood

Lemon Sandalwood Bar Soap

Very cleansing and purifying to the skin. Lemon oil is highly antifungal, combating ringworm, athlete's foot and other fungal infections. Sandalwood has been show to protect the skin against viruses, such as the human papilloma virus, which is related to herpes.

Essential Oils: Lemon, and Sandalwood

Melaleuca Geranium Bar Soap

Designed specifically to combat acne, this soap contains highly antiseptic essential oils designed to dissolve away excess sebum and disinfect the skin.

Essential Oils: *Melaleuca alternifolia,* Tea tree (*Melaleuca ericifolia*), Geranium, and Vetiver

Morning Start Bar Soap

An invigorating blend of energizing and antifungal essential oils. It contains lemongrass which has been documented as a powerful anti-fungal agent in clinical studies. Ideal for combating ringworm, athlete's foot, and other fungal skin conditions.

Essential Oils: Lemongrass, Rosemary, Peppermint, and Juniper

Peppermint-Cedarwood Bar Soap

Offers an anti-inflammatory blend of essential oils to combat pain and itching. It is analgesic and pain-relieving and combats tendon, ligament, bone, and muscle pain.

Essential Oils: Peppermint, and Cedarwood

Sacred Mountain Bar Soap

This soap is for oily skin. Dissolves away excess sebum and gently exfoliates.

Essential Oils: Spruce, Fir, Ylang ylang, and Cedarwood

Thieves® Cleansing Bar Soap

A disinfecting soap that contains a powerful blend of highly antibacterial and antiseptic essential oils.

Essential Oils: Clove, Lemon, Cinnamon Bark, *Eucalyptus radiata*, and Rosemary

Thieves® Foaming Hand Soap

A natural hand-cleansing formula, that contains the Thieves blend of essential oils, all known for their powerful cleansing and anti-bacterial properties. Thieves essential oil blend penetrates beneath the skin's surface, providing a long-lasting barrier of protection. This gentle, foaming soap also contains ingredients such as vitamin E, aloe vera, and *Ginkgo biloba* to moisturize and soften the skin, and provide a balanced pH to support the skin's natural moisture complex.

Ingredients: Thieves essential oil blend (clove *(Syzygium aromaticum)*, lemon *(Citrus limon)*, Cinnamon Bark *(Cinnamomum verum)*, *Eucalyptus radiata*, and rosemary *(Rosmarinus officinalis))* Orange *(Citrus aurantium dulcis)* essential oil

Other Ingredients: Aloe vera (Aloe Barbadensis) Leaf Juice, Vitamin E (tocopheryl acetate), *Ginkgo biloba* Leaf Extract, Vitamin A (retinyl palmitate, Green Tea Leaf *(Camellia sinensis)* Extract, Water, Decyl Glucoside, Cocamidopropyl Hydroxysultaine, Denatured Alcohol, Cetyl Hydroxyethylcellulose, and Citric Acid

Companion Products: Thieves Household Cleaner, Thieves Spray, Thieves Wipes, Thieves Waterless Hand Purifier

Thieves® Waterless Hand Purifier

An all-natural hand cleanser designed to clean and refresh the hands, Thieves Waterless Hand Purifier conveniently promotes good hygiene whenever water or washing facilities are not available. Contains Thieves blend essential oils, known for the powerful anti-bacterial properties, which penetrate the skin as the ethanol in this hand purifier evaporates. Also contains active skin-moisturizing ingredients to prevent dry skin.

Ingredients: Thieves blend essential oil (clove *(Syzygium aromaticum)*, lemon *(Citrus limon)*, Cinnamon Bark *(Cinnamomum verum)*, *Eucalyptus radiata*, and rosemary *(Rosmarinus officinalis))* Peppermint essential oil

Other Ingredients: Denatured ethanol SD-38B (Denatured With Peppermint Essential Oil), Water, Aloe vera *(Aloe barbadensis)* Leaf, Vegetable Glycerin, and Hydroxylpropyl Cellulose

Directions: Use as often as necessary. Apply a nickel-sized amount to the palm of the hand and rub until completely absorbed.

Companion Products: Thieves Foaming Hand Soap, Thieves Cleansing Bar Soap, Thieves Household Cleaner, Thieves Spray

Valor Bar Soap

A highly moisturizing soap made with pure frankincense essential oil.

Essential Oils: Spruce, Rosewood, Blue Tansy, and Frankincense

DEODORANTS

Most deodorants today are loaded with toxic chemicals ranging from aluminum to antifreeze. As these chemical leach through the skin into the blood and tissues, these can create a toxic buildup in the body that can lead to cancer, liver damage, and neurological diseases.

Studies of Aluminum Toxicity

UNIVERSITY OF WESTERN ONTARIO

"Regardless of the host, the route of administration, or the speciation, aluminum is a potent neurotoxicant."

— MJ Strong, Department of Clinical Neurological Sciences, University of Western Ontario, Canada

UNIVERSITY OF STIRLING

"Aluminium is acutely toxic to fish in acid waters. The gill is the principal target organ and death is due to a combination of ionoregulatory, osmoregulatory and respiratory dysfunction. The mechanism of epithelial cell death is proposed as a general mechanism of aluminium-induced accelerated cell death."

— C Exley, University of Stirling, Scotland

BIOFACTORS

"Experimental evidence is summarized to support the hypothesis that chronic exposure to low levels of aluminum may lead to neurological disorders."

— JG Joshi, Aluminum, a neurotoxin which affects diverse metabolic reactions. Biofactors (1990 Jul)

THOMAS JEFFERSON UNIVERSITY

"This data defines a new model in which aluminum kills liver cells by mechanisms distinct from previously recognized pathways of lethal cell injury. It is hypothesized that aluminum binds to cytoskeletal proteins intimately associated with the plasma membrane. This interaction eventually disrupts the permeability barrier function of the cell membrane, an event that heralds the death of the hepatocyte."

— JW Snyder et al., Department of Pathology, Thomas Jefferson University, Philadelphia, Pennsylvania (Arch Biochem Biophys 1995)

STATE UNIVERSITY AT GENT, BELGIUM

"Epidemiological studies from Norway and England suggest a relation between the frequency of Alzheimer's disease and the concentration of aluminum in the drinking water. Estimates, made in this study, show that the role of aluminum from tooth pastes may be even more important than that from the drinking water. For that reason we determined in samples of tooth pastes taken from the BENELUX market which brands contained aluminum. This appeared to be the case for about 22% of the brands which according to the manufacturers cover about 60% of the market."

— RM Verbeeck, Laboratory for Analytical Chemistry, State University, Gent, Belgium (Acta Stomatol Belg 1990 Jun)

UNIVERSITY OF VIRGINIA

"Attention was first drawn to the potential role of aluminum as a toxic metal over 50 years ago… the accumulation of aluminum is associated with the development of toxic phenomena; dialysis encephalopathy, osteomalacic dialysis osteodystrophy, and an anemia. Aluminum has also been implicated as a toxic agent in the etiology of Alzheimer's disease, Guamiam amyotrophic lateral sclerosis, and parkinsonism-dementia."

— CD Hewitt et al., University of Virginia Health Sciences Center, Charlottesville

Perils of Aluminum

Glen Scott, MD, of Cincinnati and Patricia Saunders, a government microbiologist, warned of aluminum neurotoxicity, causing the FDA to require aluminum-bearing antiperspirants to carry a renal dysfunction warning (June 9, 2003).

According the Antiperspirant Products Final Monograph, the FDA is "concerned that people with renal dysfunction may not be aware that the daily use of antiperspirant products containing aluminum may put them at higher risk because of exposure to aluminum in the product." Young children are "at higher risk resulting from exposure to aluminum." Parents and others "must keep these products away from children, and to seek professional assistance if accidental ingestion occurs."

Sources of Aluminum Exposure

Over the Counter: Deodorants, antiperspirants, baby wipes, skin creams, suntan lotions, toothpaste, buffered asprin.

Medical: Vaccinations, intervenous solutions, wound and antacid irrigation, ulcer treatment, blood oxygenization, bone or joint replacement and burn treatments.

Foods: Aluminum cans, foils, containers, baking powder, cake mixes, frozen dough, pancake mixes, self-rising flour, grains, processed cheese.

Aromaguard - Meadow Mist

The first deodorant stick in the world to use an aluminum-free, petrochemical-free essential oil formula made from edible ingredients and therapeutic-grade essential oils.

Ingredients: Fractionated coconut oil (*Cocos nucifera*), Pure beeswax (Cera alba), Pure vegetable esters, Zinc oxide, and Vitamin E

Essential Oils: Lemon, Geranium, Rosemary, Rosewood (*Aniba rosaeodora*), Lavender, Tea tree (*Melaleuca alternifolia*), Niaouli, Clove, and Peppermint (*Mentha piperita*)

Aromaguard - Mountain Mint

The first deodorant stick in the world to use an aluminum-free, petrochemical-free essential oil formula made from edible ingredients.

Ingredients: Fractionated coconut oil (*Cocos nucifera*), Pure beeswax (Cera alba), Pure vegetable esters, Zinc oxide, Tocopherol acetate (vitamin E)

Essential Oils: Clove, Lemon, Peppermint, Rosemary, *Eucalyptus radiata*, and White fir

TOOTHPASTES

The Dirtiest Place on the Body

It is common medical knowledge the dirtiest part of the body is not the colon or bowels but the mouth. The back of the tongue is literally teeming with pathogenic microorganisms. According to Dr. John Richter founder of the Richter Center for the Diagnosis and Treatment of Breath Disorders, "more bacteria per square inch live [on the back of the tongue] than on any other part of the body."

The problem is that few people use a toothbrush to remove these bacteria. And even if the tongue were to receive a thorough scrubbing, many would remain and quickly repopulate the mouth.

The Heart Disease Link

At the 2001 annual session of the American College of Cardiology, researchers were stunned by new research that showed that gingivitis is actually linked to heart disease. "There is sufficient evidence to conclude that oral lesions, especially advanced periodontopathies, place certain patients at risk for cardiovascular disease and stroke," stated Louis F. Rose, DDS, MD, of the University of Pennsylvania.

The same oral pathogen *Porphyromonas gingivalis* that causes gum disease, also contributes to the inflammation along arteries and arterial damage that leads to heart and vascular disease.

Brushing Is Not Enough

Most toothpastes work to prevent cavities by merely hardening the tooth enamel with fluoride or using abrasive salts to mechanically scrub away microorganisms from teeth and gums.

The problem is that brushing is not enough to eliminate bacterial, fungal, and viral presence in the mouth. Such microorganisms typically hide between teeth and under the tongue. While brushing mechanically removes some of the plaque and pathogens, it still leaves 40 to 70% of microorganisms behind unscathed to later repopulate the mouth. Oral hygiene could be vastly improved by adding proven and potent antiseptics to the toothpaste matrix, rather than relying on either fluoride or scrubbing.

Antibacterial and Antiseptic

Essential oils are ideal for use in oral care products because they are both antiseptic and non-toxic—a rare combination. Jean Valnet, M.D., who used essential oils for decades in his clinical practice emphasized this: "Essential oils are especially valuable as antiseptics because their aggression toward microbial germs is matched by their total harmlessness toward tissue."

Dentarome, Dentarome Plus and Fresh Essence Mouthwash use therapeutic-grade essential oils at the heart of their formulas. These oils include peppermint, wintergreen, eucalyptus, thyme, and a proprietary blend of therapeutic-grade essential oils, including clove, lemon, cinnamon, and rosemary. This blend was tested at Weber State University in Ogden, Utah, and found to dramatically inhibit the growth of many types of bacteria (both gram negative and gram positive), including *Micrococcus luteus* and *Staphylococcus aureus*. Even more remarkably, this blend exhibited a 99.96 percent kill rate against tough gram negative bacteria, like *Pseudomonas aeruginosa*. These bacteria, because of their thicker cell walls, tend to be far more resistant to antiseptics.

The essential oils of thyme, clove and cinnamon possess significant inhibitory affects against 23 different genera of bacteria.

—International Journal of Food Microbiology

Essential oils constituents, such as thymol, menthol and eucalyptol, have been used in mouth rinses for over 100 years [and] have been documented to be antibacterial in laboratory tests. With the association of microorganisms and plaque formation, and [their] suspected involvement with carious lesions (tooth decay) and gingivitis, the effect of essential oils takes on new interest.

—Journal of the Soc. of Cosmetic Chemists

The Truth about Thyme

A comprehensive 2002 survey of medical literature has shown that thyme oil is one of the strongest natural antiseptics known. Researchers found that thyme oil kills over 60 different strains of bacteria (both gram negative and gram positive) and 16 different strains of fungi. A 1995 study by Nicole Didry at the College of Pharmaceutical and Biological Sciences in Lille, France, found that

thyme oil at even very small concentrations (500 parts per million or less), killed the pathogenic organisms responsible for the tooth decay, gingivitis, and bad breath, *Streptococcus mutans, Streptococcus sanguis, Streptococcus milleri, Streptococcus mitis, Peptostreptococcus anaerobius, Prevotella buccae, Prevotella oris,* and *Prevotella intermedia.*

Clinical Research on Essential Oils in Dental Hygiene

Over 100 studies have documented how essential oils kill the microbes that cause tooth decay and gingivitis. According to Christine Charles and colleagues in a study published by the *Journal of the American Dental Association*, "The efficacy of an essential-oil-containing antiseptic mouthrinse has been demonstrated in numerous double-blind clinical studies."[1,2,3,4,5]

Researchers at the University of Maryland have also stated in the *Journal of Clinical Periodontology* that "Antiseptic mouthrinses are well known for their antibacterial effectiveness and are widely used for the prevention and treatment of periodontitis and to prevent the formation of supragingival plaque."[6]

Bacteria	Cinnam Aldehyde from cassia/cinnamon EO	Thymol from thyme EO	Carvacrol from oregano EO	Eugenol from clove EO
Streptococcus mutans	250	250	250	500
Streptococcus sanguis	250	125	125	250
Streptococcus milleri	31	125	125	125
Streptococcus mitis	125	125	125	250
Peptostreptococcus anaerobius	500	500	500	1000
Prevotella buccae	125	250	250	500
Prevotella oris	63	250	250	500
Prevotella intermedia	125	125	125	250

MIC μg/ml (PPM or parts per million)

Didry et al., 1995

1. CH Charles et al., "Comparative efficacy of an antiseptic mouthrinse and an antiplaque/ antigingivitis dentifrice. A six-month clinical trial." *J Am Dent Assoc.* 2001 May;132(5):670-5.

2. IG DePaola et al., "Chemotherapeutic inhibition of supragingival dental plaque and gingivitis development." *J Clin Periodontol.* 1989 May;16 (5):311-5.

3. CD Overholser et al., "Comparative effects of 2 chemotherapeutic mouthrinses on the development of supragingival dental plaque and gingivitis." *J Clin Periodontol.* 1990 Sep;17 (8):575-9.

4. KR Eldridge et al., "Efficacy of an alcohol-free chlorhexidine mouthrinse as an antimicrobial agent." *J Prosthet Dent.* 1998 Dec;80(6):685-90.

5. BG Riep et al., "Comparative antiplaque effectiveness of an essential oil and an amine fluoride/ stannous fluoride mouthrinse." *J Clin Periodontol.* 1999 Mar;26(3):164-8.

6. AA Baqui et al., "In vitro effect of oral antiseptics on human immunodeficiency virus-1 and herpes simplex virus type 1." *J Clin Periodontol.* 2001 Jul;28(7):610-6.

Excess Abrasion Destroys Tooth Enamel

The problem with many common brand toothpastes is that they contain very large-sized abrasive particles that can quickly wear away tooth enamel. Because tooth enamel is not regenerated by the body, its loss is permanent. It is never replaced. As tooth enamel is lost, the softer dentin material underneath is exposed and thereby greatly enhances the risk of dental decay and tooth loss.

To preserve dental enamel, a toothpaste (dentifrice) should have extremely fine particle size: Particles fine enough to not damage or abrade irreplaceable enamel, but yet sufficiently strong to remove the biofilm of dental plaque (caused by *Streptococcus mutans* bacterial) that can cause tooth decay, gingivitis and dental disease.

Removing Tarter Naturally

Most toothpastes use questionable chemicals such as pentasodium triphosphate and tetrasodium pyrophosphate to control tartar, the scale that builds up on teeth and irritates gums, leading to gingivitis, tooth loss, and periodontal disease. However, recent studies published in the *American Journal of Dentistry* have documented the significant tartar-reducing effects of zinc citrate. Among these clinical

ABOVE: Shown at 500 times magnification are scanning electron microscope photos of ultrafine particle zinc oxide (top) and calcium carbonate (bottom) which form the base of the most advanced toothpastes in the world. These ultrafine particle sizes allow for gentle removal of dental plaque with minimal erosion of tooth enamel.

NEXT PAGE: Shown at 500 times magnification are scanning electron microscope photos of three common brand toothpastes. The top photo shows a popular toothpaste which has article sizes so large that a single grain nearly fills up the entire image area. Such huge particles are extremely corrosive to teeth, cleaning teeth while at the same time accelerating the erosion of enamel. The middle photo shows the large angular structure of a leading whitening toothpaste, whose sharp oversized structure whitens teeth by stripping away enamel with a sandpaper-like action. The lower photo shows a popular household toothpaste with less anguler but large particle sizes with a rough, coarse, abrasive texture that can be highly damaging to dental structure. Long term use of such dentrifices can hasten the loss of enamel and eventually increase the risk of tooth loss.

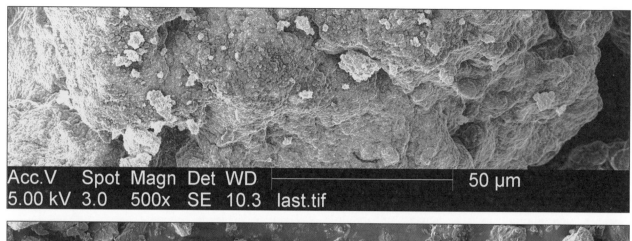

Acc.V   Spot Magn Det WD   50 μm
5.00 kV 3.0   500x SE   10.3   last.tif

Acc.V   Spot Magn Det WD   50 μm
5.00 kV 3.0   500x SE   10.0   last.tif

Acc.V   Spot Magn Det WD   50 μm
5.00 kV 3.0   500x SE   9.9   last.tif

studies was a randomized, double-blind six-month trial which showed that a zinc-citrate containing toothpaste could reduce tartar by 26%.[7]

Essential Oils as Effective Antiseptic Mouthrinses

Essential oils have proved to be even more effective as antiseptic mouthrinses than even FDA-recognized plaque-control antiseptic drugs such as stannous fluoride. A 1999 study published in the Journal of Clinical Periodontology found that an essential oil mouthrinse containing thymol, methyl salyicilate (wintergreen), menthol (peppermint), and eucalyptol (Eucalyptus globulus) was far more effective than a stannous fluoride antiseptic.

Thieves® Dentarome Toothpaste

Dentarome is formulated with pure, natural edible ingredients, such as vegetable glycerine, sodium bicarbonate, ionic minerals, and steviocide (a natural, intensely-sweet extract from a tropical plant native to South America). In addition, Dentarome

7. SL Santos et al. Anticalculus effect of two zinc citrate/essential oil-containing dentifrices. Am J Dent. 2000 Sep;13(Spec No):11C-13C.

Comparing Toothpastes

	Dentarome Ultra	Common Brand
Active Ingredients	Thieves* blend Eucalyptus Oil Peppermint Oil Thyme Oil Wintergreen Oil	Sodium Fluoride Sodium Monofluorophosphate
Foaming Agent	None	Sodium Laurel Sulfate (SLS) **
Tartar Control	Zinc Citrate	Pentasodium triphosphate
Tooth Health Agent	Wintergreen Oil	Tetrasodium pyrophosphate
Moisturizer	Vegetable Glycerine	Glycerine, sorbitol
Sweetener	Xylitol	Sodium saccharin
Coloring	None	Titanium Dioxide FD&C Blue #1
Cleansing Agent	Ultrafine Calcium Carbonate	Abrasive Silica Synthetic Glycerine
Flavoring	Therapeutic-grade Essential Oils	Artificial Sources Natural Sources
Thickener	Xanthum Gum	Xanthum Gum, Cellulose Gum

* A proprietary blend of clove, lemon, cinnamon, *Eucalyptus radiata*, rosemary.
** Also known as sodium laureth sulfate.

uses an exclusive formula of uniquely antiseptic and antimicrobial therapeutic-grade essential oils to combat plaque-causing microorganisms. Dentarome leaves the mouth fresh, fragrant, and clean.

Dentarome was tested at Weber State University and found to have potent antimicrobial properties against a wide range of oral microbes, including *Streptococcus oralis, Streptococcus pneumoniae,* and *Candida albicans*.

INGREDIENTS:

Water, Sodium bicarbonate, Glycerine, Xanthan Gum, Ionic Trace Minerals, Stevia *(Sevia Rebaudiana)* Leaf

(Contains NO fluoride, sodium lauryl sulfate, sugar, synthetic chemicals or colors)

ESSENTIAL OILS:

Peppermint *(Mentha piperita)*, Wintergreen *(Gaultheria procumbens)*, Clove *(Syzygium aromaticum)*, Lemon *(Citrus limon)*, Cinnamon Bark *(cinnamomum verum)*, Eucalyptus Radiata *(Eucalyptus radiata)*, Rosemary *(Rosmarinus officinalis)*

Thieves Dentarome Plus Toothpaste

Includes a higher concentration of thymol and eugenol for extra antiseptic action. Thymol is derived from thyme oil *(Thymus vulgaris)* and eugenol is derived from clove oil *(Syzygium aromaticum)*.

INGREDIENTS:

Water, Sodium Bicarbonate, Vegetable Glycerine, Xanthan gum, Ionic Trace Minerals, Eugenol, Thymol

(Contains NO fluoride, sodium lauryl sulfate, sugar, synthetic chemicals or colors)

ESSENTIAL OILS:

Peppermint *(Mentha piperita)*, Wintergreen *(Gaultheria procumbens)*, Clove *(Syzygium aromaticum)*, Lemon *(Citrus limon)*, Cinnamon Bark *(cinnamomum verum)*, Eucalyptus Radiata *(Eucalyptus radiata)*, Rosemary *(Rosmarinus officinalis)*

Thieves® Dentarome Ultra Toothpaste

This high-powered essential oil toothpaste has a special two-part essential oil system that has:

- Anti-stain whitening enzymes
- Time-released essential oil mouthwash
- Therapeutic-grade essential oils of Thieves (EO of clove, cinnamon, rosemary cineol, and lemon)
- Low abrasion formula contains the smallest particle-size commercially available calcium carbonate and zinc oxide
- Special tartar-control agents
- All food-grade edible ingredients

Patented Liposome Technology

- Uses only water and lecithin
- Emulsifies and protects essential oils from oxidation
- Binds essential oils to the mucus membranes in the mouth for unmatched breath-freshening and oral hygiene

INGREDIENTS:

Calcium Carbonate, Water, Zinc Oxide, Xylitol, Vegetable glycerine, Xanthan gum, Papain (from papaya extract), Lecithin, Zinc Citrate, Stevia *(Stevia Rebaudiana)* Leaf

(Contains NO fluoride, sodium lauryl sulfate, sugar, synthetic chemicals or colors)

ESSENTIAL OILS:

Peppermint *(Mentha piperita)*, Clove *(Syzygium aromaticum)*, Thyme *(Thymus vulgaris)*, Eucalyptus globulus *(Eucalyptus globulus)*, Lemon *(Citrus limon)*, Cinnamon Bark *(Cinnamomum verum)*, Eucalyptus Radiata *(Eucalyptus radiata)*, Rosemary *(Rosmarinus officinalis)*, Wintergreen *(Gaultheria procumbens)*

Thieves® Dental Floss

Flossing is an essential part of the tooth-cleaning process because it removes plaque from between teeth and at the gum line, where periodontal disease often begins. Thieves dental floss combines the traditional benefits of regular dental floss with the anti-bacterial benefits of Thieves blend essential oils. The floss is infused with essential oils which help fight infection and cavities.

ESSENTIAL OILS:

Thieves blend (clove *(Syzygium aromaticum)*, lemon *(Citrus limon)*, Cinnamon Bark *(Cinnamomum verum)*, *Eucalyptus radiata*, and rosemary *(Rosmarinus officinalis)*) Peppermint essential oil

MOUTHWASH AND LOZENGES

Essential Oil Mouthrinses Reduce Plaque and Fight Tooth Decay

A number of clinical studies over the past 20 years have documented the ability of essential oil mouthrinses to control plaque and fight gingivitis. Typical of these is 1999 study at Humboldt University in Berlin, Germany. Researchers using an observer-blind, randomized, cross-over design found that median plaque reductions generated by twice-daily essential oil mouthrinses were 23% greater than a placebo. The essential oils used were thyme, peppermint, wintergreen, and eucalyptus. (Riep et al., 1999).

Comparing Mouthwashes

Active Ingredients	Thieves Fresh Essence Mouthwash	Common Brand
Thieves*		
Thyme oil	Thymol	
Eucalyptus oil	1,8 cineol	
Wintergreen oil	Methyl Salicylate	
Peppermint oil	Menthol	
Base	Water	Alcohol, SD Alcohol
Sweetener	Steviocide Sorbitol	Sodium saccharin
Coloring	None	D&C Yellow #10 FD&C Green #3 FD&C Blue #1 FD&C Yellow #5
Flavoring	Peppermint	Artificial Sources
Preservatives	None	Benzoic Acid Polysorbate 80
Dispersant	Natural Lecithin	Poloxamer 403 Sodium Hydroxide (Lye) Synthetic Glycerine

* A proprietary blend of clove, lemon, cinnamon, *Eucalyptus radiata*, rosemary.

A six-month, double blind controlled clinical study at the University of Maryland similarly found that the essential oils of thyme, peppermint, wintergreen, and eucalyptus dramatically improved oral hygiene, killing the bacteria that cause plaque, tooth decay, and gingivitis. In this case, 20 ml of mouthrinse used twice daily produced a 34% inhibition of both plaque and gingivitis compared with a control.

Slow Release Systems for Oral Soft Tissues

Liposomal systems that adhere to mucus membranes are designed to slowly release beneficial chemical compounds in the mucus membranes of the mouth and nose. This is useful in the slow release of flavors. For example, a breath lozenge containing menthol that is contained in a mucin-binding system can provide extended oral freshness longer than a standard menthol lozenge (Fig. 1).

In another experiment, two thymol-based mouthwashes were compared side by side. The first was a standard commercial product with no liposome-based delivery; the second used a liposomal delivery system. The results of the experiment are illustrated in Fig. 2. The level of thymol measured in saliva over a period of five minutes was measured. With the

Comparison of Coolness
Retention of menthol flavor in the mouth

Figure 2. Lozenges made with mucin-binding system to release menthol flavor slowly are compared to control menthol lozenges. Timing began when the lozenge was completely dissolved in the mouth.

Controlled Release
Retention of thymol in the mouth

Figure 3. The retention of thymol was measured over a period of five minutes in various saliva samples. The level of thymol remaining in the saliva dropped off rapidly following usage of the commercial product. However, following usage of the liposome-based mouthwash, there was a significantly higher level of thymol in each saliva sample analyzed.

Liposomal Binding to Teeth

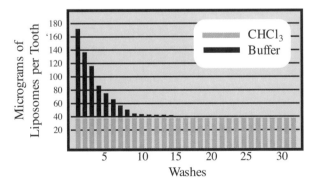

Figure 1. A saliva-coated human tooth was dipped in a solution of dental liposomes and rinsed repeatedly with 1.0 ml of water.

Critical Kill Time Against Representative Oral Pathogens

	TYPES of MOUTHRINSES		
	Essential Oil	Stannous Fl	Sterile Water Control
Fusobacterium nucleatum	<0.5 min	<0.5 min	>5 min
Streptococcus mutans	<0.5 min	<1 min	>5 min
Prevotella intermedia	<0.5 min	<2 min	>5 min
Lactobacillus casei	<0.5 min	>2 min	>5 min
Candida albicans ATCC 28366	<0.5 min	>5 min	>5 min
Candida albicans ATCC 18804	<0.5 min	>5 min	>5 min

Pan et al., 1999

commercial product, thymol levels dropped off quickly, whereas with the liposome-based mouthwash, there was a significantly higher level of thymol in each saliva sample.

Benefits of Liposomes in Thieves Fresh Essence Mouthwash

Controlled-release liposomes are a key ingredient in Fresh Essence Mouthwash. These liposomes adhere to either tooth enamel or mucus membranes in the mouth. The two primary benefits of using liposome technology are:

1. **Controlled release of active ingredients**

2. **Ingredient protection**

The controlled-release aspect of liposome technology is enhanced through the use of a patented "liposome anchoring" system. Liposomes that adhere to dental enamel can be used to improve dental health, because they contain active materials to prevent plaque formation, treat periodontal disease, and prevent dental caries. These active materials can be released slowly, enhancing their benefits.

The ability of dental liposomes to slowly release their therapeutic cargo is demonstrated in Fig. 3. A saliva-coated tooth is dipped into a solution containing dental liposomes. The liposomes contain a test material. The tooth is sequentially washed with 1.0 ml of buffer 30 times. The test material is removed slowly with the washes. Even after 30 washes, some active material is retained on the tooth.

Thieves® Lozenges, Soft

A special throat lozenge that contains the essential oil blend of Thieves, university tested for it's ability to kill 99.6% of bacteria tested.

INGREDIENTS:

Xylitol is important for maintaining good oral hygiene.

Sorbitol is a noncarcinogenic flavoring agent.

ESSENTIAL OILS:

Clove has been shown to inhibit over 60 strains of gram negative and positive bacteria and 13 types of fungi according to over two dozen clinical studies.

Lemon *(Citrus limon)* promotes leukocyte formation and increases immune function, decreases platelet stickiness and improves blood flow. It has limonene which is good for the heart.

Cinnamon is one of the strongest known antimicrobial, antiviral, and antifungal essential oils.

Eucalyptus radiata has been used to purify the air for centuries. It is rich in eucalyptol, a powerful antimicrobial agent, found in many antiseptic mouth rinses.

Rosemary is a special chemotype of rosemary in rich in eucalyptol, on the key ingredients in antiseptic mouthwashes.

Orange is fungicidal. It is also rich in limonene, a powerful antioxidant, and a superb natural flavoring.

Peppermint is antibacterial and pain-relieving.

Also contains cellulose, silica, sugar cane, and palm oil.

Thieves® Lozenges, Hard

A special throat lozenge that contains the essential oil blend of Thieves, university tested for it's ability to kill 99.6% of bacteria tested.

INGREDIENTS:

Malitol is a noncarinogenic flowing agent

Pectin is a natural thickening agent.

Steviocide *(Stevia rebaudiana)* is a natural sweetener.

Xylitol is important for maintaining good oral hygiene.

Sorbitol is a noncarcinogenic flavoring agent.

ESSENTIAL OILS:

Clove has been shown to inhibit over 60 strains of gram negative and positive bacteria and 13 types of fungi according to over two dozen clinical studies.

Lemon *(Citrus limon)* promotes leukocyte formation and increases immune function, decreases platelet stickiness and improves blood flow. It has limonene which is good for the heart.

Cinnamon is one of the strongest known antimicrobial, antiviral, and antifungal essential oils.

Eucalyptus radiata has been used to purify the air for centuries. It is rich in eucalyptol, a powerful antimicrobial agent, found in many antiseptic mouth rinses.

Rosemary is a special chemotype of rosemary in rich in eucalyptol, on the key ingredients in antiseptic mouthwashes.

Peppermint is antibacterial and pain-relieving.

CHAPTER 17
Personal Care Products for Children

KidScents Bath Gel

A shower gel with a neutral pH, perfect for young skin. pH neutral and noncomedogenic.

Ingredients: Deionized water, Decylpolyglucose, Glycerin, Sorbitol, MSM (Methylsulfonyl-methane), Aloe vera gel, Panthenol, Tocopheryl acetate (vitamin E), Chamomile extract, Comfrey extract, PG-hydroxyethycellulose cocodimonium chloride, Coneflower extract, Kiwi nut oil, Jojoba *(Simmondisia chinensis)* oil, Citrus seed extract, Babassu oil, Grape seed extract, Dimethicone copolyol meadowfoamate, Soap bark extract, Soapwort extract, Hyaluronic acid, Wheat germ oil, Keratin, Linoleic acid, and Linolenic acid

Essential Oils: Cedarwood, and Geranium

Companion Products: KidScents Shampoo, and Kidscents Moisturizing Lotion

KidScents Lotion

An extraordinarily gentle lotion with the ideal pH for young skin. pH neutral and noncomedogenic.

Ingredients: Dionized water, MSM (Methylsulfonyl-methane), Glyceryl stearate, Stearic acid, Glycerin, Grape seed extract, Sodium hyaluronate, Sorbitol, Rosehip *(Rosa rubiginosa)* seed oil, Shea butter, Mango butter, Wheat germ oil, Green tea *(Camellia oleifera),* Kukui nut oil, Lecithin, Safflower oil, Apricot oil, Almond oil, Tocopheryl acetate (vitamin E), Retinyl palmitate (vitamin A), Jojoba oil, Sesame *(Sesamum indicum)* oil, Calendula extract, Chamomile extract, Orange blossom extract, St. John's wort *(Hypericum perforatum)* extract, Algae extract, Aloe vera gel, Ascorbic acid (vitamin C), and *Ginkgo biloba* extract

Essential Oils: Cedarwood, Rosewood, Western Red Cedar, and Geranium

Companion Products: KidScents Tender Tush Ointment, KidScents Bath Gel, and KidScents Shampoo

KidScents Shampoo

Contains the finest and most nontoxic natural ingredients for gently cleansing young, delicate hair. Perfectly pH-balanced formula.

Ingredients: Deionized water, Decylpolyglucose, MSM, Aloe vera gel, Panthenol, Tocopheryl acetate (vitamin E), Chamomile extract, Coneflower extract, Kiwi nut oil, Jojoba oil, Citrus seed extract, Babassu oil, Grape seed extract, Dimethicone copolyol meadowfoamate, Hyaluronic acid, Wheat germ oil, Keratin, and Linoleic acid, and Linolenic acid

Essential Oils: Tangerine, Lemon, and Blue Tansy.

Companion Products: KidScents Bath Gel, Kidscents Moisturizing Lotion, and Lavender Volume Conditioner

KidScents Tender Tush Ointment

An ointment designed to protect and nourish young skin and promote healing. This gentle ointment is pH neutral and noncomedogenic.

Ingredients: Virgin coconut oil, cocoa butter, Pure bees wax *(Cera alba)*, Wheat germ oil, Organic olive *(Olea europea)* oil, and Almond oil

Essential Oils: Sandalwood, Rosewood, Roman Chamomile, Lavender, Cistus, Blue Tansy, Lemon, and Frankincense.

Directions: Apply as needed to areas with diaper rash, redness, or irritation.

Companion Products: Rose Ointment, German Chamomile, and Roman Chamomile

KidScents Toothpaste

KidScents Toothpaste is a revolutionary all-natural, vegetarian formula with edible ingredients. Ultra-fine calcium carbonate, a natural tooth-health agent, gently scrubs plaque and debris from teeth without damaging enamel. Contains xylitol which has been proven to reduce tooth decay. Also contains an antiseptic, antimicrobial complex of essential oils which kill the oral bacteria responsible for gingivitis, periodontal disease, and tooth decay.

Ingredients: Calcium carbonate, Natural Strawberry Flavor, Vegetable glycerine, Zinc oxide, Xanthum gum, Trace minerals, Xylitol, and Steviocide

Essential Oils: Peppermint, Rosemary, Thieves, Spearmint, Orange, and Lemon

Companion Products: Thieves, Fresh Essence Plus Mouthwash, and Thieves Soft Lozenges

KidScents MightyMist Oral Spray

A special easy to administer and swallow spray multivitamin with wolfberry polysaccharide and therapeutic-grade essential oils.

INGREDIENTS:

	Child %DV	Adult %DV
Vitamin A (palmitate)		
3600 IU	720%	68%
Vitamin B1 (thiamin HCL)		
1.5 mg	166%	100%
Vitamin B2 (riboflavin)		
1.7 mg	154%	100%
Vitamin B3 (niacinamide)		
5 mg	41%	25%
Vitamin B5 (pantothenic acid)		
10 mg	**	100%
Vitamin B6 2 mg	181%	100%
Vitamin B7 (biotin)		
30mcg	**	10%
Vitamin B9 (folic Acid)		
400 mcg	533%	100%
Vitamin B12 6 mcg	600%	100%
Vitamin C (ascorbic acid)		
60 mg	133%	100%
Vitamin D (cholecalciferol)		
400 IU	100%	100%
Vitamin E (d-alpha-tocopherol acetate)		
7IU	70%	20%
Vitamin K (menadione)		
80 mcg	400%	100%
Magnesium (amino acid chelate)		
40 mg	30%	10%
Zinc (zinc gluconate)		
1.5mg	15%	10%
Selenium (amino acid chelate)		
7 mcg	35%	10%
Manganese (amino acid chelate)		
200 mcg	**	10%
Proprietary MightyMist Blend		
55 mg	**	**

Ningxia Wolfberry polysacharrides & Echinacea root extract

Other Ingredients:

Aloe vera leaf extract, Deionized water, Vegetable glycerin, Pure grain alcohol, Colloidal trace mineral complex, Amino acid complex, Phosphatidylcholine, Ginkgo biloba leaf extract, PABA (Vitamin B10), Inositol (Vitamin B8), Stevia leaf extract, Potassium sorbate, Natural fruit flavoring

Directions: Spray inside mouth three times between meals.

Companion Products: MightyVites, and Mightyzymes

KidScents MightyVites Daily Whole Food Multi-nutrient

A great-tasting (wild berry and orange cream flavors), chewable multivitamin formulated from whole food extracts, especially for children in their early growth years (and also for adult maintenance in late years.) Made with Ningxia wolfberry (*Lycium barbarum*) MightyVites uses nutrient-dense superfruits, plants, and veggies to deliver the full-spectrum of vitamins, minerals, antioxidants, and phytonutrients, all in their whole, synergistic and easily-absorbable form.

INGREDIENTS:

Ningxia wolfberry (Lycium barbarum) fruit
Tocotrienols (from natural palm oil)
Lecithin (soy)
Malic acid from apples
Olive (Olea europea) leaf extract
Curcumins (from tumeric rhizome)

KidScents MightyVites Whole Food Multi-nutrient
NUTRITION FACTS:

		%DV Adults	%DV Children Age 4-12
Calories	5		
Total Carbohydrate	1 g	*	<1%
Sugars	1 g	*	*
Vitamin A (alpha and beta carotene)	1,500 IU	30%	68%
Vitamin C (as ascorbic acid) from oranges	28.4 mg	48%	108%
Vitamin D (as cholecalciferol)	100 IU	25%	50%
Vitamin E (as d-α tocopheryl acid succinate)	2 IU	10%	19%
Vitamin K (as phytonadione)	95 mcg	119%	164%
Thiamin (Vitamin B1 as thiamine mononitrate)	950 mcg	63%	150%
Riboflavin (Vitamin B2)	950 mcg	56%	150%
Niacin (as niacinamide)(Vitamin B3)	9.5 mcg	48%	113%
Vitamin B6 (as pyridoxine HCl)	1.9 mcg	95%	301%
Vitamin B6 (as pyridoxal-5-phosphate)	950 mcg	48%	150%
Folate (as folic acid)	400 mcg	100%	200%
Vitamin B12 (as methylcobalamin)	3.8 mcg	63%	301%
Biotin (Vitamin H)	190 mcg	63%	150%
Pantothenic acid (as d-calcium pantothenate)	4 mcg	40%	133%
Iodine (as potassium iodide)	95 mcg	63%	106%
Magnesium (as magnesium oxide)	19 mcg	5%	15%
Zinc (from zinc yeast complex)	1mg	13%	38%
Selenium (from selenium yeast complex)	19 mcg	27%	63%
Copper (from copper yeast complex)	190 mcg	10%	43%
Chromium (from chromium yeast complex)	9.5 mcg	8%	63%
Choline (from soy lecithin)	23 mg	4%	*

* Daily value not established

Broccoli (Brassica oleracea) floret
Barley (Hordeum vulgare) grass
MSM (methylsulfonylmethane)
Spirulina (S. platensis) algae
Boron (as boron AAC)
Lutein (from marigold flowers)

Other Ingredients: Orange juice powder, cherry juice powder, grape skin powder (30% polyphenols), strawberry juice powder, and other natural flavors, sorbitol, fructose, citric acid, silica, magnesium stearate, and dicalcium phosphate

Directions: Children 6 – 12 years old: take three chewable tablets daily. Can be taken before breakfast, lunch, or dinner, or in one daily dose.

Companion Products: Body Balance, Protein Complete, Mightyzymes, Mightymist, Wolfberry Crisp, YL Manna Bars

KidScents MightyZymes

A special formulation by D. Gary Young of 9 different digestive enzymes and several other nutrients designed to support healthy digestion for children. Also for relief of occasional symptoms including fullness, pressure, bloating, gas, pain or minor cramping that may occur after eating.

Ingredients: Enzyme complex (including Protease 3.0, Protease 4.5, Protease 6.0, Amylase, Peptidase, Bromelain, Cellulase, Lipase, Phytase), Alfalfa leaf, Carrot root, Peppermint leaf, Apple Syrup, Virgin coconut oil, Silicon dioxide, Citric acid, Folic acid, Dextrose, Calcium carbonate, and Fructose

Directions: Take one tablet three times daily, prior to or with meals.

Companion Products: KidScents MightyVites, and KidScents MightyMist

CHAPTER 18

Household Care

Thieves® Antiseptic Household Cleaner

A nontoxic, biodegradable, cleansing solution that uses therapeutic-grade essential oils as emulsifiers and germ-killers. It contains Thieves Essential Oil Blend, which is documented to kill over 99.96% of bacteria it comes into contact with (ie., *Pseudonomas aeroginosa*).

Ingredients:

Cleansing solution base: Nontoxic, biodegradable

Soy Lecithin is used as a natural emulsifier.

Thieves Essential Oil Blend:

Clove *(Syzygium aromaticum)*
Lemon *(Citrus limon)*
Cinnamon Bark *(Cinnamomum verum)*
Eucalyptus Radiata *(Eucalyptus radiata)*
Rosemary *(Rosmarinus officinalis)*

Thieves® Antiseptic Spray

An all-natural petro-chemical-free antiseptic spray that uses therapeutic-grade essential oils. It contains Thieves Essential Oil Blend, which is documented to kill over 99.96% of bacteria it comes into contact with (ie., *Pseudonomas aeroginosa*).

Ingredients:

Coconut oil - Fractionated

Pure Grain Alcohol is denatured with pure cinnamon essential oil; non-toxic, and no harmful or synthetic denaturants used.

Soy Lecithin is used as a natural emulsifier.

Thieves Essential Oil Blend:

Clove *(Syzygium aromaticum)*
Lemon *(Citrus limon)*
Cinnamon Bark *(Cinnamomum verum)*
Eucalyptus Radiata *(Eucalyptus radiata)*
Rosemary *(Rosmarinus officinalis)*

Thieves® Antiseptic Wipes

A pack of 30 essential-oil-impregnated wipes using Thieves Essential Oil. documented to kill over 99.96% of bacteria it comes into contact with (ie., *Pseudonomas aeroginosa*).

Ingredients:

Coconut oil - Fractionated

Pure Grain Alcohol is denatured with pure cinnamon essential oil; non-toxic, and no harmful or synthetic denaturants used.

Soy Lecithin is used as a natural emulsifier.

Thieves Essential Oil Blend:

Clove *(Syzygium aromaticum)*
Lemon *(Citrus limon)*
Cinnamon Bark *(Cinnamomum verum)*
Eucalyptus Radiata *(Eucalyptus radiata)*
Rosemary *(Rosmarinus officinalis)*

Thieves® Foaming Hand Soap

A natural hand-cleansing formula, that contains the Thieves blend of essential oils, all known for their powerful cleansing and anti-bacterial properties. Thieves essential oil blend penetrates beneath the skin's surface, providing a long-lasting barrier of protection. This gentle, foaming soap also contains ingredients such as vitamin E, aloe vera, and *Ginkgo biloba* to moisturize and soften the skin, and provide a balanced pH to support the skin's natural moisture complex.

Essential Oils: Thieves essential oil blend (clove *(Syzygium aromaticum)*, lemon *(Citrus limon)*, Cinnamon Bark *(Cinnamomum verum)*, *Eucalyptus radiata*, and rosemary *(Rosmarinus officinalis)*) Orange *(Citrus aurantium dulcis)* essential oil

Other Ingredients: Aloe vera (Aloe Barbadensis) Leaf Juice, Vitamin E (tocopheryl acetate), *Ginkgo biloba* Leaf Extract, Vitamin A (retinyl palmitate, Green Tea Leaf *(Camellia sinensis)* Extract, Water, Decyl Glucoside, Cocamidopropyl Hydroxysultaine, Denatured Alcohol, and Citric Acid

Companion Products: Thieves Household Cleaner, Thieves Spray, Thieves Wipes, Thieves Waterless Hand Purifier

Thieves® Waterless Hand Purifier

An all-natural hand cleanser designed to clean and refresh the hands, Thieves Waterless Hand Purifier conveniently promotes good hygiene whenever water or washing facilities are not available. Contains Thieves blend essential oils, known for the powerful anti-bacterial properties, which penetrate the skin as the ethanol in this hand purifier evaporates. Also contains active skin-moisturizing ingredients to prevent dry skin.

Ingredients: Thieves blend essential oil (clove *(Syzygium aromaticum)*, lemon *(Citrus limon)*, Cinnamon Bark *(Cinnamomum verum)*, *Eucalyptus radiata*, and rosemary *(Rosmarinus officinalis)*) Peppermint essential oil

Other Ingredients: Denatured ethanol SD-38B (Denatured With Peppermint Essential Oil), Water, Aloe vera *(Aloe barbadensis)* Leaf, Vegetable Glycerin, and Hydroxylpropyl Cellulose

Directions: Use as often as necessary. Apply a nickel-sized amount to the palm of the hand and rub until completely absorbed.

Companion Products: Thieves Foaming Hand Soap, Thieves Cleansing Bar Soap, Thieves Household Cleaner, Thieves Spray

CHAPTER 19

Animal Care and Horses

PRODUCTS

Animal Scents Shampoo

This shampoo is designed to clean all types of animal fur and hair. It has insect-repelling and killing properties, and is designed to rid hair of lice, ticks, and other insects.

Ingredients: Saponified oils of coconut and olive, Glycerin, Guar gum (*Cyamopsis tetragonoloba*), Aloe vera (*Aloe barbadensis*), and Rosemary (*Rosmarinus officinalis*) extract

Essential Oils: Citronella, Lavandin, Lemon, Geranium, and Spikenard

Animal Scents Ointment

This ointment has been tested in the field for many years. It is designed to cover and seal infected wounds and seal in essential oils.

Ingredients: Mink oil, Lecithin, Bees wax (*Cera alba)*, Lanolin, Sesame *(Sesamum indicum)* seed oil, Wheat germ oil, Carrot seed oil *(Daucus carota)*, and Rosehip seed oil

Essential Oils: Palmarosa, Geranium, Patchouli, Idaho balsam fir, *Melaleuca alternifolia*, Myrrh, Tea tree *(Melaleuca alternifolia)*, and Rosewood

VETERINARY MEDICINE

Essential oils have been used very successfully on many different kinds of animals from kittens to 2,000-pound draft horses. Animals generally respond to essential oils in much the same way as humans do.

How Much Should I Use?

Most animals are even more sensitive to the effects of the oils than humans. They often seem to have a natural affinity to the healing influence of the oils. Adjust dosage proportionately, based on body weight. If the protocol for a human being (at about 160 lbs.) calls for 3-5 drops, then a horse (at 1600 lbs. or more) could use as much as 10 times that amount, while a dog (at 16 lbs.) would need as little as one tenth that amount. Generally speaking, if you have never put oils on an animal before, you should start carefully, applying them only to the feet, paws, or hooves (on the frog and cornet bands) at first.

In the case of cats and small dogs, essential oils should ALWAYS be diluted before applying, because they are actually MORE sensitive to the biochemicals in the oils than humans. Be careful to avoid high phenol oils, such as oregano and thyme, on cats because they can be extremely sensitive to these stronger oils. They should only be used in high rates of dilution (90%) and the diluted oil should only be applied to the paws.

General Guidelines:

For small animals: (cats and small dogs) Apply 3-5 drops DILUTED (80-90%) oil mixture per application.

For larger animals: (large dogs) Apply 3-5 drops NEAT (dilute if using oils high in phenol) per application.

For large animals: (cattle and horses) Apply 20-30 drops NEAT (dilute if using oils high in phenol) per application.

Use Special Caution with Cats

Cats metabolize things very differently from dogs and other animals. Certain oils are potentially toxic to cats and could result in injury or even death, if applied incorrectly. For example, cats generally have adverse reactions to citrus products, and citrus oils are sometimes used to deter cats from frequenting an area. Also, cats are very sensitive to strong odors. A safe alternative, when in doubt, would be to mist them lightly with floral water. Consulting with a veterinarian is a good policy before applying oils to cats for the first time.

How to Administer EOs Internally

For internal use (ingestion), essential oils can be put into a capsule and mixed with the feed. A few drops could be added to gravy on food when administering to dogs or cats.

On large animals, the animal's bottom lip can be pulled out and (for example, in the case of a horse) 10 or 15 drops of oil put in. The animal will feel the effect quickly because capillaries in the lip will carry the oil into bloodstream immediately. For a large dog, 1 to 3 drops is sufficient.

When treating animals with essential oils internally, make certain the oils used are pure and free of chemicals, solvents, and adulterants. Always seek the advice of a qualified veterinarian before allowing the animals to ingest essential oils.

Other Helpful Tips:

- When treating large animals for viral or bacterial infection, arthritis, or bone injury, generally use the same oils and protocol recommended for humans.
- For applying to large open wounds or hard-to-reach areas, it helps to put the oils in a spray bottle dilute with vegetable oil (olive) and spray them directly on location.
- After an oil application to an open wound, cover the wound with Animal Scents Ointment to seal it and protect it from further infection. The ointment will also prevent the essential oils from evaporating.
- There is no right or wrong way to apply essential oils. Every animal is a little different. Use common sense and good judgment as you experiment with

different methods. Observe carefully how the animal responds to the treatment.

- Take special care not to get essential oils in the animal's eyes.
- Make sure the animal is drinking pure water. **Chlorinated water will suppress thyroid and immune function** in animals even quicker than in humans, and when that happens, you will suppress the healing process of that animal whether it is a dog, a horse or a cat. (see CHAPTER 12: WATER TREATMENT).
- Quality protein is vitally important to promote healing, which makes the use of organic feed essential. Unfortunately many commercial feeds contain bovine byproducts that have high risk for BSE disease and make them unfit for animal care. Avoid these at all costs. Enzymes are also essential to maximize digestion and protein assimilation.

Where to Apply Essential Oils to Animals:

For non-ungulate animals (not having hooves) such as dogs or cats, oils (neat or diluted) can be applied to paws for faster absorption.

For hoofed animals, sprinkle a few drops on the spine or flanks and massage them in. Also apply on the gums, tongue, or underneath the top lip; also apply on the frog and cornet bands of hooves. These are all good locations for oils to be applied to cows, horses, etc. (all animals with hooves). Oils can also be applied to auricular points of the ears.

When the Animal is Jittery and Resists:

If you have a high-spirited, jittery animal that won't be still to receive the application, apply Peace & Calming and/or Valor on yourself first. As you approach the animal, it should react calmer as it perceives the aroma. Kneel down or squat beside the animal and remain still for several minutes, so that it can become accustomed to the smell. As the animal breathes in the fragrances, it will become calmer and easier to manage.

Essential Oils First Aid Kit for Animals

- **Animal Scents Ointment** to seal and disinfect open wounds.
- **Exodus II** for infection, inflammation; to promote tissue regeneration.

- **Helichrysum** as a topical anesthetic.

- **Idaho Tansy** is one of the most versatile oils for animals. It is purifying, cleansing, tissue-regenerating, anti-inflammatory, and anesthetic, and is used for bruised bones, cuts, wounds, and colic. It repels flies.

- **Laurel** for bruising and soreness.

- **Lavender** for tissue regeneration, desensitizing wound.

- **Melrose** for disinfecting and cleaning wounds.

- **Mountain savory** for reducing inflammation.

- **Myrrh** for infection, inflammation; to promote tissue regeneration.

- **Ortho Ease** to dilute essential oils and act as a pain-reliever and anti-inflammatory.

- **PanAway:** If the pain originates from a broken bone rather than an open wound, use PanAway to kill pain in points where there is no open, raw tissue. NOTE: Do not apply PanAway to open wounds because it will sting and traumatize the animal. Instead use helichrysum and balsam fir to reduce bleeding and pain.

- **Purification** is more effective than using iodine or hydrogen peroxide for washing and cleansing wounds. It repels ticks and mites.

- **Roman chamomile** for tissue regeneration, desensitizing wound.

- **Thieves** for inflammation, infection and bacteria; for proudflesh (where new tissue continues to rebuild itself causing excessive granulation) to promote tissue regeneration.

- **Valerian** can be used internally and externally for controlling pain.

- **Vetiver** can be used internally and externally for controlling pain.

Animal Treatment A to Z

ARTHRITIS: (common in older animals and purebreds):

Ortho Ease or PanAway (massage on location or put several drops in animal feed).

Use Raindrop-like application of PanAway, wintergreen, pine, or spruce and massage the location. For larger animals use at least 2 times

more oil than a normal Raindrop Technique would call for on humans.

For prevention: Put Power Meal and Sulfurzyme in feed or fodder. Small animals: 1/8 to 1/4 serving per day. Large animals: 2-4 servings per day.

BIRTHING:

Gentle Baby.

BLEEDING:

Geranium, helichrysum (Shave the hair over the area being treated.)

BONES: (pain, spurs—all animals):

R.C., PanAway, wintergreen, lemongrass, and spruce. All conifers are very powerful in the action for bones and in promoting bone health. For more effective absorption, it is helpful to shave the fur/hair away from the area being treated. BLM is an excellent supplement for building animal bones.

BONES: (fractured or broken):

Mix PanAway with 20-30 drops of wintergreen and spruce. Cover the area. After 15 minutes rub in 10-15 more drops of wintergreen and spruce. Cover with Ortho Sport Massage Oil. BLM can be used as a supplement to help speed bone healing.

CALMING:

Peace & Calming, Trauma Life, lavender (domestic animals respond very quickly to the smell).

COLDS AND FLU:

For small animals put 1-3 drops Exodus II, ImmuPower, or Di-Gize in feed or fodder. For large animals, use 10-20 drops.

COLIC:

For large animals (cows) put 10-20 drops of Di-Gize in feed or fodder. For small animals, use 1-3 drops.

FLEAS AND OTHER PARASITES:

Single oils: Lemongrass, tea tree, eucalyptus (all types), citronella, and peppermint.

Blends: Di-Gize. Also add 1-2 drops of lemongrass to Animal Scents shampoo, and use to shampoo the animal.

Oils repel fleas and other external parasites. Wash blankets with oils added to the wash during the rinse cycle. Also, place 1-2 drops of lemongrass on collar to help eliminate fleas.

For internal parasites, daily rub Di-Gize on the pads (bottom) of the feet. Many people have reported that they have seen the parasites eliminated from the animal within days after starting this procedure.

INFLAMMATION:

Apply Ortho Ease, PanAway, pine, wintergreen, or spruce on location. Put Sulfurzyme in feed. Mineral Essence may also be good.

INSECT REPELLENT:

Put 10 drops each of citronella, Purification, *Eucalyptus globulus,* and peppermint in 8 ounce spray bottle with water. Alternate formula: Put 2 drops pine, 2 drops Eucalyptus globulus, and 5-10 drops citronella in a spray bottle of water. Shake vigorously and spray over area. Floral waters, such as peppermint and Idaho tansy, can also be used.

LIGAMENTS/TENDONS (torn or sprained):

Apply lemongrass and lavender (equal parts) on location and cover area. For small animals or birds, dilute essential oils with V-6 Mixing Oil (2 parts mixing oil to 1 part essential oil).

MINERAL DEFICIENCIES:

Mineral Essence. (In one case, an animal stopped chewing on furniture once his mineral deficiency was met).

MITES (ear mites):

Apply Purification and peppermint to a Q-Tip and swab just the inside of the ear.

NERVOUS ANXIETY:

Valor, Trauma Life, Roman or German chamomile, geranium, lavender, and valerian.

PAIN:

Helichrysum, PanAway, Relieve It, clove, or peppermint diluted 50-50 with V6 Oil Complex.

SHINY COATS:

Rosemary and sandalwood, or sulfurzyme will be beneficial as well.

SINUS PROBLEMS:

Diffuse Raven, R.C., pine, myrtle, and *Eucalyptus radiata* in animal's sleeping quarters or sprinkle their on bedding. Thieves, Super C, Exodus, Exodus II, and ImmuneTune have been reported as being extremely beneficial for sinus and lung congestion.

SKIN CANCER:

Frankincense, lavender, clove, and myrrh. Apply neat.

TICKS:

To remove ticks, apply 1 drop cinnamon or peppermint on cotton swab and swab on tick. Then wait for it to release the head before removing from animal's skin.

TRAUMA:

Trauma Life, Valor, Peace & Calming, melissa, rosewood, Gentle Baby, lavender, valerian, and chamomile.

TUMORS OR CANCERS:

Mix frankincense with ledum, lavender or clove and apply on area of tumor.

WORMS AND PARASITES:

ParaFree Softgels and Di-Gize.

WOUNDS (open or abrasions):

Melrose, helichrysum, and Animal Scents Ointment.

Further Helps for Equine Care

BRUISED ANKLE (ie., from hobble injury):

Apply bay laurel, Melrose, and mountain savory to reduce tenderness, bruising, and inflammation.

CANCER:

Shave area near the tumor and inject with a hypodermic needle. Keep saturated with frankincense. If the area is open, put a plug in the opening to hold the oil in the tumor cavity. Alternate with clove oil every four days. Continue for six months.

COLIC: (The leading cause of death in horses.)

Symptoms:
- Pawing the ground with head down
- Trotting in circles
- Lying down and looking bloated
- No churning or rumbling in the stomach. Quiet is a sign of colic.

Causes:
- Eating off the ground and mineral imbalance (getting too much dirt in the gut). The accumulated dirt can cause the gut to twist, abscess, and spasm.
- Parasites
- Eating too much alfalfa and not enough feed. Alfalfa can stress kidneys and liver in horses. In general, grass hay is best for horses of all kinds. As a rule of thumb, the more a horse works, the more alfalfa he needs and can tolerate.
- Getting too hot.

Treatment Protocol:
Keep the horse standing or walking. If the horse lies down, keep the animal's head tied up to prevent him from rolling.

1st hour:
Internal Use:
8 to 10 Detoxzyme capsules
15 drops of DiGize

Put into animal's feed grain or drop inside lip. You can open the capsules and make an enzyme/oil paste to put inside the horse's lip.

Massage
- Rub 10 drops DiGize up each flank and massage out towards umbilical area.
- Rub 10 drops DiGize around the coronet band.
- Rub DiGize on auricular points of ears.

Enema
Mix 30 drops of Di-Gize in 6 ounces olive oil or V-6 oil and insert in the horse's rectum as enema. Do not use castor oil-it dehydrates the colon.

2nd hour:
Put 10 to 20 drops Di-Gize in the mouth and on the flanks and coronet band.

4th hour:
Repeat 1st hour protocol except for enema.

6th hour:
Repeat 1st hour protocol, adding 5 drops of peppermint to the 15 drops of Di-Gize.

8th hour:
Repeat 1st hour except for enema and add 1 scoop of Power Meal (add to water if the animal is drinking).

10th hour:
Continue administering 6-8 Detoxzyme capsules every 2 hours until the horse's bowels are moving well.

DISTEMPER, WHOOPING COUGH OR ASTHMA

Daily Regimen:
- Mix 30 drops each of R.C. and Raven in 4 ounces of V-6 Oil Complex and insert into the rectum.
- Put 15 drops each of R.C. and Raven in the bottom lip.
- Massage oils on the chest between the front legs and auricular points of ears.
- Raindrop Technique down the spine and neck hair.
- 4 Longevity Softgels.

FRACTURES/BONE CHIPS

Shave area around affected bone
Apply mixture of
5 drops wintergreen
5 drops balsam fir
2 drops oregano

Add to feed: 2 tablespoons Sulfurzyme
Continue the above daily for 3 months

Case History:
In 1997 a horse's back hock was fractured, with two 50-cent-sized pieces splintered off. The animal was diagnosed at stage 5 lameness and the vet urged euthanizing the animal. After wintergreen essential oil was applied for several months, the bone regenerated and the break healed. Today the horse Goliath is ridden in jousting tournaments. Note: Other oils that may be effective for this condition include helichrysum, spruce and Idaho balsam fir. Sulfurzyme can be used internally.

HIDE INJURIES

Case History:

A 4-month-old colt had the hide on one side of its body stripped off. The wound was sprayed with Melrose to disinfect and helichrysum to control pain. The wound was then sealed with the formula now known as Animal Scents Ointment. Within several months the hair and skin had completely grown in and the animal had made a full recovery.

HOOF INFECTIONS

Case History:

In 2000, a show horse received some kind of severe bite on the pastern. Although the vet diagnosed a rattlesnake bite, it may have been caused by something else. Two weeks later, the entire pastern and coronet band were inflamed (the size of a cantaloupe) and the rotting, decaying flesh revealed a large hole where the bone was visible and had separated from the hoof. The vet suggested amputating the foot. Instead the following protocol was initiated:

Day 1: Wound was cleaned and disinfected with Thieves and helichrysum and the foot was bandaged. This treatment decreased pain enough to allow the mare to put weight on the foot.

Day 2: Swelling dropped by 50 percent.

Wound was again cleaned with Thieves and helichrysum and then packed with Animal Scents Ointment

Day 3 to 14: Wound was washed morning and night with Thieves, melrose and helichrysum and packed with Animal Scents Ointment.

RESULT: The animal today walks with no discomfort. A brand new hoof has appeared with only a small scar where the wound was. Although there was minor swelling in the pastern for a while, it faded 8 months later.

IMPRINTING ON NEW FOALS

Recommended Essential Oils:

Valor, Highest Potential, Sacred Mountain, Joy, Surrender, Acceptance

As soon as a colt is born, pick up the foal, hold it in your arms. Massage 5-6 drops of oil along the spine and a drop on each ear; then rub oils all over colt's body, a few drops at a time. Lay the colt in your lap. Lay its head back, stroke its neck, and pass over its nose (avoid putting any oils on the nose; it is very sensitive). Repeat every day for 21 days.

JITTERINESS:

To calm a horse, apply a few drops of oil on the hands; then put one hand on the base of the tail and the other on the withers. The animal should relax. Relaxation is the first step to healing.

Put several drops of Trauma Life, Surrender or Peace & Calming in your hand and briefly hold it up to the animal's muzzle or nostrils. If the horse pulls away and returns to it several times--perhaps out of curiosity or perhaps thinking that food may appear--feed him some grain as a reward and then put your hand with oil on his muzzle and gently rub it in. As he relaxes, work your hand around the side of his jaw and up along the neckline to the ears. Then rub his ears and top of head/crop. As he further relaxes, you can add more oil to the palm of your hand (Peace & Calming or valerian) and continue rubbing his ears, head and crop.

KIDNEY FAILURE:

- Administer 10 drops (about 1/2 dropper) K & B tincture morning and night
- Raindrop-type application on the spine: 5 drops each of cypress and juniper daily for 10 days

LAXATIVE FOR FOALS:

Put 4 drops of Di-Gize in bottom lip daily until bowels are moving.

OPEN WOUNDS

Case History:

A large thoroughbred gelding was attacked by a cougar who clawed a chunk of flesh out of the horse's buttocks half the size of a soccer ball. The horse bled terribly, blood squirting from ruptured blood vessels. The vet said the prognosis was grim because there was too much torn, damaged, and removed tissue. Even if the horse didn't die, the wound would leave a size-able scar and indentation.

TREATMENT PROTOCOL:

DAY 1:

To reduce pain and stop bleeding, a 5cc hypodermic syringe was filled with helichrysum and sprayed into the wound. The horse became less jittery and the bleeding stopped.

Several minutes later a larger 10cc syringe of Purification was sprayed into the open wound
It took over 15 ml of Purification to spray down and cover the entire wound.

After several hours, the wound was sprayed with Melrose to disinfect it and packed with the formula now known as Animal Scents Ointment. To keep hair out of the wound and reduce the possibility of infection, the tail was wrapped and tied up. Because there was no way to cover or close the wound, the horse was kept in the stable to prevent him from moving around. The animal was closely monitored to reduce the possibility of reinfection caused by the animal lying down, rolling around, and scratching the wound.

DAY 2-7

The horse's grain was supplemented with enzymes (crushed up Essentialzyme--Polyzyme is also helpful--and four scoops of Power Meal, which is dense in the nutrients required for healing and tissue rebuilding. Three times daily the open wound was irrigated with Purification and helichrysum. The vet came regularly to monitor the horse's progress. He remarked that he had never seen muscle tissue regenerate to such a degree.

WEEKS 2 to 4

Two times a day the open wound was irrigated with Purification and helichrysum

WEEKS 4 to 8

Once a week the wound was irrigated with Purification and helichrysum until it was closed.

RESULTS:

Today no indentation or concavity is visible, only a small circular two-inch scar.

PUNCTURE WOUNDS

Put 1cc of Thieves in a hypodermic syringe, insert the needle deeply into the wound, and irrigate thoroughly. Repeat 1 to 2 times a day for 2 to 3 days if still infected or swollen continue for up to 10 days.

SADDLE SORES and RAW SPOTS

(ie., where packs rub against flesh):

Use Melrose and Animal Scents ointment for at least 3 days.

SCOURS (diarrhea caused by bacteria):

- Put 5 drops Di-Gize in the horse's lower lip and rub 5-8 drops up in flank,
- Put I.C.P. in water or pouring it down the throat. Continue for four days.

SCREW WORM

There is a round worm called a bore or screw worm that bores into the spine of a horse (especially wild horses). It will cause a huge boil-like abscess on the spine. When lanced a larva worm will come out of that abscess. Sometimes the abscess will actually break open and ooze. Pour Thieves into the hole to flush out the larva worm and then fill the hole with a mixture of 12 drops Melrose and 5 drops mountain savory.

STRANGLES (*Streptococcus equi* infection):

- Perform Raindrop Technique with Thieves.
- 4 drops of Thieves on the inside of the bottom lip (for a large horse, 8 drops).
- After 2 hours repeat RT with oregano and thyme; Put 2 drops of oregano and 2 drops of thyme on the inside of the bottom lip (for a large horse, 4 drops each).

Repeat the last two steps every 2 hours until the horse begins to improve. As the horse continues to improve, alternate treatments every four hours, every 6 hours, and then morning and night.

SWOLLEN SHEATH

Geldings and stallions occasionally suffer swollen sheath, with an abscess and infection. It can be caused by

1. Eating hay too rich in protein (ideal levels of protein should be 12 to 15%; alfalfa hay can have protein as high as 26%).

2. Not extracting the penis and letting it clean off.

TREATMENT:

1. Put on rubber gloves.
2. Clean inside the sheath and remove debris with soap and water. (Use half a cap of

Thieves household cleanser diluted in a half gallon of water).

3. Clean outside of the sheath, apply myrrh oil and rosemary with bay laurel. The ratio is 15 drops of myrrh, 15 drops of rosemary, and 10 drops of laurel.

4. Perform cleaning and disinfecting morning and night until infection and swelling subsides.

5. Maintenance: The sheath should be cleaned out once a month Make sure the horse is fed adequate water and grass hay and gets sufficient exercise to increase circulation.

6. Perform Raindrop Technique with oregano, thyme and mountain savory every three to six months.

UMBILICAL CORDS OF NEWBORN FOALS:

Instead of iodine, put myrrh oil on the umbilical cord of newborn foals. Myrrh will dry the umbilical cord and facilitate a good separation. Exodus II can also be used to treat infections in a foal's umbilical cord.

Tips on Performing Raindrop Technique on Horses

Although many veterinarians have developed their own variations on this technique, the simplicity of this procedure is what makes it effective. RT for horses is similar to that for humans except that there must be practical modifications because of the difference in size and shape of the patient. Trying to exactly duplicate the human-version of Raindrop Technique on animals is not advised.

STARTING POINT:

Apply 6 drops of Valor to the tailbone (the base of the tail where it connects with the spine). Then place one hand on the withers and the other on the tailbone and hold for 5 minutes. There is no difference energetically, whether you use your right or left hand in these spots. Once the horse relaxes (i.e., drops its head and eyelids droop) the procedure can start.

DON'TS:

- Do not spend too much time stroking the horse's spine. Usually three repetitions is sufficient

- Avoid dripping oils on the hair of the horse's spine and stroking them in. You will be stroking against the grain of the hair and oil will be flicked off the spine rather than rubbed in. (This is not so important with animals with fine hair).

- Once you make contact with the animal you are applying oils, never break it.

- Don't work on the animal with multiple partners. RT is more effective when only one pair of hands makes continuous contact with the animal because:
  1) The energy stays the same.
  2) Animals get skittish when two or more people touch them at the same time.

HOW TO APPLY OILS:

- Where feasible, shave the spine area for direct application of the oil (you will use less oil).

- If shaving is not feasible, stand the hair up and part it; then drip the oil down through the hair so the oil contacts the spine. Hold the oil six inches above the spine as you drop it in.

- For coarse-haired animals stroke in the oils using small, circular motions, working from the base of the tail to the shoulders of the spine.

- For fine-haired animals, stroke in oils using regular Raindrop Technique straight-strokes

- Spend enough time massaging to get oils down into the skin and not sitting on top of the hair

When dripping the oils on spine, use
- 12 drops on a draft horse
- 6 drops on a saddle horse
- 3-4 drops on a miniature horse, Shetland or Welch pony

ADDITIONAL TIPS:

Carefully use your fingertips and thumb tips to perform Vita Flex along the auricular points of the ear. Be gentle. If you inflict a little discomfort, the horse will distrust you and pull away.

Stretching the spine is problematic in horses, so instead place one hand over the tail, the other hand on the withers and focus moving the energy along the spine.

Rubbing oils around the coronet band will allow them to reach the bloodstream and travel through the nerves in the legs to the spine.

Drip Marjoram and Aroma Siez into the hair of the outside muscles away from the spine and rub in with a larger circular motion massages. (Idaho tansy, Bay Laurel or Melrose--which are anti-inflammatory, anaesthetic, insect-repelling, relaxing and healing--can also be used). This is important because horses used for packing, riding, or working have extra stress to the spine and muscles in the back.

Avoid having two people working on opposite sides of the horse at the same time. No two people's energy are the same and this produces an energetic imbalance.

Use a stool (mounting block) to reach both sides of the spine without having to break contact, potentially creating tension in the animal.

Some people mistakenly believe that if they don't have all the oils in the Raindrop kit, they can't do a raindrop. One does not need to apply every single oil to have an effective treatment. You can perform an excellent, beneficial Raindrop procedure with one oil, if that's all you have. Using just oregano and thyme or even Idaho tansy can produce excellent results. Similarly, Melrose, tea tree, mountain savory, or bay laurel can also be used.

Is it OK to stroke oils down off the hips and down the legs? Yes

Is it OK to put a hot towel on the spine? Yes, it is recommended.

Following a raindrop, you can apply a saddle blanket then a horse blanket and leave the animal standing in the stall. Usually after about 10 minutes they will lie down and go to sleep.

EO TESTIMONIALS FROM ANIMAL OWNERS

The following is a small selection of the dozens of testimonials received from animal owners:

"My cat developed a pink bald spot, near his tail, which was losing hair by the day. The veterinarian didn't know what it was, so she tested for a virus and sold me antibiotics to give him just in case. She mentioned that it had the appearance of a burn.

"When I got home, I decided to re-think the antibiotic idea: If it might be a burn, why not simply put on lavender, I asked myself? So I applied less than a drop on that spot, by just barely touching it. In the morning it was clearly improved. I applied lavender again the same way, a second time only. His fur grew back in so fast I didn't worry about it again.

"Later I learned that this is a common spot where a cat will scratch another when it runs away from a standoff. In hindsight, I believe the bald spot was just that: a cat scratch infection."

— *Barbara J. Ullrich, Tacoma, WA*

"I recently used the oils in a case with a mare that had colic, and they seemed to work just like the drug, Banamine. I had on hand three oils that were suggested for use on smooth muscles (intestines) in the Desk Reference--marjoram, clary sage and lavender. For each application, I used 5 drops of the same oils on each flank with a warm compress. Each application took effect in about 30 minutes and kept the mare calm and comfortable for 2.5-3 hours. I alternated oils throughout the night with each application. Marjoram and clary sage seemed to work better than lavender. By 7:30 the next morning, the mare showed marked improvement and went for water."

— *Janis Early, Tallahassee, FL*

"My cat Nigel has to be rushed to three different animal hospitals one night due to a ruptured urethra. He was in severe pain and had been anesthetized twice over the course of about 6 hours.

"By 11:00 pm we were wearily on our way to the third hospital, which was over an hour away, when I thankfully found my Young Living lavender oil in my coat pocket. After applying several drops to my forehead, temples and neck to help calm me down, I simply held the open bottle next to Nigel's carrier where he was loudly despairing and restlessly trying to stand despite his dizziness from the anesthesia.

"Within seconds of introducing the oil to him, he became silent. I was so amazed that I had to check to make sure he was still alive! I left the bottle open for the duration of the trip. He remained calm for the remainder of the drive, meowing only occasionally, and made it through his final surgery beautifully. Thanks to the lavender oil, Nigel and I got through the final hours of that very long, traumatic night with comfort and ease."

— *Sarah George, Newburyport, MA*

"Three years ago, my corgi, Dickens, ruptured a disc in his back. As a result, his back legs were paralyzed. He was 5 years old at the time. He underwent surgery and recovered very well, but he was left with an odd gait, with swinging hips. He was able to run and play, go on long walks and, most importantly, was pain free.

But a year and a half ago, while laying on the sofa, he rolled over on his back and immediately began yelping in pain. We had no idea what was wrong. Since it was 8 pm on a Friday night, we took him to an emergency animal clinic. He was examined and x-rayed. Nothing showed up on the x-ray, but Dickens continued to howl and shake, so the vet thought that maybe he had a pinched nerve in his neck. She gave him a shot for pain and a cortisone shot, and prescribed both pain and cortisone pills. We took him to our regular vet the following Monday, who agreed the problem was most likely a pinched nerve, and gave us enough pills to last 2 weeks. Dickens did fine for two weeks, and after a final check up, the vet released him. He recommended that we use a harness, not a leash, to relieve any neck stress.

"Things went along well for about 10 days. Then all at once, Dickens started howling in pain. This time I decided to try my own therapy. I got out a 15 ml bottle and made up a "Raindrop concoction" consisting of 5 ml Valor, 2 ml Aroma Siez and 1 ml each of oregano, thyme, basil, wintergreen, cypress, marjoram, and peppermint.

"I applied 5-7 drops of this mixture along his spine, starting at the atlas and moving down to his tail bone. I massaged it in, and then applied a little V6 Oil Complex to "seal" it. I repeated this treatment 3-4 times daily. On the second day, Dickens was running and playing again. I continued the treatment for about 3 weeks. Several times since then, Dickens has come over to me and stared expectantly until I got out the "Raindrop concoction" and applied it to his back.

"Now over 8 years old, he has remained healthy and happy, and I know what to do if the condition flares up again."

— *Linda Chandler, Carmel, CA*

278

"Early one morning I received a call from Marie, one of my massage clients I had seen the day before. Her 14 year old dog, Precious, had been to the groomer--whom she doesn't like--and fell off the table while the groomer wasn't watching. The dog could not walk or squat. Marie took her to the vet, who examined and x-rayed Precious and found no broken bones. Precious received a shot and an anti-inflammatory, but she still could not walk. Marie wanted me to come help with her dog. Although Marie had complete faith in my abilities, I was hesitant to go. I suggested other things that might help, but Marie was insistent. I told her I would be there within the hour.

"On the way I was sorting out what I could do for the dog. I had the essential oil blend, PanAway, with me, but I wasn't sure the dog would like the aroma, and I wondered if an animal in pain would allow me to work on it. I know Precious, so that was a help. She was glad to see me. She was on Marie's bed and that was a good place to work.

"I tried gentle massage to the back and spinal area. It was soon evident she liked what I was doing and seemed to know I was trying to help her. After about 10 or 15 minutes, we encouraged her to get up. She stood, but her hind legs were rubbery and she could not walk. As she lay down I noticed her left back leg was stuck, out straight. I massaged the left leg, hip, and knee with PanAway, especially the tendons in the knee, and we then took Precious outside. She emptied her bladder, came inside under her own power, drank a whole bowl of water and ate a little food. (She had not been drinking or eating.) Marie called me the next day to say Precious was walking and feeling fine. 'It's a miracle!' she said."

— *Kathy Smith, CMS, NMT, Atlanta GA*

"My horse Katie, is a beautiful Shire draft horse, of the type used in jousting. Katie had a serious abscess on the bottom of her foot. Fixing this involves digging a huge hole into the foot to get the abscess out, and is a painful situation for the horse--which is very rarely anaesthetized. My vet was trying to get to the abscess and of course Katie was skittish. The farrier was helping him, but Katie weighs a ton (yes, a ton--as I said, she is a jousting-type horse), and it was very slow going. She was upset, scared, and I knew she was in pain. It's hard because you can't tell an animal it's "going to be all right" when the doctor is done. I didn't know what to do.

"So I had my friend go to my car to get some Peace & Calming, as I figured anything could help. She mistakenly brought back PanAway, and before realizing it was a different blend, I put it up to Katie's nose. At that moment, I realized it was not the oil I had intended to use and had my friend go back to the car to get the Peace & Calming. The thing was, as soon as I had put the PanAway to Katie's face, she had gotten "interested" in the small; her ears had pricked forward and she had stopped moving around as much. Then when I put the P & C up to her nostrils, it calmed her down *immediately*. The vet was able to 'doctor' her up and an unpleasant task became manageable. In fact, the farrier didn't even have to continue to help the vet. Katie relaxed so much that you could see her shoulder go down and she stopped trying to pull her foot away from the vet. There was blood all over her hoof from the vet trying to dig out that abscess! My friend and I were honestly amazed that 'suddenly' she just relaxed and even dropped her head down. Now, mind you, I used almost the entire bottle of the P & C, because the work on the abscess took a long time. But from the moment I put it up to her nostrils until the vet packed her foot up and wrapped it with an enormous bandage, her shoulders were relaxed, and her head was down (a good sign with horses that they are not stressed). The vet didn't even give me a 'butte' (horse painkiller); he just said "whatever you were doing, keep doing that.""

— *Sandra Shepard, CMT, JD, Petaluma, CA*

SECTION 6

Vita Flex Technique

Vita Flex Technique means "vitality through the reflexes." It is a specialized form of hand and foot massage that is exceptionally effective in delivering the benefits of essential oils throughout the body. It is said to have originated in Tibet thousands of years ago, and was perfected in the 1960s by Stanley Burroughs long before acupuncture was popular in Western medicine.

It is based on a complete network of reflex points that stimulate all the internal body systems. Essential oils are applied to contact points, and energy is released through electrical impulses created by contact between the fingertips and reflex points. This electrical charge follows the nerve pathways to a break or clog in the electrical circuit usually caused by toxins, damaged tissues, or loss of oxygen. As

**Vita Flex
Foot Chart**

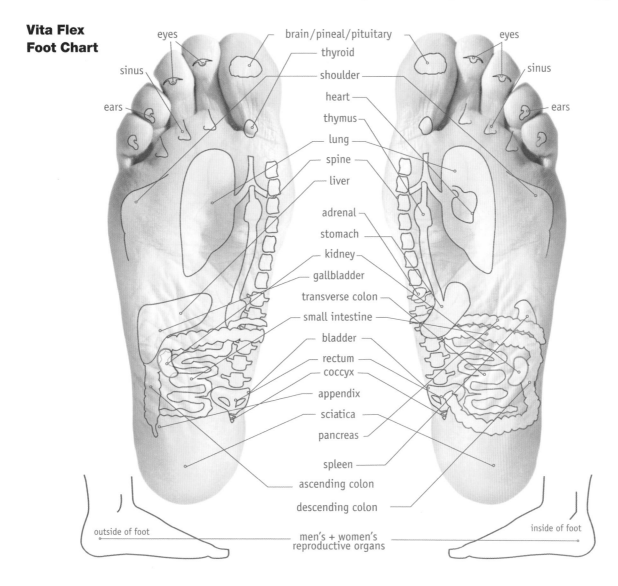

eyes
brain/pineal/pituitary
eyes
thyroid
sinus
sinus
shoulder
heart
ears
thymus
ears
lung
spine
liver
adrenal
stomach
kidney
gallbladder
transverse colon
small intestine
bladder
rectum
coccyx
appendix
sciatica
pancreas
spleen
ascending colon
descending colon
outside of foot
inside of foot
men's + women's
reproductive organs

with acupressure there are hundreds of Vita Flex reflex points throughout the human body, encompassing the entire realm of body and mind, that are capable of releasing many kinds of tension, congestion, and imbalances.

In contrast to the steady stimulation of reflexology, Vita Flex uses a rolling and releasing motion that involves placing fingers flat on the skin, rolling onto the fingertips, and continuing over onto the fingernail using medium pressure. Then moving forward about half the width of the finger, this rolling and releasing technique is continually repeated until the Vita Flex point, or area, is covered. This movement is repeated over the area three times.

Combine this technique with 1-3 drops of essential oil applied to those areas of the feet that correspond to the system of the body you wish to support (see the diagram on previous page). Rapid and extraordinary results are experienced when combining essential oils with Vita Flex stimulation, as it increases the effect of both.

The diagram below shows the nervous system connection to the spine for the electrical points throughout the body.

Nervous System Connection Points

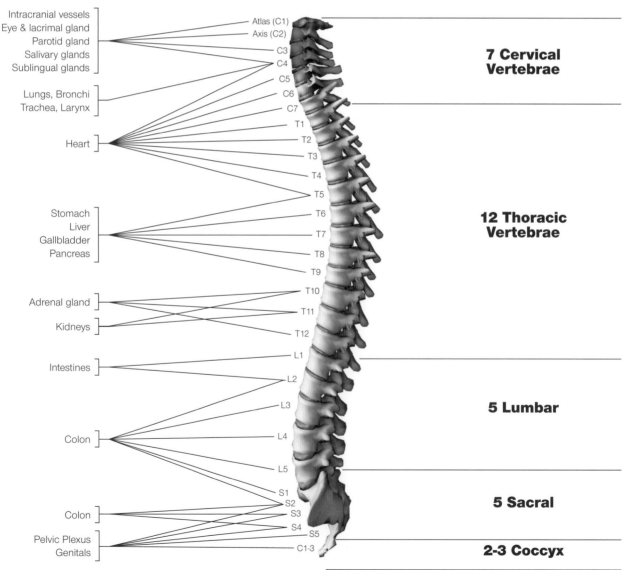

CHAPTER 21
Raindrop Technique®

D. Gary Young developed the Raindrop Technique® (RT) based on (1) his research with essential oils as antimicrobial agents, (2) his knowledge of the Vita Flex technique and its reflex points in the feet, and (3) fascinating information on effleurage (finger stroking) and its effect on the muscles and the nervous system that he learned from the Lakota people in South Dakota.

While visiting with the Lakota people, Gary learned that for several generations, before the US/Canadian border was established, the Lakota Indians migrated across the Canadian border into the northern regions of Saskatchewan and Manitoba. There, they often witnessed the Northern Lights, or Aurora Borealis. Those who were ill or had complicated health problems would stand facing the Aurora Borealis, hold their hands toward the lights, and inhale deeply. The Lakota believed that when the Aurora Borealis was visible, the air was charged with healing energy. They would mentally 'inhale' this energy, allowing it to pass through their spine and on to other afflicted areas of the body through neurological pathways. Many experienced dramatic healing effects through this practice.

Eventually, after the border made migrations impossible, the Lakota began to use effleurage, or feathered finger stroking, which became associated with this healing technique. Additionally, the Lakotans continued their practice of mentally processing energy, coupled with effleurage, to distribute healing energy throughout the body.

Gary Young found that when this Lakota practice of effleurage was coupled with the energy created by essential oils and Vita Flex, its effects were greatly heightened. Since its formal adoption in 1989, Raindrop Technique has received an enormous amount of praise from users all over the world for its help with relaxation, emotional release, tissue cleansing and help with spinal misalignments.

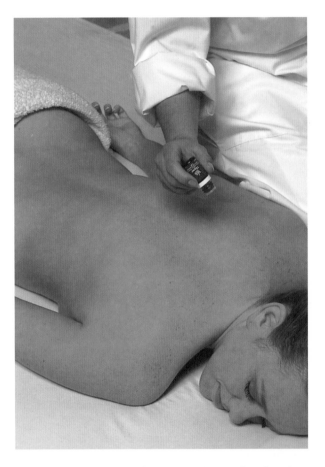

In 2001, David Stewart, PhD, circulated a questionnaire to over 2000 health practitioners, massage therapists, aromatherapists and their clients, to gain insight on the results that were accruing from RT. He received 422 responses summarizing the experiences of some 14,000 Raindrop sessions. His findings are summarized in his booklet, *A Statistical Validation of Raindrop Technique* (available through Essential Science Publishing). Overall, the 416 respondents who had received RT rated it positive (97%), pleasant (98%), resulted in improved health (89%) and resulted in an improved emotional state (86%). 99.9% of receivers said they would choose to receive RT again.

Another foundation principle behind RT is the idea—now being explored and verified in a number of scientific studies—that some types of spinal misalignment are caused by viruses or bacteria that lie dormant along the spine. These pathogens create inflammation, which, in turn, contorts and disfigures the spinal column.

RT is a powerful, non-invasive technique utilizing the antiviral, antibacterial and anti-inflammatory action of several key essential oils to assist the body in maintaining normal spinal curvature. During the past 18 years it has helped alleviate or resolve many cases of scoliosis, kyphosis, and chronic back pain and has eliminated the need for back surgery for hundreds of people.

Consistent with the French Model

The use of undiluted essential oils in RT is consistent with the French model for aromatherapy—which is the most extensively practiced and studied model in the world. With over 40 years of experience using essential oils clinically, the French have consistently recommended neat (undiluted) use of essential oils. An illustrious roster of 20th century French physicians provides convincing evidence that undiluted essential oils have a valuable place in the therapeutic arsenal of clinical professionals. René Gattefossé, PhD; Jean Valnet, MD; Jean-Claude Lapraz, MD; Daniel Pénoël, MD, and many others have long attested to the safe and effective use of undiluted essential oils and the dramatic and powerful benefits they can impart. According to Dr. Pénoël, "What happens when we use [essential oils] without diluting them? With many current essential oils, nothing dangerous or serious can happen."

In the case of Raindrop Technique®, the use of certain undiluted essential oils typically causes minor reddening and "heat" in the tissues. Normally, this is perfectly safe and not something to be overly concerned about. Blondes, redheads, and persons whose systems are toxic are more susceptible to this temporary reddening. Should the reddening or heat become excessive, it can be remedied within a minute or two by the immediate application of several drops of pure, quality vegetable oil to the affected area. This effectively dilutes the oils and the warming effect. Temporary mild warming is normal for RT. Typically it is even milder than that of many capsicum creams or sports ointments. Indeed, rather than being a cause of concern, this warming indicates that positive benefits are being imparted. In cases where the warmth or heat exceeds the comfort zone of the recipient, as mentioned before, the facilitator can apply any pure vegetable oil to the area until the comfort level is regained and reddening dissipates (usually within 2 minutes).

NOTE: If a rash should appear, it is an indication of a chemical reaction between the oils and synthetic compounds in the skin cells and interstitial fluid of the body (usually from conventional personal care products). Some misconstrue this as an allergic reaction, when in fact the problem is not caused by an allergy but rather by foreign chemicals already imbedded in the tissues.

A number of medical professionals throughout the United States have adopted RT in their clinical practice and have found it to be an outstanding resource for aiding sciatica, scoliosis, kyphosis, and chronic back pain. Ken Krieger, DC, a chiropractor practicing in Scottsdale, Arizona, states, "As a chiropractor, I believe that the dramatic results of RT are enough for me to rewrite the books on scoliosis." Similarly, Terry Friedmann, MD, of Westminster, Colorado, stated that "these essential oils truly represent a new frontier of medicine; they have resolved cases that many professionals had regarded as hopeless."

Do Infections Cause Scoliosis and Sciatica?

A growing amount of scientific research shows that certain microorganisms lodge near the spinal cord and contribute to deformities. Studies at Western General Hospital in Edinburgh, Scotland, linked virus-like particles to idiopathic scoliosis.[1,2] Researchers at the University of Bonn have also found the varicella zoster virus can lodge in the spinal ganglia throughout life.[3]

Research in 2001 further corroborated the existence of infectious microorganisms as a cause of spine pain and inflammation. Alistair Stirling and his colleagues at the Royal Orthopedic Hospital in Birmingham, England, found that 53 percent of patients with severe sciatica tested positive for

1. Green RJ, Webb JN, Maxwell MH. The nature of virus-like particles in the paraxial muscles of idiopathic scoliosis. J Pathol. 1979 Sep;129(1):9-12.

2. Webb JN, Gillespie WJ. Virus-like particles in paraspinal muscle in scoliosis. Br Med J. 1976 Oct 16;2(6041):912-3.

3. Wolff MH, Buchel F, Gullotta F, Helpap B, Schneweiss KE. Investigations to demonstrate latent viral infection of varicella-Zoster virus in human spine ganglia. Verh Dtsch Ges Pathol. 1981;65:203-7.

Example of kyphosis (hunchback) caused by an infectious microorganism (tuberculosis) in the spine. The above X-rays show two views of the spine of a 62 year-old man with a 3-month history of increasing back pain and inflammation due to kyphosis. The problem had become so severe that he could no longer walk unaided; however, there was no history of tuberculosis. The X-rays show the collapse of the seventh thoracic vertebra. He subsequently underwent back surgery to help correct the problem. Specimens taken during the surgery did not immediately show a bacterial infection, but after 12 weeks of incubation, the presence of Mycobacterium tuberculosis was detected, confirming the original diagnosis of spinal tuberculosis.

Source: Jenks, Peter J. and Stewart, Bruce. Images in Clinical Medicine. Vertebral Tuberculosis. New England Journal of Medicine, 1998 June 4, 338 (23);1677.

chronic, low-grade infection by gram-negative bacteria (particularly Propionibacterium acnes) which triggered inflammation near the spine. Stirling suggested that the reason these bacteria had not been identified earlier was because of the extended time required to incubate disc material (7 days).[4]

The tuberculosis mycobacterium has also been shown to contribute to spinal disease and possibly deformations. Research at the Pasteur Institute in France, published in The New England Journal of Medicine, documented increasing numbers of patients showing evidence of spinal disease (Pott's disease) caused by tuberculosis.[5, 6, 7, 8]

In addition, vaccines made from live viruses have been linked to spinal problems. A 1982 study by Pincott and Taff found a connection between oral poliomyelitis vaccines and scoliosis.[9]

Powerful Infection-Fighters

Essential oils are some of the most powerful inhibitors of microbes known, and as such are an important new weapon in combating many types of tissue infections. A 1999 study by Marilena Marino and colleagues found that thyme oil exhibited strong action against stubborn gram-negative bacteria.[10] Similarly, basil essential oil also demonstrated strong bactericidal action against microorganisms Aeromonas hydrophila and Pseudomonas fluorescens.[11] A study at the Central Food Technological Institute in Mysore, India, found that a large number of essential oil components had tremendous germ-killing effects, inhibiting the growth of Staphylococcus, Micrococcus, Bacillus, and Enterobacter strains of bacteria. These compounds included menthol (found in peppermint), eucalyptol (found in rosemary, eucalyptus, and geranium), linalool (found in marjoram), and citral (found in lemongrass).[12] A 2001 study conducted by myself, Diane Horne, Sue Chao, and colleagues at Weber State University in Ogden, Utah, found that oregano, thyme, peppermint, and basil exhibited very strong antimicrobial effects against pathogens such as Streptococcus pneumoniae, a major cause of illness in young children and death in elderly, and immune-weakened patients.[13] Many other studies confirm these findings.[14]

The ability of essential oils to penetrate the skin quickly and pass into bodily tissues to produce therapeutic effects has also been studied. Hoshi University researchers in Japan found that cyclic monoterpenes (including menthol, which is found in peppermint) are so effective in penetrating the

4. Stirling AL, et al., Association between sciatica and Propionibacterium acnes. Lancet 2001:V357.

5. Nagrath SP, Hazra DK, Pant PC, Seth HC. Tuberculosis spine—a diagnostic conundrum. Case report. J Assoc Physicians India. 1974 May;22(5):405-7.

6. Jenks PJ, Stewart B. Images in clinical medicine. Vertebral tuberculosis. N Engl J Med. 1998 June 4;338(23):1677.

7. Monaghan D, Gupta A, Barrington NA. Case report: Tuberculosis of the spine—an unusual presentation. Clin Radiol. 1991 May;43(5):360-2.

8. Petersen CK, Craw M, Radiological differentiation of tuberculosis and pyogenic osteomyelitis: a case report. J Manipulative Physiol Ther. 1986 Mar;9(1):39-42.

9. Pinott JR, Taffs LF. Experimental scoliosis in primates: a neurological cause. J Bone Joint Surg Br. 1982;64(4):503-7.

10. Marino M, Bersani C, Comi G. Antimicrobial activity of the essential oils of Thymus vulgaris L. measured using a bioimpedometric method. Journal of Food Protection, Vol. 62, No. 9, 1999 pp. 1017-1023.

11. Wan J, Wilcock A, Coventry MJ. The effect of essential oils of basil on the growth of Aeromonas fluorescens. Journal of Applied Microbiology, 1998, 84, 152-158.

12. Beuchat LR. Antimicrobial properties of spices and their essential oils. Center for Food Safety and Quality Enhancement, Department of Food Science and Technology, University of Georgia, Griffin, Georgia.

13. Horne D, et al., Antimicrobial effects of essential oils on Streptococcus pneumoniae. Journal of Essential Oil Research, (September/October 2001). 13, 387-392.

14. Moleyar V, Narasimham P. Antibacterial activity of essential oil components. International Journal of Food Microbiology, Vol. 16 (1992) 337-32.

skin that they can actually enhance the absorption of water-soluble drugs.[15] North Dakota State University researchers have similarly found that cyclic monoterpenes such as limonene and other terpenoids such as menthone and eugenol easily pass through the dermis, magnifying the penetration of pharmaceutical drugs such as tamoxifen.[16]

It is interesting to note that many essential oils used in RT—in addition to being highly anti-microbial—are also among those classified as GRAS (Generally Regarded As Safe) for internal use by the U.S. Food and Drug Administration. These include basil, marjoram, peppermint, oregano, and thyme. These and many other GRAS essential oils have a decades-long history of being consumed as foods or flavorings with virtually no adverse reactions.

In sum, RT is one of the safest, noninvasive techniques available for spinal health. It is also an invaluable tool to promote healing from within using topically applied essential oils.

Introduction to the Technique

Gary Young incorporated into RT nine of the most potent therapeutic-grade essential oils. All of these oils have been heavily researched. They were selected to synergistically combine to simultaneously kill viral and bacterial pathogens, reduce inflammation, support the immune system, ease respiratory discomfort, relax stressed muscles, curb digestive upset and relieve body and joint discomfort, as well as balance energy, lift the spirit, restore calm and increase the ability to concentrate. The seven single essential oils used include:

- Oregano (Origanum compactum)
- Thyme (Thymus vulgaris)
- Basil (Ocimum basilicum)
- Cypress (Cupressus sempervirens)
- Wintergreen (Gaultheria procumbens)
- Marjoram (Origanum majorama)
- Peppermint (Mentha piperita)

In addition, two essential oil blends, Valor and Aroma Seiz are incorporated into RT to further facilitate energy balancing (Valor) and muscle relaxation (Aroma Seiz).

The oils are dispensed like drops of rain from a height of about six inches above the back and feathered and massaged along the vertebrae and back muscles. Although the entire technique takes from 45-60 minutes to complete, the oils continue

to work in the body for up to one week following RT, often with continued re-alignment taking place during this time.

Caution: RT is not a cure-all or a magic bullet. A healthy balanced body is the result of a well-rounded program of exercise and proper diet. Health is everything we do, say, hear, see, and eat. RT is only one tool to help restore balance in the body. Healthy eating habits and a positive, open mind will also help prepare the body and skin to accept the oils better and more rapidly.

Although this technique is explained as simply as possible, you may want to contact Essential Science Publishing to purchase a demonstration video. Every step of the technique is carefully demonstrated in an actual hands-on presentation. You can order the video by visiting the ESP website at www.essentialscience.net or by calling toll-free 800-336-6308. Viewing this video and following the outline presented here will make this revolutionary technique easy to understand and easy to put into practice.

OVERVIEW

Before explaining the detailed steps and massage techniques of RT, it is helpful to see the 12 steps or stages of the entire process in overview. This will help you understand the detailed description of these steps in their proper context, which follows after this overview.

Note: Drop counts listed for each step are guidelines and can generally be increased or decreased to fit the size and/or preference of the receiver.

There is a significant list of items that need to be arranged in preparation for RT, because it is very inconvenient to make these preparations once the procedure has started. This list of steps is provided in detail under the heading "Preparation."

In describing the technique, "facilitator" refers to the person giving the Raindrop Technique; "receiver" refers to the person receiving it.

The following are items that should be prepared and available in the room before treatment starts:
- Massage table (ideally) or a comfortable flat surface for the recipient to lie on. The surface

15. Obata Y, et al. Effect of pretreatment of skin with cyclic monoterpenes on permeation of diclofenac in hairless rat. Biol Pharm Bull. 1993 Mar;16(3)312-4.

16. Zhao K, Singh J. Mechanisms of percutaneous absorption of tamoxifen by terpenes: eugenol, d-limonene and menthone. Control Release. 1998. Nov 13;55(2-3)253-60.

should be high enough that the facilitator can perform RT without back strain. It is best to cover the surface with sheets or towels that are expend-able as several of the oils may stain certain fab-rics. Also, some of the oils can react with the vinyls used to cover massage tables so be sure vinyl surfaces are covered well.

- A twin-sized bed sheet or similar sized towel to help protect the modesty of the receiver. It is impor-tant to protect the receiver's modesty at all times. Make sure the environment and all actions promote a sense of security and protection for the receiver.

- A stable table or tray on which to place the oils and instructions, if needed, near the receiver.

- Each of the 10 different oils needed for RT: The seven single oils, two blends (Valor and Aroma Seiz) and a quality vegetable oil (V6).

Step 1: Balance Energy: The starting step for all RT is to apply Valor to the soles of the feet (and, optionally, to the shoulders).

Step 2: Using Vita Flex, apply seven essential oils to the spinal reflex area on each foot. This Vita Flex application is essential to prepare the body for subsequent steps performed directly on the spine. It is also highly relaxing.

Step 3: Apply 3-5 drops oregano, evenly-spaced, directly on the spine and feather the oils using 5-step feathering technique. (Note: the 5-step feathering technique is used with each of the oils as they are applied on the spine. It helps to stimulate the cell receptors and activate energy centers along the spine, as well as distribute the oil drops so they penetrate rapidly.)

Step 4: Apply 3-5 drops thyme directly on the spine; and feather.

Step 5: Apply 5-8 drops basil on the spinal muscles on each side of the spine; feather; then perform Spinal Tissue Pull

Step 6: Apply 5-8 drops cypress directly on the spine; feather; then perform Spinal Finger Straddle.

Step 7: Apply 5-8 drops wintergreen directly on the spine; feather; then perform Vita Flex Thumb Roll

Step 8: Apply 8-10 drops marjoram over the entire back; feather; then perform Circular Hand Massage

Step 9: Apply 8-10 drops Aroma Seiz over the entire back; feather; then perform Palm Slide.

Step 10: Apply 3-5 drops peppermint directly on the spine; and feather.

Step 11: Apply 8-10 drops Valor over the entire back; and feather.

Step 12: Stimulate the lymphatic system using Finger Pump

PERFORMING THE RAINDROP TECHNIQUE®

Preparation

- It is recommended that RT be performed in a quiet, semi-darkened area, free of distractions. Soft and relaxing music will make the recipient more comfortable.

- The temperature should be cool enough to prevent sweating, but warm enough to be comfortable, as the recipient's back and legs will be exposed.

- Both the facilitator and the recipient should remove all jewelry. This includes watches, pendants, chains, rings, bracelets, belts, earrings, etc. These items produce an electrical energy and may interfere with the technique. Metal eyeglass frames are acceptable.

- RT should only be performed if the facilitator is feeling balanced and focused. Time should be spent developing clarity and energy for transfer to the receiver during the technique.

- Inquire as to whether the receiver has been exposed to chemicals or worked in a toxic environment. This may result in skin reactions to the oils.

- Suggest the receiver use the restroom before beginning RT.

- Both facilitator and receiver should be relaxed and comfortable. Appropriate clothing should be worn. It will be necessary to access the receiver's back for application of the oils. Clothing that fully

---

If you intend to offer the Raindrop Technique® as a service, please be advised that some states require that you be a licensed massage therapist, aesthetician or chiropractor prior to offering any service where physical touch is involved. Please check the regulations for your jurisdiction.

exposes the spine (i.e. a hospital gown) works best. If modesty can be preserved, remove all clothing from the waist up for easier application.

- The facilitator should make sure his/her fingernails are closely clipped and filed to prevent scratching the receiver's skin, particularly when performing the Vita Flex technique. Nails should also be free of all polish. Essential oils can remove polishes and lacquers.

- The receiver should lie on his/her back, face-up on the massage table, with their heels at the very end, or just over the edge of the massage table. The recipient should lie as straight as possible with the hips flat on the table. It is preferable not to use a pillow under the knees or head, as this makes it more difficult for the facilitator to detect misalign-ments and changes in the recipient's body. Arms should rest alongside the body with the palms touch-ing the thighs just below the hips. This will help direct the flow of energy and keep it connected to the receiver.

- The facilitator should request permission from the receiver to begin the RT.

- The facilitator should maintain constant physical contact with the receiver, once the RT has commenced, to prevent feelings of insecurity, anxiousness or abandonment.

- It is anticipated that RT will create structural change in the body. Use caution when working on the spine or applying any pressure.

- Have plenty of pure water available for the receiver to drink once RT is complete.

- Be prepared to provide detailed instructions for the receiver for post-RT care.

- Offer assistance to the receiver when dismounting from the table.

Step 1: Balance Energy Using Valor on the Feet (and Shoulders)

The Valor blend and oregano and thyme oils are the foundation of all RT work. RT always starts with the application of Valor to the feet and, optionally, to the shoulders. This is one of the most important steps for a successful RT because it works on the physical, electrical, spiritual and emotional levels, supporting the physical and energy alignment of the body. The key to using Valor to balance energies is patience. Once the frequencies begin to balance, a structural alignment will much more likely begin to occur.

Fig. 1 — Placing hands on the recipient's feet

Fig. 2a — Dipping fingertips into essential oil

This first step forms the foundation for everything that follows:

Foot Application:

The facilitator, standing at the feet of the receiver, puts 6 drops of Valor in each hand. Then, places the palms of each hand on the soles of each foot, right palm on the sole of the right foot; left palm on the sole of the left foot. This will require the facilitator to cross arms, as shown in Figure 1. Facilitator should close his/her eyes and concentrate, holding this position for at least 5 minutes, feeling for subtle changes such as increased warmth, smooth pulsing sensations, or vibrations. Once the facilitator senses the energy in both hands, he/she can release and proceed to the next step.

Shoulder Application:

The facilitator stands at the receiver's head and puts 3 drops of Valor in each hand. Then, with

Fig. 2b — Vita Flex along the spinal reflex point, step 1
(Side view and bottom view)

Fig. 2d — Vita Flex at the big toe, step 1

Fig. 2c — Vita Flex along the spinal reflex point, step 2
(Side view and bottom view)

Fig. 2e — Vita Flex at the big toe, step 2

palms down, places the right hand on the right shoulder and the left hand on the left shoulder of the recipient.

(This optional step is ideally performed by a second facilitator at the same time the foot application is taking place. However, a single facilitator can perform this step after the foot application.)

Step 2: Vita Flex seven essential oils into the spinal reflex area of both feet

The seven oils in application sequence are: oregano, thyme, basil, cypress, wintergreen, marjoram, and peppermint. The following sequence is followed for each of the seven oils.

Stand at the feet of the recipient with the right hand in line with the right foot of the receiver.

Starting with oregano, place 2-3 drops of essential oil (small feet may only require 1-2 drops) in the palm of the left hand. Dip the fingertips of the

right hand in the oil and stir clockwise three times to energize the oil. See Figure 2a.

With the right hand, apply the oil to the right foot using Vita Flex technique, along the spinal reflex area (bottom inside edge of the foot from heel to the tip of the big toe — see chart on page 2) as follows:

A. Cup the hand so the four fingertips rest on the spinal reflex area at the heel while the thumb rests on the top of the foot, as shown in Figure 2b. In a quick motion, rock the hand over so that the nails end up flat against the bottom of the foot, as shown in Figure 2c. Then rock backward to the original position. Apply constant, mild pressure and do not break contact with the skin.

B. Continue this technique all the way up the foot to the tip of the big toe (Figures 2d and 2e). End with several Vita Flex movements on the neck and center of the big toe. Repeat two times before moving to the left foot, massaging any excess oil into the sole of the foot.

Fig. 3a — Applying oregano up the spine

Fig. 3c — 12-15 inch Feather Strokes up the spine

Fig. 3b — 6-8 inch Feather Strokes up the spine

Fig. 3d — 12-15 inch Feather Strokes up the spine

C. Switch to the left foot. Place 2-3 drops of the same essential oil in the palm of the right hand. Dip the fingertips of the left hand in the oil and stir clockwise three times to energize the oil. With the left hand, apply the oil, using Vita Flex technique, along the spinal reflex area of the left foot, as described above.

D. Repeat this same sequence for each of the seven oils, starting on the right foot, then complet-ing the left foot before going on to the next oil.

Step 3: Apply 3-5 drops oregano essential oil to the spine and perform 5-step feathering technique (explained below).

Have the receiver turn over and lay on his/her stomach. Be sure the receiver is comfortable and his/her modesty is respected. The receiver should place his/her arms comfortably along the sides of the body. The entire back needs to be exposed for application of the Raindrop oils. Oils will be applied from the very base of the spine (sacrum) to the base of the neck (atlas).

The oils used in the next several steps mirror those used in the Vita Flex foot application and are applied in the same sequence. Before beginning to apply the oils to the back, observe the receiver's spine. Look for areas of discoloration or distortion. Variations of the spine may indicate regions of structural compromise. A comparative assessment before and after RT may serve as a gauge for effectiveness.

Apply the oregano oil by holding the bottle six inches above the skin and evenly spacing 3-5 drops directly over the spine from bottom (sacrum) to top (atlas) as shown in Figure 3a.

Immediately after applying oregano, feather stroke the oil into the spine as described in the 5-step feathering technique below.

Fig. 3e — 6-8 inch Fan Strokes up the spine

Fig. 3f — Full length Fan Strokes up the spine

The feathering technique, described below, is used in all remaining steps of Raindrop Technique, after applying the oils.

Visually divide the entire back into three equal regions: bottom (sacrum), middle (lumbar) and top (thorax). 'Feathering' is performed by brushing the backs of the fingertips, extremely lightly, up the spine, so that they are barely felt. This creates a tingling effect for the recipient, commonly bringing them to goose bumps. The purpose of this feathering is to stimulate energy centers and awaken the receptors along the spine.

1. Using strokes that go up the same line along the center of the spine, brush the bottom (sacrum) segment using 6-8" strokes three times, alternating hands (right, left, right). See Figure 3b. Continuing the feather stroking in a fluid motion, move up to the middle (lumbar) region and perform the same process of three alternating strokes (left, right, left). Finally, move up to the top (thorax) region and perform the same process of three alternating strokes (right, left, right).

2. Start feathering again with longer strokes, this time feathering in 3 alternating strokes up the length of both the bottom and middle regions of the back, directly up the center of the spine. These strokes will be 12-15" long. See Figure 3c. After completing 3 longer strokes on the combined bottom and middle regions, in a fluid motion move to the middle and top regions and perform 3 alternating longer strokes there. See Figure 3d.

3. Complete this series by feathering up the entire length of the back in three long strokes, from sacrum to atlas, alternating hands.

Remember: feather strokes should be very light, using only the very tips of the fingers. Their purpose is to stimulate the nerves and receptors. A good sign that this is happening is the appearance of goosebumps on the receiver's back.

4. Start fan feather strokes at the very base of the bottom region (sacrum) of the spine by placing both hands side-by-side, backs of the fingertips facing down. Center the hands on the spine (left hand on the left side of the spine; right hand on the right of the spine, over the spinal muscles). Feather up 6-8", moving both hands together up the spine, then fan each hand off in a perpendicular direction to the spine, the right hand flaring to the far right side of the back and the left hand flaring to the far left side of the back. Repeat these simultaneous strokes two more times making a total of 3 fan strokes for this region. Then, in a fluid, continuing motion, move to the middle (lumbar) region of the back and do the same process, moving both hands together up the spine, then flaring them to either side three times. See Figure 3e. Finally complete this step by doing the same 3 fan strokes on the top (thorax) region of the back.

5. Finally, complete the fan feather stroke process with a set of three, simultaneous, full-length strokes from the base of the spine to the base of the neck, fanning at the top across the shoulders, the right hand flaring to the right and the left hand flaring to the left. See Figure 3f. This completes the feathering technique, and all five steps of the technique are used in every step of Raindrop Technique after application of the oils.

Fig. 5a — Applying basil on each side of spine

Fig. 5c — Spinal Tissue Pull continuing up the spine

Fig. 5b — Spinlal Tissue Pull starting at the base of the spine

Step 4: Apply 3-5 drops thyme essential oil to the spine, using the feathering technique, exactly as in Step 3.

Hold the bottle 6 inches above the skin and evenly space 3-5 drops of thyme essential oil directly over the spine, from bottom to top.

Immediately after applying the oil drops, feather the oil into the spine using the 5-step feathering technique, described above.

Step 5: Apply 4-8 drops basil essential oil to the muscles on both sides of the spine, perform the feathering technique and then do the Spinal Tissue Pull

Holding the bottle 6 inches above the skin, evenly drop 4-8 drops of basil essential oil along the muscles on both sides of the spine, from bottom to top, i.e. 2-4 drops in a line along the spine about 1" to the right of the spine and 2-4 drops in a line along

the spine about 1" to the left of the spine. See Figure 5a. This differs from the previous two steps where the oil was dropped directly on the spine.

Feather the oil into the spinal muscles using the feathering technique described in step 3.

After feathering is complete, stand at the receiver's right side and place the pads of the fingertips of both hands, side by side, along the edge of the spine. Starting at the base of the spine, using small, circular (1-2" diameter) clockwise motions, massage the muscles on the right side of the spine as shown in Figure 5b.

Do not work directly on the spine, but on the muscles on the right edge of the spine. Do not cross over the spine. Never apply direct pressure to the vertebrae. With each clockwise circular motion, use the gentle pressure of the fingertips to pull the tissue away from the spine. After performing 3 clockwise rotations, move up the spine one hand width, and do 3 more clockwise rotations. Make the overall movement as fluid as possible, so that it looks like one continuous movement. Continue moving up the spine, one hand width at a time until you reach the base of the neck, as shown in Figure 5c.

After finishing the right side of the spine, put a hand on the receiver's back, walk around to the left side of the receiver and begin the process on the left side, starting at the base of the spine. If the skin becomes dry and this massage is causing too much friction, sprinkle extra basil over the muscles as needed, to reduce friction on the skin.

Repeat the above process, working up the right side, then the left side, two more times for a total of three times.

Fig. 6 — Finger Straddle massage up the spine

Fig. 7a — Thumb Roll up spine, step 1

Fig. 7b — Thumb Roll up spine, step 2

Step 6: Apply 5-8 drops cypress essential oil to the spinal muscles, use the feathering technique and then do Finger Straddle Massage up the spine

The cypress essential oil is dropped from a height of 6 inches above the skin directly on the spine, 5-8 drops total, spaced evenly, followed by feathering technique.

Begin the Finger Straddle massage by standing at the receiver's left side, near his/her waist, facing toward the receiver's feet. Straddle the base of the spine with the index and middle fingers of the left hand. Do not raise the left hand too high; the heel of the left hand should be no more than a finger's width above the back. The full pads of the straddling fingers above the first knuckle should be in contact with the back. Place the bottom edge of the right hand, pinky side down, just below the middle joints of the two straddling fingers. See Figure 6.

Simultaneously perform the following motions: (1) Pull the straddling fingers slowly to the top of the spine; (2) applying downward pressure, "saw" with the right hand using short, rapid 1" back and forth motions. The right hand should NOT slip or slide over the left hand; rather it should transmit a rocking motion to the bottom hand. This rocking motion is pulled the full length of the spine by the moving bottom hand.

Upon reaching the neck, at the very base of the skull (occiput) with the two hands still in place, perform 3 gentle pushes with the right hand, pushing the straddling fingers toward the head. This stretches the muscles at the top of the spine, allowing the oils to better penetrate to the brain stem.

Repeat this entire process two more times for a total of three times.

Step 7: Apply 5-8 drops wintergreen essential oil to the spinal muscles, use the feathering technique and then do Vita Flex Thumb Roll up the spine

As with cypress, wintergreen essential oil is dropped from 6 inches above the skin directly on the spine, 5-8 drops total, spaced evenly, followed by feathering technique.

Begin the Vita Flex Thumb Roll by placing both thumbs, one inch apart, on either side of the spine at the base, with one thumb slightly higher than the other to avoid bumping thumbs on the inward roll.

Start the Thumb Roll by rolling both thumbs inward, in a quick motion, over the edge of the thumbs to the nail side, then roll back to the starting position. Apply constant, mild pressure with the thumbs, and do not break contact with the skin between rolls or when changing hand position. Continue this rolling motion, back and forth, working up the spine in 1" increments from the bottom to the top. See Figures 7a and 7b.

Fig. 8— Circular hand massage along the sides of the back

Fig. 9b — Palm rub massage on the back, step 2

Fig. 9a — Palm rub massage on the back, step 1

to access the deeper tissues, but not jerky. Rotate hands in 3 large (4-6" diameter), clockwise circles. Then move the hands up one hand's width and do the 3 clockwise circles again, as shown in Figure 8. Continue this process moving up to the base of the neck. This massaging motion should include areas along the outer edges of the rib cage and shoulders that have not been previously worked.

Maintaining body contact, move to the left side of the receiver and repeat the same process moving up the left side of the back

Repeat this cycle two more times, alternating sides, for a total of three times.

Note: if the skin absorbs the marjoram oil and becomes dry, additional drops may be added as needed, to maintain a reasonable level of lubrication.

Step 9: Apply 8-10 drops of Aroma Seiz all over the back; use feathering technique and then perform the Palm Slide

Hold the bottle 6 inches above the skin and apply a total of 8-10 drops of Aroma Seiz over the entire back. Use free-form feather strokes to distribute the oil evenly. Follow with feathering technique, the same as in step 8.

Begin the Palm Slide by placing both hands at the base of the receiver's back, palms down, with one hand close to you and one hand on the far side of the back. Then slide the palms, using mild downward pressure, in opposite directions, from one side of the rib cage to the other side, working slowly up the back, toward the neck. See Figures 9a and 9b. Continue this back and forth movement until you reach the base of the neck. Repeat this massage up the back two more times for a total of 3 times.

It is essential the facilitator's thumbnails be filed down as short as possible, with no sharp edges, so as not to cause discomfort to the receiver during this step.

Step 8: Apply 8-10 drops marjoram essential oil over the entire back, use feathering technique and then perform the Circular Hand Massage

Hold the bottle 6 inches above the skin and apply 8-10 drops of marjoram essential oil all over the back. Use free-form feather strokes as needed to distribute the oil evenly. Follow with 5-step feathering technique.

Begin the Circular Hand Massage by standing on the receiver's right side and placing the palms of both hands, side-by-side, thumbs overlapped, on the lower right side of the back. The palms should be flat, so the hands 'cup' the receiver's back on the right side of the spine. The massage should be somewhat firm

Fig. 12 — Finger pump

Step 10: Apply 3-5 drops peppermint essential oil on the spine, then use feathering technique.

Holding the bottle 6 inches above the skin, apply 3-5 drops of peppermint essential oil, directly on the spine. Stimulate the spine using feathering technique.

Step 11: Apply 8-10 drops Valor over the entire back; then use feathering technique.

Holding the bottle 6 inches above the skin, apply 8-10 drops of Valor all over the back, Use free-form feather strokes to distribute the oil evenly. Stimulate the spine and back area using feathering technique.

Step 12: Stimulate the lymphatic system using Finger Pump.

Have the receiver turn over onto his/her back. Be careful to keep the receiver covered to protect modesty.

Sit at the recipient's head and cup your hands under the base of the skull with the palms up and the fingers curving around the bottom of the occipital region (the bottom back edge) of the skull, so the fingertips touch the very base of the skull. The index fingers should be positioned just underneath the mastoid process. The little fingers of each hand should be next to each other. The forearms should be placed on the table and should not move. Move the index and middle fingers of both hands toward you, creating a firm pull. The movement is like pulling a trigger. See Figure 12.

Repeat this process for 1 minute, so that it becomes a flowing movement of pull-relax-pull-relax. When this movement is performed correctly, you will see the receiver's toes rock forward 1-2" with each pull. After one minute of pulling, rest for 60 seconds, then repeat for another minute, then rest once more for 60 seconds and repeat a third time.

Make sure the fingertips are at the bottom of the occipital bone, and not further down on the neck muscles, in order to achieve good movement. While this is a firm movement, it should not cause discomfort for the receiver. This movement provides an excellent lymphatic pump effect.

For optimum results, the receiver should drink extra pure water for the first few days following RT. This will aid the body in flushing toxins from the tissues.

Customizing Raindrop Technique® to Address Specific Health Issues

Raindrop Technique can be customized to address different health issues that are not directly related to back problems. Lung infections, digestive complaints, hormonal problems, liver insufficiencies, and other problems can all be dealt with by substituting standard RT essential oils with other oils that are specifically targeted for that body system.

As a rule, when customizing RT, you will generally want to start with Valor, oregano, and thyme. These three oils form the basis or "hub" of all Raindrop applications. (For extra antiviral effect, add mountain savory.) The other essential oils such as basil, wintergreen, marjoram, thyme, or cypress can be omitted or replaced by essential oils specific for the condition being treated.

For example, if a lung infection is present, basil and wintergreen should be replaced with ravensara, cypress replaced with Eucalyptus radiata, and marjoram replaced with mountain savory. (See diagram on page 299)

There are several variations to the basic Raindrop Technique. These variations are not easy to explain and require class instruction and demonstration.

Live Blood Analysis Comparison

In 2007, a before-and-after experiment was conducted with Raindrop Technique in Queensland, Australia. Live and Dry Blood analyses were performed on a 68 year-old female, named Janice, both before and after Raindrop. The blood tests were performed by a lab technician with many years of experience working for Australian Biologics, a firm that specializes in live blood analysis. Janice had been experiencing symptoms of fatigue (she is a full-time care-giver for her husband who is a stroke victim). The following images illustrate the immediate impact Raindrop Technique can have.

COMPARISON 1

BEFORE   AFTER

COMPARISON 2

BEFORE   AFTER

COMPARISON 3

BEFORE   AFTER

COMPARISON 4

BEFORE   AFTER

Photos courtesy of The Health Garden, PTY LTD, Queensland, Australia

Comparison 1: Chaining/Clumping of red blood cells

In the 'before' image, a degree of clumping can readily be seen in the red blood cells. This suggests higher than normal protein in the blood, likely due to compromised digestion. When this clumping occurs, oxygen cannot be transported as effectively throughout the body. This affects all cells in all body systems and will produce symptoms of fatigue. Note in the 'after' image that the cells are clearly more separated. In the actual video, the cells are also more active, moving around and through one another, obviously more able to transport their oxygen content.

Comparison 2: Inflammation

In this dry blood analysis of Janice's blood, the white patches in the 'before' image are referred to as 'ROTS masses' and are an indicator of inflammation and oxidation/free radical damage in the lymphatic system. Inflammation in Janice's lymphatic system could have been amplified by a viral infection she had a week earlier. In the 'after' image, these white patches are greatly reduced, suggesting a lowering of inflammation levels. Raindrop Technique has a demonstrable antioxidant effect on Janice's blood.

Comparison 3: Inflammation and Yeast

These images are a magnified picture of the insides of the ROTS masses, providing a closer look at inflammation indicators. Note how large the blue/gray ROTS mass is in the 'before' image, compared with the 'after' image. Also, the white dots in ROTS mass represent yeast in the blood, perhaps due to a candida infection. In the 'after' picture, there is significantly less evidence of yeast in the blood.

Comparison 4: Adrenal Status

Using the dry blood analysis, there is an indication of a change in adrenal function. The absence of white spots in the 'before' picture suggests Janice is producing little or no adrenalin. This can occur in a patient whose life is very peaceful and calm, but that is not the case with Janice. The reason for the absence of adrenalin in her case is due to adrenal exhaustion, due to the high levels of stress in her life. Note that there are white spots in the 'after' picture, suggesting that Raindrop Technique has moved Janice from a condition of adrenal burnout to a level of some adrenalin production. This would help to explain why Janice felt substantially revitalized and re-energized after receiving Raindrop Technique.

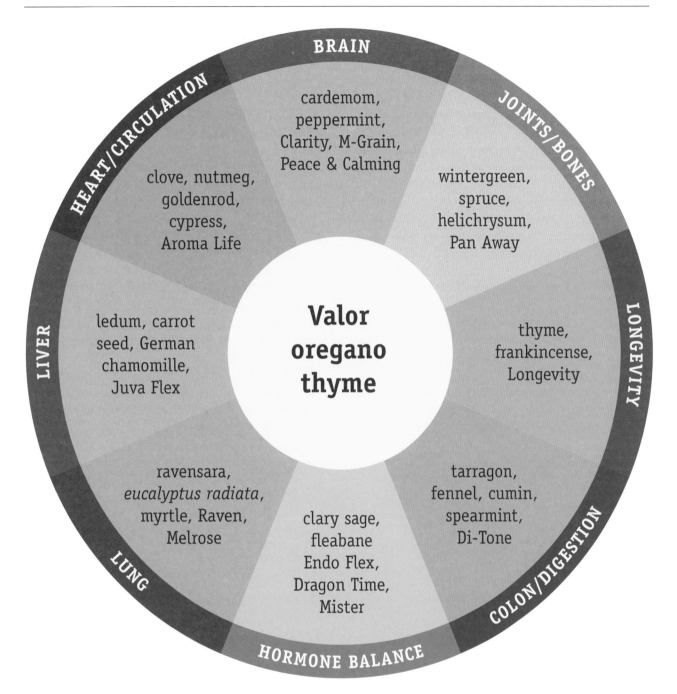

BRAIN
cardemom, peppermint, Clarity, M-Grain, Peace & Calming

JOINTS/BONES
wintergreen, spruce, helichrysum, Pan Away

HEART/CIRCULATION
clove, nutmeg, goldenrod, cypress, Aroma Life

LONGEVITY
thyme, frankincense, Longevity

LIVER
ledum, carrot seed, German chamomille, Juva Flex

Valor oregano thyme

LUNG
ravensara, *eucalyptus radiata*, myrtle, Raven, Melrose

COLON/DIGESTION
tarragon, fennel, cumin, spearmint, Di-Tone

HORMONE BALANCE
clary sage, fleabane Endo Flex, Dragon Time, Mister

SUMMARY

Raindrop Technique (RT) is a powerful tool that assists both professionals and lay people to achieve true balance in the body. Out of the thousands of RT sessions that have been performed, there have been hundreds of instances where the results were amazingly profound and immediate. Here are just a few examples:

A young man from Denver, Colorado who suffered from chronic scoliosis was able—for the first time in eight years—to fully bend over after the application of RT. With an overhead camera televising an image of his spine as he bent over, an audience of over 400 watched the vertebrae in his spine literally move into place. When he stood up, he was measured and had gained an inch in height.

Another case involved a professional model in her early 40s, who had developed early adult-onset scoliosis. She had to alter clothing so it would fit properly for modeling sessions. She wasn't able to sit still for any length of time. After receiving RT, her spine straightened to such a degree that she, too, gained an inch in height. She followed up with more RT in the next few months and reported that all discomfort was gone. She now dances and rides horses pain-free.

It is quite common that individuals with scoliosis who receive RT will gain 1/2 an inch or more in stature from a single application. Many others have reported pain relief, congestion relief, and cold and flu relief as a result of RT. This is why RT has captured so much interest among those involved in the healing arts.

Answers to frequently asked questions

Older children can benefit from RT, but it is critical to adjust the amount of oil used in proportion to their body size. Amounts should be adjusted to reflect the difference in body size relative to an adult.

Every person is biochemically different, and what works for one may not work for another. Different body types respond to the applications in ways you may not expect. Learn to be sensitive to the person on whom you are working so that you can respond to their needs.

The question is often asked, "How long do the effects of this application last?" Again, each person responds differently. Generally speaking, a high level of health and proper diet are key factors, as are exercise and attitude. The effects of one application may last several months for one person, but for another it may be necessary to have repeated applications weekly until the body begins to respond. The goal is to retrain the tissues of the body. This may take a few weeks or even a full year.

Spinal alignment may have a completely different look when the individual is lying down, rather than sitting. There is more torque on the spine in a sitting or standing position, so these are the positions in which X-rays are usually taken. The spine may appear to be totally corrected when the receiver is lying down, but then appear to be crooked when they are in a sitting position. This variance is normal and may be apparent until a total retraining of the muscles occurs. The object is to achieve proper alignment in all positions.

CHAPTER 22
Lymphatic Pump

Maintaining lymph circulation is one of the keys to keeping the immune system adequately functioning. This technique is designed to promote lymph circulation. It is an excellent tool for those who are sedentary or bedridden.

1. With the recipient lying on their back, hold one leg with one hand just above ankles with your palm on the underside of the leg (covering the Achille's tendon).

2. Place the other hand on the bottom of the recipient's foot with your palm over the ball of their feet and your fingers curled around their toes.

3. Push the top of the recipient's foot away from you. (See Fig. A)

4. Then, pull the recipient's foot toward you by the toes until the ball of the foot is as close to the table as possible. (See Fig. B)

5. Check with the recipient during the pump to verify that the muscles in their feet are not being overextended. This should be an active process, but not a painful one.

6. Pull and push their foot using this "pumping motion" at least 10 times on each leg for maximum benefit. Note that their entire body should move during each step of the Lymphatic Pump.

Fig. A — Pushing the foot

Fig. B — Pulling the foot

CHAPTER 23

Auricular Aroma Technique

D. Gary Young developed auricular aroma technique, the integration of essential oils with standard auricular technique, after using essential oils in acupuncture applications in his clinic. He found that using essential oils in conjunction with acupuncture was extremely beneficial. He also found that acupuncture stimulation with essential oils was noticeably greater than either acupuncture or essential oil applications by themselves.

Emotional Ear Chart

Mother

Father

Depression

Overwhelmed

Sympathy & Guilt

Self Pity

Bearing the Burden of the World

Rejection

Anger & Hate

Self Expression

Vision

Fear

Heart

Open

Acupuncture with essential oils seems to enhance benefits substantially. As Gary left his first clinical practice and began researching, farming, and teaching, he knew he could not continue the practice of acupuncture, so he started developing a simplified technique that everyone could use. That technique is called auricular probe technique, using a small, pen-shaped instrument with a rounded end to apply the oils to the acupuncture meridians or Vita Flex points on the ears. This concept can be used in both the emotional and physical realm.

For working the spine and dealing with neurological problems that exist because of spinal cord injury, auricular probe technique was found to be extremely beneficial to deliver the oils to the exact location of the neurological damage.

Auricular probe technique is a program that Gary continues to research and develop, and teach to doctors. It has shown tremendous potential and will grow to be a well-known modality in the future.

Physical Ear Chart

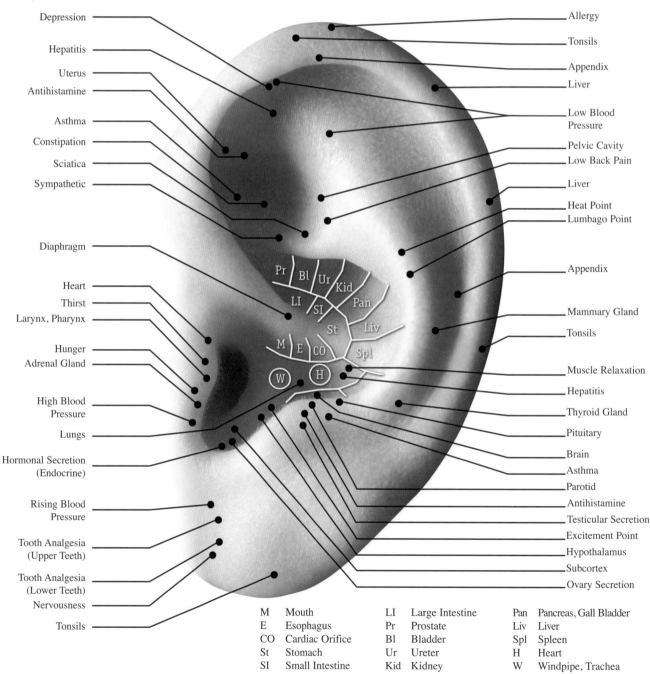

Depression
Hepatitis
Uterus
Antihistamine
Asthma
Constipation
Sciatica
Sympathetic
Diaphragm
Heart
Thirst
Larynx, Pharynx
Hunger
Adrenal Gland
High Blood Pressure
Lungs
Hormonal Secretion (Endocrine)
Rising Blood Pressure
Tooth Analgesia (Upper Teeth)
Tooth Analgesia (Lower Teeth)
Nervousness
Tonsils

Allergy
Tonsils
Appendix
Liver
Low Blood Pressure
Pelvic Cavity
Low Back Pain
Liver
Heat Point
Lumbago Point
Appendix
Mammary Gland
Tonsils
Muscle Relaxation
Hepatitis
Thyroid Gland
Pituitary
Brain
Asthma
Parotid
Antihistamine
Testicular Secretion
Excitement Point
Hypothalamus
Subcortex
Ovary Secretion

M	Mouth	LI	Large Intestine	Pan	Pancreas, Gall Bladder
E	Esophagus	Pr	Prostate	Liv	Liver
CO	Cardiac Orifice	Bl	Bladder	Spl	Spleen
St	Stomach	Ur	Ureter	H	Heart
SI	Small Intestine	Kid	Kidney	W	Windpipe, Trachea

CHAPTER 24
Emotional Response with Essential Oils

Today we live in a society of emotional turmoil. More and more the evidence is accumulating that our emotional health can have a profound effect on our physical health. More than ever before researchers are probing the impact that emotional states have on the physical condition of the body. Many doctors are recognizing the possibility that a number of diseases are caused by emotional problems that link back to infancy and childhood— and perhaps even to the womb. These emotional problems can compromise body systems and even genetic structuring through a process that translates creates the equivalent of a molecular 'memory' in key organs and structures of the body.

The idea that memories and traumas can be embedded in the brain is not new, but scientists are now saying that these brain imprints may extend throughout the body. Well-known author and Georgetown University research professor, Candace Pert states, "Repressed traumas caused by overwhelming emotion can be stored in a body part, therafter affecting our ability to feel that part or even move it."

"To some degree, all of the organ systems in the human body have 'memory,' agrees Bruce D. Perry, MD, PhD. "All nerve cells 'store' information in a fashion that is contingent upon previous patters of activity," he noted. Dr. Perry is with the Child Trauma Program sponsored jointly by Baylor College of Medicine and Texas Children's Hospital. Perry says further that the ability to "carry elements of previous experience forward in time is the basis of the immune, the neuromuscular, and the neuroendocrine systems."

As scientists have studied to understand the neural basis of emotion, they have discovered that the limbic system of the brain plays a vital role in interpreting and channeling intense experiences, particularly memories of fear or trauma. Interestingly, the two parts of the limbic system which play a major role in emotional processing—the amygdala and the hypothalamus—are located less than an inch of the olfactory nerve (see chart on previous page and also the Limbic System chart on page 2).

In 1989, researchers agreed that the amygdala— one on each side of the inner brain—play a major role in storing and releasing emotional trauma and that aromas have a profound effect in triggering responses from the amygdala. Joseph Ledoux, MD, of the New York Medical University was one of the first to suggest that the use of aroma could be a major breakthrough in helping to trigger the release of pent-up emotional trauma.

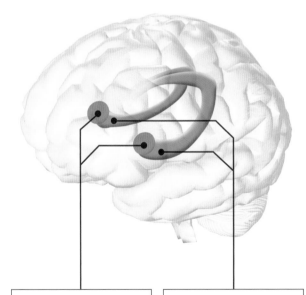

Amygdala	**Hippocampus**
Influences behaviors and activities. It is also concerned with emotions such as anger and jealousy, as well as drives such as hunger, thirst and sexual desire.	Involved with recognizing new experiences, learning and memory - especially sort-term memory

Energy Centers (Chakras) and Associated Glands

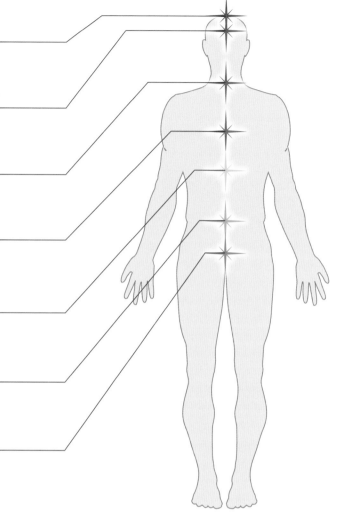

CROWN—Thought—*Violet*
   Pineal: Controls cerebrum, right brain hemisphere, central nervous system, right eye.

3RD EYE—Light—*Indigo*
   Pituitary: Controls endocrine system, left brain hemisphere, left eye, nose, ears, sinuses and parts of nervous system.

THROAT—Ether/Sound—*Blue*
   Thyroid: Controls jaw, neck, throat, voice, airways, upper lungs, nape of neck, arms.

HEART—Air/Touch—*Green*
   Thymus: Controls heart, blood circulation, immune system, lower lungs, rib cage, skin, upper back, hands.

SOLAR PLEXUS—Fire/Sight—*Yellow*
   Pancreas: Controls liver, digestive system, stomach, spleen, gall bladder, muscles, autonomic nervous system, lower back.

SACRAL—Water/Taste—*Orange*
   Adrenal: Controls all solid parts—spinal column, bones, teeth, nails. Also blood and building of cells, kidneys and bladder.

BASE/ROOT—Earth/Smell—*Red*
   Reproductive: Controls pelvic area, sex organs, potency, and fluid functions.

Fear and trauma can produce conditioned emotional responses that—unless released—will not only hamper our ability to live and enjoy life fully, but can also limit the ability of some body systems to function properly, particularly the immune system. This can result in unexplained pain and illness as well as depression and other psychological 'issues.'

Many of the biochemicals in essential oils—particularly sesquiterpenes—can increase blood oxygen levels in the brain. The stimulation of both aroma and oxygenation seems to affect the amygdala in ways that facilitate the release of stored emotional blocks, both in the subconscious and in various body systems. Combining essential oil aromas and oxygenation regularly over time—accompanied by mental focus and intent—has proven to be effective in many cases for resolving unexplained physical problems that were rooted in past emotional trauma.

Another way in which essential oils can assist in helping people to move beyond emotional blocks is through their relaxing effect. The aldehydes and esters of certain essential oils are very calming and sedating to the nervous system (including both the sympathetic and parasympathetic systems). These substances allow us to relax instead of getting caught up in an anxiety spiral. Anxiety creates an acidic condition that activates the transcript enzyme which then transcribes that anxiety on the RNA template and stores it in the DNA. That emotion then becomes a predominant factor in our lives from that moment on.

The process of emotional release using essential oils should not be dramatic, but gentle, occurring step-by-step over a period of time. Application of the oils accompanied by mental focus and relaxation should occur multiple times per day. Some emotional blocks will require only a day or two to begin releasing, others may require weeks.

There are many essential oil blends that have been created precisely for the purpose of helping to release emotional patterns. Twelve of them deserve specific mention as they are part of an extended protocol, developed by D. Gary Young. The protocol, outlined below is one that can be used very flexibly. One can use just the first step or two, or a selection of steps, or use all 12 steps, depending on inclination and need. Each succeeding step involves another blend which may further stimulate the release process.

It is important to remember that this process should not be uncomfortable. As you reach a step during which you begin to feel uncomfortable, there is no need to go further. Rather, it is okay to wait for a future application when you feel confident before going to that next step. The applications should be accompanied by mental effort focusing on reprogramming negative emotions with positive emotions and images.

For a much more thorough explanation of using essential oils in emotional release, and for specific emotional issues, consult the book, *Releasing Emotional Patterns* by Dr. Carolyn L. Mein. It is available through Essential Science Publishing at www.essentialscience.net.

Emotional Clearing Protocol using 12 essential oil blends:

Step 1. VALOR should be the first blend used and applied to the bottoms of the feet when starting an emotional clearing. It helps balance the energies within the body, helping to give courage, confidence and self-esteem. Apply 3-6 drops on each foot and hold the right food in the right hand; left foot in the left hand for a minute or two until balance is felt.

Step 2. The **3 WISE MEN** was formulated to open the subconscious mind through pineal stimulation to release deep-seated trauma encoded in the DNA. This blend opens the crown chakra and stimulates the limbic system, bringing a sense of grounding and uplifting through positive memory recall. Place 2-3 drops on the crown of the head.

Step 3. HARMONY is an exquisite blend of 12 essential oils, which promotes physical and emotional healing through harmonic balance of the energy centers of the body, enabling energy to flow more efficiently. It helps reduce stress and creates an overall sense of well-being. Apply 2 drops on the energy meridians either directly on or along the side of the body.

Step 4. FORGIVENESS blend has high electrical frequencies, which can help release negative memories to facilitate forgiveness, letting go, and moving on. Apply 1-2 drops around the navel, massaging in a clockwise motion.

Step 5. JOY is an exotic blend of ylang ylang, bergamot and pure Bulgarian rose oil, which produces a magnetic energy to attract love and enhance self-love, bringing joy to the heart. Apply 1-2 drops over the heart area massaging in a clockwisemotion.

Step 6. PRESENT TIME blend has an empowering fragrance, which gives a feeling of being 'in the moment.' One can only progress through emotional release when in the present time. Apply 1-2 drops on the thymus (top of the sternum) in a circular motion.

Step 7. RELEASE blend is formulated to support the release of traumatic memories from the cells of the liver. Many energy medicine doctors believe that anger and hate energy is stored in the liver. Apply 1-2 drops over the liver area in a circular motion.

Step 8. INNER CHILD blend is a formula that may stimulate childhood memory. When children experience abuse or trauma, they can become 'disconnected' from their inner child or identity. This disconnection may not be apparent until many years later, manifesting itself as a 'mid-life crisis.' The inner child fragrance may stimulate memory response, helping one re-connect with his or her fundamental identity. This is an essential step or condition to achieving emotional balance. Apply 1 drop under the nose and 1 drop around the navel.

Step 9. GROUNDING may be helpful in situations where one is over-excited about new ideas or wants to escape into a protective fantasy. In this kind of mental state, it is easy to make choices which lead to bad relationships, bad business

decisions and other unfortunate circumstances. We seek for an escape because we have no anchor to know how to deal with negative emotions. GROUNDING's aroma helps restore confidence and peace, enabling us to deal logically and peacefully with life's decisions. Apply 1-2 drops to the back of the neck and the sternum.

Step 10. HOPE blend is formulated to reconnect with a feeling of strength and optimism for the future. Hope must be in place in order to move forward in life. Hopelessness can cause a loss of vision of goals and dreams, making it impossible to release emotional blocks. This aroma may also help in overcoming tendencies toward depression. Massage 1 drop on the outer edge of each ear.

Step 11. SARA blend is an essential oil blend formulated specifically for opening the limbic system to release the memories of serious trauma connected with Sexual And/or Ritual Abuse. Apply one drop over the energy centers, navel and chest.

Step 12. WHITE ANGELICA is an amazing blend of 18 different oils, some of which were used during ancient times to increase the aura around the body, bringing a delicate sense of strength and protection. Its frequency protects against negative energies and helps to create a feeling of wholeness and oneness with the Creator. Apply 1-2 drops on the crown and on the shoulders.

Step 13. Meditate on positive images and emotions for 20 minutes. (Note this step should be included regardless of how many of the first 12 steps are taken.)

Oils for Specific Emotional Challenges
ABUSE
Single Oils: Geranium, ylang ylang, sandalwood.
Blends: SARA, Hope, Joy, Peace & Calming, Inner Child, Grounding, Trauma Life, Valor, Forgiveness, White Angelica

AGITATION
Single Oils: Bergamot, cedarwood, clary sage, frankincense, geranium, juniper, lavender, myrrh, marjoram, rosewood, rose, ylang ylang, sandalwood.
Blends: Peace & Calming, Joy, Valor, Harmony, Forgiveness

ANGER
Single Oils: Bergamot, cedarwood, frankincense, lavender, lemon, marjoram, myrrh, orange, rose, Roman chamomile, sandalwood, ylang ylang.
Blends: Release, Valor, Sacred Mountain, Harmony, Hope, Forgiveness, Present Time, Trauma Life, Joy, Surrender, Christmas Spirit, White Angelica

ANXIETY
Single Oils: Orange, Roman chamomile, ylang ylang, lavender.
Blends: Valor, Hope, Peace & Calming, Joy, Present Time, Citrus Fresh, Surrender, Believe

APATHY
Single Oils: Frankincense, geranium, marjoram, jasmine, orange, peppermint, rosewood, rose, sandalwood, thyme, ylang ylang.
Blends: Joy, Harmony, Valor, 3 Wise Men, Hope, White Angelica, Motivation, Passion, Highest Potential

ARGUMENTATIVE
Single Oils: Cedarwood, Roman chamomile, eucalyptus, frankincense, jasmine, orange, thyme, ylang ylang.
Blends: Peace & Calming, Joy, Harmony, Hope, Valor, Acceptance, Humility, Surrender, Release

BOREDOM
Single Oils: Cedarwood, spruce, black pepper, Roman chamomile, cypress, frankincense, juniper, lavender, rosemary, sandalwood, thyme, ylang ylang.
Blends: Dream Catcher, Motivation, Valor, Awaken, Passion, Gathering, En-R-Gee

CONCENTRATION
Single Oils: Cedarwood, cypress, juniper, lavender, lemon, basil, helichrysum, myrrh, orange, peppermint, rosemary, sandalwood, ylang ylang.
Blends: Clarity, Awaken, Gathering, Dream Catcher, Magnify Your Purpose, Brain Power

CONFUSION
Single Oils: Cedarwood, spruce, cypress, peppermint, frankincense, geranium, ginger, juniper, marjoram, jasmine, rose, rosewood, rosemary, basil, sandalwood, thyme, ylang ylang.
Blends: Clarity, Harmony, Valor, Present Time, Awaken, Brain Power, Gathering, Grounding

DAY-DREAMING

Single Oils: Ginger, spruce, lavender, helichrysum, lemon, myrrh, peppermint, rosewood, rose, rosemary, sandalwood, thyme, ylang ylang.

Blends: Sacred Mountain, Gathering, Valor, Harmony, Present Time, Dream Catcher, 3 Wise Men, Magnify Your Purpose, Envision, Brain Power, Highest Potential

DEPRESSION

Single Oils: Frankincense, lemon, sandalwood, geranium, lavender, angelica, orange, grapefruit, ylang ylang.

Blends: Valor, Motivation, Passion, Hope, Brain Power, Present Time, Envision, Sacred Mountain, Harmony, Highest Potential, Joy

DESPAIR

Single Oils: Cedarwood, spruce, clary sage, frankincense, lavender, geranium, lemon, orange, lemongrass, peppermint, spearmint, rosemary, sandalwood, thyme, ylang ylang.

Blends: Joy, Valor, Harmony, Gathering, Grounding, Forgiveness, Motivation, Hope

DESPONDENCY

Single Oils: Bergamot, clary sage, cypress, geranium, ginger, orange, rose, rosewood, sandalwood, ylang ylang.

Blends: Peace & Calming, Inspiration, Harmony, Valor, Hope, Joy, Present Time, Gathering, Inner Child, Trauma Life, Envision

DISAPPOINTMENT

Single Oils: Clary sage, frankincense, geranium, ginger, juniper, lavender, spruce, orange, thyme, ylang ylang.

Blends: Hope, Joy, Valor, Present Time, Harmony, Dream Catcher, Gathering, Magnify Your Purpose, Passion, Motivation

DISCOURAGEMENT

Single Oils: Bergamot, cedarwood, frankincense, geranium, juniper, lavender, lemon, orange, spruce, rosewood, sandalwood.

Blends: Valor, Sacred Mountain, Hope, Joy, Dream Catcher, Into the Future, Magnify Your Purpose, Envision, Believe

FEAR

Single Oils: Bergamot, clary sage, cypress, Roman chamomile, geranium, juniper, marjoram, myrrh, spruce, orange, sandalwood, rose, ylang ylang.

Blends: Valor, Present Time, Hope, white Angelica, Trauma Life, Gratitude, Highest Potential

FORGETFULNESS

Single Oils: Cedarwood, Roman chamomile, frankincense, rosemary, basil, sandalwood, peppermint, thyme, ylang ylang.

Blends: Clarity, Valor, Present Time, Gathering, 3 Wise Men, Dream Catcher, Acceptance, Brain Power, Highest Potential

FRUSTRATION

Single Oils: Roman chamomile, clary sage, frankincense, ginger, juniper, lavender, lemon, orange, peppermint, thyme, ylang ylang, spruce.

Blends: Valor, Hope, Present Time, Sacred Mountain, 3 Wise Men, Humility, Peace & Calming, Surrender, Gratitude

GRIEF/SORROW

Single Oils: Bergamot, Roman chamomile, clary sage, *Eucalyptus globulus*, juniper, lavender.

Blends: Valor, Release, Inspiration, Inner Child, Gathering, Harmony, Present Time, Magnify Your Purpose

GUILT

Single Oils: Roman chamomile, cypress, juniper, lemon, marjoram, geranium, frankincense, sandalwood, spruce, rose, thyme.

Blends: Valor, Release, Inspiration, Inner Child, Gathering, Harmony, Present Time, Magnify Your Purpose, Gratitude

IRRITABILITY

Single Oils: All oils except eucalyptus, peppermint, black pepper.

Blends: Valor, Hope, Peace & Calming, Surrender, Forgiveness, Present Time, Inspiration

JEALOUSY

Single Oils: Bergamot, *Eucalyptus globulus*, frankincense, lemon, marjoram, orange, rose, rosemary, thyme.

Blends: Valor, Sacred Mountain, White Angelica, Joy, Harmony, Humility, Forgiveness, Surrender, Release, Gratitude

MOOD SWINGS

Single Oils: Bergamot, clary sage, sage, geranium, juniper, fennel, lavender, peppermint, rose, jasmine, rosemary, lemon, sandalwood, spruce, yarrow, ylang ylang.

Blends: Peace & Calming, Gathering, Valor, Dragon Time, Mister, Harmony, Joy, Present Time, Envision, Magnify Your Purpose, Brain Power

OBSESSIVENESS

Single Oils: Clary sage, cypress, geranium, lavender, marjoram, rose, sandalwood, ylang ylang, helichrysum.

Blends: Sacred Mountain, Valor, Forgiveness, Acceptance, Humility, Inner Child, Present Time, Awaken, Motivation, Surrender

PANIC

Single Oils: Bergamot, Roman chamomile, myrrh, frankincense, lavender, marjoram, wintergreen, rosemary, sandalwood, thyme, ylang ylang, spruce.

Blends: Harmony, Valor, Gathering, White Angelica, Peace & Calming, Trauma Life, Awaken, Grounding, Believe

RESENTMENT

Single Oils: Jasmine, rose, tansy.

Blends: Forgiveness, Harmony, Humility, White Angelica, Surrender, Joy

RESTLESSNESS

Single Oils: Angelica, bergamot, cedarwood, basil, frankincense, geranium, lavender, orange, rose, rosewood, ylang ylang, spruce, valerian

Blends: Peace & Calming, Sacred Mountain, Gathering, Valor, Harmony, Inspiration, Acceptance, Surrender

SHOCK

Single Oils: Helichrysum, basil, Roman chamomile, myrrh, ylang ylang, rosemary CT cineol.

Blends: Clarity, Valor, Inspiration, Joy, Grounding, Trauma Life, Brain Power, Highest Potential, Australian Blue

SECTION 7

CHAPTER 25

Cleansing and Diets
Using Essential Oils and Supplements

The Risks of Internal Pollution

As the human body ages there is a risk of greater and greater buildup of chemical contamination in our tissues. As toxins accumulate, the body is more likely to suffer the energy-robbing effects of poor health and degenerative diseases.

This is why cleansing the body is so important. When the body is purged of heavy metal contamination, undigested foods, and internal pollution, it relieves enormous stress on the organs and tissues. Immune function is enhanced and particularly the stress on the liver is reduced.

Cleansing becomes especially important whenever animal products are consumed, such as meats and dairy products. These foods are loaded with naturally-occurring, disease-related microbes. According to Robert O. Young, PhD, DSc, meats contain an average of 300,000 to 3 million microorganisms per gram, or roughly 336 million per serving. Cheese contains from 300,000 to 1 million microorganisms per gram; milk, 20,000. These animal products can be a major source of internal pollution. Clean plant food, on the other hand, contains only 10 microbes per gram.

Humans were built to be primarily plant-eaters, not meat-eaters. Our long intestinal tracts are similar to many plant-eating species and are specifically designed by nature to digest a high-fiber, high-roughage, plant-based diet. Its long length allows enzymes a chance to unlock the nutrient value of the food. This contrasts markedly with the short intestines of flesh-eating animals, which are designed to quickly digest and pass through meats, without allowing them to putrefy, feed fungi, and create illness.

What happens when meats and dairy products are consumed by humans without adequate fiber? Lacking fiber, these proteins move through our lengthy intestines very slowly and easily become trapped in the intestine's many nooks and crannies. Acting like toxic time bombs, putrefying pockets of maldigested food gradually release their payload of heavy metals, chemicals, hormones, and toxins directly into the blood and tissues. Even worse, this undigested debris is fermented by our body's naturally-occurring yeast and fungi, polluting us with toxic by-products called mycotoxins. These mycotoxins have been linked to many diseases.

Who Needs Cleansing?

Everyone needs cleansing. All of us are stressed, to a lesser or greater degree, by an ever-mounting buildup of toxins, chemicals, bacteria, and parasites. A distinguished medical researcher, Kenneth Bock, M.D., states that humans are "walking toxic dumps." Why? Because of the industrial wastes, herbicides, pesticides, additives, and heavy metals we unknowingly absorb from our food, cosmetics, air, and water—even the mercury fillings in our teeth. Moreover, humans are at the top of the food chain meaning we are subjected to concentrated doses of potentially harmful chemicals from the meats and dairy products we consume.

According to a large 1990 survey by the Environmental Protection Agency, every single person tested showed some evidence of petro-chemical pollution in their tissues and fats. Some of the chemicals found included styrene (used in plastics), xylene (a solvent in paint and gasoline), benzene (a chemical found in gasoline), and toluene (another carcinogenic solvent).

Inflamation is one of the main factors contributing to disease in the human body today—heart disease being a prime example. Many people do not understand how someone relatively healthy, with low cholesterol levels, normal arterial function, and healthy arterial walls can unexpectedly suffer a heart attack, yet it happens all too often. The explanation is inflammation.

What causes this inflammation and how does it occur in the body? Inflammation has various causes: bacterial infection (such as clamydia pneumoniae), poor diet, chemicals, hormonal imbalance, or physical injury.

A protein called "C-reactive" is released by the liver when inflammation is present. The level of this protein indicates the degree of inflammation in places like the linings of the arteries of the heart. Accumulation of C-reactive protein and an excess of blood protein plasma can change pH in the blood and cellular function and hasten the onset of tumors and a predisposition for heart disease. In fact, C-reactive protein testing may help doctors predict heart attack or stroke risk.

Cleansing allows the body to work towards fighting off the disease and not be encumbered or overloaded with the accumulation of toxins, mucous, and parasites that have built up over the years.

Understanding a Complete Cleansing

The ideal cleansing program should combine high water consumption with high-potency herbs, digestive enzymes, and therapeutic-grade essential oils. Essential oils have a special lipid-soluble makeup, which gives them a remarkable ability to penetrate cell membranes, break up undigested food, and oppose toxins. Essential oils also deliver oxygen, which has an unparalleled ability to inhibit the growth of many types of microbes. In fact, many essential oils have been studied for their unique antimicrobial, antifungal, and antiparasitic properties. Some oils, like rosemary, have demonstrated significant antiseptic activity, with documented research appearing in many scientific journals.

Consult your physician

Anyone cleansing or fasting for more than three days should do so under the supervision of a health care professional. Never begin a shut-down fast unless you have been fasting regularly for at least two years. This type of a fast should always be done under supervision.

A cleansing program should target many different parts of the body (colon, intestine, stomach, liver, pancreas) and cover many different types of internal pollution, including waste buildup, heavy metals, parasites, fungi, and yeast.

When Should You Cleanse?

Cleansing your system should not be just a once- or twice-a-year event. It should be continuous.

Cleansing is especially important for anyone over 40. With age comes a greater buildup of debris in our bodies caused by decreased production of the stomach acids and enzymes. Without proper enzyme production, we lack the ability to properly break down undigested proteins and other fermenting debris that obstruct our digestive system and impede the assimilation of nutrients.

To get the most out of any cleansing regimen, one must drink plenty of distilled or purified water (never chlorinated tap water) throughout the day. A good rule of thumb is to divide your body weight (in pounds) by half, then drink that number of ounces of water. For example, a 150 pound person should drink 75 ounces (about 7-8 glasses) of water daily.

The Stanley Burroughs' Master Cleanse or Lemonade Diet

The Master Cleanser is not a fast, but a cleansing program. A true fast consists only of water, while the original Master Cleanser incorporates a mixture of lemon juice, Grade B maple syrup, and cayenne pepper that is consumed throughout the day and is a source of calories, vitamins, and minerals.

NOTE: Clinical experience has shown that many people do better when the Grade B Maple Syrup is replaced with Blue Agave nectar, as shown in the program below. Stanley Burroughs never had the opportunity to test this during his lifetime, so his recipe remains with the maple syrup.

The Master Cleanser is ideal for anyone who is not diabetic and can safely cleanse for at least 7-10 days. The ideal duration of this cleanse is actually 10-15 days, depending on experience and need. As with any program of caloric restriction, however, it is strongly recommended that you consult with your health care professional before undertaking any extended fast or cleanse.

Program:

- Squeeze the juice from ½ fresh lemon(preferably organic)
- Mix juice into 8 oz. of distilled water
- Add 1-2 tablespoons of blue agave nectar (or, using Burroughs' original recipe, Grade B Maple syrup)
- Add up to 1/10 tsp. cayenne (red) pepper.

Start with a pinch or two of cayenne and gradually increase to 1/10 tsp. Do not put cayenne pepper (capsicum) in capsules and take separate from the lemonade drink. It changes the action of the formula, and if sent directly to the stomach can cause inflammation and excessive mucous secretion. This may lead to sinusitis or to bowel mucus, and can even contribute to inflammatory bowel syndrome.

Drink 6 to 12 of these ten ounce glasses of lemonade daily during waking hours. Each time you begin to feel hunger, have another glass of the lemonade. No other food should be taken during the cleansing period.

Blue Agave nectar and Grade B maple syrup are two of the most balanced of all sugars, containing a balance of positive and negative ions. Neither enters the bloodstream as rapidly as honey or sugar which is better for people who react adversely to sugars, (becoming restless, sleepless and energetic after consuming sugar), or may be borderline or pre-diabetic. Diabetics should definitely substitute blue agave for the maple syrup, using up to ¼ tablespoon. (If you have difficulty locating Grade B maple syrup in your area, it is often available through Creer Labs in Utah (801-418-8870).

Contrary to popular belief, lemon is not acidic in the body. It turns alkaline in the mouth. If an acid-like reaction is observed when using lemon with water, it is because of the minerals in the water. Distilled water will not react in this manner.

Cayenne pepper is a blood vessel dilator, a thermal warmer, and provides vitamin A. People who have type O blood tend to have poor circulation. As a result their body temperature may drop during a cleanse. Because cayenne is an herb known for its ability to warm and restore circulation, it may be taken internally and used topically (especially on the feet, but in small amounts).

Cayenne pepper is also thermogenic. When used in a dietary program, it can facilitate an increase in the body's ability to burn fat. Mild exercise also enhances the cleansing action of the program.

During the middle and later phases of the cleanse (typically on about day 3 and about day 7), the body chemistry changes, and energy levels may begin to increase. One may experience minor discomforts, such as headaches, upset stomach, or low energy, as toxins and parasites are released from the body. These symptoms will be short-lived.

Helping the Cleansing Action

The more you can assist Nature to eliminate poisons, the better. If you feel discomfort or tension, you may not be eliminating sufficiently. You should be having 2-3 or more bowel movements daily in order to eliminate the waste that is being loosened from the various organs and intestines. A laxative herb tea is an excellent 'helper' for most people. If your elimination slows, take a good laxative herb tea right from the beginning---the last thing at night and first thing in the morning.

Another Cleansing Aid:
Internal Salt Water Bathing

It is not recommended that enemas or colonics be used in conjunction with the Master Cleanser diet. A better and very inexpensive method for helping to cleanse the entire digestive tract is to use salt water.

Directions: add two level teaspoons of uniodized salt to a quart of lukewarm water. (Don't use regular iodized salt as it will not work properly.) Drink the entire quart of salt water first thing in the morning, on an empty stomach. The salt water will quickly wash through the entire tract in about one hour. Multiple eliminations will occur, moving loosed toxic waste through the system that might not otherwise be cleanly eliminated.

An approach that works very well for most people is to take the herb laxative tea at night to loosen, then the salt water each morning to wash it out. If the salt water cannot be taken in the morning, then the herb laxative should be taken night and morning.

For more information on the Master Cleanser, consult Stanley Burroughs' book, "The Master Cleanser," or Tom Woloshyn's book, "The Complete Master Cleanse," available through Essential Science Publishing.

Learning to Fast

It is important to have a positive attitude during cleansing or fasting. If you are unaccustomed to the process, you can prepare yourself by fasting one day a week. Sunday, or your Sabbath day, is a wonderful day for this purpose. The biggest obstacle to successful cleansing is fear of failure and not knowing what to expect.

To fast for 24 hours, it is easiest if you begin at noon and finish at noon on the following day or from one dinner to the next.

Again, drink plenty of water.

As you begin to fast, you may experience some unpleasant side effects of cleansing, such as headache, nausea, bloating, or irritability. These symptoms are part of the cleansing response and are often a result of toxins and waste matter being purged from the body which usually takes place within 12 to 36 hours.

If you experience these symptoms, you can cut back on your fluid intake, and turn to vegetable juices: carrot juice, carrot and celery—and 50/50 mixes, carrot with celery, spinach, and broccoli is really good. Carrot with a little apple juice or carrot, apple, and a little lemon juice is good to facilitate the continuation of the cleansing. Six ounces of carrot juice, one ounce of apple, and 1/2 ounce of lemon juice will help keep the pH steady, slow the diarrhea, and keep the cleansing action going.

If you are feeling nauseated and bloated, it is an indication of two possibilities: (1) poisons are being released at a very rapid rate and may be backing up into the liver. Keeping the liver cleansed and flushed is extremely important. So it would be good to take ledum essential oil in a capsule at night or early morning. Ledum has a very strong effect on the liver and kidneys as a diuretic and a bile duct dilator.

The second reason for feeling ill is that the colon may not be eliminating as well because of spastic colon, loss of peristalsis (the wavelike motion of the intestines that moves waste matter out of the body), and/or from prolapsing with restrictions from kinks, loops, or twists in the colon. Hydro Colon therapy is a powerful treatment for cleansing the body and assisting in restoring peristalsis. You can call a colon hydrotherapist or buy a colima board. Portable colon hydrotherapy units that are available for use in the home are available and can usually be found searching the Internet.

Colon Hydrotherapy Mixture

Mix:
- 5 drops rosemary
- 5 drops basil
- 4 drops fennel

Add to colonic water and mix well.

In any case, you may also want to consult your health care professional.

During cleansing you may have an unexpected emotional clearing. There are various essential oil blends designed to help control your emotions, and modulate and facilitate the emotional release. Herbs, such as St. John's wort, kava, and hops extract, are excellent for managing stress and negative emotions. The essential oils of valerian, Roman and German chamomile, and lavender, are exceptionally beneficial. Essential oil blends, with tangerine, lavender, Roman chamomile, blue tansy, are calming and relaxing. Lemon oil is also calming. Most citrus oils containing aldehydes can be very calming in these situations. Vitamin B12 and folic acid are also important for emotional stability.

Ideally, these herbs or oils should be taken using oral infusion therapy (sprayed into the inside of the mouth where they can be most efficiently delivered into the blood).

The first 2 to 4 days of the fast are often the most difficult, since you will be overcoming the powerful psychological need to eat. As your body is cleansed of parasites and putrefying toxins, you will experience a sudden surge in energy and well being. Tapeworms, pinworms, and roundworms often start to appear in your stools after 4 to 6 days. Physical hunger will fade away. As the cleansing progresses, your mind will become sharper, your memory will improve, and your spirit will become more buoyant.

Remember: It is crucial to drink plenty of distilled water throughout the day, at least 8 to 10 eight ounce glasses. Water is crucial for not only flushing out toxins, but maintaining the metabolic machinery of your cells and tissues in proper working condition.

The Complete Cleanse

It is difficult to control internal pollution with a simple one-time fix or a single magic-bullet type solution. Complete cleansing requires a battery of different solutions all targeted at specific systems of the body. Cleansing the liver needs different herbs, oils and minerals than cleansing the colon which requires a different cleansing solution than the intestines.

Complete cleansing also requires a broad array of products that are effective against a wide variety of contaminants and microorganisms—not just one or two. Contaminants, like heavy metals, need a different set of tools to deactivate and purge them from the body than parasites do.

An important part of a complete cleansing program is essential oils. Highly antibacterial, antifungal, antiviral, and anti-inflammatory, essential oils help dissolve and chelate toxic chemicals and poisons in the body. They also promote digestive function by promoting the secretion and production of natural enzymes that enhance colon peristalsis that is the cornerstone of waste elimination.

The Herbal Colon Cleanse: ComforTone

Some of the best natural laxatives include cascara sagrada, diatomaceous earth, buckthorn bark, licorice root, apple pectin, bentonite, and black current extract. These herbs are particularly effective in cleansing the colon (large intestine) and can help counteract bloating and constipation. Purging the colon of toxins and impurities is just as important as cleaning the small intestine. Waste products and gases that are held in the colon have a far higher concentration of toxic byproducts than those in the small intestine. When these leach into the organs and tissues, they can wreak havoc in our bodies.

The essential oils of *Melaleuca alternifolia, rosemary officinalis cineol,* tarragon artemisa, bergamot, fennel, St. John's wort, German chamomile, and melissa along with basil eugenol, promote peristalsis and increase digestive secretions in the intestinal tract in helping to promote more and better digestion. Peppermint oil also promotes peristalsis.

Program:

Take two capsules every morning and two every night for two days.

Bowel movements should increase to 3-4 daily.

If elimination does not improve, then increase capsules to 3 each night and morning.

Do not exceed 8 capsules per day without advice from your physician.

If you feel cramping without results, you may have a dehydrated colon, spastic colon, loss of peristalsis, or a prolapsed colon.

Hydro colon therapy may be helpful. You can also drink 8 ounces of aloe vera and/or prune juice daily, which will work as a lubricant.

You should drink half your body weight of water in fluid ounces daily. When cleansing, you need 20 percent more water. However, water is not a lubricant. It works to soften and flush. Clay-like and hard stools and spastic colon indicate dehydration caused by not drinking enough fluids.

When bowel movements occur 3 to 4 times per day, ComforTone has done its job. If you retain this regularity, after stopping ComforTone, you have taken enough. An ideal bowel movement is 1 movement for each meal consumed per day; i.e.: 3 meals per day equal 3 bowel movements per day. When the movement slows to 1 or 2 per day or you begin to feel sluggish, begin again with ComforTone. You may be able to completely reduce your ComforTone dosage to zero or you may find that you need 1-2 capsules daily for a few weeks until you feel you do not need it any more.

Anyone, including pregnant women, should stop ComforTone if diarrhea occurs for more than 1 or 2 days. Restart again with a smaller amount. Other than this, it is safe to take the supplement through the entire pregnancy.

ComforTone and JuvaTone should not be taken together as they might cause a release of too many toxins at the same time, creating nausea, vomiting, dizziness or real discomfort. They are best taken at least one hour apart to allow them to work separately within the body.

The Intestinal Fiber Cleanse: ICP

Coarsely ground grains rich in soluble and semi-soluble fiber are some of the best intestinal cleansers known. Psyllium powder and husks, rice bran, oat bran, flax seed, and fennel seed all help loosen and expel undigested and fermenting materials from the intestines that may block nutrient absorption and poison the body's internal environment.

Fibers act as a biochemical sponge for the body, absorbing impurities, gases, and toxins. They also speed up the flow of waste matter through the intestines, helping to minimize the exposure to harmful substances. The slower the "transit time," or movement of waste matter through the gastrointestinal tract, the higher the incidence of disease.

Fiber satisfies the appetite by giving people a feeling of fullness without adding excessive calories. Fiber may also help balance blood sugar levels. It also helps maintain regularity as we grow older, preventing and overcoming constipation, diarrhea, and gas. Essential oils, such as fennel, tarragon, ginger, lemongrass, rosemary, basil, St. John's wort, bergamot, German chamomile, lemon verbena, and melissa, not only help dissolve and chelate toxins, but they also combat pathological microorganisms that reside in the intestines.

Program:

Take 1 tbs. ICP, mixed in a glass of water, morning and night for two or three days.

After 2-3 days, increase dosage to 2 tbs. morning and night while you cleanse and drink plenty of water.

Maintenance dosage: 2 tbs., 3-4 time per week.

Beta carotene, found in carrot juice and beet juice, also helps elimination.

Carrot seed oil detoxifies the liver, and in combination with geranium and lemongrass essential oils, may help in eliminating gallstones, cleaning the bowel, and relieving flatulence. For kidney stones, ledum, juniper, and geranium are best. To relieve flatulence, use fennel oil, St. John's wort, tarragon, and peppermint.

To maintain a healthy colon, it is best to stay away from processed and pasteurized dairy products, including all cheeses except goat cheese. Other items to avoid are refined white sugar, white flour, processed salt, starchy processed foods and fried foods. These are deadly to the intestinal tract. Also avoid bread made from hybrid wheats and grains that are damaging to the digestive tract. White bread is converted into sugar by the body and the sugar will turn to fat.

If ComforTone or ICP produce heartburn, this indicates that the digestive system is not working properly. If the cleansing process reduces the intestinal flora, add the following to the program:

- Essentialzyme: 1-3 tablets per meal and up to 6 with heavy meat meals late in the day or at night. Oils that can accelerate digestion are tarragon, fennel, St. John's wort, anise seed, and German chamomile. Take 3 or 4 drops of each of the above in a double 00 capsule taken before or after a meal to enhance digestion.

- Yogurt: Take 1/2 hour before meals on an empty stomach.

These supplements provide the stomach with the friendly bacteria and enzymes necessary for good digestion, conversion, and assimilation. True Source Multivitamins and Mineral Essence provide trace minerals that the body requires to make enzymes.

When taken together, ComforTone and Essentialzyme have synergistic effects, so less of each is required to achieve similar benefits.

The Enzyme Cleanse: Essentialzyme

Enzymes help break down foods and proteins that might otherwise ferment and putrefy in the gastrointestinal tract. Undigested foods tax our bodies, sap our energy, and spur the overgrowth of yeast, fungi, parasites, bacteria, and microorganisms that contribute to viral conditions, gastritis, Crohn's disease, and inflammatory diverticulitis. Inadequate digestive enzyme activity has also been linked to chronic inflammations elsewhere in the body, such as fibromyalgia, herpes, inability to gain or lose weight, bad breath, body odor, skin rashes, and migraines. Enzymes like pancreatin, pancrelipase, chymotrypsin, and trypsin are very efficient in breaking down proteins.

However, if the body is acidic, the chymotrypsin, trypsin, and enzymes will not effectively activate in the body. Vegetable enzymes from the unripe papaya and pineapple (papain and bromelain) provide enzyme support.

Digestive enzymes promote complete digestion and help those who have difficulty digesting and assimilating food. The older we get and the more food we consume, the more enzymes we need for complete digestion. Enzymes are essential in unlocking and metabolizing the vitamins, minerals, and amino acids in food.

Enzymes help digest cooked and processed foods that lack the natural enzymes of fresh foods.

Program:

For maintenance: 2-3 Essentialzyme or Polyzyme tablets 3 times daily. Best taken before meals.

Eating out: Carry tablets with you or take them when you return home. After a heavy meal at night and before going to bed, make sure to take tablets to help prevent fermenting.

A, B, and AB blood types: 2-4 tablets

O blood types: 3-6 or more tablets if you feel it necessary.

Cancer or other degenerative diseases

Use the following Ramping Enzymes Program

Ramping Enzymes Program:

Phase 1: Take 3 tablets 3 times daily. Increase by one tablet every day until you become nauseated. Then discontinue Essentialzyme for 24 to 36 hours.

Phase 2: Take 4 tablets 3 times daily. Increase daily by one tablet until you become nauseated. Rest (discontinue) again for 24-36 hours.

Phase 3: Take 5 tablets 3 times daily. Increase daily by one tablet until you become nauseated. Rest again for 24-36 hours.

Phase 4: Start again with the amount that was being taken before nausea occurred the third time. For example: If you were taking 30 tablets when you became nauseated, you would then start Phase 4 with 29 tablets spread out over each day. Continue with this amount for 6 weeks.

Phase 5: In the 7th week, start the enzyme ramping program all over again. This means that you begin Phase 1 and increase the amount by one each day until nausea or vomiting starts again. Repeat and continue for 6 weeks as previously described.

If your doctor determines that you are in remission, you can maintain with 20-30 tablets daily for one year, 6 days a week.

Maintenance: 6 Essentialzyme tablets, 2 times daily.

Caution: This is a very rigorous program so you should consult with your doctor before starting and have your doctor monitor your progress during the program.

The Liver Cleanse: JuvaTone, JuvaFlex and Juva Cleanse

The liver is one of the most important organs in the body. It is pivotal for purifying the blood and plays a key role in converting carbohydrates to energy, as well as storing energy in the form of glycogen and fats. An overburdened liver can affect our energy, digestion, skin and blood.

Fats and bile within the liver can easily become saturated with toxic chemicals and heavy metals. As these toxins accumulate, the liver becomes taxed and becomes unable to properly detoxify the blood. Symptoms of a stressed and poorly functioning liver include skin conditions (ie., rashes, eczema, dermatitis), fatigue, headaches, pallor, dizziness, irritability, and poor digestion.

Several nutrients are essential for cleansing the liver. Choline, inositol, milk thistle, schizandra, and dl-methionine, have been researched for their ability to protect, defat and purge toxins from the liver. Oregon grape root is a source of berberine, a compound researched for its ability to slow the liver damage and scarring (cirrhosis) associated with alcohol consumption and hepatitis B and C.

Some essential oils can also be valuable in increasing the flow of bile from the liver. These oils include ledum, German chamomile, carrot seed, helichrysum, and geranium. Carrot seed oil is well-regarded by herbalists for its role in liver cleansing.

Mercury Toxicity

Mercury is present in harmful amounts in almost every person in the Unites States, due to consumption of seafood (methyl mercury levels in canned tuna are especially problematic) and amalgam dental fillings (which are about 50% mercury). It is estimated that every year, 22 million pounds of mercury are put in peoples mouths in the form of fillings. It is estimated that a person who consumes a 6 oz can of one of the top 5 brands of tuna fish will (with over 0.64 ppm methyl mercury levels) have consumed over 20 times the mercury considered safe by the Environmental Protection Agency.

According to the Centers for Disease Control, statistics show that one in eight women of childbearing age in the United States suffers from tissue levels of mercury that can be dangerous to a developing fetus.

Heavy metals are some of the most toxic poisons on earth and can slowly accumulate in human tissues and cause neurological diseases, cardiovascular problems and some types of cancers. [1]

The problem is that heavy metals such as mercury and lead form insoluble metallic salts that become trapped in the fat and in the kidneys and cannot be quickly excreted by the liver. Because liver plays a major role in trapping and stabilizing mercury, liver cleansing using essential oils can be an outstanding treatment in purging the body of heavy metal contamination that can contribute to many chronic neurological diseases. [2,3,4,5,6]

Clincial Studies Using Helichrysum, Ledum, Celery Seed Essential Oils (JuvaCleanse)

Clinical studies show that an essential oil blend of helichrysum, ledum, and celery seed (JuvaCleanse) dramatically amplified the elimination from the body of heavy metals, especially mercury, one of the most toxic of all non-radioactive metals. Mercury is particularly damaging to the brain and nervous system because it can pass through blood-brain barrier and accumulate indefinitely in motor neurons.

A 2003 clinical study involving a group of four patients tested the effect of three essential oils on the urinary output of mercury.

Four healthy individuals (ages 27 to 69) took two capsules per day (approximately 1,500 mg) of a blend of helichrysum, ledum, and celery seed (JuvaCleanse). The first urine collection occurred prior to essential oil therapy, with the second and third urine collections occurring two and four days after essential oil therapy had begun. The results showed that all four participants more than doubled their urinary elimination of mercury over the four days of evaluation.

Liver Cleanse Regimen:

Week 1: Take 3 JuvaTone tablets, 3 times daily for one week.

Week 2: Increase to 4 tablets, 3 times daily for one week.

Week 3: Increase to 5 tablets, 3 times daily for one week.

Week 4: Increase to 6 tablets, 3 times daily for 1 week.

Then decrease in the reverse order.

Rest for two weeks after completing the 8 week cycle.

The above regimen can be significantly enhanced with the addition of 10 drops daily of Juva Cleanse (taken in a capsule, in the morning upon rising, with 12 oz of pure water) and 1-3 tsp daily of Juva Power, added as a seasoning to foods.

JuvaFlex Essential Oil Blend may be massaged over the liver once daily and may also be applied in a hot compress application (see Compress method in Applications Methods at beginning of Chapter 30). A combination compress can be made with JuvaFlex and a castor oil poultice. Compresses may be applied several times a day. JuvaFlex may also be applied on the bottom of the feet through the Vita Flex technique over the liver points. It may also be taken as a dietary supplement, 4 drops twice daily mixed in soy/rice milk.

Nausea or vomiting indicates a toxic liver. Stop and rest 2-3 days and then start again with 1-2 tablets per day. Gradually increase amount.

JuvaTone and ComforTone should not be taken together as they might cause a release of too many toxins at the same time creating nausea, vomiting, dizziness or discomfort. They are best taken an hour apart to allow them to work individually as the body needs.

For more information on liver cleansing and a detailed daily protocol, consult "Re-JUVA-nate Your Health," a book on liver cleansing by D. Gary Young.

For more information on JuvaTone, see Chapter 10 - DIETARY SUPPLEMENTS. For more information on JuvaFlex and Juva Cleanse, see Chapter 7 - BLENDS.

1. Grandjean P, et al., "Cardiac autonomic activity in methylmercury neurotoxicity: 14-year follow-up of a Faroese birth cohort." *J Pediatr.* 2004 Feb;144(2):169-76.

2. Stankovic RK, et al., "The expression and significance of metallothioneins in murine organs and tissues following mercury vapour exposure." *Toxicol Pathol.* 2003 Sep-Oct;31(5):514-23.

3. Kennedy CJ. "Uptake and accumulation of mercury from dental amalgam in the common goldfish, Carassius auratus." *Environ Pollut.* 2003;121(3):321-6.

4. Song KB, et al., "Mercury distribution and concentration in rats fed powdered dental amalgam." *Arch Oral Biol.* 2002 Apr;47(4):307-13.

5. Zalups RK, Lash LH. "Depletion of glutathione in the kidney and the renal disposition of administered inorganic mercury." *Drug Metab Dispos.* 1997 Apr;25(4):516-23.

6. Stoltenberg M et al., "Autometallographic tracing of mercury in pilot whale tissues in the Faroe Islands." *Int J Circumpolar Health.* 2003 May;62(2):182-9.

The Parasite Cleanse: ParaFree Softgels

Almost everyone has parasites in one form or another. For the most part, they go entirely unnoticed until they begin to cause fatigue and unwellness.

Pure essential oils have some of the strongest antiparasitic properties known. Some of these oils include thyme, clove, anise, nutmeg, fennel, vetiver, Idaho tansy, cumin, *Melaleuca alternifolia*, ledum, melissa, bergamot, and bay laurel.

Select three or four of the oils. Mix in equal proportions and fill a double 00 capsule. Take 3 to 6 a day for 7 days, resting for 7 days and repeating for 7 days. repeat this 3 week cycle seven times.

Oils that may be helpful for natural chelation would be helichrysum, orange or lime, cypress, and ledum.

Program:

The duration of this program depends on the individual.

Take 3-6 ParaFree Softgels, 2 times daily for one week. Rest for one week to allow the parasite eggs to hatch and become active.

Resume dosage for a minimum of 3 weeks and then rest for 3 weeks. Repeat this cycle three times.

The Heavy Metal Cleanse: Chelex Tincture

Heavy metals such as lead, mercury and cadmium in microscopic amounts can cause severe damage to our bodies. They disrupt normal functions and can cause allergic reactions, fatigue, headache, muscle pains, digestive disturbance, dizziness, depression and mental confusion.

Of even graver concern is their tendency to accumulate in the brain, kidneys, nerves, immune system, and fatty tissues. Some highly poisonous heavy metals, such as cadmium, can remain in the body for up to 30 years. As a result, they can lead to degenerative diseases including Alzheimer's, multiple sclerosis, and even cancer.

Herbs such as astragalus, garlic, sarsaparilla, and red clover have the ability to bind heavy metals so they can be expelled from the body. Essential oils also have a natural ability to dissolve insoluble heavy metal salts so that they can be eliminated.

Program:

Put 3-4 droppers of Chelex Tincture in distilled water and drink 3-4 times daily for up to 120 days. Depending on the type of mineral or chemical toxicity, it may be necessary to follow this regimen for as long as 18 months.

Maintenance: 1-2 droppers, 2 times daily, 5 days a week.The duration of this program depends on one's own knowledge of exposure and contamination.

Hair analysis may help in determining the proper duration of this program.

Blood Cleanse: Rehemogen Tincture

This tincture contains herbs that were traditionally used by Chief Sundance and Native Americans for cleansing and purifying the blood. It builds red blood cells and is recommended for any blood disorder. It works as a strong companion with Chelex.

Program:

Chelation (use with above Chelex program): 2 droppers Rehmogen (50 drops) in water 2-3 times daily.

Blood disorders: Put 2-3 droppers Rehmogen (50-75 drops) in distilled water every 2-3 hours.

JuvaTone with Rehemogen is invaluable.

Maintenance Cleansing

Our lifestyles should incorporate cleansing at all times. The intensity of the cleansing depends on the individual. ComforTone, Essentialzyme and ICP taken at the same time, provide a powerful, synergistic cleansing force.

Program:

ComforTone: 3-5 capsules AM and PM.

Essentialzyme: 3 tablets, 3 times daily to continue the digestion of toxic waste in your body from everyday metabolism.

ICP: 1 tbsp. in a glass of water, A.M. and P.M.

JuvaPower: 1 Tbsp 2 x daily

Babies and Children

Babies and children respond very well to oils and supplements. The only difference from adult use is smaller dosage.

Babies: Put 1-2 drops of oil in your hand and rub them together until the hands are practically dry. Then hold them over any particular area of the baby. This works very well without direct application.

Direct application: Mix 1-2 drops of an essential oil in V-6 Mixing oil or Massage Oil Base and apply to bottom of feet.

Children: Put 1-2 drops on bottom of feet or anywhere else on the body as long as the oil is diluted in V-6 Mixing oil, Massage Oil Base, or any vegetable or massage oil. The dilution is always the important factor in comfortability.

Balancing Body Frequency

Much of the cause of imbalance is in the endocrine glands, which create the electrical balance throughout the physical body.

Where the imbalance is due to allergy in sinuses, throat, or pituitary insufficiency, apply the complementary oil to the crown of the head, the forehead, and the thymus.

The blend Release stimulates harmony and balance by releasing memory trauma from liver cells, which store emotions of anger, hate, and frustration. Apply neat over liver, apply compress over liver, or massage Vita Flex points on feet and hands.

Sandalwood oxygenates the pineal/pituitary gland, thus improving attitude and body balance. Rose has a frequency of 320 MHz, the highest of all oils. Its beautiful fragrance is aphrodisiac-like and almost intoxicating. The frequency of every cell is enhanced, bringing balance and harmony to the body. Rose is stimulating and elevating to the mind, creating a sense of well being.

Lavender is very good unless it is an oil that is disliked. Harmony will probably work in most situations. Inner Child is also excellent.

For overall body electrical imbalance, put a couple of drops of the complementary oil in each palm, have the person hold the right palm over the navel and the left palm over the thymus and take three slow, deep breaths. Place the dominant hand over the navel and the other hand over the thymus and rub clockwise three times. This works through the body's electrical field by pulling the frequency in through the umbilicus, the thymus, and the olfactory to the limbic system in the brain to create electrical balance.

Apply Thieves on the bottom of the feet. Sage is good for balancing frequencies when disease lowers body frequency.

Harmony on the energy centers (or chakras) helps balance the body, enhancing the healing process and facilitating the release of stored emotions.

The energy points corresponding to the endocrine glands are:

- The crown (top) of the head (pineal)
- Forehead (pituitary)
- Neck (thyroid)
- Thymus
- Solar plexus (adrenal)
- Navel (pancreas)
- Groin (ovaries/gonads)

Other oils that can be used are frankincense, myrtle, Valor, 3 Wise Men, and Joy.

Blood Types and Food Supplements

In 1996, Dr. Peter J. D'Adamo's book, *Eat Right 4 Your Type*, presented the concept of separate diets for each of the four blood types.

People with blood type A and AB are natural vegetarians and have the easiest time converting to a vegetarian diet. However, these people also have a tendency for thyroid problems and tend to be overweight. For them, exercise that increases heart rate is necessary to have weight reduction.

People with type B blood are probably the most balanced in nutritional needs and can more easily be either vegetarians or meat-eaters.

People with type O blood need additional protein, possibly through meat consumption. They have a more difficult time converting to vegetarianism. These people can get all the protein they need if they consume the correct portions of seeds, nuts and grains. Multi Greens should be a mainstay for this group. These people often have digestive deficiencies. They eat more but assimilate less, have excess gas, get full quickly but are hungry sooner, and tend to weigh less.

People who have type O blood tend to have poor circulation and as a result tend to be cold when fasting. Cayenne pepper improves this situation. One can also put some cayenne in one's shoes and socks when they are worn. Cayenne becomes damp from foot perspiration creating warmth to the feet.

During fasting, O blood types may require more protein. During the first two weeks these people should take Body Gize twice a day and should also take Multi Greens three times per day. These supplements will provide the necessary proteins. After two weeks, the supplements should be discontinued, because protein intake must be zero in order to effect DNA memory change. The body will convert its minimal protein requirements as needed.

Blood type is one of many variables to be considered in selecting what you eat and the supplements you take.

Building the Body

Nutritional supplements enhanced with essential oils can help support and balance body systems. The following products will nourish, strengthen and build your body.

Program:

Power Meal—The all-vegetarian protein drink with Chinese wolfberries.

Use 2 scoops (4 tbs.) in liquid 2-3 times per day. Mix in water, rice or soy milk. It can be mixed in orange or apple juice, but this may make it too sweet and lower the pH. It also may be mixed with cereal, fruits, desserts, and other foods.

Combine equal parts Power Meal and Body Gize for a high-powered protein blend.

Drink as needed.

True Source Multivitamins—Premium multivitamin, mineral, and amino acid supplements.

O Blood Type: 3-4 packets daily.

B Blood Type 2-3 packets daily.

A Blood Type 1-2 packets daily.

Essentialzyme—Enzyme function for mental clarity and physical activity.

O Blood Type: 3-5 tablets daily (depending on type of food eaten and time of day).

B Blood Type: 4-6 tablets daily.

A Blood Type: 5-7 tablets daily (A types tend to have more digestive needs).

Note: When eating heavy protein foods after 3:00 p.m., it is very helpful to additionally take Polyzyme before going to bed.

Exodus—Supercharged antioxidant formula for immune supporting.

O Blood Type: 6-8 capsules daily.

B Blood Type: 6-7 capsules daily.

A Blood Type: 4-6 capsules daily.

Multi Greens—Protein-rich chlorophyll formula.

O Blood Type: 8-10 capsules daily.

B Blood Type: 6-8 capsules daily.

A Blood Type: 4-6 capsules daily.

Ultra Young—Supports healthy pituitary and growth hormone secretion.

Apply 3 sprays on the inside of the cheeks to maximize absorption. Avoid swallowing as long as possible to promote more buccal cavity absorption.

Age 15-30: 3 sprays, 2 times daily (for immune support).

Age 30-45: 3 sprays, 2-3 times daily.

Age 45-65: 3 sprays, 4-6 times daily.

Juvenile Pituitary Retardation: 3 sprays, 3-6 times daily.

Spray 6 days a week for 3 weeks and rest for one week and then repeat.

ImmuneTune

O Blood Type: 6-8 capsules daily.

B Blood Type: 6 plus capsules daily.

A Blood Type: 4 plus capsules daily.

Super C

1 tablet daily for maintenance.

2 tablets daily for reinforcing immune strength.

Super Cal

2-6 capsules daily or as needed.

Mineral Essence

3-6 droppers (75 to 150 drops) in water 1-2 times daily.

Sulfurzyme

Start: 1-2 tsp daily for 1-2 days

Increase: 1-2 tbs 2 times daily for maximum results.

The Clock Diet

The Clock Diet was originated by Dr. Charlotte Holms who maintained a private practice even at 100 years of age in 1989. This diet was based on the fact that stomach acid and enzyme production (pepsin and hydrochloric acid) begins in the morning (about 6 a.m.) and tapers off during the afternoon (between 1:00 and 3:00 p.m.).

This diet mandates that we should schedule our consumption of animal and plant protein to coincide with the highest output of stomach acid and enzymes. Unless our body produces the enzymes to break down protein, high-protein foods will merely ferment in the stomach and lead to fungal and bacterial overgrowth, laying the groundwork, not only for indigestion, but also for disease.

Ideally, we should consume all of our high-protein foods once a day during the morning meal. These foods include grains, such as oats, cornmeal, millet, soy milk, and brown rice, and animal products, such as cheese, milk, and meats.

When the stomach's production of acid and enzymes drops during midafternoon, the best foods to eat consist of simple and complex carbohydrates such as fresh fruits and cooked and raw vegetables. Avoid mixing protein and carbohydrates in the same afternoon or night meal.

Daily Maintenance

The human body has a daily need for nutrients to keep it in peak condition. The nutritional products listed below contain essential oils to help support normal digestive function and nutrient absorption.

Power Meal or Body Gize—Complete protein foods.

Combine or use individually: 1-2 scoops in water, rice milk, oat milk, or other liquid.

Multi Greens—Protein-rich chlorophyll formula very beneficial for vegetarians and O blood types.

O Blood Type: 8-10 capsules daily.

B Blood Type: 6-8 capsules daily.

A Blood Type: 4-6 capsules daily.

True Source Multivitamins—Premium vitamin, mineral, and amino acid complexes.

O Blood Type: 3-4 packets daily.

B Blood Type: 2-3 packets daily.

A Blood Type: 1-2 packets daily.

ComforTone—All natural colon cleanser.

Fasting

Fasting has been called nature's single-greatest healing therapy. Fasting is the avoidance of solid food with liquid intake varying from no liquids to just water to fresh juices. A fast can last 24 hours or several weeks. Fasting has long been a tradition in Judaism, Christianity and the Eastern religions. Religious fasting can involve purification, penitence or preparation for approaching God. An increasing number of doctors are recognizing that fasting can be physically healing while allowing us to focus our energy inward, bringing clarity and change.

Gabriel Cousens, M. D. writes that "fasting in a larger context, means to abstain from that which is toxic to mind, body and soul. A way to understand this is that fasting is the elimination of physical, emotional and mental toxins from our organs, rather than simply cutting down on or stopping food intake. Fasting for spiritual purposes usually involves some degree of removal of oneself from worldly responsibilities. It can mean complete silence and isolation during the fast which can be a great revival to those of us who have been putting our energy outward.

Fasting is generally safe but those with medical conditions should check with their health care professional.

Eldon M. Haas, M. D. notes that fasting is a catalyst for change and an integral part of transformational medicine. He writes, "Fasting clearly improves motivation and creative energy; it also enhances health and vitality and lets many of the body systems rest."

An extremely important benefit of fasting is the elimination of toxins. By minimizing the work our digestive system must do, we allow it to repair itself and clean up stored toxins. In the beginning of a fast, the liver will convert stored glycogen to energy. As the fast continues, some proteins will be broken down unless juices provide calories.

The best way to convert to vegetarianism is by fasting. To be healthy, have energy, be free of sickness and disease, you must learn to discipline yourself and listen to the needs of your body.

Our bodies do not need meat to maintain good health, even though many of us have programmed ourselves through years of meat consumption to have the desire to eat meat. Our bodies can get all the protein required from a diet containing a wide variety of non-meat foods: beans, lentils, vegetables, whole grains, seeds, some cheeses, dairy products (preferably unpasteurized and naturally colored), and occasionally eggs. However, you must be sure to eat enough protein to maintain a balanced, healthy body.

Exercise makes fasting work better, particularly if one is trying to lose weight.

NOTE: Pregnant mothers or lactating mothers should not fast, and seek medical supervision before beginning a fast.

Fitness

Power Meal—2 scoops, 4-6 times daily in water or rice milk or as needed.

Be-Fit—Women, 2 capsules before workout and 2 capsules after workout. For men to increase muscle mass, 6 capsules before and six capsules after workout.

Capsules may be increased or decreased as needed according to body weight and blood type.

Multi Greens—As desired, anywhere from 4-10 capsules daily.

True Source Multivitamins—As desired, anywhere from 2-4 packets daily.

Fortifying the Immune System

The immune system is the most important body system. It must be strong and responsive in order to combat infectious diseases and counteract toxins. Some 40 percent of immune system function is found in the intestinal tract and is called *pirus patchet*. Another 40 percent is accounted for by the thymus gland, which produces immune-stimulating cells.

Dietary supplements containing essential oils can boost immune system function.

ImmuPro—a complex of polysaccharides, beta glucans, minerals and essential oils that is regarded as the strongest immune stimulant known.

Maintenance: 1 chewable once a day before retiring.

Deficiencies: 2-4 chewables before retiring; 1-2 morning and afternoon.

Therapeutic Dosages: 4-8 chewable before retiring; 2-3 morning and afternoon.

Exodus II—blended with oils referenced in the Old and New Testaments.

Massage 3-6 drops on bottom of feet, thymus, throat, or wherever desired.

Exodus—a strong immune builder.

Maintenance: 2-4 capsules daily; O blood types may increase amount.

For weaker system: Take 6-10 capsules, 3 times daily for 10 days and then reduce. Type A's may want to use less.

Sulfurzyme—contains MSM and Chinese Wolfberry.

> **Maintenance:** 1-2 tsp. daily in water or juice. May increase as needed.

> **Deficiencies:** Begin 1-2 tsp. daily and work up to 3-4 tbs. daily or more if desired.

ImmuPower—a blend to strengthen, build, and protect the body.

> **Maintenance:** 1 capsule a day 3 or 4 times a week.

> **Deficiencies:** For pneumonia, flu or colds, 4 capsules a day for 10 days, resting 4 days, and then 1 capsule a day for another 10 days.

ImmuneTune—has strong antioxidant, anti-inflammatory, and anti-tumoral properties. Helps maintain electrolyte and pH balance.

> **Maintenance:** 2-4 capsules daily.

Super C—a special formula of ascorbic acid, scientifically balanced with rutin, bioflavonids, and trace minerals to balance electroytes and assist in the absorption of vitamin C. The essential oils of grapefruit, tangerine, lemon, and mandarin may increase the oxygen and bioflavonoid activity.

Thyromin—a special blend of glandular extracts, herbs, amino acids, minerals, and essential oils to support the thyroid. This gland regulates body metabolism and temperature and is important for immune function.

Mineral Essence—a precisely balanced complex of essential oils and more than 60 trace minerals that are essential to a healthy immune system. It includes well-known antioxidants and immune-supporters such as zinc, selenium and magnesium.

Other Products for Supporting the Immune System

Single oils:

- Frankincense with ravensara, thyme, helichrysum, oregano, rosemary, chamomile, Idaho tansy, mountain savory, melissa, lavender, grapefruit, lemon, cinnamon, clove, cumin, cistus, melaleuca, myrrh, myrtle, rose, vetiver, or lemongrass.

Blends:

- Frankincense with Thieves, ImmuPower, Abundance, Acceptance, Humility, R.C., or 3 Wise Men.

Supplements:

Super B, Multi Greens, Power Meal, Rehemogen, AlkaLime, Ultra Young, JuvaTone, and Wolfberry Bar.

Other Steps for Maintaining a Healthy Immune System

1. Cleanse the colon and liver of toxins and accumulated waste that can sap energy and down-regulate immune response.

   — ICP/ComforTone/Essentialzyme (The Cleansing Trio) is a complete cleansing solution.

2. Avoid excess fear, anxiety, and depression, which can undermine and compromise immune function. Continual daily use of essential oils is optimal to overcome stress (see STRESS in the Personal Usage section, Chapter 30).

3. Avoid physical and mental overexertion which can down regulate immune response. Essential oils, such as lavender, can have powerful relaxant effect on the mind and body, and thus stimulate immune function.

4. Maintain a healthy, balanced diet. A diet high in minerals, such as magnesium, potassium, selenium, zinc, and folic acid play a crucial role in optimizing immune response.

   — Berry Bars are loaded with essential minerals, phytonutrients, and FOS (to enhance mineral absorption).

5. Avoid contaminated or chlorinated water.

   Chlorine inhibits thyroid function interfering with its uptake of iodine and the amino acid tyrosine and therefore slows down metabolism, circulation, and immune function. Chlorine has also been linked to birth defects in children (see Chlorine Research, Appendix Q).

   — Add 1 drop of lemon, peppermint, or spearmint to drinking water.

— Use chlorine-free water for showering and bathing. The RainSpa shower head is specially designed to accept bath salts loaded with essential oils.

6. Stimulate the immune system using selected essential oils and supplements.

— Grapefruit, lemon, lemongrass, and R.C. promote leukocyte (white blood cell) formation.

— ImmuneTune, ImmuPro (polysaccharide complex) and Exodus (herbal complex) build and support the immune system. Exodus II (essential oil blend) is a companion to both supplements.

— Multi Greens encourages healthy blood and boosts immune function.

7. Diffuse essential oils to reduce airborne pathogens and viruses that can overwhelm the immune system.

— ImmuPower and Thieves.

NOTE: Do not diffuse Thieves more than 15 to 30 minutes at a time as the cinnamon may irritate the nasal passages. Also be sure that the room is well ventilated.

8. Inhalation of essential oils can increase immune function through their ability to stimulate the hypothalamus. According to studies conducted by Dr. Asawa of Japan and Dr. Richardson of England, inhalation of unadulterated essential oils increase blood flow to the brain by 15 percent and brain blood oxygen levels by 25 percent.

9. Eliminate parasites which compromise immune function by overloading the system (see PARASITES).

10. Use essential oils in massage applications or take as dietary supplements. Research from the Universities of Cairo, Geneva, and Paris indicate that essential oils are one of the highest known sources of antioxidants.

— Thieves, Exodus II, mountain savory, Abundance, ImmuPower.

Dilute 1 or 2 drops in massage oil or V-6 Mixing Oil and massage on the thymus, bottom of feet, and throat. These oils can also be used as dietary supplements: Use 3 drops, four to six times daily for seven days. Repeat the cycle again, if needed, after four days rest.

11. Support the thyroid gland. The thyroid is crucial to regulating body metabolism, energy levels, and balancing immunity.

— Thyromin strengthens the thyroid (see THYROID).

12. Use antioxidants.

— Longevity is the highest antioxidant supplement.

— Super C contains vitamin C and bioflavonoids and acts as a strong immune support.

13. Reduce candida and fungal overgrowth in the body. These can seriously impair and overload immune function. Alkaline ash whole foods and FOS (fructoligosaccharides) can minimize fungal growth.

(See BODY pH ACID/ALKALINE BALANCE)

14. Increase intake of antioxidants when exposed to radiation. If you know you have been exposed to radiation, feeling fatigued from it, or if you are flying with commercial airlines (because of the greater exposure to radiation due to the high altitude) an increased daily amount of antioxidant supplements is needed. When flying, increase intake 10 days before the trip and continue this higher dosage for 10 days after the trip.

Guidelines for the Healthiest Diet

Breakfast is the most important meal of the day. Some people work for an hour or two prior to having breakfast to promote appetite and prime the digestive system.

Eat breakfast between 6 and 7 a.m. Do not consume any fruit, sugar, or high glycemic index foods. The exception to this is strawberries or raspberries with cereal. Sugar-free yogurt is a good source of acidophilus and bifidobacteria cultures essential of proper intestinal flora. Cereals can include oatmeal, millet, wheat, barley, triticale, or a mixture of these, with coconut milk, rice milk, soy milk, whey powder, or goat milk. Since we do not have enough enzymes to handle multiple foods, it is best to not mix over 3 grains or different foods at a time. Bread should always be toasted; this changes it from a wet food to a dry food, making it more digestible. But eat sparingly. A and B blood types will gain weight eating any type of bread simply because the grains are all hybrid today.

As a rule, breakfast is the best meal of the day for eating proteins, such as beans, rice, eggs, fish, etc. Avoid meat after the noon meal. This will provide more energy and stamina in the afternoon. Always consume Polyzyme with high protein meals. Lunch should consist of carbohydrates and complex carbohydrates and proteins in the form of pasta (a high gylcemic index food, eat sparingly), mixed vegetables, particularly greens and light meats—freshwater fish, cage-free chicken. Drink water with the meal.

For the person engaged in body-building, consume proteins before 3 p.m. by having it at breakfast, mid-morning, lunch, and mid-afternoon. Eat carbohydrates and complex carbohydrates for the evening meal, and have fresh fruit for a snack.

Dinner should be eaten as close to 3 p.m. as possible. It is better not to eat late at night. Both fruit and solid vegetables are suitable for evening meals. If one must eat a large, heavy meal late in the day or evening, an extra portion of Essentialzyme or Polyzyme is needed to promote proper digestion, reduce gas, and prevent putrefaction and fungal growth in the intestines.

Be patient. It may take 2 to 2 1/2 years of very diligent work to establish good digestive function. Listen to your body and modify the program as your body changes.

Hering's Four Laws of Healing

Constantine Hering, a German homeopath who emigrated to the United States in the 1830s, is considered the father of American homeopathy. He formulated four fundamental principles of healing:

1. Healing progresses from the deepest part of the organism—the mental and emotional levels and the vital organs—to the external parts, such as the skin and extremities.

2. As healing progresses, symptoms appear and disappear in the reverse of their original chronological order of appearance.

3. Healing progresses from the upper to the lower parts of the body. This means that head symptoms may clear before stomach symptoms. Deep toxins in the colon or liver will be released before the more surface areas.

4. The most recent illnesses will be the first to leave. This means that flu symptoms experienced a month ago will leave earlier in the healing than the bronchitis suffered two years before.

Radiation Treatments

Restoring proper flora in bowels

If taking antibiotics or undergoing chemotherapy or radiation: Take a full dose of a good probiotic (acidophilus and bifidus, such as Life 5) daily for one week after finishing with antibiotics or medical intervention.

Plain, unflavored yogurt taken before lighter meals also helps provide friendly bacteria. The need for yogurt is sometimes indicated by an intolerance of dairy products.

For patients undergoing radiation, saturate the site 10 days prior to treatment with melaleuca alternifolia and melaleuca ericifolia. Take 4 double 00 capsules per day, before, during radiation, and for 30 to 60 days following the treatment.

CHAPTER 26

Liver Health and pH Balance

Liver and pH

The pH of the blood is very tightly controlled by the body. When serum pH becomes too acidic, then calcium is robbed from the bones and biochemical changes begin to slowly tax and stress liver tissues.

The Importance of Liver Health

Proper liver function is essential for life. The liver is responsible for removing and neutralizing toxins and germs from the blood, promoting digestion, maintaining hormone balance, regulating blood sugar levels, and making proteins that regulate blood clotting.

Cumulative liver stress caused by toxins, poor diet, or disease inevitably lead to irreversible liver damage and death. The first stage is a condition known as fatty liver in which fat deposits accumulate and poison the liver. It has been estimated that 5% of the general population and 25% of patients with obesity and diabetes suffer from fatty liver. With time, fatty liver eventually progresses to cirrhosis, a condition in which non-functioning scar tissue replaces working tissue; it is the 8th leading cause of death by disease, killing over 22,000 people a year.

Signs of an Overloaded or Toxic Liver

- Loss of appetite
- Nausea
- Weakness
- Weight loss
- Edema and ascites. When the liver stops making albumin, water increases in the leg (edema) and abdomen (ascites).
- Bruising and bleeding. Caused when liver slows production of clotting proteins.
- Jaundice. Yellowing of the skin and eyes.
- Itching. Bile products deposited in the skin may cause intense itching
- Gallstones
- Forgetfulness, poor concentration, or disturbed sleep
- Sensitivity to medication. Because the liver does not remove drugs from the blood at the usual rate, drugs act longer than expected.
- Portal hypertension. The flow of blood through the portal vein is slowed, which increases the pressure inside.
- Varices. Blood from the intestines and spleen backs up into blood vessels in the stomach and esophagus. These vessels swell and are more likely to burst.
- Lowered immunity. Cirrhosis can result in immune system dysfunction, leading to infection.

Liver Dangers

- Exposure to Chemicals, Toxins, Pharmaceutical Drugs, and Parasites. Many pesticides, petrochemicals, and environmental toxins are potent liver stressors. Acetaminophen can also stress the liver as can reactions to prescription drugs. Parasitic infection (schistosomiasis) can also contribute to cirrhosis.

- Poor Diet. Excess intake of refined carbohydrates, transfatty acids, and sugars can cause fatty liver or liver degeneration over time.

- Iron Overload. Excess iron in the diet can stress the liver, especially in individuals who are genetically unable to dispose of or sequester dietary iron (hemochromatosis). Creates a haemo-type liver pathology.

- Diabetes, Protein Malnutrition, Obesity, and Corticosteroid Use. Any of these can cause Non-alcoholic Steatohepatitis (NASH). NASH results in deadly fat buildup and eventual cirrhosis in the liver.

- Viruses. The hepatitis B and C viruses are major causes of chronic liver disease and cirrhosis in the United States. Hepatitis viral infections cause inflammation and low-grade damage to the liver that eventually leads to cirrhosis and death.

A 2003 study conducted by Roger Lewis MD at the Young Life Research Clinic in Provo, Utah evaluated the efficacy of helichrysum, ledum, and celery seed in treating cases of advanced Hepatitis C. In one case of a male age 20 diagnosed with a Hepatitis C viral count of 13,200. After taking two capsules (approx. 750 mg each) of a blend of helichrysum, ledum, and celery seed (JuvaCleanse) per day for a month with no other intervention, patients showed that viral counts dropped to 2,580, an over 80 percent reduction.

- Inherited diseases. Alpha-1 antitrypsin deficiency, Wilson's disease, galactosemia, and glycogen storage diseases are inherited disorders that result in malproduction, malprocessing, and malstorage by the liver of enzymes, proteins, and metals.

- Blocked bile ducts. When the ducts that carry bile out of the liver are blocked, bile backs up and damages liver tissue (biliary cirrhosis).

The Importance of Alkalinity to Health

As the liver's filtered ability becomes impaired the blood becomes increasing acidic. Unfriendly bacteria and fungi that populate our intestinal tracts thrive in an acid environment and are responsible for secreting mycotoxins, which are the root cause of many debilitating human conditions. In fact, many researchers believe that most diseases can be linked to blood and intestinal acidity, which contributes to an acid-based yeast and fungus dominance.

The symptoms of excess internal acidity include:

- Fatigue / low energy
- Unexplained aches and pains
- Overweight conditions
- Low resistance to illness
- Allergies
- Unbalanced blood sugar
- Headaches
- Irritability / mood swings
- Indigestion
- Colitis / ulcers
- Diarrhea / constipation
- Urinary tract infections
- Rectal itch / vaginal itch

The ideal pH for human blood is between 7.4 and 7.6. Preserving this alkalinity (pH balance) is the bedrock on which sound health and strong bodies are built. When the blood loses its alkalinity and starts to become more acidic, the foundation of health is undermined. This creates an environment where we become vulnerable to disease and runaway yeast and fungus overgrowth.

The naturally occurring yeast and fungi in the body thrive in an acidic environment. These same yeast and fungi are responsible for secreting a large number of poisons called mycotoxins, which are believed to be one of the root causes of many diseases and debilitating conditions.

When yeast and fungus decline in the body, so does their production of mycotoxins, the poisonous waste products and byproducts of their life cycles. There are numerous varieties of these mycotoxins, many of which are harmful to the body and must be neutralized by our immune systems. When our bodies are overwhelmed by large quantities of these toxins, our health becomes impaired, and we become susceptible to disease and illness.

Many cancers have been linked to mycotoxins. For example, the fungus *Aspergillus flavus*, which infests stored peanuts, not only generates cancer in laboratory animals but has been documented as the prime culprit in many liver cancers in humans.

By balancing the body's pH and creating a more alkaline environment, you can rein in the microbial overgrowth and choke off the production of disease-producing mycotoxins. With pH balance restored, the body can regain newfound vigor and health.

How to Restore Alkalinity

An alkaline environment is hostile to fungi, which require acidity to survive and thrive. Lowered yeast and fungus populations translate into lower levels of body-damaging, disease-inducing mycotoxins.

Some of the most common varieties of pathogenic bacteria, yeast, and fungi that live in the intestines are inactive. However, when the body is weakened by illness, stress, and excess acidity caused by stress, these bacteria become harmful and active, changing into an invasive mycelic form.

1. **Carefully monitor your diet.** Avoiding yeast- and fungus-promoting foods is a crucial factor in combating excess acidity and fungus overgrowth. Meats, sugars, dairy products, pickled and malted products can be especially acidic. On the other hand, garlic is excellent for controlling fungi and yeast. Other high-alkaline, fungus-inhibiting foods include green and yellow vegetables, beans, and whole uncracked nuts.

   The natural ratio between alkaline and acid foods in the diet should be 4:1—four parts alkaline foods to one part acid. JuvaPower and JuvaSpice are mixtures of extremely alkaline and high-antioxidant foods that nourish the liver and combat toxic acidity.

   The pH of a raw food does not always determine its acidity or alkalinity in the digestive system. Some foods, like lemons, might be acidic in their natural state but when consumed and digested are converted into alkaline residues. Thus, the true determinant of a food's pH is whether it is an alkaline-ash or acid-ash food. In this case, lemons are an alkaline-ash food.

2. **Avoid the use of antibiotics.** The overuse of antibiotics for incidental, minor, or cosmetic conditions not only increases the resistance of pathogenic microorganisms, but it kills the beneficial bacteria in your body, leaving the mycotoxin-generating yeast and fungi intact. This is why many women suffer outbreaks of yeast infections after antibiotic use.

3. **Use essential oils.** Many essential oils possess important antimicrobial, antibacterial and anti-fungal properties. Clove and Thyme essential oils have been documented to kill over 15 different strains of fungi.

Essential oils work best when blood and tissues are alkaline. When our systems become acidic—due to poor diet, illness, or emotional stress—essential oils lose some of their effects. So the best way to enhance the action of essential oils is to alkalize your body.

4. **Using alkaline minerals.** Increasing intake of calcium can dramatically boost blood and intestinal alkalinity. Calcium and magnesium-rich supplements such as SuperCal and MegaCal can help alkalinize both blood and body tissues. AlkaLime is an outstanding source of alkaline salts that can help reduce internal acidity. JuvaPower and JuvaSpice are also rich in minerals and yeast-fighting phytonutrients.

5. **Lower stress.** Emotional and psychological tension can be especially damaging to bodily systems and act as a prime promoter of acid formation in the body. To properly appreciate how acidic stress can be, just think back to the last time you were seriously stressed-out and had to reach for an antacid tablet to soothe your heartburn or stomach discomfort.

   Blends of essential oils high in sesquiterpenes, such as frankincense, myrrh, and sandalwood, can produce profound balancing and calming effects on emotions. They work by affecting the limbic system of our brain, the seat of our emotions.

6. **Boost friendly flora.** From three to four pounds of beneficial bacteria permanently reside in the intestines of the average adult. Not only are they the first line of defense against foreign invaders, but they are absolutely essential for health, energy, and optimum digestive efficiency. These intestinal houseguests not only control mucus and debris, but they produce B vitamins, vitamin K, and maintain the all-important pH balance of the body.

   These friendly flora are also important in counteracting and opposing yeast and fungus overgrowth. When our natural cultures are compromised or disrupted by taking antibiotics or by poor dietary practices, yeast and fungus start growing unopposed and begin colonizing and invading larger swaths of our internal terrain, secreting ever-increasing volumes of poisonous mycotoxins.

Using an acidophilus and bifidus (such as Life 5) supplement may be especially valuable in boosting levels of naturally occurring beneficial bacteria in the body and preventing fungal and yeast overgrowth. They also help the body maintain proper pH balance for nutrient digestion and absorption. Ideally, the lactobacillus acidiphilus and bifidobacterium bifidus cultures must be combined with plantain to promote implantation on the intestinal wall.

Research indicates a significant proportion of bacteria from many acidophilus supplements do not reach the lower intestine alive, or they arrive in such a weakened state that they are not of much benefit. This is why combining the acidophilus and bifidus cultures with plantain is so important because plantain helps these cultures adhere to the intestinal walls.

An even more effective means of fortifying the friendly flora in our intestines is by consumption of fructooligosaccharides (also known as FOS). FOS is one of the most powerful natural agents for feeding our friendly flora. FOS is made up of medium-chain sugars that cannot be used by pathogenic yeast and fungi. The end result is that FOS starves fungi while feeding the acidophilus and bifidus cultures that are our main defense against disease.

But FOS is far more than just an outstanding means of rebuilding and protecting the beneficial bacteria inside the body. Over a dozen clinical studies have documented the ability of fructooligosaccharides to prevent constipation, lower blood sugar and cholesterol levels, and even prevent cancer. (Hidaka et al., 1991; Briet et al., 1995); Bouhnik et al., 1996; Kawaguchi et al., 1993; Luo et al., 1996); Rochat et al., 1994; Tokunaga et al., 1993).

Testing Your pH

You can easily test your pH at home by purchasing small litmus-paper strips at your drug store or pharmacy. To get the most accurate reading, expose the strip to a sample of your saliva immediately after awakening in the morning and before eating breakfast. Color changes on the litmus paper will determine pH; check the instructions of your kit for specific details on how to read the litmus paper.

Many of today's health concerns are caused by so-called modern conveniences. Increased use of sugars, artificial sweeteners, contaminated water, and even microwave ovens can all be harmful to health.

Sugars and Sweeteners

Nothing stresses the human body as much as refined sugar. Called a "skeletonized food" and a "castrated carbohydrate" by Edward Howell, PhD, and a "metabolic freeloader" by Ralph Golan, MD, sugar actually drains the body of vitamins, minerals, and nutrients in the process of being burned for energy. Sugar also stresses the pancreas, forcing it to pump out a surge of unneeded digestive enzymes.

Sugars also undermine and retard immune response. One study measured the effects of 100 grams of sugar (sucrose) on neutrophils, a form of white blood cell that comprises a central part of immunity. Within one hour of ingestion, neutrophil activity dropped 50 percent and remained below normal for another four hours (Castleman, 1997).

Population studies have also linked sugar consumption with diabetes and heart disease. According to researcher John Yudkin, the reason sugar elevates the risk of heart disease is due to an automatic built-in safety switch inside the body. To protect itself from being immediately poisoned from excess sugar, the body converts it into fats, like triglycerides. So instead of killing you quickly, the body defends itself by clogging its arteries, thereby killing you on the installment plan.

Aspartame

The worst dangers, though, are not found in natural sugars but in the use of artificial sweeteners. Seventy-five percent of the adverse reactions reported to the U. S. Food and Drug Administration come from a single substance: the artificial sweetener, aspartame.

Aspartame is marketed today as NutraSweet, Equal, Spoonful and Equal-Measure. With so many Americans on one diet or another, the market for aspartame is simply enormous. And it matters not that aspartame users are suffering from symptoms ranging from headaches, numbness and seizures to joint pain, chronic fatigue syndrome, multiple sclerosis, and epilepsy.

This toxic artificial sweetener is made up of three chemicals: aspartic acid, phenylalanine and methanol. What these chemicals do in our bodies is anything but sweet.

A recent book by Dr. Russell L. Blaylock, professor of neurosurgery at the Medical University of Mississippi, *Excitotoxins: The Taste That Kills*, explains that aspartame is a neurotransmitter facilitating the transmission of information from one neuron to another. Aspartame allows too much calcium into brain cells, killing certain neurons, earning aspartame the name of "excitotoxin." With aspartame now in over 9,000 products such as instant breakfasts, breath mints, cereals, frozen desserts, "lite" gelatin desserts and even multivitamins, it is no surprise that there is a virtual epidemic of memory loss, Alzheimer's disease, and multiple sclerosis. In a move much like a telephone company selling your phone number to telephone solicitors and then charging you to block their calls, G. D. Searle (the Monsanto company that manufactures aspartame) is searching for a drug to combat memory loss caused by excitatory amino acid damage most often caused by aspartame.

Phenylalanine

The chemical phenylalanine, a by-product of aspartame metabolism, is an amino acid normally found in the brain. You may have heard of testing infants for phenylketonuria (PKU), a condition where phenylalanine cannot be metabolized, which can lead to death. It has been shown that excessive amounts of phenylalanine in the brain can cause serotonin levels to decrease. Does it seem that half the people you know are on Prozac? Perhaps the flooding of American foods and soft drinks with aspartame is contributing to this need for drugs like Prozac and Zoloft.

But depression is not the most worrisome result of excessive phenylalanine levels in the brain. Dr. Blaylock writes that schizophrenia and susceptibility to seizures can occur as a result of these high levels. The Massachusetts Institute of Technology surveyed 80 people who suffered seizures following the ingestion of aspartame. The Community Nutrition Institute concluded that these cases met the FDA's own definition of an imminent hazard to the public health, but the FDA made no move to remove this dangerous product from the market.

Do you fly the friendly skies? You may be interested to know that both the Air Force's magazine, *Flying Safety,* and *Navy Physiology,* the Navy's publication, detailed warnings about pilots being more susceptible to seizures after consuming aspartame. The Aspartame Consumer Safety Network notes that 600 pilots have reported acute reactions to aspartame including grand mal seizures in the cockpit. Many other publications have warned about aspartame ingestion while flying, including a paper presented at the 57th Annual Meeting of the Aerospace Medical Association.

Methanol

Another by-product of aspartame is methanol. Free methanol results when aspartame is heated higher than 86 degrees F. If you cook a sugar-free pudding that contains aspartame, you are creating free methanol. If methanol were a criminal in a police lineup, it would wear a sign saying, "aka wood alcohol." For those desperate enough to drink it, wood alcohol can lead to blindness and even death. One quart of aspartame-sweetened beverage contains about 56 mg of methanol. The EPA states that methanol is "considered a cumulative poison due to the low rate of excretion once it is absorbed."

Methanol is truly criminal after it enters your body. It breaks down into formic acid and formaldehyde. Formaldehyde is a known carcinogen and can cause birth defects by interfering with DNA replication. Our Desert Storm troops were treated to free diet drinks that sat in the hot sun of Saudi Arabia. Many of the unusual symptoms found in Desert Storm veterans are similar to those of people chemically poisoned by formaldehyde.

The artificial sweetener aspartame would certainly not sell if people knew what kind of a toxic chemical stew they were ingesting.

Natural Low-Glycemic Sweeteners

Blue Agave Nectar (Organic)

The blue agave cactus grows in Central America. It produces a sweetener that is about 68 percent fructose, 22 percent glucose, 4 percent fructoligosaccharides. Because of its heavy fructose concentration, blue agave is 32 percent sweeter than table sugar but has a low glycemic index (about 34). This means that when consumed, blue agave has a minimal impact on blood sugar levels following consumption. It is much better suited for people with candida infections.

Grade B Maple Syrup

The US and Canada have slightly different grading systems for maple syrup. What is classified as Grade B maple syrup in the US is the same as grade C maple syrup in Canada. This grade is the best sweetener and the most balanced sugar. It is processed from the last tapping of the maple sap, so it is richer in invert sugars and minerals.

Grade B Maple Syrup is also a lower glycemic index food, resulting in a slow, gradual rise in blood sugar levels. The best maple syrup is currently produced in Vermont because it is strictly regulated for purity and authenticity by government law. Some unscrupulous marketers in other areas have been known to add refined sugars to colored diluted genuine maple syrup to produce a cheaper product. Also, a number of years ago, there was a problem with some Canadian and US producers inserting formaldehyde pellets in their sugar maples trees to keep tap holes open longer, increasing yields.

Fructose

Fructose is a natural sweetener that has one of the lowest glycemic indexes of any food. A glycemic index measures the impact that a food has on blood sugar levels two to three hours after ingestion. The lower the glycemic level, the lower the rise in blood sugar levels.

With a glycemic index of only 20, fructose has one of the lowest of any food and many times lower than standard breads and processed grains. Fructose has a glycemic index that is only a third of that of glucose, a fourth of the glycemic index of white bread, and a fifth of the glycemic index for boiled potatoes.

Stevia

Known as *Stevia rebaudiana* by botanists and yerba dulce (honey leaf) by the Guarani Indians, stevia has been incorporated into many native medicines, beverages, and foods for centuries. The Guarani used stevia separately or combined with herbs like yerba mate and lapacho.

Fifteen times sweeter than sugar, stevia was introduced to the West in 1899, when M. S. Bertoni discovered natives using it as a sweetener and medicinal herb. With Japan's ban on the import of synthetic sweeteners in the 1960's, stevia began to be seriously researched by the Japanese National Institute of Health as a natural sugar substitute. In 1994, the U.S. Food and Drug Administration permitted the importation and use of stevia as a dietary supplement. However, its adoption by American consumers as a noncaloric sweetener has been very slow because the FDA does not currently permit stevia to be marketed as a food additive. This means that stevia cannot be sold as a sweetener (all sweeteners are classified as food additives by the FDA). Moreover, stevia faces fierce opposition by both the artificial sweetener (aspartame) and sugar industries in the U.S.

Stevia, however, is more than just a non-caloric sweetener. Several modern clinical studies have documented the ability of stevia to lower and balance blood sugar levels, support the pancreas and digestive system, protect the liver, and combat infectious microorganisms. (Oviedo et al., 1971; Suzuki et al., 1977; Ishit et al., 1986; Boeckh, 1986; Alvarez, 1986.) (See Appendix M)

Water

There is nothing more refreshing when you are hot and thirsty than clear, cold spring water. Water is not only refreshing but absolutely essential to life. The only nutrient more important to the body than water is oxygen.

Water is the crucial ingredient in our body's self-cleansing system. We are very aware of the body's normal elimination processes, but may not realize that unwanted substances are also eliminated through exhaled breath and perspiration, both of which also require water. Certainly our kidneys will not be able to cleanse efficiently if there is not enough water in our system to carry away waste.

Finding pure drinking water is becoming a challenge. Our increasingly polluted world has made it necessary for the Environmental Protection Agency to set water standards. The EPA screens for the presence of suspended solids, oil and grease, fecal coliform bacteria, chemicals and heavy metals. Unfortunately, the major source of pollution (65 percent in 1990) comes not from industrial sites, which can be regulated, but from storm-water run-off. Rainfall coming in contact with pollutants from agricultural and industrial operations absorbs these chemicals and transports them into lakes and rivers. Only 9 percent of water pollution came from actual industrial sites in 1990.

Municipal water should be avoided if possible. Most municipal waters have a high concentration of aluminum due to the use of aluminum hydroxide for water treatment. Moreover, the addition of chlorine results in the creation of cancer-causing chemicals when dissolved organic solids are chemically altered by chlorination. While there is a trend toward replacing chlorination with peroxide treatment of water, it will be decades before peroxide is adopted as a standard.

We may turn to expensive bottled waters, but regulation in this industry is vague. Regardless of cost, the bottled water you buy may simply be tap water put through a filtration process. You may wish to invest in a water purifier for your home or drink distilled water to be sure you are getting pure water.

Distilled water washes out the system. With the help of essential oils and distilled water, the body can excrete petroleum residues, metals, inorganic minerals, and other toxins.

Essential oils, like lemon, also make outstanding water purifiers. One drop per glass is generally enough. Put the oil in a glass or container first, then run the water in. Since oils do not mix with water, this will distribute them through the water. Or, put several drops in the out end of the carbon filter of a water purification system. This can drop nitrate levels by up to 3,000 ppm.

Since chlorine damages thyroid function, drink water that has the chlorine removed. You can either distill the water or let it stand unsealed (which allows the chlorine to evaporate over time). You can also add a drop of lemon or other oil. To obtain chlorine-free water for showering and bathing, get a shower head filter or aromatherapy shower head like the RainSpa. Avoid public swimming pools. While carbon filters are good for removing chlorine from water, the best water distillers have pre-flash or pre-boiling chambers, to flash off volatile gases, such as chlorine and petroleum products. The steam should rise at least 15 inches to balance the pH and fall 15 inches to oxygenate again.

One very popular water purification system is the ion exchange used in areas of the country with "hard" water or water with dissolved minerals. Water is passed through a filter exchanging charged particles (ions) in the water for charged particles in the filter. Most units use salt, with sodium and chloride ions exchanging for the contaminated ions in the water. Since the minerals are replaced with salt, at least one cold water tap needs to be left out of the system so that drinking water is not loaded with sodium.

The ideal amount of water to consume is half your body weight in ounces per day. That means if you weigh 160 pounds, you should drink 80 ounces of water (or about ten, 8 ounce glasses per day. Avoid drinking any chlorinated water.

Microwave Ovens

Microwave ovens can be found in almost every home and restaurant because they are extremely convenient for thawing and heating food. Yet we are paying a great price for this convenience. In a study by Dr. Radwan Farag of Cairo University, it was discovered that just two seconds of microwave energy destroys all the enzymes in a food, thus increasing our enzyme deficiency and altering the frequency of the food. Heating proteins in the microwave for 10 minutes or more may create a new, harmful type of protein. You may decide that this is a high price to pay for convenience.

Also, microwave radiation has been known to leak and could disrupt the delicate balances in cellular growth. Our bodies are regulated by electrical frequencies and electromagnetic fields. It would be wise to avoid disrupting these frequencies.

And there is this to think about: the University of Minnesota warned that microwaving a baby's bottle can cause slight changes in the milk. In the case of a hip-surgery patient in Oklahoma, microwaving blood for a transfusion killed the patient. Warming blood for a transfusion is routine; unfortunately, using a microwave caused enough changes in the blood to be deadly.

For those who cannot give up convenience, please remember that plastic molecules could end up in your food if you microwave in plastic dishes or use plastic wrap to cover open dishes.

A research project with 20 volunteers was conducted in 1980 with microwave cooking. Ten volunteers in group A and 10 in group B fasted on liquids for 10 days. Then both groups were fed the same foods for another 10 days with only one exception: Group A foods were steamed, while group B foods were microwaved. After 10 days, stool samples were taken and analyzed. Group A stools appeared to be normally digested, while group B stools were of a plastic texture. Ultrasound scans showed adhesive food particles stuck to the stomach wall. In the stool sample, altered enzymes were found, as well as protein with altered molecular structure which could not be absorbed.

CHAPTER 28

Longevity/Anti-aging Therapies

Essential oils and aromatics were some of the most highly prized natural medicines of the ancient world. References to cassia, clove, frankincense, myrrh, spikenard, cinnamon, and rosemary appear in many historical writings, including the Old and New Testaments as well as the writings of Hippocrates, Avicenna, and ancient Egyptian hieroglyphics.

Intriguing new research offers a tantalizing glimpse into the far-reaching potential of essential oils like thyme (Thymus vulgaris) to reverse or slow the aging process by acting as powerful antioxidants that protect tissues and organs from oxidative stress and damage. Other oils, such as clove (Syzygium aromaticum) and lemon (Citrus limon) have not only been shown to act as powerful antioxidants, but also to protect cellular DNA from damage and to act as potent antiseptics with broad-spectrum germ-killing properties.

What Causes Aging?

There is still some controversy concerning the cause of aging and premature death. Some researchers believe that declining levels of hormones from the pituitary and hypothalamus are the culprits. Others point an accusing finger at the crosslinking of collagen, a key protein of the soft tissues that constitutes a third of all protein in the body. Still others blame the buildup of lipofuscin, a brownish pigment that accumulates inside the cells, particularly nerve and heart muscle cells.[1]

However, the oxidative stress/free radical theory of aging is the most persuasive and substantiated. This rationale posits that aging is caused by cumulative oxidative stress to the cell walls, receptors, and DNA. Rogue electrons that are generated from normal metabolic and immune functions attack proteins and disrupt DNA, eventually overwhelming the natural repair abilities of the body and sometimes leading to disease and death.[2,3,4]

While many researchers have focused on damage to the DNA (the blueprint for cellular operations) as the cause of aging, few have appreciated how devastating free radical damage can be to fats—especially the unstable polyunsaturated fatty acids (PUFAs) that form the phospholipid membranes of almost every cell in the body. When these fatty membranes are attacked by free radicals, ion transport and hormone receptors are disrupted.[5] As cell membranes become less fluid, they lose their ability to function normally. This can hasten the onset of tissue and organ damage and lead to premature death.

One of the most easy-to-understand examples of the detrimental effects of cell membrane brittleness occurs in the blood vessel walls. As the blood vessels lose their flexibility, the risk of hypertension (high blood pressure) increases, as does the incidence of arteriosclerosis.

Why does free radical damage escalate with age? Because antioxidant protection declines as we grow older. Free radical scavengers such as superoxide dismutase (SOD) and glutathione peroxidase chart a steady decline along with other antioxidants. This means that the older body is less efficient in neutralizing free radicals and combating the oxidative damage that gradually weakens and eventually destroys key organs.

1. Hayflick, L. How and Why We Age. Ballantine Books, New York, 1994.

2. Harmon, D, Ageing: a theory based on free radical and radiation chemistry. J. Gerontology 11, (1956): 298-300.

3. Harmon, D, Free radical theory of ageing: Effect of free radical inhibitors on the mortality rate of male LAFmice. J. Gerontology 23 (1968): 476-482.

4. Harmon, D, Free radical theory of ageing: Effect of the amount and degree of unsaturation of dietary fat on mortality rate. J. Gerontology 26 (1971): 451-457.

5. Stubbs CD & Smith AD, The modification of mammalian membrane polyunsaturated fatty acid composition in relation to membrane fluidity and function. Biochimica et Biophysica Acta 779, (1984)89-137.

Essential Oils vs. Fatty Oils

Fatty oils are very different from essential oils. Fatty oils, such as cottonseed, almond, olive, corn, sunflower, and canola oil, are usually pressed from a seed or fruit. They are greasy in texture and have little odor, being simple mixtures of several different fatty acids (ie., capric, stearic, and oleic).

In contrast, essential oils are usually steam distilled from leaves, flowers, roots, and bark. They have strong odors and are not greasy. Because many are lighter than water, they float and tend to evaporate very easily. Essential oils are complex mosaics of hundreds of aromatic molecules (ie., terpenes, sesquiterpenes, and phenols) that usually have a ring-like structure.

THYMOL
(from thyme ess. oil)

CAPRIC FATTY ACID
(from coconut oil)

Methyl end   Acid end

H-C-C-C-C-C-C-C-C-C-C

Levels of polyunsaturated fats such as DHA (decosahexaenoic acid) are also crucial for healthy brain and eye function. DHA occurs in unusually high concentrations in the cerebral cortex—the most advanced part of the brain structure where logic and reasoning take place. When DHA becomes oxidized and loses its double bonds because of free radical attacks, brain and cognitive function can deteriorate. This can lead to memory loss, dementia, and even death. By protecting fats like DHA from free radical attack, hydrolysis, or oxidation, brain health can be significantly improved.[6,7,8,9]

The crux of the problem is that DHA and other long chain PUFAs are very unstable and are vulnerable to chemical alteration and oxidation. This means that the antioxidant systems of the body must work overtime to protect them in order to sustain health. An even greater problem is that the liver slows down PUFA production with age, so it becomes less and less able to replace through desaturase activities the dwindling supply of PUFA needed to sustain the brain, tissues, and other organs.[10]

Thus the longevity of the organism is strongly linked to preserving the integrity of the polyunsaturated fats that comprise cells, nerves, and other tissues. Preventing the degradation of these fats from free radical damage can forestall the signs of accelerated aging.

Preserving the Integrity of Fats *In Vitro*

In the late 1980s, Dr. Radwan Farag of the biochemistry department of the University of Cairo was among the first to show in vitro how selected essential oils were able to significantly slow the rancidity (oxidation) of fatty oils such as cottonseed oil. He dosed samples of cottonseed oil with 200 ppm of thyme oil (55.7% thymol and 36% p-cymene) and 400 ppm of clove oil (85.3% eugenol). After comparing the essential oil-treated samples with untreated control samples, he found that both thyme and clove oil afforded significant protection against rancidity to the cottonseed oil as determined by lowered peroxide and TBA values. Thyme oil generated a 20% reduction in rancidity while clove oil triggered almost a 30% drop.[11]

A second study by Dr. Farag and his colleagues showed that essential oils such as thyme, clove, rosemary (Rosmarinus officinalis), and sage (Salvia officinalis) arrested the oxidation of linoleic acid, a polyunsaturated omega-6 fatty acid.[12]

In addition, Dr. Farag demonstrated the safety of these essential oils in vivo. When he added thyme and clove oils to rat feed rations at up to six times

6. Barja de Quiroga G, et al., Antioxidant defences and peroxidation in liver and brain of aged rats. *Biochemical Journal* 272 (1990), 247-250.

7. Lamptey MS & Walker BL, A possible dietary role for linolenic acid in the development of the young rat. Journal of Nutrition 106, (1976) 86-93.

8. Okuyama H, Minimum requirements of n-3 and n-6 essential fatty acids for the function of the central nervous system and for the prevention of chronic disease. *Proceedings of the Society for Experimental Biology and Medicine* 200, (1992) 174-176.

9. Yamamoto N, et al, Effects of dietary alpha-linolenate/linolenate balance of brain lipid composition and learning ability of rats. *Journal of Lipid Research* 28, (1987) 144-151.

10. Bourre et al., Function of dietary polyunsaturated fatty acids in the nervous system. *Prostaglandins, Leukotrienes, and Essential Fatty Acids* 48 (1993): 5-15.

11. Farag et al., Antioxidant activity of some spice essential oils on linoleic acid oxidation in aqueous media. *JAOCS* June 1989;66: 792-799.

12. Farag et al., Inhibitory effects of individual and mixed pairs of essential oils on the oxidation and hydrolysis of cottonseed oil and butter. *FASC*, 1989; 40: 275-279.

Farag et al., 1989

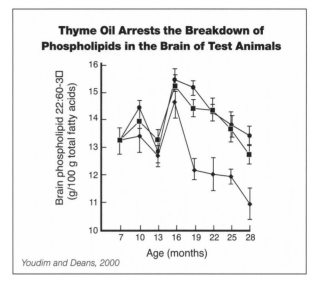

Youdim and Deans, 2000

the minimum concentration needed to stall fat oxidation, none of the rats studied suffered any negative side effects. Essential oil-fed rats exhibited no difference in protein, cholesterol, and liver enzyme levels (SGPT, SGOT) when compared with a control group.[13]

Protecting Fats and Phospholipids in Animals

Almost a decade after Farag's groundbreaking research, another series of more intensive in vivo studies were begun at the Scottish Agricultural College in the United Kingdom and the Semmelweis University of Medicine in Hungary. In these clinical trials, researchers found that daily lifelong feeding of thyme and clove oils to laboratory animals

preserved key antioxidant levels in the liver, kidneys, heart, and brain. Even more importantly, essential oils arrested the oxidation and destruction of long-chain PUFAs throughout the organism.

One of the first studies to document these remarkable antioxidant effects was conducted at the Semmelweis University of Medicine in 1993. Researchers fed different groups of mice with daily doses of 0.72 mg of essential oils including thyme (Thymus vulgaris), clove (Syzygium aromaticum), nutmeg (Myristica fragrans), and pepper (Piper nigrum). Groups of younger mice (6 months old) were treated for five weeks, while groups of 22 month-old mice were treated for 21 weeks. Following treatment, the livers of the animals were examined for levels of C20 and C22 polyunsaturated fatty acids, which declines substantially during the animal's lifetime.

The results were phenomenal. According to the researchers, "dietary administration of the volatile oils to the aging mice had a marked effect on fatty acid distribution by virtually restoring the proportions of the polyunsaturated fatty acids within the phospholipids to the levels observed in young mice."

Another randomized, controlled animal study at Semmelweis University in 1997 showed that these same essential oils—thyme, clove, nutmeg, and pepper—restored DHA in the eyes to much younger levels. As a long-chain polyunsaturated fatty acid (PUFA) that is very fragile and easily oxidized,

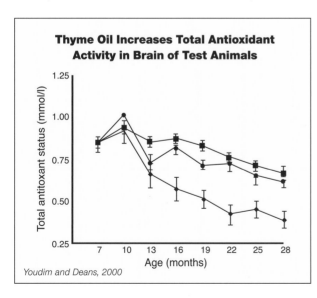

Youdim and Deans, 2000

13. Farag et al., Safety evaluation of thyme and clove essential oils as natural antioxidants. *Afr J Agr Sci.* 1991;18: 169-17.

DHA is absolutely crucial for normal eye health. Declining levels of DHA have been directly linked to heightened risk of age-related macular degeneration, the leading cause of blindness in old age.[14,15]

In this case, dietary supplementation of just 3.9 mg per day of essential oils to laboratory animals over a 17-month period was sufficient to markedly slow DHA loss in their eyes.

Preserving Brain Function

The brain is another organ where DHA is essential to health. Karesh Youdim and his colleagues at the Scottish Agricultural College tested the ability of essential oils to preserve DHA levels in the brain of 100 animal subjects. Feeding them a daily dose (42.5 mg/K of body weight) of thyme oil (48% thymol) over the course of their lifetime (28 months), the researchers achieved stunning results: Thyme oil dramatically slowed age-related DHA and PUFA degradation in the brain. In other words, the essential oil of thyme was able to partially prevent brain aging through protection of essential fatty acids. An analysis of the data showed that the DHA levels in 28 month-old animals' brains was almost the same as that of 7 month-olds. In human terms, this was equivalent to an 80-year-old having the brain chemistry of a 20-year-old![16]

Thyme oil supplements also slowed the decline of total brain antioxidant levels that occurs with age. Lifelong supplementation with thyme oil in laboratory rats resulted in antioxidant levels dropping by only 29%, compared with a 45% fall for untreated animals.

Even more startling is the fact that thyme essential oil also preserved levels of PUFAs in the animals' hearts, livers, and kidneys, while at the same time raising total antioxidant levels—including key antioxidants such as glutathione peroxidase and superoxide dismutase. This was accomplished by feeding laboratory rats daily thyme oil supplements (42.5 mg/K of body weight) throughout their lives.[17]

Clove Oil Affords Protection Against Cancer

Clove oil also has potent antioxidant-boosting properties. Animal studies conducted at LKT Laboratories in Minneapolis, Minnesota, found that five compounds within clove oil significantly increased levels of GST (glutathione S-transferase), one of the most important detoxifying enzymes in the human body that is critical for neutalizing potential cancer-causing chemicals. Just 60 mg of each of the five compounds (b-caryophyllene, b-

14. Rotstein et al., Effects of aging on the composition and metabolism of docosahexaenoate-containing lipids of retina. Lipids, 1987 Apr;22(4):253-60.

15. Neuringer M & Connor WE, N-3 fatty acids in the brain and retina: evidence for their essentiality. *Nutrition Reviews* 44, 285-294.

16. Youdim KA, et al., Effect of thyme oil and thymol dietary supplementation on the antioxidant status and fatty acid composition of the ageing rat brain. *Br J Nutr.* 2000 Jan;83(1):87-93.

17. Youdim KA, Deans SG., Dietary supplementation of thyme (Thymus vulgaris L.) essential oil during the lifetime of the rat: its effects on the antioxidant status in liver, kidney and heart tissues. *Mech Ageing Dev.* 1999 Sep 8;109(3):163-75.

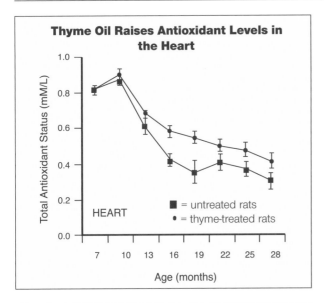

Thyme Oil Raises Antioxidant Levels in the Heart

(Graph: Total Antioxidant Status (mM/L) vs Age (months))
■ = untreated rats
● = thyme-treated rats
HEART

How 5 Constituents in Clove Oil Raise Glutathione Levels

Compound	Liver Levels of GST	Small Bowel Levels of GST
Control	0.74	0.25
Compound 1	1.92	0.75
Compound 2	2.13	1.20
Compound 3	1.47	0.63
Compound 4	1.54	0.81
Compound 5	1.26	0.59

Zheng et al., 1992.

caryophyllene oxide, a-humulene, a-humulene epoxide I, and eugenol) fed to rats over the course of six days (3 doses of 20 mg each) resulted in a doubling of GST activity in the liver and a quadrupling of GST level in the small bowel mucosa. The authors concluded that "these sesquiterpenes show promise as potential anticarcinogenic agents."[18]

Many other researchers have shown that clove essential oil exhibits pronounced antitumoral and DNA-protectant effects.[19,20]

Essential oils may do more than just raise antioxidant levels and block damage to PUFAs. They may also protect cellular DNA from damage that can eventually lead to mutations and subsequent tumor growth. In a 1986 study, Yokota et al., found that a diet including 5% eugenol (the chief constituent in clove oil) helped protect test animals against the mutagenic and cancer-causing affects of the chemical benzo-a-pyrene.[21]

Potent Weapons Against Microbes

Another method by which aromatics and essential oils may exert a life-lengthening effect is through their ability to inhibit the growth of bacteria, fungi, and viruses. Some bacteria, such as Chlamydia pneumoniae have been implicated as one of the true causes of heart disease. Viruses, such as HIV and hepatitis, have resulted in liver failure and premature death. Fungi like Candida albicans have been implicated in cancer due to their secretion of mycotoxins.

One of the most comprehensive studies to probe the powerful antimicrobial effects of essential oils was conducted with D. Gary Young and Sue Chao at Weber State University. Using disc diffusion assays, they tested the killing power of 67 different essential oils against a variety of yeast, molds, gram negative bacteria, and gram positive bacteria. Cinnamon, clove, thyme, peppermint, oregano, and mountain savory exerted the strongest antimicrobial properties.[22]

The following year they tested the ability of thyme, oregano, and clove essential oils to destroy colonies of Streptococcus pneumoniae, the bacteria responsible for many types of throat, sinus, and lung infections.[23]

Essential Oils: Treatments for Arthritis, Heart Disease, and More

A growing body of clinical research during the last several decades indicates that essential oils have enormous potential to treat conditions ranging from acne to obesity.

18. Zheng GQ, et al. Sesquiterpenes from clove (Eugenia caryophyllata) as potential anticarcinogenic agents. *J Nat Prod.* 1992 Jul;55(7):999-1003.

19. Rompelberg et al. Antimutagenicity of eugenol in the rodent bone marrow micronucleus test. *Mutat Res.* 1995 Feb;346(2):69-75.

20. Sukumaran et al. Inhibition of tumour promotion in mice by eugenol. *Indian J Physiol Pharmacol.* 1994 Oct;38(4):306-8.

21. Yokota H, et al., Suppressed mutagenicity of benzo[a]pyrene by the liver S9 fraction and microsomes from eugenol-treated rats. *Mutat Res.* 1986 Dec;172(3):231-6.

22. Chao, et al., Screening for Inhibitory Activity of Essential Oils on Selected Bacteria, Fungi, and Viruses. *Journal of Essential Oil Research*, 1997.

23. Chao et al., Antimicrobial Effects of Essential Oils on Streptococcus pneumoniae. *JEOR,* 2001.

Peppermint (Mentha piperita) has been reviewed for its ability to block pain, relieve headaches [24], combat indigestion [25], boost mental alertness [26,27], induce weight loss [28], kill lice [29], and inhibit tumor growth.[30]

Melaleuca (Melaleuca alternifolia) has been used to treat acne [31], kill fungi [32], and inhibit bacteria growth.[33,34]

Lavender (Lavandula angustifolia) fights travel sickness [35], reduces atherosclerosis [36], protects blood vessels [37], acts as a local anaesthetic [38], and has anticonvulsant properties.[39]

Clove (Syzygium aromaticum) has been researched for its action against tooth decay [40] as well as its antifungal [41] and anticonvulsant activities.[42]

Rosemary (Rosmarinus officinalis) has been shown to enhance alertness [43], combat fungi such as Candida albicans, and act as an antioxidant.[44]

Orange (Citrus aurantium) halts fungus infection [45,46] and inhibits tumor formation.[47] Limonene, an important component of orange and lemon oil has demonstrated similar tumor-suppressing effects in studies at Indiana University.[48]

Basil (Ocimum basilicum) has been shown to have anticancer properties.[49]

Eucalyptus (Eucalyptus radiata) has been studied for reducing inflammation [50], improving cerebral blood flow [51], inhibiting Candida growth [52], and treating bronchitis.[53]

Many other documented benefits of aromatics have been recorded in recent medical literature.[54-66]

Longevity Nutrition

During the last five years, D. Gary Young has traveled throughout the world investigating the regions inhabited by most long-lived peoples on earth: the Ningxia province in China, Hunzaland in Pakistan, southern Ecuador, the Talish Mountain region of Azerbaijan, and the Copper Canyon of central Mexico. After intensively examining the dietary habits of these cultures, he found one common denominator: an active lifestyle and a mineral-rich diet exceptionally high in antioxidant foods, such as wolfberries and apricots.

In particular, he found that Chinese wolfberries (Ningxia variety) and potassium-rich apricots were two foods consumed by people routinely reaching 110 and 120 years of age.

D. Gary Young's book, *Longevity Secrets,* discusses the scientific reasons why these foods may confer important anti-aging properties. This is certainly due to their extremely high content of

24. Gobel et al. Effect of peppermint and eucalyptus oil preparations on neurophysiological and experimental algesimetric headache parameters. *Cephalalgia.* 1994 Jun;14(3):228-34; 182.

25. Dalvi et al. Effect of peppermint oil on gastric emptying in man: a preliminary study using a radiolabelled solid test meal. *Indian J Physiol Pharmacol.* 1991 Jul;35(3):212-4.

26. Dember WN, et al., Olfactory Stimulation and Sustained Attention, *Compendium of Olfactory,* (Avery N. Gilbert, Editor) pp. 39-46.

27. Miltner et al. Emotional qualities of odors and their influence on the startle reflex in humans. *Psychophysiology.* 1994 Jan;31(1):107-10.

28. Hirsch, Alan. A Scentsational Guide to Weight Loss. Rockport, MA: Element, 1997.

29. Veal L. The potential effectiveness of essential oils as a treatment for headlice, Pediculus humanus capitis. *Complement Ther Nurs Midwifery.* 1996 Aug;2(4):97-101.

30. Russin, et al. Inhibition of rat mammary carcinogenesis by monoterpenoids. *Carcinogenesis.* 1989 Nov;10(11):2161-4.

31. Bassett et al. A comparative study of tea-tree oil versus benzoylperoxide in the treatment of acne. *Med J Aust.* 1990 Oct 15;153(8):455-8.

32. Nenoff et al. Antifungal activity of the essential oil of Melaleuca alternifolia (tea tree oil) against pathogenic fungi in vitro. *Skin Pharmacol.* 1996;9(6):388-94.

33. Cox et al. The mode of antimicrobial action of the essential oil of Melaleuca alternifolia (tea tree oil). J Appl Microbiol. 2000 Jan;88(1):170-5.

34. Carson et al. Antimicrobial activity of the major components of the essential oil of Melaleuca alternifolia. *J Appl Bacteriol.* 1995 Mar;78(3):264-9.

35. Bradshaw et al. Effects of lavender straw on stress and travel sickness in pigs. *J Altern Complement Med.* 1998 Fall;4(3):271-5.

36. Nikolaevskii et al. Effect of essential oils on the course of experimental atherosclerosis. *Patol Fiziol Eksp Ter.* 1990 Sep-Oct;(5):52-3.

37. Siurein S A. Effects of essential oil on lipid peroxidation and lipid metabolism in patients with chronic bronchitis]. *Klin Med* (Mosk). 1997;75(10):43-5.

38. Ghelardini et al. Local anaesthetic activity of the essential oil of Lavandula angustifolia. *Planta Med.* 1999 Dec;65(8):700-3

39. Elisabetsky et al. Anticonvulsant properties of linalool in glutamate-related seizure models. *Phytomedicine.* 1999 May;6(2):107-13.

40. Cai and Wu .Compounds from Syzygium aromaticum possessing growth inhibitory activity against oral pathogens. *J Nat Prod.* 1996 Oct;59(10):987-90.

41. Covello et. al. Determination of eugenol in the essence of "Eugenia caryophyllata". Titration in non-aqueous solvent and comparison with other methods of analysis. *Boll Chim Farm.* 1966 Nov;105(11):799-806.

42. Pourgholami M.H. et.al. Evaluation of the anticonvulsant activity of the essential oil of Eugenia caryophyllata in male mice. *J Ethnopharmacol.* 1999 Feb;64(2):167-71.

43. Diego Migul A. et al. Aromatherapy positively affects mood, EEG patterns of alertness and math computations. *Int J Neurosci.* 1998 Dec;96(3-4):217-24.

44. Lopez-Bote et. al. Effect of dietary administration of oil extracts from rosemary and sage on lipid oxidation in broiler meat. *Br Poult Sci.* 1998 May;39(2):235-40.

45. Ramadan W. et. al. Oil of bitter orange: new topical antifungal agent. *Int J Dermatol.* 1996 Jun;35(6):448-9.

46. Alderman G, and Elmer H., Inhibition of Growth and Aflatoxin Production of Aspergillus Parasiticus by Citrus Oils. Z. Leb. Unt-Forsch 1976: 353-58.

47. Wattenberg L.W. et. al. Inhibitory effects of 5-(2-pyrazinyl)-4-methyl-1,2-dithiol-3-thione (Oltipraz) on carcinogenesis induced by benzo[a]pyrene, diethylnitrosamine and uracil mustard. *Carcinogenesis.* 1986 Aug;7(8):1379-81.

48. Crowell P. L. Prevention and therapy of cancer by dietary monoterpenes. *J Nutr.* 1999 Mar;129(3):775S-778S.

49. Aruna, K. and V.M. Sivaramakrishnan. "Anticarcinogenic Effects of the Essential Oils from Cumin, Poppy and Basil." Food Chem Toxicol. 1992;30(11):953-56.

50. Juergens et. al. The anti-inflammatory activity of L-menthol compared to mint oil in human monocytes in vitro: a novel perspective for its therapeutic use in inflammatory diseases. *Eur J Med Res.* 1998 Dec 16;3(12):539-45.

51. Nasel et.al. Functional imaging of effects of fragrances on the human brain after prolonged inhalation. *Chem Senses.* 1994 Aug;19(4):359-64.

52. Steinmetz et. al.,Transmission and scanning electronmicroscopy study of the action of sage and rosemary essential oils and eucalyptol on Candida albicans. *Mycoses.* 1988 Jan;31(1):40-51.

53. Ulmer et. al., [Chronic obstructive bronchitis. Effect of Gelomyrtol forte in a placebo-controlled double-blind study]. Fortschr Med. 1991 Sep 20;109(27):547-50.

54. Cao G, et al, Antioxidant capacity in different tissues of young and old rats. *Proceedings of the society for Experimental Biology and Medicine* 211(1996), 359-365.

55. Chao et al., Antimicrobial Effects of Essential Oils on Streptococcus pneumoniae. *JEOR*, 2001.

56. Deans SG, et al, Natural antioxidants from aromatic and medicinal plants. *Role of Free Radicals in Biological Systems*, pp. 159-165 (1993a) [J Feher, A Blazovics, B Matkovics and M Mezes, editors]. Budapest: Akademiai Kiado.

57. Farag et. al. Acute hepatic damage in rats impairs metharbital metabolism. *Pharmacology.* 1987;34(4):181-91.

58. Halliwell B & Gutteridge JMC, *Free Radicals in Biology and Medicine*, 2nd Edition. (1989), Oxford: Clarendon Press.

59. Inhibition of growth and aflatoxin production of Aspergillus parasiticus by citrus oils. *Z Lebensm Unters Forsch.* 1976 Apr 28;160(4):353-8.

60. Kaplan RJ & Greenwood CE, Dietary saturated fatty acids and brain function. *Neurochemistry Research* 23, (1989)615-626.

61. Ramadan W. et. al. Oil of bitter orange: new topical antifungal agent. *Int J Dermatol.* 1996 Jun;35(6):448-9.

62. Recsan Z, et al, Effect of essential oils on the lipids of the retina in the aging rat: a possible therapeutic use. *J Ess Oil Res* 9, (1997) 53-56.

63. Scott BL & Bazan NG, Membrane docosahexaenoate is supplied to the developing brain and retina by the liver. *Proceedings of the National Academy of Sciences USA* 86, (1989) 2903-2907.

64. Socci DJ, et al, Chronic antioxidant treatment improves the cognitive performance in aged rats. *Brain Research* 693, (1995) 88-94.

65. Wahnon R, et al, Age and membrane fluidity. *Mechanisms of Ageing and Development* 50, (1989) 249-255.

66. Youdim KA, et al., Effect of thyme oil and thymol dietary supplementation on the antioxidant status and fatty acid composition of the ageing rat brain. *Br J Nutr.* 2000 Jan;83(1):87-93.

essential minerals such as magnesium and potassium, as well as a their rich supply of potent natural antioxidants.

Research also indicates that foods high in antioxidants, such as wolfberries, blueberries, strawberries, raspberries, and spinach can dramatically increase glutathione levels and actually reverse the signs of aging.

A new test developed by USDA researchers at Tufts University in Boston, Massachusetts, has been able to identify the highest known antioxidant foods. Known as ORAC (oxygen radical absorbance capacity), this test is the first of its kind to measure both time and degree of free radical inhibition.

The Ningxia wolfberry was documented to have the highest ORAC score of any food tested. A special variety grown on the Yellow River in the Ningxia Province of central China, the Ningxia cultivar is very different from any other type of wolfberry. Among the 17 types of wolfberry identified, the Ningxia wolfberry has by far the highest levels of immune-stimulating polysaccharides. It also possesses over 33 times the antioxidant power of oranges and an incredible 120 times the antioxidant potential of carrots. In addition, the Chinese wolfberry is one of the most nutrient-dense foods known, rich in many vitamins and minerals including calcium, magnesium, B vitamins, and vitamin C.

A diet high in antioxidants can combat the free radical damage in the body that is associated with premature aging and degenerative diseases.

The Hunza People— Limited Caloric Intake

The Hunzakuts living in the remote Hunza Valley in northern Pakistan are renowned for their longevity. The Hunzakuts (as they call themselves) routinely live past ages 100, 110 and even 120. They also share another remarkable trait: the near absence of degenerative disease.

It is known that the diet of the Hunza people is high in potassium and low in sodium. Apricots, barley, millet, and buckwheat are the main staples of their diet along with mineral-rich water with a pH of 8.5. But there is yet another unusual factor that may protect the health of the Hunza people and increase their longevity: their limited food intake.

Because the land provides just enough food to cover their basic caloric expenditures, the Hunzakuts rarely indulge in overeating. In fact, prior to the construction of the Korakoram Highway, they annually endured near-fasting conditions for several weeks each spring, a time when the previous year's food was depleted and the current year's harvests had not yet begun.

Restricted caloric intake such as fasting can have powerful effects on longevity because it increases blood levels of growth hormone which is one of the most significant anti-aging hormones to be identified during the last two decades. Secreted by the pituitary gland, growth hormone production steadily declines with age. By age 70, the human body produces less than one-tenth of the growth hormone it did at age 20.

Clinical studies have repeatedly shown that growth hormone production is stimulated by low glucose levels. Because fasting depresses glucose levels, it leads to a surge in natural growth hormone production (Khansari et al., 1991).

Other studies have shown that the practice of caloric restriction (providing all necessary nutrients but limiting calorie intake) results in increased longevity and postponement of disease. Clive McCay at Cornell University showed that rats fed a diet low in calories but high in vitamins, minerals, and nutrients lived up to twice as long as rats fed on a regular diet (McCay et al., 1939). Ray Walford of the University of California in Los Angeles found that in studies on mice, the greater the reduction in calories, the longer the animal lived—as long as the vitamin and mineral content remained constant and the calories consumed did not drop below 40 percent of the normal (Walford et al., 1987).

CHAPTER 29
Enzyme Therapy

Importance of Enzymes

Digestive enzymes are absolutely vital to human health. They break down and digest food in order to liberate the essential nutrients, vitamins, and minerals that sustain life. Some digestive enzymes are present in the food we eat; some are produced by the body itself.

A lack of digestive enzymes in the diet forces the body to overproduce its own digestive enzymes and limits its ability to produce metabolic enzymes which are also crucial for health and normal metabolism. This limitation occurs because both digestive enzymes and metabolic enzymes are created from the same enzyme precursors. The production of these precursors is limited in the human body, so when the digestive system must overproduce digestive enzymes (due to an enzymeless diet), it causes a harmful underproduction of metabolic enzymes.

How important are metabolic enzymes? Metabolic enzymes are involved in every process of the human body. The immune system, circulatory system, liver, kidneys, spleen, pancreas, and even our ability to see, breathe, and think, depend upon metabolic enzymes.

When the diet is supplemented with digestive enzymes that are naturally present in whole, raw, or uncooked foods, two powerful benefits are unleashed:

1. The body can extract maximum nutritional value from food.

2. The body can reduce its internal production of digestive enzymes, which allows for higher production of metabolic enzymes, crucial for daily metabolism, health, and detoxification.

Categories of Enzymes:

Metabolic enzymes

These enzymes work in the blood, tissues, and organs. Our organs are run by metabolic enzymes. These enzymes convert food substances into healthy cells. One researcher found over 98 enzymes carrying out metabolic functions in the arteries alone.

Digestive enzymes produced by the body

These include trypsin, chymotrypsin, and pepsin, which contain a broad spectrum of protein, starch, and fat-digesting enzymes. Some typical animal-derived enzymes include pancrelipase (from pigs) and pancreatin (from cows).

Protein digesting enzymes: protease 4.5 (this number refers to the pH environment that the enzyme works best in), protease 6.0, protease 3.0, and peptidase

Fat-digesting enzymes: lipase

Starch-, sugar-, and carbohydrate-digesting enzymes: alpha-galactosidase, sucrase, maltase, invertase, lactase, cellulase, amylase, glucomylase, hemicellulase, phytasemalt, and diastase

Digestive enzymes found in food

These are present naturally in raw food and jump start the digestive process. They are broadly classified into proteases (protein-digesters), lipases (fat-digesters), and amylases (starch digesters). There are also many different subcategories of enzymes.

Broad-spectrum plant enzymes: papain and bromelain

Amylase is the only digestive enzyme that does not exist in a newborn infant. It can only be obtained through mother's milk. Children who use formulas and cow's milk do not receive this enzyme. This may be the reason some children are born with allergies or develop allergies as they begin growing.

In the food chain, nature has strategically placed enzymes in many raw or whole foods to assist our own body's enzymes in the digestive process.

Ancient cultures prized the natural enzymes in foods—especially meats. They worked hard to conserve the natural enzymes present in their food-stuffs because they knew how valuable they were for strength and health. This is why many ancient cultures "aged" or cured meats. This allowed the natural enzymes present in the flesh to predigest it, thereby easing the burden on their own digestive system and conserving their own limited pool of enzymes.

When meat is predigested, it places less stress on the body's own enzyme bank. Predigestion also enhances the breakdown of peptide chains and proteins into free form amino acids, the building blocks of every major body function, from immunity to growth.

Every protein that enters the human body via digestion has to be broken down into amino acids before it can be fully utilized. Meats that are not completely digested contain large protein fragments that cannot benefit the body. In fact, these protein fragments can cause allergic reactions if the body's antibodies mistake them for foreign microorganisms. Even worse, these protein fragments can become trapped in the intestines where they will ferment and promote parasite infestation.

Cathepsin is a natural enzyme present in all animal flesh. The aging or "curing" process allows cathepsin, an enzyme that is within the flesh, to slowly digest the meat. This is not unlike the process that ripens bananas. A green banana starts out high in starch. As it ages or ripens, the natural amylase in the banana converts the starches into sugar. In effect, the amylase is digesting the banana, eventually turning it brown.

As soon as an animal is dead, cathepsin begins to predigest the meat. It begins splitting large peptide (protein) chains into smaller, more digestible ones. When this meat is eaten after it has been hung for two to three weeks, the digestive system now has a far easier job completing its breakdown and liberating the vital free-form amino acids, the building blocks of all bodily processes.

The remarkable physical strength and endurance exhibited by the pioneers and Native Americans may have been due to their consumption of enzyme-rich raw and unprocessed foods, despite the sometimes meager rations of less than four ounces of food a day. We have been taught that you must eat to have strength. But there is more to it than that.

You must be able to digest and assimilate the nutrients that you take in, in order to sustain health and strength.

On the average, only 8 percent of the food we consume is metabolized to sustain normal bodily function. The remainder passes through us undigested. Even worse, only 1 to 2 percent of the nutrient value of the food that we consume reaches our cells.

Many people today suffer wheat and grain allergies. This may be due to the fact that grains are not grown and prepared as they used to be.

Egyptian hieroglyphics depict the ancient process of grain harvesting. The grain was cut with a scythe, tied into sheaves and left to stand in the field for several days. It was then loaded into ox carts, hauled to the threshing site and thrown into a big stone grinder operated by an ox team. The stone rolled around on the grain, cracking the hulls. With the sifting of the wind, the chaff was blown off, and the grain picked up by slaves and carried in baskets to the storehouse.

Stone-ground, whole-wheat bread which is rich in enzymes, vitamin E, and other nutrients, sadly, is a thing of the past. Today, modern technology brings grain to us via a machine called a combine. The combine cuts the grain, almost instantly separates the kernel from the husk and delivers the grain ready for market on the same day it was cut. It is then further processed to strip out the vitamin E and other oils. Most of it is then bleached leaving only a tiny fraction of the grain's initial enzymes.

To maximize the enzymes in a food, the fruit of the plant needs to mature on the stalk/stem to the point of 'ripening,' or readiness to sprout. This is when the enzyme content of the food is the highest. Unfortunately, many fruits, vegetables and grains are harvested when they are immature and assumed to ripen "in transit." This results in a food that has a far lower enzyme content.

In order for grains to fully digest in the human body, they must contain a full complement of their natural enzymes. Every food has its own specific enzymes. In order for a grain to have viable enzymes, it must have time to germinate. Once it germinates, its enzymes are released from the bondage of enzyme inhibitors. This is why sprouted grains are so health-giving, because the enzyme inhibitors have been deactivated and can no longer counteract the natural enzymes present in the food.

What are some of the early signs of enzyme deficiency? Digestive complaints, heartburn, gas, bloating, fatigue, headaches, stomach aches, diarrhea, constipation, chronic fatigue, yeast infections, nutritional deficiencies, pain, joint stiffness; colon, liver, pancreas, and intestinal problems, skin eruptions, psoriasis, and eczema.

Many enzymes are not only deficient but also inactive. At the Young Life Research Clinic in Springville, Utah, Gary Young tested over 21 different enzyme products from 21 different manufacturers and did not find a single one that was effective in a clinical environment. The patients were closely monitored, their food intake measured; their blood and digestive systems regularly measured and analyzed. The clinic staff found that patients were simply not obtaining value from their foods because their enzymes were inactive.

How are enzymes destroyed or rendered inactive?

1. Chemical cultivation. When natural food is grown in an artificial, chemical environment created by chemical fertilizers, herbicides and pesticides, enzyme content suffers.

2. Heat. Enzymes begin breaking down at 118° F and are totally destroyed at 129° F.

3. Pasteurization, Sterilization, Freezing, Microwaving. All these modern processes render enzymes inactive.

D. Gary Young has traveled the world studying cultures renowned for their longevity: The Vilcabamba in Ecuador, the Aszerbijani people of the Talish Mountains, the Georgian people in the Caucasus region, the Inner-Mongolian people in the province in Ningxia, and the Hunzakut people in Northern Pakistan. All these people share two common traits: They practice fasting on a regular basis and they live to be over 120 years of age. Fasting allows the body to slow down the secretion of digestive enzymes, thereby permitting an increase in metabolic enzymes that help the body to repair and rejuvenate tissue that has been damaged or destroyed. In effect, the fasting process rebuilds the body.

In addition, fasting spurs an increase in growth hormone release, which is important for preventing premature aging.

The human body has the potential to live for 120 years and beyond. However, devitalized, enzyme-deficient foods deplete our enzyme stores and unduly stress the organs and major physical processes. This can hasten the onset of many degenerative diseases. Hence, one of the most effective ways of preventing disease is to maintain an ample reserve of enzymes in the body.

Medical research shows that food enzyme supplements can fight illness, slow the development of life-threatening diseases, and slow the effects of aging.

Dr. Francis Pottinger conducted an amazing study with over 900 cats. He fed one group of cats raw milk and meat. They lived healthy and disease free. They produced healthy litters generation after generation. He fed another group of cats pasteurized milk and cooked food. After the first generation, this group became lethargic and began to suffer from allergies, infections, and other diseases, including heart, kidney, and lung diseases. Each succeeding generation of cats that ate cooked food suffered more diseases. By the third generation, the cats were unable to reproduce.

Another study showed that after eating cooked food, the human body reacted just as if suffering an acute illness. Within 30 minutes of eating cooked food, white blood cell counts increased dramatically, as though the body were fighting an infectious disease.

In a very interesting experiment, one group of pigs was fed enzyme-rich raw potatoes and another group enzyme-deficient cooked potatoes. The pigs eating cooked potatoes gained weight rapidly. The pigs that were eating raw potatoes did not get fat.

An area of deep concern is obesity. Dr. David Galton at the Tufts University School of Medicine tested people weighing 230-240 pounds. He found that almost all of them were lacking lipase enzymes in their fatty tissues. Lipase, found abundantly in raw foods, is a fat-splitting enzyme that aids the body in digestion. Lipase activity breaks down and dissolves fat throughout the body. Without lipase, fats are kept and stored in tissues. We see this manifest around the waistline, hips, and thighs.

It is astounding to see the obesity levels of America's children. According to 1998 statistics, a minimum of 25 percent of our children are overweight today—an increase of 33 percent since 1978. This obesity may be due to chronic enzyme deficiency.

Tansy

SECTION **8**

How Essential Oils Work

Essential oils can work through inhalation, ingestion, topical application, or rectal/vaginal retention.

Although topical use is perhaps best known, dietary use of essential oils may be one of the most effective ways of unlocking their health benefits. Many essential oils have been used as food flavorings or as a part of patent medicines for centuries, endowing them with a long history of safe use. Recent research suggests that certain high ORAC essential oils act as potent antioxidants that can actually raise antioxidant levels in the body and prevent premature aging.

Many of the oils listed in this section are classified as "GRAS" by the U.S. Food and Drug Administration. This means they are "generally regarded as safe" for human consumption. An appendix of GRAS oils appears in Appendix C.

Topical application is probably the most common means of using essential oils. According to researcher Jean Valnet, MD, an essential oil that is directly applied to the skin can pass into the bloodstream and diffuse throughout the tissues in 20 minutes or less. More recent studies have also documented the ability of essential oils to penetrate the stratum corneum (the upper layer of skin) to reach the subdermal tissues and blood vessels beneath.[1,2]

Some of the compounds in essential oils that work synergistically to enhance permeation include alpha-pinene (frankincense, valerian, basil, cistus), beta-pinene (galbanum, hyssop, fir, rosemary), alpha-terpineol (bay laurel, *Melaleuca ericifolia*, ravensara), 1,8-cineole or eucalyptol (*Eucalyptus globulus*, *E. radiata*, *E. dives*, rosemary) and d-limonene (white fir, tangerine, orange, lemon, grapefruit).

Inhalation is also an effective means of therapeutically using and delivering an essential oil. The fragrance of an essential oil can have a direct influence on both the body and mind due to its ability to stimulate the brain's limbic system (a group of subcortical structures including the hypothalamus, the hippocampus, and the amygdala). This can produce powerful effects that can effect everything from emotional balance and energy levels to appetite control, heart, and immune function. (See Limbic System chart on page 2.)

Some researchers believe that the inhalation of an essential oil can also enhance the body's frequency, which can have a direct impact on disease. Disease and emotional trauma foster a negative frequency that may be disrupted or broken by essential oils. Oils with higher frequencies can elevate the entire frequency of the body whether topically or orally administered, thereby creating an internal environment that opposes the establishment of some disease conditions.

When to Mix Oils and Blends

The essential oils and blends that are listed for a specific condition can be used either separately or together. By combining a single oil with another recommended single oil or blend, a synergistic or additive effect is produced that results in stronger total effect than the sum of the actions produced by each oil or blend separately.

As a rule, when a list of oils or blends is recommended and does not list specific quantities, usually 1-3 drops of each oil should be used. For example, if the list reads, "Lavender, lemongrass, marjoram, ginger," this means that 1 drop of lavender should be mixed with one drop of any 1-3 of the other listed oils for a synergistic blend. It is best to avoid using more than 3 oils in any given blend at a time.

---

1. Taiwan Huang, Fang, Hung, Wu, Tsai "Cyclic monoterpene extract from cardamom oil as a skin permeation enhancer for indomethacin: in vitro and in vivo studies." *Biological and Pharmaceutical Bulletin* 1999 Jun;22(6):642-6.

2. Ogiso, Iwaki, Paku "Effect of various enhancers on transdermal penetration of indomethacin and urea, and relationship between penetration parameters and enhancement factors." *Journal of Pharmaceutical Sciences.* 1995 Apr;84(4):482-8.

How to Choose an Essential Oil

The essential oils listed for a specific condition are not designed to be a comprehensive or complete list; they are merely a starting point. Other oils that are not listed can also be effective.

In addition, essential oils are not listed in any particular order. This is because one oil might be more compatible with one person's unique body chemistry than another's for aromatic purposes and skin sensitivity, not necessarily for physical response. If results are not felt within several minutes, try another oil, blend, or combination, on the next application.

How to Use Essential Oils

Essential oils should be used in moderation as they are highly concentrated. Use with VITA FLEX, massage, or acupuncture-point applications. In most cases, one or two drops is sufficient to produce significant effects. It is strongly recommended that most essential oils be diluted in vegetable oil prior to either topical or internal application (particularly if you have not used essential oils previously). Specific directions for each oil are listed in Appendixes E, R, S and T.

When using essential oils topically, first do a skin test with 1 drop of essential oil on the inside of the upper arm. If any redness or irritation results, cleanse skin thoroughly and reapply. If skin irritation persists, discontinue using that oil or oil blend. Use no more than 10 to 20 drops during one topical application.

Many essential oils can be used as dietary supplements, and a list of these oils appears in

Helpful Conversions

1 drop	=	approximately 60 mg
1 ml	=	1/5 teaspoon
1 ml	=	approximately 16 drops
1 ml	=	fills one 00 capsule
5 ml	=	1 teaspoon
5 ml	=	approximately 80 drops
15 ml	=	1 tablespoon
15 ml	=	1/2 fluid ounce
240 ml	=	1 cup (depends on product)
30 ml	=	1 fluid ounce
28 grams	=	1 ounce

Address the overall health of the body when considering a specific solution. Although essential oils have powerful therapeutic effects, they are not, by themselves, a total solution. They must be accompanied by a program of internal cleansing, proper diet, and supplementation. This may also include lifestyle changes, such as exercise, meditation/yoga, and stress-free situations.

Step 1. Cleanse

Cleansing the colon and liver is the first and most important step to take when dealing with any disease. Many imbalances can be corrected by cleansing alone. Products that cleanse the body include: Cleansing Trio (Essentialzyme, ComforTone, and ICP), Chelex, ParaFree Softgels, JuvaTone, and JuvaFlex (See Cleansing programs in Chapter 25).

Step 2. Balance and Build

Once the body has been cleansed, various systems of the body can be balanced and nourished. This includes rebuilding and nourishing beneficial intestinal flora, and remineralizing the blood and tissues. Products that build the body include: Mineral Essence, True Source Multivitamins, MultiGreens, Power Meal, and Super Cal.

Step 3. Support

Supporting the endocrine and immune system comprises the third phase. Products include: ImmuPro, ImmuneTune, Exodus, Be-Fit, Wolfberry Crisp bars, Super C, and Super B.

NOTE: Infants or children under 8 should not undergo a colon and liver cleanse. Instead, use 3 drops of Di-Gize in a tsp. of V-6 Mixing Oil or Massage Oil Base, rub around the navel, and place warm hot packs over the stomach. Also apply Di-Gize or fennel on bottom of the feet.

Appendix C. All essential oils should be diluted prior to ingestion unless directed otherwise by a physician or one trained in the oral use of essential oils. No more than 2-4 drops should be consumed at one time (in a single serving, usually in a gelcap) unless indicated otherwise. The simplest way to dilute essential oils for ingestion is to mix a drop in a teaspoon of honey (do not give honey to children age 1 or under) or a cup of almond or rice milk. If taste is a problem, oils can be diluted 50:50, placed in a gelatin capsule and swallowed.

When using essential oils always increase fluid intake because the oils can accelerate the detoxification process in the body. If you are not taking in adequate fluids, toxins could recirculate causing nausea, headaches, etc.

Avoid Petrochemicals

Exercise caution when applying essential oils to skin that has been exposed to cosmetics, personal care products, or soaps and cleansers containing synthetic or petroleum-based chemicals. Essential oils may react with such chemicals and cause skin irritation, nausea, or headaches.

Essential oils can also react with toxins built up in the body from chemicals in food, water, and the work environment. If you experience a reaction to essential oils, temporarily discontinue their use and start an internal cleansing program (30 days using ICP, ComforTone, Essentialzyme--See Chapter 25) before resuming regular use of essential oils.

How to Use This Reference Guide

This Guide has two parts, which must be used together in order to correctly and safely develop regimens for essential oil application.

The first part of the guide is a list of 18 standard application methods found on the next two pages. For each of these applications, dilution rates, mixtures and procedures are listed in detail. These applications are grouped by five basic types: TOPICAL, INHALATION, INGESTION, ORAL, and RETENTION. The details of each application method are listed here at the beginning of this chapter to avoid unnecessary repetition throughout the remainder of the chapter. It is recommended that you read through all these application methods to familiarize yourself with them before using the second part of the guide.

Consult Your Health Care Professional

Consult your health care professional about any serious disease or injury. Do not attempt to self-diagnose or prescribe any natural substances such as essential oils for health conditions that require professional attention.

The second part of the guide, comprising most of the chapter, includes application suggestions for over 300 different illnesses and injuries with single essential oils, blends, dietary supplements and topical treatments, which are appropriate for those conditions. Each topic contains some or all of the following headings pointing to the products to use and how to use them:

FIRST RECOMMENDATIONS
Other Singles Oils
Other Blends
EO APPLICATION METHODS
OTHER DIETARY SUPPLEMENTS
Topical Treatments

Within each 'EO Application Methods' heading is a listing of keywords indicating which of the 18 application methods are most appropriate and effective for that condition. It is important to note that abbreviated keywords are listed in the body of this guide. Readers must return to the application methods explanations on the next two pages to get the full detail of how to use the oils in each particular application method. Failure to do so could result in improper application.

As explained in earlier sections of this book, essential oils are very concentrated natural substances—easily 100 times more concentrated than the natural herbs from which they are distilled. So dilution of an essential oil is a very important aspect of using it therapeutically. Some essential oils are so mild that dilution is simply not necessary, even for use on infants. Others are so strong that dilution is mandatory. (See Appendix E for a list of recommended safe dilutions for all the oils mentioned in this book).

A Sample Lookup

Here is an example of how to develop an application program using the two parts of the guide. Let's say that you are experiencing a sore throat and want to know what you can do to treat that condition with the products in this reference book.

Step 1: Locate the disease/injury topic alphabetically in the Personal Usage Guide

In this case, the heading you are looking for is a subhead located under the main heading of THROAT INFECTIONS. It is found on page 481.

Step 2: Note the recommended essential oils and oral treatment in the FIRST RECOMMENDATIONS heading.

These should be your starting point. Other oils and supplements listed should be considered for supplemental effect, or if you are not completely satisfied with using the First Recommendations products.

In this case, the section on Sore Throat lists two essential oils under the FIRST RECOMENDATIONS heading. These would be your starting point. Additionally, under other headings there are 9 other single oils, 3 other blends, and 2 custom blends that all may be helpful when used according to the methods listed in the EO Applications section.

Although this listing shows 14 possible oils, only 1-3 oils or blends should be used at any given time. You will need to select 1-3 oils or blends that you will use based on availability, budget and aroma (for example, some oils are strong enough that you may not want to be using or wearing them at work.)

Step 3: Make a list of the recommended essential oil (EO) applications listed for the illness/injury you are checking.

In this case, under the *Sore Throat* heading, quite a variety of methods is listed. Altogether 10 different application methods are listed, ranging from Direct Inhalation to Raindrop Technique. (Not all conditions have this many application methods. Most recommend only two or three.) The 10 listed application methods for a sore throat are intended to show all possible application methods for using essential oils in treating that condition.

Normally, only 1-2 different application methods should be used at any given time. This is a matter of both convenience and safety. If someone were to attempt all 10 applications for a sore throat at once, it would require an enormous investment of time, be extremely inconvenient and would put more essential oil in that person's body than is needed or helpful.

CAUTION: Always cross check the keyword application method descriptions with the detailed application descriptions on this page and the opposite page. This will provide critical additional information, such as dilution rates and frequency of application, which is needed in order to perform the application safely and properly.

Step 4: Note any additional dietary supplements and topical treatments listed for the condition.

More detailed information on recommended usage for these products can be found in the product listings in chapters 6-19.

Step 5: Make a written personal regimen that includes the 1-3 oils you have selected, the 1-2 EO application methods you will be using, and the dietary supplements and the topical treatments, if any.

This will save you from having to look up everything again each time you do your applications.

Step 6: Make sure you understand the proper essential oil dilution levels.

If you do not properly link oils with their application method details, you could make a mistake here. For example, one of the applications for sore throat is Direct Inhalation, in which the oils are used in their 'neat,' or undiluted state. However, for Topical Application to the skin, the dilution rate is 50:50 or 1 part essential oil to 1 part vegetable oil. (V6 Oil Complex)

Step 7: Be faithful with your regimen.

Therapeutic-grade essential oils are wonderful, natural, healing substances, and they work extremely well with the body's own defenses to solve problems. However, they are not drugs, and they may not always work in seconds, or even minutes. Essential Oils will enhance and speed up the benefits of dietary supplements, but it is still a 'natural' process. Sometimes it can take hours or even days to see the improvement.

The 18 Basic Essential Oil Application Methods

NOTE: Please read this information carefully as all directions in the following personal guide section will refer to the 18 methods outlined here.

TOPICAL (On the skin surface)

- NEAT: Apply neat (undiluted) as directed to affected area. (See Appendix E)

- DILUTE 50:50: 1 part essential oil (s) to 1 part V6 Oil Complex. (See Appendix E)

- DILUTE 20:80: 1 part essential oil(s) to 4 parts V6 Oil Complex. (See Appendix E)

- VITA FLEX: Apply 1-3 drops neat to the Vita Flex points on the feet as directed. See Vita Flex chart found in Chapter 20 for point locations.

- COMPRESS: Dilute 1 part essential oil(s) with 4 parts V6 Oil Complex and apply 8-10 drops on affected area. Cover with a warm, moist hand towel. Then cover the moist towel with a dry towel for 10-15 minutes. Can also use a cool, moist hand towel instead of a hot one, to create a COLD compress.

- BATH SALT: Mix thoroughly 10-15 drops of essential oil into 2 tablespoons of Epsom salts or baking soda. Dissolve in warm bathwater as tub is filling and soak for at least 20 minutes before using soap or shampoo; or place in special shower head designed to hold salt/essential oil mixture and shower for 10 minutes.

- BODY MASSAGE: Apply diluted in a 20:80 ratio (1 part essential oils to 4 parts V6 Oil Complex) in a full-body massage.

- RAINDROP Technique: (See Chapter 21)

INHALATION

- DIFFUSION: Diffuse neat in a cold-air diffuser. (Cold air diffusers are not designed to handle vegetable oils because they are thicker and may clog the diffuser mechanism).

- DIRECT: Apply 2-3 drops of essential oil(s) to the palm of one hand; rub palms together; cup hands over nose and mouth (being careful not to touch the skin near your eyes) and inhale vapors deeply 6-8 times.

- VAPOR: Run hot, steaming water into a sink or large bowl. Water should be at least 2 inches deep to retain heat for a few minutes. Drape a towel over your head, covering the hot water also, enclosing your face over the steaming water. Add 3-6 drops of essential oil(s) to the hot water. Inhale vapors as deeply as possible several times, through the nose, as they rise with the steam. Recharge vapors with additional hot water.

INGESTION

- CAPSULE: Unless directed otherwise, use a clean medicine dropper to fill the larger half of an empty gelatin capsule (available at health food stores) half-way with essential oil(s); then fill the remainder with V6 Advanced Oil Complex or a high quality cold-pressed vegetable oil, seal with the other half of the gel cap and take as directed.

There are two basic dosages used for capsules, indicated by capsule size. '00' size capsules (which contain a 400 mg dose when filled with a 50:50 dilution of essential oil) and '0' size capsules (which contain a 200 mg dose when filled with a 50:50 dilution of essential oil). If '0' size capsules are not readily available, you can half fill '00' size capsules.

- RICE MILK: Add the essential oil to rice milk and take as directed. Use 3-5 drops in 1/2 cup of rice milk. Goat milk may be substituted for rice milk.

- SYRUP: Add the essential oil to Blue Agave nectar or Grade B Maple Syrup. Use 3 drops in 1 tsp. maple syrup. Hold in mouth for 30 seconds before swallowing. Blue Agave nectar (a low-glycemic natural sweetener derived from the Agave plant) seems to work more effectively than maple syrup.

ORAL

- GARGLE: Add 2-3 drops essential oil with 4 tablespoons purified water, shake or mix vigorously. Gargle for 30 seconds.

- TONGUE: Apply 1 drop of essential oil neat to the back of the tongue with cotton swab or fingertip. Retain, allowing oil to combine with saliva, for at least 1 minute, then swallow. Note: this should NOT be done with essential oils which have a **20:80** application code. (See Appendix E)

RETENTION

- RECTAL: Dilute the recommended essential oil(s) in 40:60 ratio (4 parts essential oil to 6 parts V6 Oil Complex), insert 1-2 tablespoons in rectum with a bulb syringe and retain up to 8 hours or overnight.

- TAMPON: Dilute the recommended essential oil(s) in 40:60 ratio (4 parts essential oil to 6 parts V6 Oil Complex). Apply 1-2 tablespoons to a tampon and insert into vagina (for internal infection) OR apply to a sanitary pad (for external lesions). Retain up to 8 hours or overnight. Use only tampons or sanitary pads made with non-perfumed, non-scented organic cotton.

ABSCESS (Skin)

(See SKIN DISORDERS)

ABSENTMINDEDNESS

Clinical studies on Ningxia wolfberry *(Lycium barbarum)* have shown that it has an anti-senility effect. Clinical studies at University of Colorado Health Sciences Center found that high antioxidant foods such as spinach (found in JuvaPower) and blueberry (found in Ningxia Red) dramatically improved learning and cognition.[3,4]

(See BRAIN DISORDERS)

FIRST RECOMMENDATIONS:
Cardamom, Brain Power, Peppermint, Ningxia Red

Other Single Oils:
Vetiver, frankincense, sandalwood, rosemary, basil

Other Blends:
Clarity, M-Grain

EO APPLICATION METHODS:
Inhalation:
DIFFUSION, 15 min every 2 hours, as needed
DIRECT, 2-4 times daily, as needed
Topical:
NEAT, 1-2 drops on temples and/or back of neck, as needed.

DIETARY SUPPLEMENTATION:
PD 80/20, Omega Blue Softgels, Progessence Cream, Ningxia Red, True Source Multivitamins

ABUSE (mental and physical)

The trauma from mental and physical abuse can result in self-defeating behavior that can undermine success later in life. Through their powerful effect on the limbic system of the brain (the center for stored memories and emotions), essential oils can help release pent-up trauma, emotions, or memories.

FIRST RECOMMENDATIONS:
Trauma Life, SARA, Release

Other Single Oils:
Geranium, sandalwood, melissa.

Other Blends:
Acceptance, Forgiveness, Surrender, Humility, White Angelica, Inner Child, Harmony," Hope, Brain Power, Valor, Valor Roll-on, Tranquil Roll-on

EO APPLICATION METHODS:
Inhalation:
DIFFUSION, 15 min. every 2 hours as needed
DIRECT, 2-3 times daily, as needed
Topical:
NEAT, 1-2 drops on temples and/or back of neck as needed. Also apply 2- 3 drops on the Vita Flex liver point of the right foot. Also apply a trace under the nose.

DIETARY SUPPLEMENTATION:
Omega Blue Softgels, Super C, Super C Chewable, Super B

Specific types of abuse:

Physical Abuse: Begin with application of 2-3 drops Forgiveness, unless suicidal. It is most effective around the navel. Follow with 1-2 drops Release over the Vita Flex points, especially the liver point of right foot, and under the nose.

Parental, Sexual or Ritual Abuse: 1-3 drops SARA over the area where abuse took place; then Forgiveness, Trauma Life, Release, Joy, or Present Time.

Spousal Abuse: Use Forgiveness, Trauma Life, Acceptance, Release, Valor, Valor Roll-on, Joy, or Envision.

Feelings of Revenge: 1-2 drops of Surrender on the sternum over the heart, 2-3 drops of Present Time on the thymus, and 2-3 drops Forgiveness over navel.

Suicidal: 2 drops Hope on rim of ears. Melissa, Brain Power, or Present Time may be beneficial also.

Protection/Balance: 1-2 drops of White Angelica on each shoulder, 1-2 drops Harmony over thymus and on energy centers or chakras of the body.

3. Galli RL et al., "Fruit polyphenolics and brain aging: nutritional interventions targeting age-related neuronal and behavioral deficits." *Ann N Y Acad Sci.* 2002 Apr; 959: 128-32.

4. Bickford PC et al., "Antioxidant-rich diets improve cerebellar physiology and motor learning in aged rats." *Brain Res.* 2000 Jun 2; 866(1-2): 211-7.

ACID/ALKALINE BALANCE

(See ACIDOSIS, ALKALOSIS)

ACIDOSIS

Acidosis is a condition where the pH of the blood serum becomes excessively acidic. This condition should not be confused with acid stomach (See Heartburn under DIGESTIVE PROBLEMS). Acidic blood can stress the liver and eventually lead to many forms of chronic and degenerative diseases. Dietary modification is the first course to pursue in raising the serum pH (making it more alkaline). Rudolf Wiley, Ph.D., recommends courses of action to accomplish this in *BioBalance: The Acid/Alkaline Solution to the Food-Mood-Health Puzzle.*

To raise pH, avoid acid-ash foods, overuse of antibiotics, and monitor the pH of the saliva (6.4-6.5) and blood (7.3-7.6). (See Appendix B)

Cleansing is an essential dietary step in balancing pH. (See Chapter 25).

FIRST RECOMMENDATIONS:
Essentialzyme, MultiGreens, JuvaPower

DIETARY SUPPLEMENTATION:
Mega Cal, Polyzyme, AlkaLime

OTHER REGIMENS:
Take Polyzyme with peppermint until acid level is balanced, then add Essentialzyme.

To reduce acid indigestion and prevent fermentation that can contribute to bad dreams and interrupted sleep: 1 tsp. AlkaLime in water before bedtime.

To raise pH, take 2-6 capsules of MultiGreens 3 times daily and take 1 tsp. AlkaLime in water one hour before or two hours after meals each day. For maintenance, take 1 tsp. AlkaLime once per week.

To stimulate enzymatic action in the digestive tract: Mix together or use individually, raw carrot juice, alfalfa, trace minerals, and papaya.

(See also FUNGAL INFECTIONS)

ACNE

(See SKIN DISORDERS)

A.D.D.

(See ATTENTION DEFICIT DISORDER)

ADDICTIONS

Many food and chemical dependencies, such as addictions to tobacco, caffeine, drugs, alcohol, and sugar may originate in the liver. Cleansing and detoxifying the liver is a crucial first step toward breaking free of these addictions. Increasing intake of alkaline calcium can help bind bile acids and prevent fatty liver. A colon and tissue cleanse is also important.

Using stevia, stevioside, or FOS can help reduce sugar cravings. Stevia is a supersweet noncaloric extract derived from an ancient South American herb, while FOS is a sweet-tasting indigestible sugar derived from chicory roots and Jerusalem artichokes with no calories and important health benefits. (See Appendix M)

Trace mineral and mineral deficiencies can also play a part in some addictions. Magnesium, potassium, calcium, and zinc should all be included in the diet.

Cleansing also plays an important role in helping the body overcome physical addictions. (See Chapter 25).

See also Chapter 24 on Emotions

FIRST RECOMMENDATIONS:
Detoxzyme, Omega Blue Softgels, ComforTone, ICP

Other Blends:
Harmony, Peace & Calming, JuvaCleanse, JuvaFlex

EO APPLICATION METHODS:
Inhalation:
DIFFUSION, 15 min every 2 hours as needed
DIRECT, 2-3 times daily, as needed
Topical:
NEAT, 1-2 drops on temples and/or back of neck 4 times daily
COMPRESS, warm, over liver

DIETARY SUPPLEMENTATION:
JuvaTone, JuvaPower/Spice, Stevia, Mega Cal, Essentialzyme, Balance Complete

(See also LIVER and SMOKING CESSATION)

ADDISON'S DISEASE

(See ADRENAL GLAND IMBALANCE)

ADRENAL GLAND IMBALANCE

The adrenal glands consist of two sections: An inner part called the medulla produces stress hormones and an outer part called the cortex secretes critical hormones called glucocorticoids and aldosterone. Because of these hormones, the cortex has a far greater impact on overall health than the medulla does.

Why are aldosterone and glucocorticoids so important? Because they directly affect blood pressure and mineral content and help regulate the conversion of carbohydrates into energy.

Addison's Disease

In cases like Addison's disease, adrenal cortex hormones are no longer produced or severely limited. This can lead to life-threatening fluid and mineral loss unless these hormones are replaced.

Because Addison's disease is an autoimmune disease in which the body's own immune cells destroy the adrenal glands, it may help to supplement with MSM. MSM is an important source of organic sulfur that has been shown to have positive effects with many types of autoimmune diseases, including lupus, arthritis, and fibromyalgia.

Adrenal Glands

> ### Supporting the Adrenal Glands
>
> Add the following amounts of essential oils to 1/4 teaspoon of massage oil and apply as a warm compress over the adrenal glands (located on top of the kidneys).
>
> - 3 drops clove
> - 3 drops nutmeg
> - 7 drops rosemary

If adrenal insufficiency is accompanied by a lack of thyroid hormone, the condition is known as Schmidt's syndrome.

Symptoms:
- Severe fatigue
- Lightheadedness when standing
- Nausea
- Depression/irritability
- Craving salty foods
- Loss of appetite
- Muscle spasms
- Dark, tan-colored skin

Essential oils can play a part in correcting deficiencies in adrenal cortex function. Nutmeg, for example, has adrenal-like activity that raises energy levels.

FIRST RECOMMENDATIONS:
Nutmeg, German chamomille

Other Single Oils:
Clove

Blends:
EndoFlex, En-R-Gee

EO APPLICATION METHODS:
Topical:
COMPRESS, warm, over the adrenal gland area (on back, over the kidneys)
Ingestion:
CAPSULE, 00 size, 2 daily

DIETARY SUPPLEMENTATION:
MultiGreens, Balance Complete, Sulfurzyme, Mega Cal, Mineral Essence

Cushing's disease

Cushing's disease is the opposite of Addison's disease. It is characterized by the overproduction of adrenal cortex hormones, such as cortisol. While these hormones are crucial to sound health in normal amounts, their unchecked overproduction can cause as much harm as their underproduction. This results in the following symptoms:

- Slow wound healing
- Low resistance to infection
- Easily-bruised skin
- Weak or wasted muscles
- Obesity
- Acne
- Moon-shaped face
- Osteoporosis

Although Cushing's disease can be caused by a malfunction in the pituitary, it is usually triggered by excessive use of immune-suppressing corticosteroid medications—such as those used for asthma and arthritis. Once these are discontinued, the disease often abates.

The key to reducing excess cortisol is often reducing stress.

FIRST RECOMMENDATIONS:
Peace & Calming, lemon, Acceptance, Grounding

Other Single Oils:
Spearmint

Other Blends:
Harmony, Endoflex

EO APPLICATION METHODS:
Topical:
COMPRESS, warm, over adrenal area (on back, over kidneys)
Ingestion:
CAPSULE, 00 size, 2 daily

DIETARY SUPPLEMENTATION:
ImmuPro, PD 80/20, ImmuneTune, Mineral Essence, Cortistop Women's, Digest & Cleanse Softgels

AGE-RELATED MACULAR DEGENERATION (AMD)

(See EYE DISORDERS)

AGITATION

Agitation is often a byproduct of a congested liver. (See LIVER DISORDERS and Chapter 24 on Emotions.)

FIRST RECOMMENDATIONS:
Peace & Calming, ImmuPro, Super B, valerian

Single Oils:
Lavender, orange, Roman chamomile

Blends:
Forgiveness, Surrender, Humility

EO APPLICATION METHODS:
Inhalation:
DIFFUSION, 15 min. every 2 hours, as needed
DIRECT, 2-3 times per day, as needed
Topical:
NEAT, 1-2 drops on temples and/or back of neck
VITA FLEX, 1-2 drops on brain and heart points

DIETARY SUPPLEMENTATION:
JuvaTone, Mega Cal

AIDS (Acquired Immune Deficiency Syndrome)

The AIDS virus attacks and infects immune cells that are essential for life.

Frankincense and myrrh gum resins and essential oils have immune building properties. Other oils like cumin *(Cuminum cyminum)* have an inhibitory effect on viral replication. In May 1994, Dr. Radwan Farag of Cairo University demonstrated that cumin seed oil had an 88 to 92 percent inhibition effect in vitro against HIV, the virus responsible for AIDS. Other antiviral essential oils include oregano, sandalwood, tea tree and peppermint.

FIRST RECOMMENDATIONS:
ImmuPro, cistus, cumin, Dried wolfberries, Raindrop Technique (see Chapter 21)

Other Single Oils:
Cumin, blue cypress, sandalwood, tea tree, myrrh (gum resin and essential oil), frankincense (gum resin and essential oil)

Other Blends:
Valor, Thieves, Inner Defense, Release, Acceptance, Valor Roll-on

DIETARY SUPPLEMENTATION:
Exodus, Ningxia Red, Power Meal, Balance Complete, Longevity

(See also LIVER DISORDERS. See Chapter 24 on Emotions and Chapter 25 on Cleansing

ALCOHOLISM

FIRST RECOMMENDATIONS:
Orange, JuvaPower/Spice, milk thistle extract

Single Oils:
Lavender, Roman chamomile, ledum

Blends:
JuvaCleanse, Forgiveness, Acceptance, Valor Roll-on, Motivation, Valor, White Angelica

EO APPLICATION METHODS:
Ingestion:
CAPSULE, 6 drops in a 0 size capsule, once a day
Inhalation:
DIFFUSION, 15 min every 2 hours as needed
DIRECT, 2-3 times daily, as needed
Topical:
NEAT, 1-2 drops on temples and/or back of neck 4 times daily
COMPRESS, warm, over liver

DIETARY SUPPLEMENTATION:
JuvaTone, ICP, ComforTone, Super B, Power Meal, Detoxyme

(See also ADDICTIONS, LIVER DISORDERS)

ALKALOSIS

(See also ACIDOSIS)

Alkalosis is a condition where the pH of the intestinal tract and the blood becomes excessively alkaline. While moderate alkalinity is essential for good health, excessive alkalinity can cause problems and result in fatigue, depression, irritability, and sickness.

The best solution is to lower, or acidify, the internal pH of the body using a high protein diet. (See Appendix B) Ultrafiltered whey is an excellent solution for excess alkalinity. Rudolf Wiley, Ph.D., recommends courses of action to accomplish this in *BioBalance: The Acid/Alkaline Solution to the Food-Mood-Health Puzzle.*

Cleansing should be a part of any pH balancing regimin. (See Chapter 25)

FIRST RECOMMENDATIONS:
Protein Complete, Balance Complete

OTHER DIETARY SUPPLEMENTATION:
Essentialzyme, ICP, Comfortone, Digest & Cleanse Softgels

ALLERGIES

Allergies can be triggered by food, pollen, environmental chemicals, dander, dust, and insect bites and can impact:

Respiration—wheezing, labored breathing
Mouth—swelling of the lips or tongue, itching lips
Digestive tract—diarrhea, vomiting, cramps
Skin—rashes, dermatitis
Nose—sneezing, congestion

Food Allergies

Food *allergies* are different from food *intolerances*. The former involve an immune system reaction, whereas the latter involves a gastrointestinal reaction (and is far more common). For example, peanuts often produce a lifelong allergy in adults due to peanut proteins being targeted by immune system antibodies as foreign invaders. In contrast, intolerance of pasteurized cow's milk that causes cramping and diarrhea is due to the inability to digest lactose (milk sugar) because of a lack of the enzyme lactase.

Food allergies are often associated with the consumption of peanuts, shellfish, nuts, wheat, cow's milk, eggs, and soy. Infants and children are far more susceptible to food allergies than adults, due to the immaturity of their immune and digestive systems.

A thorough intestinal cleansing is one of the best ways to combat most allergies. Start with ICP, Comfortone, Essentialzyme and JuvaTone.

See Chapter 25 on Cleansing and Diets.

Hay fever (allergic rhinitis)

Hay fever is an allergic reaction triggered by airborne allergens (pollen, animal hair, feathers, dust mites) that cause the release of histamines and subsequent inflammation of nasal passages and sinus-related areas. A more serious form of respiratory allergy is asthma, which manifests in the chest and lungs.

Symptoms: Inflammation of the nasal passages, sinuses, and eyelids that causes sneezing, runny nose, watery, red, itchy eyes, and wheezing.

FIRST RECOMMENDATIONS:
German chamomille, wintergreen, Polyzyme

Single Oils:
Lavender, Roman chamomile

Blends:
Harmony, Valor, Juva Cleanse, Valor Roll-on

EO APPLICATION METHODS:
Inhalation:
DIFFUSION, 15 min every 2 hours, as needed
DIRECT, 2-4 times daily, as needed
Ingestion:
CAPSULE, 00 size, 2 times daily

DIETARY SUPPLEMENTATION:
Sulfurzyme, Detoxzyme, Essentialzyme, MultiGreens, ICP/ComforTone/JuvaTone

ALOPECIA AREATA (Hair Loss)

Alopecia is an inflammatory hair-loss disease that is the second-leading cause of baldness in the U.S. A randomized, double-blind study at the Aberdeen Royal Infirmary in Scotland found that certain essential oils were extremely effective in combating this disease.[5,6]

FIRST RECOMMENDATION:
Rosemary

Single Oils:
Thyme, lavender, cedarwood

Alopecia Areata Blend:
4 drops rosemary
4 drops thyme
4 drops lavender
4 drops cedarwood

EO APPLICATION METHODS:
Topical:
Dilute 20:80, (5 drops essential oils in 20 drops olive, grapeseed or fractionated coconut oil). Massage into scalp before sleep nightly

ALUMINUM TOXICITY

(See METAL TOXICITY, Aluminum)

ALZHEIMER'S

(See BRAIN DISORDERS)

ANALGESIC

An 'analgesic' is defined as a compound that binds with a number of closely related specific receptors in the central nervous system to block the perception of pain or affect the emotional response to pain. A number of essential oils have analgesic properties.

FIRST RECOMMENDATIONS:
PanAway, clove, peppermint

Single Oils:
Elemi, wintergreen, lavender, helichrysum, copaiba

Other Blends:
Thieves, Inner Defense, Deep Relief Roll-on

Additional blend for pain relief:
Equal parts wintergreen, spruce and black pepper

EO APPLICATION METHODS:
Topical:
DILUTE 50:50, apply 4-6 drops on location, as needed.

ANEMIA

(See BLOOD DISORDERS)

ANEURYSM

(See also CARDIOVASCULAR CONDITIONS)

Aneurysms are weak spots on the blood vessel wall which balloon out and may eventually rupture. In cases of brain aneurysms, a bursting blood vessel can cause a hemorrhagic stroke, which can result in death or paralysis (with a fatality rate of over 50 percent).

---

5. Hay, Jamieson, Ormerod "Randomized trial of aromatherapy. Successful treatment for alopecia areata." *Archives of Dermatology.* 1998 Nov;134(11):1349-52.

6. Kalish, Gilhar "Alopecia areata: autoimmunity--the evidence is compelling." *The Journal of Investigative Dermatology Symposium Proceedings* 2003 Oct;8(2):164-7.

See your physician for treatment immediately if you have, or suspect you have, an aneurysm.

Some essential oils and nutritional supplements support the cardiovascular system. Cypress strengthens capillary and vascular walls. Helichrysum helps dissolve blood clots.

FIRST RECOMMENDATION:
Aroma Life

Single Oils:
Helichrysum, cypress

Aneurysm blend:
- 5 drops of frankincense
- 1 drop helichrysum
- 1 drop cypress

EO APPLICATION METHODS:
Topical:
DILUTE 50:50, on affected area 3-5 times daily
Inhalation:
DIFFUSION, 15 minutes, 4-6 times daily
Ingestion:
CAPSULE, 00 size, 2 times daily

DIETARY SUPPLEMENTATION:
Dried wolfberries, Ningxia Red

ANGINA

(See CARDIOVASCULAR CONDITIONS)

ANOREXIA

While psychotherapy remains indispensable, the inhalation of essential oils may alter emotions enough to effect a change in the underlying psychology or disturbed-thinking patterns which support this self-destructive behavior. This is accomplished by the ability of fragrance to directly impact the emotional hub inside the brain known as the limbic system. Essential oils such as lemon and ginger when inhaled regularly can combat the emotional addiction that leads anorexics to premature death.

Many people with anorexia believe they don't deserve to be healthy or loved unless they are "slender."

Anorexia nervosa is an eating disorder characterized by total avoidance of food and virtual self-starvation. It may or may not be accompanied by bulimia (binge-purge behavior).

Many anorexics suffer life-threatening nutrient and mineral deficiencies. The lack of magnesium and potassium can actually trigger heart rhythm abnormalities and cardiac arrest. Replacement of calcium, magnesium, potassium, and other minerals is absolutely essential for this condition.

FIRST RECOMMENDATION:
Lemon, tangerine, ginger, MegaCal

Single Oils:
Mandarin, ginger

Blends:
Valor, Motivation, Brain Power, Valor Roll-on

EO APPLICATION METHODS:
Inhalation:
DIFFUSION, 15 minutes every 2 hours
DIRECT, 2-3 times daily, as needed
Topical:
NEAT, 1-2 drops on temples and/or back of neck 4 times daily
COMPRESS, warm, over liver area

DIETARY SUPPLEMENTATION:
Mineral Essence, Balance Complete

(See also ADDICTIONS, LIVER DISORDERS, Chapter 24 on Emotions and Chapter 25 on Cleansing)

ANTHRAX

Caused by the bacteria *Bacillus anthracis*, anthrax is one of the oldest and deadliest diseases known. There are three predominant types: the **external** form acquired from contact with infected animal carcasses, the **internal** form is obtained from breathing airborne anthrax spores, and **battlefield anthrax**, which is a far more lethal variety of internal anthrax that was developed for biological warfare. When the airborne variety of anthrax invades and lungs, it is 90 percent fatal unless antibiotics are administered at the very beginning of the infection. Often anthrax goes undiagnosed until it is too late for antibiotics.

External varieties of anthrax may be contracted by exposure to animal hides and wool. While vaccination and antibiotics have stemmed anthrax infection in recent years, new strains have developed that are resistant to all counter measures.

According to Jean Valnet, MD, thyme oil may be effective for killing the anthrax bacillus.[7] Two highly antimicrobial phenols in thyme, carvacrol and thymol, are responsible for this action.

FIRST RECOMMENDATIONS:
Thyme, manuka, Thieves, Inner Defense

Other Single Oils:
Oregano, clove, cinnamon, citronella, lemongrass

Other Blends:
Exodus II

EO APPLICATION METHODS:
Topical:
DILUTE 20:80, on hands and exposed skin areas
Inhalation:
DIFFUSION, 5 minutes 4-6 times daily to purify air
Ingestion:
CAPSULE, 00 size, 4 times daily

DIETARY SUPPLEMENTATION:
ImmuPro, ImmuneTune, Super C Chewable

OTHER:
Topical treatments to help prevent contracting or spreading anthrax include Thieves, Inner Defense, Thieves Household Cleaner, Thieves Spray and Thieves Wipes.

(See also INFECTIONS)

ANTIBIOTIC REACTIONS

Synthetic antibiotic drugs indiscriminately kill both beneficial and harmful bacteria. This can result in yeast infections (including candida), diarrhea, poor nutrient assimilation, fatigue, degenerative diseases, and many other conditions and symptoms.

The average adult has 3-4 pounds of beneficial bacteria permanently residing in the intestines.

These beneficial flora:
- Constitute the first line of defense against bacterial and viral infection
- Produce B vitamins
- Maintain pH balance
- Combat yeast and fungus overgrowth
- Aid in the digestive process

DIETARY SUPPLEMENTATION:
Life 5, Balance Complete

During antibiotic treatment, take 2-3 servings of probiotics daily on an empty stomach before meals. After completing antibiotic treatment, continue using probiotics for 10-15 days.

ANTISEPTIC

Antiseptics prevent the growth of pathogenic microorganisms. Many essential oils have powerful antiseptic properties. Clove and thyme essential oils have been documented to kill over 50 types of bacteria and 10 types of fungi. Other potent antiseptics include, cinnamon/cassia oil, tea tree, oregano, and mountain savory.

FIRST RECOMMENDATIONS:
Tea tree, manuka, Thieves, Inner Defense, Melrose

Single Oils:
Thyme, clove, oregano, rosemary, mountain savory, eucalyptus (all types), lavandin, cinnamon, cassia, ravensara

Blends:
Purification, Melrose, R.C., Breath Again Roll-on

EO APPLICATION METHODS:
Topical:
DILUTE, According to application code (see Appendix E) and apply to affected area 2-10 times daily as needed

OTHER:
Products to maintain a clean, antiseptic environment both in the home and on the skin include Thieves Cleansing Bar Soap, Thieves Household Cleaner, Thieves Spray, Thieves Wipes, Thieves Foaming Hand Soap and Thieves Waterless Hand Purifier

---

7. Jean Valnet, MD, "The Practice of Aromatherapy: A Classic Compendium of Plant Medicines & Their Healing Properties," *Healing Arts Press*, 1990, p. 197.

APNEA

Apnea is a temporary cessation of breathing during sleep. It can degrade the quality of sleep resulting in chronic fatigue, lowered immune function, and lack of energy.

FIRST RECOMMENDATION:
Valor, Valor Roll-on

Other Blend:
Clarity

EO APPLICATION METHODS:
Inhalation:
DIFFUSION, in the bedroom throughout the night while sleeping
Topical:
NEAT, 2-4 drops on soles of feet just before bedtime

DIETARY SUPPLEMENTATION:
MultiGreens, Super B, Thyromin

APPETITE, LOSS OF

Ginger has been shown to stimulate digestion and improve appetite.

FIRST RECOMMENDATIONS:
Ginger, spearmint, orange

Single Oils:
Nutmeg

Blends:
Citrus Fresh, Christmas Spirit

EO APPLICATION METHODS:
Inhalation:
DIFFUSION, 10 min., 3-5 times daily
DIRECT, 3-5 times daily, as needed
Ingestion
CAPSULE, 00 size, 1 times daily

DIETARY SUPPLEMENTATION:
Essentialzyme, Polyzyme, ComforTone

ARTERIOSCLEROSIS
(Hardening of the arteries)

(See CARDIOVASCULAR CONDITIONS)

ARTHRITIS

(See also JOINT STIFFNESS/PAIN)

Osteoarthritis

Osteoarthritis involves the breakdown of the cartilage that forms a cushion between two joints. As this cartilage is eaten away, the two bones of the joint start rubbing together and wearing down. In contrast, rheumatoid arthritis is caused from a swelling and inflammation of the synovial membrane, the lining of the joint.

Natural anti-inflammatories (blue chamomile, wintergreen) combined with cartilage builders (glucosamine/chondroitin) are powerful natural cures for arthritis. The best natural anti-inflammatories include fats rich in omega-3s and essential oils such as nutmeg, wintergreen, German (blue) chamomile, and balsam fir. The best cartilage builders include Type II collagen and glucosamine (contained in BLM powder).

Nutmeg, a source of myristicin, has been researched for its anti-inflammatory effects in several studies. It works by inhibiting pro-inflammatory prostaglandins when taken internally or applied topically. Clove exhibits similar action.

Chamazulene, the blue sesquiterpene in German chamomile, also shows strong anti-inflammatory activity when used both topically and orally.

Methyl salicylate, a major component of wintergreen, is a chemical cousin to the active agent in aspirin and also has strong anti-inflammatory and analgesic properties.

Glucosamine and chondroitin are the two most powerful natural compounds for rebuilding cartilege and are the key ingredients in the supplement BLM.

FIRST RECOMMENDATIONS:
Wintergreen, PanAway, peppermint, copaiba, Essentialzyme, BLM, MSM

Other Single Oils:
Nutmeg, German chamomile, clove, copaiba, helichrysum, Idaho balsam fir, white fir, pine, *Eucalyptus globulus*, frankincense gum resin/essential oil, myrrh gum resin/essential oil

Other Blends:
Relieve It, Aroma Siez, Ortho Ease, Ortho Sport, Deep Relief Roll-on

EO APPLICATION METHODS:
Topical:
DILUTE 5-10 drops essential oils in 1 tsp. V6 Oil Complex and apply on location. Essential oils can also be applied neat, then followed by application of V6 Oil Complex.

DIETARY SUPPLEMENTATION:
Longevity Softgels, ImmuneTune, Sulfurzyme, Mega Cal

Supplementation regiment of osteoarthritis:
- BLM: 2-4 capsules, 2 times daily
- Mega Cal: 2-3 capsules, 2 times daily
- ImmuneTune: 2-3 capsules, 3 times daily

Detoxification of the body and strengthening the joints is important. Cleanse the colon and liver. Rehemogen cleans and purifies the blood which may have toxins blocking nutrient and oxygen absorption into cells (see Circulation).

Apply oils on location followed by massage oil.

OTHER:
Regenolone is an excellent companion personal care product to support the joints.

Rheumetoid Arthritis

Rheumatoid arthritis is a painful inflammatory condition of the joints marked by swelling, thickening, and inflammation of the synovial membrane lining the joint. (In contrast, osteoarthritis is characterized by a breakdown of the joint cartilage without any swelling or inflammation.)

Rheumatoid arthritis is classified as an autoimmune disease because it is caused by the body's own immune system attacking the joints.

Other factors can aggravate arthritis such as:
- Deficiencies of minerals and other nutrients
- Microbes and toxins
- Lack of water intake

Essential oils constitute some of the most effective treatments for combating arthritis pain and combating infection in cases where it is present. Peppermint has been studied for its ability to kill pain by blocking substance P and calcium channels.[8]

In cases where arthritis is caused by infectious organisms, such as *Borrelia burgdorferi, (Lyme Disease) Chlamydia,* and *Salmonella,* essential oils may counteract and prevent infection, especially when diffused or applied topically. Highly antimicrobial essential oils include: mountain savory, rosemary, *Melaleuca alternifolia* (tea tree), and oregano. The oils can pass into the bloodstream when applied topically.

Additionally, MSM has been documented to be one of the most effective natural supplements for reducing the pain associated with rheumatism and arthritis. The subject of a number of clinical studies, MSM was used extensively by Ronald Lawrence, MD, in his clinical practice to successfully treat rheumatism and arthritis. MSM is the key ingredient in the supplement Sulfurzyme.

Also, glucosamine and chondroitin are some of the most powerful natural compounds for reducing inflammation, halting the progression of arthritis and rebuilding cartilage. These are the key ingredients in the supplement BLM.

FIRST RECOMMENDATIONS:
Wintergreen, PanAway, peppermint, copaiba, Essentialzyme, BLM, MSM

Other Single Oils:
Nutmeg, clove, helichrysum, Idaho balsam fir, white fir, pine, *Eucalyptus globulus*, copaiba, myrrh gum resin/essential oil, frankincense gum resin/essential oil

Other Blends:
Relieve It, Aroma Siez, Ortho Ease, Ortho Sport, Deep Relief Roll-on

EO APPLICATION METHODS:
Topical:
DILUTE 5-10 drops essential oils in 1 tsp. V6 Oil Complex and apply on location. Essential oils can also be applied neat, then followed by application of V6 Oil Complex.

DIETARY SUPPLEMENTATION:
BLM, Longevity Softgels, ImmuneTune, Sulfurzyme, Mega Cal

Other Topical Treatments:
Regenolone, Ortho Ease

---

8. Gobel et al., "Effect of peppermint and eucalyptus oil preparations on neurophysiological and experimental algesimetric headache parameters." Cephalalgia. 1994 Jun;14(3):228-34; discussion 182.

ASTHMA

CAUTION: Essential oils should not be inhaled for asthma-related problems. The oils should be applied to the soles of the feet or ingested (if they are GRAS – Generally Regarded As Safe--see Appendix C)

During an asthma attack, the bronchials (air tubes) in the lungs become swollen and clogged with a thick, sticky mucus. The muscles of the air tubes will also begin to constrict or tighten. This results in very difficult or labored breathing. If an attack is severe, it can actually be life-threatening.

Many asthma attacks are triggered by an allergic reaction to pollen, skin particles, dandruff, cat or dog dander, dust mites, and foods such as eggs, milk, flavorings, dyes, and preservatives. Asthma can also be triggered by respiratory infection, exercise, stress, and psychological factors.

(See ALLERGIES)

FIRST RECOMMENDATIONS:
Wintergreen, R.C., Breath Again Roll-on

Other Single Oils:
Eucalyptus radiata, lemon, lavender, rose, frankincese marjoram

Other Blends:
Raven, Inspiration, Sacred Mountain

EO APPLICATION METHODS:
Topical:
NEAT, 2-4 drops to soles of feet 2-3 times daily
Ingestion:
CAPSULE, 00 size, 2 times daily

DIETARY SUPPLEMENTATION:
MultiGreens, ImmuneTune, Essentialzyme, Carbozyme

ATHLETE'S FOOT

(See FOOT PROBLEMS)

ATTENTION DEFICIT DISORDER (ADD and ADHD)

Terry Friedmann, MD has recently completed pioneering studies using essential oils to combat ADD and ADHD. Using twice a day inhalation of essential oils including vetiver, cedarwood, and lavender, Dr. Friedmann was able to achieve clinically significant results in 60 days. Researchers postulate that essential oils mitigate ADD and ADHD through their stimulation on the limbic system of the brain.

Because attention deficit disorder may be caused by mineral deficiencies in the diet, increasing nutrient intake and absorption of magnesium, potassium, and other trace minerals can also have a significant beneficial effect in resolving ADD.

FIRST RECOMMENDATIONS:
Vetiver, lavender, cedarwood, clarity, Omega Blue Softgels

Other Single Oils:
Sandalwood, cardamom, peppermint, frankincense

Other Blends:
Brain Power, Peace & Calming, Clarity

EO APPLICATION METHODS:
Inhalation:
DIFFUSION, 15 min. 4-8 times daily
DIRECT, 4-8 times daily

DIETARY SUPPLEMENTATION:
Mineral Essence, Ningxia Red, Power Meal, Balance Complete

AUTISM

Improving diet can be the key to ameliorating cases of autism. Replacing high glycemic sweeteners (ie. sugar) with low-glycemic sweeteners (ie. Blue Agave nectar,) has produced outstanding results in numerous cases of autism.

Autism is a neurologically based developmental disorder that is four times more common in boys than girls. It is characterized by:

- Social ineptness (loner)
- Nonverbal and verbal communication difficulties
- Repetitive behavior (rocking, hair twirling)
- Self injurious behavior (head-banging)
- Very limited or peculiar interests
- Reduced or abnormal responses to pain, noises, or other outside stimuli

Autism is being increasingly linked to certain vaccinations, the MMR being most often cited by researchers. British researcher Andrew Wakefield, MD, suggests single shots for children for measles, mumps and rubella (instead of the combined MMR shot) until further research is done.

Until very recently, children were receiving large doses of mercury (from thimerosal, a vaccine preservative that contains 49.6% mercury) that were well above the limit recommended by the EPA, through vaccination. Some success in reversing autism has resulted through mercury detoxification along with nutritional supplementation.

Some researchers believe that gastrointestinal disorders may be linked to the brain dysfunctions that cause autism in children (Horvath et al., 1998). In fact, there have been several cases of successful treatment of autism using pancreatic enzymes.

Stimulation of the limbic region of the brain may also help treat autism. Aromas from essential oils have a powerful ability to stimulate this part of the brain since the sense of smell (olfaction) is tied directly into the mind's emotional and hormonal centers. As a result the aroma of an essential oil has the potential to exert a powerful influence on disorders such as ADD and autism.

FIRST RECOMMENDATIONS:
Brain Power, sandalwood, frankincese

Single Oils:
Vetiver, lavender, *Eucalyptus globulus*, melissa, cedarwood

Blends:
Valor, Valor Roll-on, Clarity, Peace & Calming

EO APPLICATION:
Inhalation:
DIFFUSION, 15 min. 4-6 times daily
DIRECT, 4-6 times daily

DIETARY SUPPLEMENTATION:
Essentialzyme, Polyzyme, Ningxia Red, Power Meal, Balance Complete

BACK INJURIES AND PAIN

(See SPINE INJURIES AND PAIN)

BALDNESS

(see also ALOPECIA AREATA)

Male pattern baldness is often a result of excess conversion of testosterone to dihydrotestosterone through the enzyme 5-alpha reductase. It can also be caused by an inflammatory condition called alopecia areata.

FIRST RECOMMENDATIONS:
Rosemary, peppermint, ProGen, PD 80/20

Single Oils:
Fleabane, black pepper

EO APPLICATION METHODS:
Topical:
DILUTE 20:80, massage into scalp before retiring. (For this application, fractionated coconut oil is recommended as the diluting oil. It's finer structure is more readily absorbed into the scalp.)

BELL'S PALSY

(See NERVE DISORDERS)

BENIGN PROSTATE HYPERPLASIA (BPH)

(See PROSTATE PROBLEMS)

BITES

(See INSECT BITES or SNAKE BITES)

BLADDER INFECTION

(See URINARY/BLADDER INFECTION)

BLEEDING

(See HEMORRHAGING)

BLEEDING GUMS

(See ORAL CARE)

BLISTERS and BOILS

Blisters are created when fluid is trapped under the skin. They can be caused by physical injury (ie., chemical burns, sunburns) or microbial infestation (ie., fungal and viral diseases such as Herpes simplex, athlete's foot, etc.).

Boils (carbuncles are groups of boils) are caused by bacterial infection which creates a pus-filled hair follicle. They can be easily treated with antiseptic essential oils including melaleuca and clove.

Blisters

FIRST RECOMMENDATIONS:
Tea tree, Melrose

Other Single Oils:
Lavender, Roman or German chamomile

Other Blends:
Purification

EO APPLICATION METHODS:
Topical:
DILUTE 50:50, apply to blistered area 3-5 times daily, as needed
Topical Treatments:
Lavaderm.

Boils

FIRST RECOMMENDATIONS:
Melaleuca ericifolia, manuka, Melrose

Other Single Oils:
Clove, thyme, oregano, tea tree

Other Blends:
Purification, Thieves, Inner Defense

EO APPLICATION METHODS:
Topical:
DILUTE 50:50, 2-3 drops on location 3-6 times daily

BLOATING/SWELLING

(See also MENSTRUAL CONDITIONS, CARDIOVASCULAR CONDITIONS, DIGESTION PROBLEMS)

Bloating is usually a result of hormonal or mineral imbalances that trigger excess fluid retention in the body. One of the best natural remedies is progesterone, which is added to creams and absorbed transdermally.

FIRST RECOMMENDATIONS:
Peppermint, Mineral Essence, Balance Complete

Other Single Oils:
Juniper berry, clary sage

EO APPLICATION METHODS:
Topical:
NEAT, 2-4 drops on soles of feet 2-3 times daily
Ingestion:
Capsules, 00 size, 1 times daily

DIETARY SUPPLEMENTATION:
PD80:20, ICP, ComforTone, Essentialzyme

OTHER:
Progessence Cream

BLOOD CLOTS

(See also CIRCULATION DISORDERS, CARDIOVASCULAR CONDITIONS, HEMATOMA, LIVER DISORDERS)

As people age, the viscosity or thickness of the blood increases and also the tendency of the blood to clot excessively.

If blood clots (also known as embolisms) occur in the brain, they cause strokes; if they obstruct a coronary artery, they cause ischemic heart attacks.

People with diabetes or high blood pressure are far more likely to die from blood clots.

Natural blood thinners, such as clove oil, wintergreen oil, and nutmeg oil can be highly effective. These oils also are some of the most powerful antioxidants known and can slow the formation of oxidized cholesterol and foam cells that are implicated in atherosclerosis. Helichrysum is also effective for preventing blood clot formation and promoting the dissolution of clots.

Foods rich in vitamin E and omega-3 fats are vital for proper blood viscosity.

FIRST RECOMMENDATIONS:
Clove, PanAway

Other Single Oils:
Helichrysum, wintergreen, nutmeg, lemon, grapefruit, cistus

Other Blends:
Longevity

EO APPLICATION METHODS:
Topical:
DILUTE 50:50, on location 4-6 times daily
COMPRESS, warm, 15 min., 2 times daily
Massage equal parts lemon, lavender and

helichrysum on location, with or without hot packs

Ingestion:
CAPSULE, 00 size, 2 times daily between meals (this works especially well with helichrysum and cistus
RICE MILK, 2 times daily

DIETARY SUPPLEMENTATION:
Longevity Softgels, Thieves, Inner Defense, Ningxia Red, Omega Blue Softgels

OTHER:
Dentarome Toothpastes (all varieties) contain clove oil, a natural blood thinner

BLOOD DISORDERS

(See also CIRCULATION DISORDERS and CARDIOVASCULAR CONDITIONS)

Anemia

Anemia is a condition caused from the lack of red blood cells (or a lack of properly functioning ones). Nutritional deficiencies such as the lack of adequate iron or vitamin B12 can contribute to this disorder.

Anemia also may be caused by improper liver function. In such cases, a liver cleanse and liver nutritional support may be effective for rebuilding red blood cell counts.

There can be many different causes of anemia. You should see your physician for proper diagnosis if you suspect anemia.

FIRST RECOMMENDATIONS:
JuvaPower/Spice, Super B

Single Oils:
German chamomille

Blends:
Juva Cleanse

EO APPLICATION METHODS:
Topical:
NEAT, 2-3 drops on Vita Flex points of feet, or on inside of wrists, 2-3 times daily
Ingestion:
CAPSULE, 00 size, 2 times daily

DIETARY SUPPLEMENTATION:
Rehemogen, MultiGreens

Blood Circulation (Poor)

FIRST RECOMMENDATIONS:
Helichrysum, orange, Ningxia Red

Other Single Oils:
Cypress, clove, Idaho balsam fir

Blends:
Longevity, Valor, Valor Roll-on

EO APPLICATION METHODS:
Topical:
NEAT, 2-3 drops on Vita Flex points of feet, or on inside of wrists, 2-3 times daily
Ingestion:
CAPSULE, 00 size, 2 times daily

OTHER DIETARY SUPPLEMENTATION:
Longevity Softgels, dried wolfberries

Essential oils when used regularly can improve circulation as much as 20 percent.

Blood Detoxification

(see LIVER DISORDERS)

Detoxified blood results in better nutrient and oxygen flow and is the key to begin combating many diseases.

FIRST RECOMMENDATIONS:
JuvaCleanse, helichrysum, Di-Gize, geranium

Other Single Oils:
German chamomile, clove, Idaho balsam fir, mountain savor

EO APPLICATION METHODS:
Topical:
NEAT, 2-3 drops on Vita Flex points of feet, or on inside of wrists, 2-3 times daily
Ingestion:
CAPSULE, 00 size, 2 times daily

DIETARY SUPPLEMENTATION:
MultiGreens, Rehemogen, ICP, JuvaPower/Spice, Sulfurzyme, Balance Complete, pure rice bran

MSM (found in Sulfurzyme) purifies the body and blood.

Blood Platelets (Low)

DIETARY SUPPLEMENTATION:
Rehemogen

To enhance effects of Rehemogen use with JuvaTone, JuvaPower/Spice

BLOOD PRESSURE, HIGH (Hypertension)

(See HIGH BLOOD PRESSURE)

BONE PROBLEMS

(see also OSTEOPOROSIS and ARTHRITIS)

Broken Bones

A health professional should always be involved in the diagnosis and setting of a broken bone or a suspected broken bone.

FIRST RECOMMENDATIONS:
Thyme, thyme borneol, Aroma Siez, PanAway, Mega Cal, BLM

Single Oils:
Helichrysum, wintergreen, peppermint, spruce, Idaho balsam fir, pine, copaiba

Blends:
Aroma Siez, Relieve It, Deep Relief Roll-on

Another blend for bone healing:
• 8 drops Idaho balsam fir
• 6 drops helichrysum
• 1 drop myrrh
• 1 drop wintergreen

EO APPLICATION METHODS:
Topical:
NEAT OR DILUTE 50:50, 2-4 drops on location, 2-4 times daily as needed
Note: Apply extremely gently if bone break is suspected

Broken Bone Blend:
The following recipe is for a blend which can help relieve pain and speed the bone mending process:
• 10 drops wintergreen
• 3 drops helichrysum
• 2 drops lemongrass
• 3 drops pine
• 4 drops ginger
• 4 drops vetiver:

Prior to casting a broken bone, mix the above blend and very gently apply 5-10 drops (depending on size) to break area, neat. If there are any signs of skin sensitivity or irritation, be prepared to apply a small amount of V-6 Oil Complex.

OTHER DIETARY SUPPLEMENTATION:
PD 80/20, Super Cal, Mineral Essence, Omega Blue Softgels

OTHER:
Ortho Ease, Ortho Sport, Regenolone, Progessence Cream

Bone Pain

FIRST RECOMMENDATIONS:
Wintergreen, PanAway, spruce, copaiba

Other Single Oils:
Pine, balsam fir, helichrysum

EO APPLICATION METHODS:
Topical:
NEAT, 2-4 drops on location, 2-5 times daily as needed

DIETARY SUPPLEMENTATION:
Mega Cal

Poor bone and muscle development can indicate HGH and/or potassium deficiency.

Seeing the Big Picture Can Produce Big Results

When selecting oils, particularly for injuries, think through the cause and type of injury and select oils for each segment. For instance, a broken bone could encompass muscle damage, nerve damage, ligament strain or tear, inflammation, infection, bone injury, and possibly an emotion. Select an oil or oils for each perceived problem and apply in rotation or prepare a blend to cover all of them. The emotion may be shock, anger, guilt, or the person may have had pain for a long time and needs to release or relieve it. They may need some joy in their lives, etc. Work through all factors of the injury.

The Brain

BRAIN DISORDERS

(See NEUROLOGICAL DISEASES)

The fragrance of many essential oils exerts a powerful stimulus on the limbic system—a part of the brain located on the margin of the cerebral cortex, including the amygdala, hippocampus, and hypophysis which interact directly with the thalamus and hypothalamus. Acting together, these glands and brain components combined are the seat of memory, emotions, and sexual arousal, They also govern aggressive behavior. (See chart on page 2)

Alzheimer's Disease

Over 4 million Americans suffer from Alzheimer's. Alzheimer's was found to nearly double in subjects with high levels of homocysteine in the Framingham Study. Aluminum continues to be linked to Alzheimer's, yet older Americans are urged to get yearly flu shots which contain aluminum as an adjuvant. Pepper, grapefruit and fennel oils have been found to stimulate brain activity.[9] Peppermint oil has been helpful in protecting against stresses and toxins in brain cells.[10]

Dr. Richard Restick, a leading neurologist in Washington, D.C., stated that maintaining normal synaptic firing would forestall many types of neurological deterioration in the body.

Essential oils high in sesquiterpenes, such as vetiver, cedarwood, patchouli, German chamomile, myrrh, melissa, and sandalwood, are known to cross the blood-brain barrier. The following oils are general cerebral stimulants:

FIRST RECOMMENDATIONS:

Cedarwood, myrrh, Brain Power, Omega Blue Softgels

Other Single Oils:

Sandalwood, ginger, nutmeg, German chamomile, spikenard, *Eucalyptus globulus*, frankincense, patchouli

Helichrysum supports neurotransmitter activity. Nutmeg is a general cerebral stimulant and also has adrenal cortex-like activity.

Other Blends:

Valor, Valor Roll-on, Clarity

EO APPLICATION METHODS:
Topical:

NEAT, As needed, apply 1-2 drops directly onto the brain reflex centers. These points include the forehead, temples, and mastoids (the bones just behind the ears). Apply oils and mild direct pressure to the brainstem area (center top of neck at base of skull) and work down the spine.
VITA FLEX, apply 1-2 drops to brain points on feet 1-2 times daily
RAINDROP Technique once every two weeks. You can also apply 3-6 drops essential oils to a natural bristle brush (essential oils may dissolve plastic bristles). Rub and brush along the brain stem and spine.

DIETARY SUPPLEMENTATION:
MultiGreens, Power Meal, Sulfurzyme

Impaired Concentration

FIRST RECOMMENDATIONS:
Brain Power, peppermint

Other Single Oils:
Basil, lemon, bergamot, cardomom, rosemary

Other Blends:
Clarity, Harmony, Valor, Valor Roll-on

9. Haze S, Sakai K, Gozu Y, "Effects of fragrance on sympathetic activity in normal adults," *Jpn J Pharmacol* 2002 Nov;903):247-53.

10. Koo HN et al., "Inhibition of heat shock-induced apoptosis by peppermint oil in astrocytes," *J Mol Neurosci* 2001 Dec;17(3):391-6.

EO APPLICATION METHODS:
Topical:
NEAT, apply 1-2 drops to brain reflex centers (see above application), as needed
Inhalation:
DIRECT, 2-4 times daily, as needed

Impaired Memory

FIRST RECOMMENDATIONS:
Cardamom, rosemary

Other Single Oils:
Peppermint, basil, vetiver, rose, lemon, lemongrass

Peppermint improves mental concentration and memory. Dr. Dember conducted a study at the University of Cincinnati in 1994 showing that inhaling peppermint increased mental accuracy by 28 percent.[11]

The fragrance of diffused oils, such as lemon, have also been reported to increase memory retention and recall.

Blends:
Brain Power, Clarity, M-Grain, En-R-Gee

Memory blend Recipe #1:
- 5 drops basil
- 10 drops rosemary
- 2 drops peppermint
- 4 drops helichrysum

Memory blend Recipe #2:
- 4 drops lavender
- 3 drops geranium
- 3 drops rosewood
- 3 drops rosemary
- 2 drops tangerine
- 1 drops spearmint
- 2 drops Idaho tansy

EO APPLICATION METHODS:
Topical:
DILUTE 50:50, apply 2-3 drops on temples, forehead, mastoids (bone behind ears) and/or brainstem (back of neck), as needed
Inhalation:
DIRECT, 2-6 times daily, as needed

DIETARY SUPPLEMENTATION:
Longevity Softgels, MultiGreens, Mineral Essence

Right Brain vs. Left Brain

The left brain is logical, rational, and judgmental. The right brain is artistic and creative.

Essential oils are believed to heighten right brain activity while increasing left brain integration.

OTHER:
Vascular cleansing may improve mental function by supporting improved blood flow, boosting distribution of oxygen and nutrients (see Vascular Cleansing).

Mental Fatigue

FIRST RECOMMENDATIONS:
Brain Power, frankincense, cardamom

Other Single Oils:
Rosemary, vetiver, cedarwood, peppermint

Other Blends:
Clarity.

EO APPLICATION METHODS:
Topical:
NEAT, apply 1-2 drops to brain reflex centers (forehead, temples, mastoids), and/or brain stem (back of neck) as needed
Inhalation:
DIRECT, as needed

Strokes

Two principal kinds of strokes can damage the brain: thrombotic strokes and hemorrhagic strokes. Thrombotic strokes are caused from a blood clot lodging in a cerebral blood vessel and cutting blood supply to a part of the brain. A hemorrhagic stroke is caused by an aneurysm, or a weakness in the blood vessel wall that balloons out and ruptures, spilling blood into the surrounding brain tissue. Strokes are very serious events and if you suspect that you may be susceptible, immediately see a physician.

To reduce your risk of stroke, essential oils can be used topically or as supplements. In particular, the essential oils of clove and nutmeg

---

11. Dember, Warm, 1994. USA. Parasuraman, Compendium of Olfactory Research

were found to exert anti-clotting action in clinical trials, and can be used as a preventative measure to reduce the risk of thrombotic stroke.

Thrombotic Strokes

(See BLOOD CLOTS in BLOOD DISORDERS)

FIRST RECOMMENDATIONS:
  Clove, helichysum, nutmeg, Longevity, Aroma Life

Single Oils:
  Cypress, juniper, grapefruit, orange, cistus

EO APPLICATION METHODS:
  Topical:
    DILUTE 50:50, apply 1-3 drops on temples, forehead, mastoids, back of neck and at base of throat just above clavicle notch
    VITA FLEX, apply 1-3 drops on brain points of feet
  Ingestion:
    CAPSULE, 00 size, 2 times daily
    RICE MILK, 2 times daily

DIETARY SUPPLEMENTATION:
  Sulfurzyme, Mega Cal, Omega Blue Softgels

These supplements are rich in essential minerals, fatty acids, and nutrients necessary for regenerating and rebuilding damaged nerve tissues.

Hemorrhagic Strokes

(See also HEMORRHAGING or BRUISING)

The essential oil of cypress may help strengthen vascular walls.

FIRST RECOMMENDATIONS:
  Cypress

Single Oils:
  Helichrysum

Blends:
  Longevity

EO APPLICATION METHODS:
  Ingestion:
    CAPSULE, 00 size, 2 times daily
    RICE MILK, 2 times daily

DIETARY SUPPLEMENTATION:
  Sulfurzyme, Super Cal

BREASTFEEDING

Dry, Cracked Nipples

FIRST RECOMMENDATIONS:
  Myrrh, KidScents Tender Tush, Essential Beauty Serum for Dry Skin, rosehip seed oil, virgin coconut oil.

Other Single Oils:
  Geranium, sandalwood

Blends:
  Valor, Valor Roll-on

EO APPLICATION METHODS:
  Topical:
    DILUTE 50:50 and massage over breast and on Vita Flex points of the feet

Mastitis (Infected Breast)

FIRST RECOMMENDATIONS:
  Tea tree, manuka, thyme

Other Single Oils:
  Roman chamomile, clove, rosemary, lavender

EO APPLICATION METHODS:
  Topical:
    DILUTE 20:80 and massage over breast and on Vita Flex points of the feet.

Breast blend #1:
  • 3 drops thyme
  • 7 drops PanAway
  • 1 tsp V6 Oil Complex

Breast blend #2:
  • 3 drops lemon
  • 4 drops thyme
  • 2 drops citronella
  • 1 tsp V6 Oil complex

Massage either of these blends on the breasts and under armpits twice daily.

BRUISING

(See also BLOOD CLOTS in BLOOD DISORDERS)

Some people bruise easily because the capillary walls are weak and break easily, particularly in the skin. Those who bruise easily may be deficient in vitamin C.

Essential oils can help speed the healing of bruises and reduce the risk of blood clot formation. Oils like cypress help to strengthen capillary walls, while oils like helichrysum help speed the reabsorption of the blood that has collected in the tissue.

FIRST RECOMMENDATIONS:

Helichrysum, geranium, lavender

Other Single Oils:

Cypress, white fir, Roman chamomille

Bruise blend Recipe 1:

- 5 drops helichrysum
- 4 drops lavender
- 3 drops cypress
- 3 drops lemongrass
- 3 drops geranium

Bruise blend Recipe 2:

- 6 drops clove
- 4 drops black pepper
- 3 drops peppermint
- 2 drops marjoram
- 2 drops geranium
- 2 drops cypress

EO APPLICATION METHODS:

Topical:

NEAT or DILUTE 50:50, 1-3 drops on bruised area, 2-5 times daily. Helichrysum is especially beneficial in healing bruises when applied neat on location.
COMPRESS, cold, on location, 2-4 times daily, as needed

DIETARY SUPPLEMENTATION:

MultiGreens, JuvaTone, JuvaPower/Spice, Super C

Regimen:

- Apply 2-3 drops of helichrysum on location neat, 2 times daily
- Super C Chewable: 1-4 tablets daily.
- MultiGreens: 2-3 capsules 3 times daily.

BURNS

(See also SKIN DISORDERS and SHOCK)

There are three types of burns:

- First-degree burns only damage the outer layer of the skin. Sunburn is typically a first-degree burn.

- Second-degree burns damage both the outer layer and the underlying layer known as the dermis. It is manifested by blisters.

- Third-degree burns not only destroy or damage skin but can even damage underlying tissues.

Burns can be caused by sunlight, chemicals, electricity, radiation, or heat. Thermal burns are the most common type.

Aloe vera gel (contained in LavaDerm) has been extensively used in the treatment of burns and has been studied for its anti-inflammatory and tissue-regenerating properties. Helichrysum, lavender, and Idaho balsam fir oils support tissue regeneration and reduce scarring and skin discoloration.

Severe burns can result in dehydration and mineral loss. Inflammation often accompanies burns, so dietary protocols should be used to lessen inflammation.

NOTE: All burns can be serious, therefore, seek medical attention if necessary. If the burn is large or severe, the individual may go into shock. Inhaling oils may help reduce the shock. (See SHOCK)

After a burn has started to heal and is drying and cracking, use Rose Ointment or body lotion with a few drops of lavender oil to keep skin soft and to promote faster healing.

DIETARY SUPPLEMENTATION:

Longevity Softgels, Sulfurzyme, Mega Cal, Omega Blue Softgels

First-Degree Burns (Sunburn)

The best prevention for sunburn is to avoid prolonged exposure to the sun. When you do go outdoors, always wear sunblock or lotion with an SPF greater than 15—especially during the summer and when you expect to be outdoors for a prolonged period of time.

In the event of a sunburn, lavender essential oil can offer excellent pain-relieving and healing benefits.

The Deadly Dehydration of Burns

The reason that burns tend to swell and blister is due to fluid loss from the damaged blood vessels. This is why it is important to keep the burn well hydrated and to drink plenty of water.

In cases of serious burns, fluid loss can become so severe that it sends the victim into shock and requires intravenous transfusions of saline solution to bring up blood pressure.

FIRST RECOMMENDATIONS:
Lavender, LavaDerm Spray

Other Single Oils:
Idaho balsam fir, helichrysum, blue cypress, rose, niaouli, German chamomille

Other Blends:
Gentle Baby, Australian Blue, Melrose, Valor, Valor Roll-on

EO APPLICATION METHODS:
Topical:
NEAT or DILUTE 50:50, 1-3 drops on burn location to cool tissue and reduce inflammation. Apply 3-6 times daily or as needed.
Other Topical Treatments:
Tender Tush Ointment, Rose Ointment

For fast relief of first-degree burns, spray burn immediately with LavaDerm Cooling Mist and continue misting as necessary to cool the area. Spray as often as 4-5 times an hour for the first two hours and follow with 2-3 drops of lavender or Idaho balsam fir oil.

Second-Degree Burns (Blisters)

(see also BLISTERS)

Spray burn immediately with LavaDerm Cooling Mist and continue misting when necessary to cool the area. Spray 4-5 times an hour for the first two hours and follow each spray with 2-3 drops of lavender oil.

Thereafter, apply LavaDerm every 15-30 minutes during the first day. (Keep LavaDerm refrigerated.) Apply 2-4 drops of lavender oil or niaouli oil as needed immediately after each LavaDerm misting.

On days 2 through 5, mist every hour and follow with 2-4 drops lavender oil or niaouli oil.

Continue using Lava Derm 3 to 6 times daily until healed. Apply Rose Ointment to keep tissue soft.

Third-Degree Burns

For third-degree burns, seek immediate medical attention and follow the health professional's advice.

BURSITIS

Bursitis is an inflammation of the bursa, which are small, fluid-filled sacs located near the joints. Bursa act as shock absorbers when muscles or tendons come into contact with bone. As the bursa become swollen, they result in pain, particularly when the affected joint is used.

Bursitis can be caused by injury, infection, or arthritis, and usually involves the joints of the knees, elbows, shoulders, and Achilles tendon. Occasionally bursitis can occur in the base of the big toe. Bursitis may signal the beginning of arthritis.

FIRST RECOMMENDATIONS:
Wintergreen, peppermint, copaiba, PanAway, Sulfurzyme

Other Single Oils:
Idaho balsam fir, basil, lavender, black pepper, Idaho tansy, elemi, oregano

Blends:
Relieve It, Sacred Mountain, Deep Relief Roll-on

EO APPLICATION METHODS:
Topical:
NEAT or DILUTE 50:50, 2-4 drops on affected area/joint 3-5 times daily, or as needed to soothe pain
COMPRESS, cold, around affected join, 1-3 times daily
OTHER DIETARY SUPPLEMENTATION:
Mega Cal, BLM

OTHER TOPICAL TREATMENT:
Ortho Ease

CANCERS

(NOTE: due to the complexity of dealing with any cancer, this section is presented in a different format to better explain the role essential oils may play in fighting this very serious condition.)

Cancer is among the most complex and difficult to treat of any human disease. A patient that has been diagnosed with cancer should always defer to his/her physician for primary care. Keeping this in mind, a number of patients have achieved successful remission while following the principles outlined in the section below.

It is important to note that many natural therapies—especially those using essential oils—work best in the early stages of cancer. In fact, citrus oils, high in d-limonene, including orange, grapefruit, and tangerine, work better as cancer preventatives than cancer treatments, although they have been shown to have powerful anti-cancer properties on all stages of cancer.

A 1996 study at Charing Cross Hospital in London, UK, achieved close to a 15% remission rate in patients with advanced colon and breast cancer using doses from 1 to 15 grams of d-limonene from orange oil as their only treatment. In patients with only weeks or months to live, limonene treatment extended patients' lives by up to 18 months in some cases.[12]

FOUNDATIONS OF NATURAL CANCER TREATMENT

Emotions and Cancer

Cancer should always be treated first by dealing with the emotions that contributed to the onset of the disease. In many cases, negative emotions and traumas not only triggered the cancer appearance, but may enhance its metastasis. Any kind of negative emotion—anger, fear, rage, helplessness, abandonment—can worsen a cancer prognosis and hasten its spread. Essential oils when used as the core of an emotional treatment program can have powerfully positive effects in improving emotions and potential disease outcomes. Essential oil blends such as White Angelica, Release, Grounding, Inner Child, Trauma Life, Peace and Calming, and SARA can form the core of any emotional treatment regimen.

(See Chapter 24 on Emotional Response with Essential Oils)

Cleansing and Removing Toxins

Industrial pollutants (ie., benzene, lead) and lifestyle toxins (ie., cigarette smoke chemicals, heterocyclic amines from overcooked meat) contribute to a vast majority of cancers. To help lower cancer risk, it is a matter of reducing exposure to these chemicals. In any cancer treatment program, these chemicals should be avoided at all cost, as they can damage DNA, decrease immunity, promote oncogenes, and accelerate cancer development.

Cleansing and Chelation

The foundation of any cancer program should begin with a period of fasting, cleansing, and chelation. Cleansing and chelation can help remove some of the toxin- and petrochemical-buildup that may have triggered the cancer initially; fasting can be one of the single most powerful anti-cancer tools available, particularly in the early stages. (It is NOT advised for cancer patients with advanced cancer or cachexia).

Essential oils that improve liver function and promote glutathione can form the core of any detoxification program. Lemon and orange oils were shown in studies at Johns Hopkins to substantially increase glutathione levels in the liver and colon, which can have beneficial effects on detoxifaction. Chelation can be particularly important in removing carcinogenic transition metals from the body. Studies in Germany have shown that transition metals such as iron, mercury, lead, zinc, nickel and cadmium can accumulate in high levels in tumors, particular in breast cancer tissue. Complexing and chelating to eliminate these metals can produce profound benefits in the earliest stage of cancer.[13]

---

12. Vigushin DM et al., Phase I and pharmacokinetic study of D-limonene in patients with advanced cancer. Cancer Research Campaign Phase I/II Clinical Trials Committee. Cancer Chemother Pharmacol. 1998;42(2):111-7.

13. Ionescu JG, et al., Increased levels of transition metals in breast cancer tissue. Neuro Endocrinol Lett. 2006 Dec;27 Suppl 1:36-9.

Rice bran is not only rich in metal-chelating Ip6, it also contains anti-cancer phytonutrients such as gamma oryzanol, and other compounds. It also rich in immune stimulating arabinoxylans that increase cancer cell death.[14]

The Ningxia wolfberry is rich in polysaccharides that similarly amplify immunity; a number of clinical research trials have shown that wolfberry compounds can dramatically improve cancer remissions, particularly when combined with immune-stimulating therapies.[15]

Cleansing and Chelation Products suitable for most cancers:

1. Essentialzyme/Polyzyme
   Take 2 to 4 capsules three times a day during the fast or cleanse; increase dosage to 6 to 12 capsules when cleanse is discontinued.
2. Calcium EDTA
   Take 500 mg three times a day for two weeks; rest one week before continuing.
3. Rice Bran (stabilized)
   Take 10 grams twice a day.

Why Fasting Works

New research has uncovered one of the properties that make cancer cells different from normal cells: insulin receptors. Cancer cells have over 10 times the number of receptors for insulin as a normal cell; excess insulin can stimulate cancer cells disproportionately compared to well-differentiated cells. Similarly, because cancer cells are fast-growing, they require far more glucose (blood sugar) than normal cells do. The most effective way of lowering both insulin levels and blood glucose levels is with a fast. Bernard Jensen ND, used a 180-day fast, composed initially of only barley grass juice, to effectively eliminate a case of advanced metastatic prostate cancer. Even partial fasts in which refined carbohydrates are eliminated and caloric intake reduced to 500 and 1000 calories can be potentially very therapeutic.

Determining Hormone Sensitivity

A number of human cancers are known as "hormone sensitive" cancers. In the case of women, hormone-receptor positive cancers require estrogen for growth; in the case men, hormone-receptor positive cancers require testosterone for growth.

In women, breast cancer, ovarian cancer, uterine cancer, all can be either estrogen receptor negative or positive. If a female has an estrogen receptor positive cancer, it is strongly recommended that she avoid all potentially estrogenic essential oils unless otherwise directed by a health care professional. Some of these oils include, fennel, clary sage, melissa, lemongrass, lemon myrtle, and geranium. Similarly, these patients should also avoid estrogenic types of foods such as soy, and estrogenic-types of herbs such as American ginseng and black cohosh.

For men, it is not known at this time whether essential oils would negatively impact men with testosterone-receptor positive cancers (i.e., prostate). In these cases, a health care professional should be consulted before herbs such as saw palmetto and essential oils such as clary sage are used.

CANCER AND ANTIOXIDANTS

It is recommended that patients seek the advise of their health care professional before embarking on any antioxidant program. Some studies have reported that certain antioxidants can reduce the effectiveness of some types of chemotherapy; however these studies only looked a small subset of cancer patients using a specific type of chemotherapy. A large number of other studies have found the opposite, showing that antioxidants can improve patient remissions and prognosis. In the case of radiation treatments, a number of well-controlled studies have similarly found that antioxidants can improve patient outcomes dramatically and counter the injury and immune suppression caused by these therapies.

14. Ghoneum M, Gollapudi S. Modified arabinoxylan rice bran (MGN-3/Biobran) enhances yeast-induced apoptosis in human breast cancer cells in vitro. Anticancer Res. 2005 Mar-Apr;25 (2A):859-70.

15. Cao GW, Yang WG, Du P. Observation of the effects of LAK/IL-2 therapy combining with Lycium barbarum polysaccharides in the treatment of 75 cancer patients. Zhonghua Zhong Liu Za Zhi. 1994 Nov;16(6):428-31.

Similar to DNA-protective essential oils, antioxidants produce their best results as cancer preventatives in the earliest stages of cancer. As cancer progresses, the likelihood of meaningful remissions using only antioxidants declines rapidly.

Groundbreaking research at Brigham Young University in Provo, Utah, has identified some of the most inhibitory essential oils against a variety of cancer cell lines. The oils were also tested for their lack of toxicity to normal cells. Those results are incorporated in the sections under the specific cancer sections included below.

INFLAMMATION AND CANCER

The link between cancer and inflammation has been strengthened in recent years. It is well known that the salicylates in aspirin which have highly anti-inflammatory effects reduce the risk of colon cancer dramatically. The natural salicylates found in the essential oil of wintergreen are very close in structure to the acetyl salicylic acid found in aspirin. According to Erica Leibert of Harvard University, wintergreen oil is 40% stronger than an aspirin equivalent with very similar anti-inflammatory properties.

Clove has been researched as a potential chemopreventive agent for lung cancer, because of its powerful anti-inflammatory effects.[16] The biochemical alpha humulene, found in balsam fir essential oil and copaiba essential oil, has also been shown to have significant cancer prevention properties through its anti-inflammatory action.[17]

Boswellic acids found in frankincense gum resin also have powerful anti-inflammatory effects. Myrrh gum has been studied for its ability to combat various cancers, include breast cancer.

ANTI-INFLAMMATORY PRODUCTS SUITABLE FOR MOST CANCERS:

1. Wintergreen essential oil
2. Frankincense gum resin
3. Myrrh gum resin
4. Clove essential oil
5. Frankincense essential oil
6. Myrrh essential oil

Immunity and Cancer

Enhancing immune function is a vital component of both traditional and complementary approaches to cancer. Typically, chemotherapy and radiation can drastically winnow down populations of T-cells and NK cells that are responsible for fighting tumor growth, and certain natural compounds can restore levels of these critical immune components.

Additionally, a heightened immune response during the earliest phases of cancer can have far greater effects than later on in the cancer cycle. It is important to note that immune stimulating products may not be suitable for all cancers, particularly patients with leukemia or non-Hodgkin's lymphoma, and for this reason these patients should be especially diligent in consulting their physician before use.

IMMUNE-ENHANCING PRODUCTS SUITABLE FOR MOST CANCERS:

1. ImmuPro
2. Dried Ningxia wolfberries
3. Essential oil of Balsam Fir (alpha humulene chemotype)

Essential oils with the broadest spectrum anti-cancer activity (breast, cervical, skin, prostate, etc.), Oils are ranked according to their potency.

1. Sandalwood
2. Balsam Fir (alpha humulene chemotype)
2. Thyme
3. Hyssop
4. Tsuga
5. Orange

Skin Cancer
1. Thyme
2. Sandalwood
3. Grapefruit
4. Hyssop
5. Tarragaon

16. Banerjee S., Panda CKL, Das S., Clove (Syzygium aromaticum L.), a potential chemopreventive agent for lung cancer. Carcinogenisis. 2006 Aug;27(8):1645-54. Epub 2006 Feb 25.

17. Legault J, Dahl W, Debiton E, Pichette A, Madelmont JC. Antitumor activity of balsam fir oil: production of reactive oxygen species induced by alpha-humulene as possible mechanism of action. Planta Med. 2003 May;69(5):402-7.

Breast Cancer
1. Sandalwood
2. Myrtle
3. Tsuga

Prostate Cancer
1. Canadian Red Cedar
2. Thyme
3. Sandalwood
4. Myrtle
5. Dill

Lung Cancer
1. Sandalwood
2. Clove
3. Thyme
4. Hyssop

Cervical Cancer
1. Patchouli
2. Sandalwood
3. Galbanum
4. Valerian
5. Frankincense
6. Tsuga
7. Douglas Fir
8. Hyssop
9. Nutmeg
10. Tarragon

DOSAGES

Essential oils recommended for inclusion in therapy should be used at initial dosages of 400 mg (approx. 7 drops) diluted 50:50 in a 00 gel capsule, twice a day. This dose can be increased as needed (up to 6 capsules per day). It may be necessary to rotate among several different essential oils over the course of 90 days so that the cancer cells do not develop a resistance to a particular essential oil. The same oil should be used for no longer than 3 to 4 weeks before rotating to a different oil.

CANDIDA

(See FUNGAL INFECTIONS)

CANKER SORES

(See also COLD SORES)

These are technically known as aphthous ulcers and are not regarded as an infectious disease and are not caused by the Herpes virus.

Canker sores tend to occur because of stress, illness, weakened immune system, and injury caused by such things as hot food, rough brushing of teeth, or dentures. They appear under the tongue more commonly than cold sores.

FIRST RECOMMENDATIONS:
Niaouli, Thieves, Inner Defense, Thieves Antiseptic Spray

Other Single Oils:
Melissa, clove, lavender, sandalwood, blue cypress, thyme

Other Blends:
Melrose

EO APPLICATION METHODS:
Topical:
NEAT, 1 drop applied gently with fingertip to canker sore 4-8 times daily
Oral:
GARGLE, 2-4 times daily
Ingestion:
SYRUP, Maple, 2-4 times daily

OTHER DIETARY SUPPLEMENTATION:
ImmuPro

CARDIOVASCULAR CONDITIONS

(See also BLOOD CLOTS, BLOOD DISORDERS, CIRCULATION DISORDERS, HEART HEALTH, DIABETES)

Angina
FIRST RECOMMENDATIONS:
Clove, helichrysum, Omega Blue Softgels

Other Single Oils:
Goldenrod, orange, lemon, wintergreen

Other Blends:
Aroma Life, Peace & Calming

EO APPLICATION METHODS:
Topical:
NEAT, massage 1-3 drops over heart area
1-3 times daily. Also apply to left chest,
left shoulder and back of neck
VITA FLEX, massage 1 drop each of 2 or
3 of the recommended oils on heart Vita
Flex points on foot, hand, and arm,
as needed

DIETARY SUPPLEMENTATION:
Dried wolfberries, Ningxia Red, Mega Cal,
Longevity

Arteriosclerosis (Hardening of the Arteries)

This condition is defined as any one of a group
of diseases which causes a thickening and a loss
of elasticity of arterial walls. It can be caused by
inflammation and is frequently an underlying
cause of heart attack or stroke.

FIRST RECOMMENDATIONS:
Longevity, clove

Other Singles:
Helichrysum, lavender, German chamomille,
cumin

Other Blends:
Aroma Life

EO APPLICATION METHODS:
Topical:
BODY MASSAGE, 2 times weekly
Ingestion:
CAPSULE, 00 size, 3 times daily

DIETARY SUPPLEMENTATION:
Longevity Softgels, Omega Blue Softgels,
Mega Cal, True Source Multivitamins, dried
Wolfberries, Ningxia Red

Blood Pressure, High (Hypertension)

(See STRESS, HIGH BLOOD PRESSURE)

Congestive Heart Failure

(See *Heart Attack*)

Coenzyme Q10 is one of the most effective
supplements for supporting the heart muscle.

FIRST RECOMMENDATION:
Clove

Other Single Oils:
Helichrysum, cypress, goldenrod

Blends:
Aroma Life, Longevity

EO APPLICATION METHODS:
Topical:
NEAT, apply 1-2 drops to heart Vita Flex
points on foot, hand, and arm as described
under the 'Heart Vita Flex' section under the
topic, HEART HEALTH.

DIETARY SUPPLEMENTATION:
HRT, CardiaCare, Mega Cal, Mineral Essence

Fibrillation

This is a specific form of heart arrhythmia that
occurs when the upper heart chambers contract at
a rate of over 300 pulsations per minute. The
lower chambers cannot keep this pace, so
efficiency is reduced and not enough blood is
pumped. Palpitations, a feeling that the heart is
beating irregularly, more strongly, or more rapidly
than normal, are the most common symptoms.

FIRST RECOMMENDATIONS:
Valerian, Omega Blue Softgels, ylang ylang

Other Single Oils:
Goldenrod, marjoram, lavender, rosemary,
Idaho tansy

Other Blends:
Peace & Calming

EO APPLICATION METHODS:
Topical:
NEAT, massage 1-3 drops over heart area
1-3 times daily. Also apply to left chest,
left shoulder and back of neck
VITA FLEX, massage 1 drop each of 2 or
3 of the recommended oils on heart Vita
Flex points on foot, hand, and arm, as needed
Inhalation:
DIRECT, as often as needed to bring calm

DIETARY SUPPLEMENTATION:
HRT, CardiaCare, Mineral Essence, Mega
Cal, Sulfurzyme, dried wolfberries,
Coenzyme Q10

Heart Attack (Myocardial Infarction)

A heart attack is a circulation blockage resulting in an interruption of blood supply to an area of the heart. Depending on the size of the area affected, it can be mild or severe.

NOTE: Contact your physical immediately if you suspect a heart attack.

Many people do not understand how someone who is relatively healthy, with low cholesterol levels, suffers a heart attack with no explanation. The explanation is actually inflammation, the fundamental cause of heart disease.

Inflammation of the heart is caused when blood vessels leading to the heart are clogged and damaged. This releases a protein into the bloodstream called C-reactive protein. The level of this protein indicates the degree of inflammation in the linings of the arteries. Certain essential oils have been documented to be excellent for reducing inflammation. German chamomile contains azulene, a blue compound with highly anti-inflammatory properties. Peppermint is also highly anti-inflammatory. Other oils also have anti-inflammatory properties such as helichrysum, spruce, wintergreen, and valerian. Clove, nutmeg and wintergreen are natural blood thinners and help reduce blood clotting.

Magnesium, the most important mineral for the heart, acts as a smooth muscle relaxant and supports the cardiovascular system. Magnesium will act as a natural calcium channel blocker for the heart, lowering blood pressure and dilating the heart blood vessels (according to Terry Friedmann, MD).

FIRST RECOMMENDATIONS:
PanAway, MegaCal, wintergreen, aspirin

Other Single Oils:
Lavender, Roman chamomile, helichrysum, Idaho tansy, clove nutmeg, copaiba

Other Blends:
Longevity, Aroma Life, Peace & Calming, Relieve It, Valor, Valor Roll-on

EO APPLICATION METHODS:
Topical:
NEAT, apply 1-2 drops to heart Vita Flex points on foot, hand, and arm as described under the 'Heart Vita Flex' section under the topic, HEART HEALTH. If there is not enough time to remove shoes to get at the feet, apply the 'pumping' action to left hand and arm points. Using 1-2 drops of Aroma Life on each point will increase effectiveness and may even revive an individual having a heart attack while waiting for medical attention.

DIETARY SUPPLEMENTATION:
HRT, Longevity Softgels, CardiaCare, Mineral Essence, Omega Blue, Sulfurzyme

High Cholesterol

FIRST RECOMMENDATIONS:
Lemongrass, Omega Blue Softgels, Essentialzyme

Single Oils:
Rosemary, clove, German and Roman chamomile, spikenard

Blends:
Aroma Life, Longevity

Cholesterol reducing blend:
- 4 drops rosemary
- 5 drops Roman chamomile
- 3 drops helichrysum
- 5 drops lemongrass

EO APPLICATION METHODS:
Topical:
NEAT or DILUTE 50:50 if needed, 2-4 drops at pulse points where arteries are close to the surface (wrists, inside elbows, base of throat), 2-3 times daily. Also rub 6-10 drops along spine 3 times daily BODY MASSAGE, 2 times weekly
Ingestion:
CAPSULE, 00 size, 3 times daily
RICE MILK, 1-2 times daily

DIETARY SUPPLEMENTATION:
CardiaCare, JuvaPower/Spice, MultiGreens, Super C Chewable, Super Cal, Longevity Softgels, ICP, Polyzyme, Balance Complete, True Source Multivitamins

Supplementation regimens:
1. Do a colon and liver cleanse using ICP/ComorTone/Essentialzyme, JuvaTone, JuvaPower/Spice, JuvaFlex and JuvaCleanse.

JuvaTone is particularly useful for high cholesterol.

2. Magnesium acts as a smooth muscle relaxant and supports the cardiovascular system. It acts as a natural calcium channel blocker for the heart, lowering blood pressure and dilating the heart blood vessels (*Dr. T. Friedmann*). Mineral Essence and Mega Cal are good sources of magnesium.

Phlebitis (Inflammation of Veins)

(See Phlebitis under CIRCULATORY DISORDERS)

Tachycardia

Another form of heart arrhythmia in which the heart rate suddenly increases to 160 beats per minute or faster.

FIRST RECOMMENDATIONS:
Peace & Calming, ylang ylang, wintergreen

Other Single Oils:
Marjoram, German Chamomile, lavender, goldenrod, Idaho tansy

Other Blends:
Aroma Life, Acceptance

EO APPLICATION METHODS:
Topical:
NEAT, massage 1-3 drops over heart area 1-3 times daily. Also apply to left chest, left shoulder and back of neck
VITA FLEX, massage 1 drop each of 2 or 3 of the recommended oils on heart Vita Flex points on foot, hand, and arm, as needed
Inhalation:
DIRECT, as often as needed to bring calm

DIETARY SUPPLEMENTATION:
CardiaCare, HRT, Sulfurzyme, Coenzyme Q10

CARPAL TUNNEL SYNDROME

(See NERVE DISORDERS)

CARTILEGE

(See CONNECTIVE TISSUE)

CATARACTS

(See EYE DISORDERS)

CELLULITE

Cellulite is one of the harder types of fats to dissolve in the body. Cellulite is an accumulation of old fat cell clusters that solidify and harden as the surrounding tissue loses its elasticity.

Excess fat is undesirable for two reasons:

1. The extra weight puts an extra load on all body systems, particularly the heart and cardiovascular system, as well as the joints (knees, hips, spine etc).

2. Toxins and petrochemicals (pesticides, herbicides, metallics) tend to accumulate in fatty tissue. This can contribute to hormone imbalance, neurological problems, and a higher risk of cancer.

Essential oils such as ledum, tangerine and grapefruit may help reduce fat cells. Cypress enhances circulation to support the elimination of fatty deposits. The essential oils of lemongrass and spearmint also may help fat metabolism. Cel-Lite Magic Massage Oil contains many of these oils and may help reduce cellulite deposits.

Cellulite is slow to dissolve, so target areas should be worked for a month or more in conjunction with weight training, a weight loss program, and drinking purified water—one-and-a-half times the body weight in ounces each day. Be patient. You should begin to see results in 4 to 6 weeks when using the oils in combination with a muscle-building and weight-loss regimen.

FIRST RECOMMENDATIONS:
Grapefruit, spearmint

Single Oils:
Rosemary, lemon, tangerine, cypress, fennel, juniper, lemongrass

Blends:
EndoFlex

Cellulite blend #1:
• 10 drops grapefruit
• 5 drops lavender
• 3 drops helichrysum
• 3 drops patchouli
• 4 drops cypress

Cellulite blend #2: (Bath):
- 5 drops juniper
- 3 drops orange
- 3 drops cypress
- 3 drops rosemary

Mix the above recipe together with 2 tablespoons Epsom salts or Bath Gel Base and dissolve in warm bath water. Massage with Cel-Lite Magic after bath.

EO APPLICATION METHODS:
Topical:
DILUTE 50:50, massage 3-6 drops vigorously on cellulite locations at least 3 times daily, especially before exercising.
BATH SALTS, 2-4 times weekly
Apply 3-5 drops of grapefruit, neat, 1-2 x daily to increase fat-reducing action in areas of fat rolls, puckers, and dimples.

DIETARY SUPPLEMENTATION:
Thyromin, ThermaBurn, Power Meal, Omega Blue Softgels, Balance Complete

Thyromin and ThermaBurn balance and boost metabolism.

Topical Treatments:
Cel-Lite Magic Massage Oil

CEREBRAL PALSY

(See MUSCLES, NEUROLOGICAL DISORDERS)

CHEMICAL SENSITIVITY REACTION

Environmental poisoning and chemical sensitivity are becoming a major cause of discomfort and disease. Strong chemical compounds, such as insecticides, herbicides, and formaldehyde found in paints, glues, cosmetics, and finger nail polish, enter the body easily. Symptoms include indigestion, upper and lower gas, poor assimilation, poor electrolyte balance, rashes, hypoglycemia, allergic reaction to foods and other substances, along with emotional mood swings, fatigue, irritability, lack of motivation, lack of discipline and creativity.

FIRST RECOMMENDATIONS:
Wintergreen, frankincense gum resin, myrrh gum resin, JuvaPower/Spice

Other Single Oils:
Frankincense, sandalwood, copaiba, *eucalyptus globulus*

Other Blends:
PanAway

EO APPLICATION METHODS:
Topical:
DILUTE 50:50, on affected areas, 2-4 times daily
Ingestion:
CAPSULE, 00 size, 1-3 times daily

OTHER DIETARY SUPPLEMENTATION:
ImmuneTune, JuvaTone, Balance Complete ICP/ComforTone/Essentialzyme, Life 5

For headache relief:
- 4 Essentialzyme
- 1/8 tsp M-Grain diluted 50:50 in vegetable oil

Drink 2-3 large glasses of water immediately after using these products.

CHICKEN POX (Herpes Zoster)

(See also COLD SORES, BLISTERS)

Chicken pox (also known as shingles, *Varicella Zoster*, or *Herpes zoster*) is caused by a virus that is closely related to the Herpes simplex virus. This virus is prone to hiding along nerves under the skin and may cause recurring infection through life.

When *Herpes zoster* infection occurs in children it is known as chicken pox; when infection occurs or reoccurs in adults, it is known as shingles.

A childhood bout with chicken pox may leave the virus dormant in sensory (skin) nerves. If the immune system is taxed by severe emotional stress, illness, or long-term use of corticosteroids, the dormant viruses may become active and start to infect the pathway of the skin nerves.

FIRST RECOMMENDATIONS:
Lemongrass, niaouli, Thieves, Inner Defense softgels

Single Oils:
Lavender, tea tree, sandalwood, melissa, clove, blue cypress, cumin, geranium, wintergreen

Blends:
Australian Blue, Melrose

EO APPLICATION METHODS:
Topical:
Add 20 drops of essential oils (using any of the above oils) to 1 tablespoon of calamine lotion or V6 Oil Complex and lightly dab on spots (lesions)

DIETARY SUPPLEMENTATION:
ImmuPro, Balance Complete

Topical Treatments:
Thieves Antiseptic Spray, Ortho Ease, LavaDerm Cooling Mist

Shingles

Shingles is a short-lived viral infection of the nervous system that starts with fatigue, fever, chills, and intestinal upset. The affected skin areas become sensitive and prone to blistering. One attack usually provides immunity for life. However, for many people, particularly the elderly, pain can persist for months, even years.

NOTE: Occurrences of shingles around the eyes or on the forehead can cause blindness. Consult an ophthalmologist (eye doctor) immediately if such outbreaks occur.

FIRST RECOMMENDATIONS:
Ravansara, niaouli, Thieves

Other Single Oils:
Blue cypress, elemi, Idaho tansy, tea tree, oregano, mountain savory, sandalwood, thyme, peppermint, tamanu (a fatty acid oil)

Other Blends:
Australian Blue, Exodus II

Shingles blend #1:
- 10 drops German chamomile
- 5 drops lavender
- 4 drops sandalwood
- 2 drops geranium

Shingles blend #2:
- 10 drops sandalwood
- 5 drops blue cypress
- 4 drops peppermint
- 2 drops ravensara

EO APPLICATION METHODS:
Topical:
DILUTE 50:50, apply 6-10 drops on affected area, back of neck and down the spine 1-3 times daily.
COMPRESS, alternating warm and cold, on spine, 1-3 times daily

Shingles regimen:
A. Layering in Raindrop Technique style, apply 3-4 drops each of oregano, mountain savory and thyme along the spine
B. Apply 15-20 drops V6 Oil Complex to the spine, massage briefly over the other oils, then cover the skin with a dry towel and apply a warm pack for 15-20 minutes). NOTE: Be cautious about warming. If the back becomes too hot, remove the warm pack immediately and add more V6 Oil Complex to cool.
C. Remove the warm pack and towel, then layer 4-8 drops each of tea tree, elemi and peppermint along the spine
D. Put the dry towel back over the skin and apply an ice pack for 30 minutes.

DIETARY SUPPLEMENTATION:
Super Cal, Sulfurzyme

CHOLECYSTITIS

(See GALLBLADDER INFECTION)

Inflammation of the gallbladder due to obstruction of the gallbladder (bile) outlet with symptoms ranging from mild edema and congestion to severe infection and perforation.

CHOLERA

Cholera is an acute diarrheal disease caused by an interotoxin produced by a gram negative bacteria called *Vibrio cholerae*. Severe cases are marked by vomiting, muscle cramps and constant watery diarrhea which can result in serious fluid loss, saline depletion, acidosis and shock. The disease is typically found in India and Southeast Asia and is spread by feces-contaminated water and food. If you suspect cholera, you should immediately seek professional medical advice.

A recent study shows that lemon—freshly squeezed juice, peel, and essential oil—act as a biocide against *Vibrio cholerae* with no harmful side effects.[18]

FIRST RECOMMENDATION:
Lemon

Other Single Oils:
Clove, thyme, rosemary, oregano

EO APPLICATION METHODS:
Ingestion:
CAPSULE, 00 size, 3 times daily with meals

CHOLESTEROL

(See CARDIOVASCULAR CONDITIONS)

CHRONIC FATIGUE SYNDROME

(See EPSTEIN-BARR VIRUS)

CIRCULATION DISORDERS

(See also BLOOD CLOTS, BLOOD DISORDERS and CARDIOVASCULAR CONDITIONS)

Good circulation is undoubtedly the foundation of good health; however, sluggish or inadequate circulation can result in tissue toxicity, starvation, and eventually, cellular death. The damage that poor or inadequate circulation can cause is best illustrated in the gangrene that often develops in the legs and arms of many advanced diabetic patients. Because the blood cannot efficiently circulate through these areas, parts of the tissues literally rot away.

Niacin (nicotinic acid) is effective for dilating blood vessels and increasing circulation. The amino acid L-arginine and cayenne pepper have similar properties.

Essential oils may be extremely useful for promoting circulation. Myrtle, lemon, and cypress have been used to strengthen and dilate capillaries and increase circulation. Helichrysum, clove and citrus oils are natural blood thinners, balancing the

viscosity or thickness of the blood, and they amplify the effects of cypress. Marjoram relaxes muscles and dilates blood vessels, while nutmeg acts as a circulatory stimulant and anti-inflammatory. Goldenrod is a vein decongestant.

FIRST RECOMMENDATIONS:
Helichrysum, cypress, Aroma Life, clove

Other Single Oils:
Goldenrod, marjoram, wintergreen, myrtle, orange, grapefruit, peppermint, geranium, nutmeg, cistus, pink pepper, copaiba

Other Blends:
Pan Away, Longevity

EO APPLICATION METHODS:
Topical:
DILUTE 50:50, 2-4 drops on affected area 2-3 times daily. Also apply over carotid arteries and pulse points, wherever arteries are close to the skin surface.
BODY MASSAGE, 2-3 times weekly, start at feet and work up to heart
Ingestion:
CAPSULE, 0 size, 2 times daily

Circulation blend #1:
- 5 drops basil
- 8 drops marjoram
- 10 drops cypress
- 3 drops peppermint

Circulation blend #2:
- 3 drops basil
- 2 drops peppermint
- 4 drops cypress
- 8 drops marjoram
- 10 drops wintergreen

EO APPLICATION:
Topical:
DILUTE either of the above recipes in 1 tsp V6 Oil Complex and massage on location, 1-3 times daily

DIETARY SUPPLEMENTATION:
Super B, Cel-Lite Magic, HRT, CardiaCare, MultiGreens, Longevity Softgels, Rehemogen, and JuvaTone, JuvaPower/Spice

---

18. de Castillo et al., "Bactericidal activity of lemon juice and lemon derivatives against Vibrio cholerae," *Biol Pharm Bull* 2000 Oct;23(10):1235-8.

Circulation support regimen:

1. Put 25 drops HRT in 1 oz. distilled water and take 3 times daily
2. Rub 2-4 drops Aroma Life on the carotid arteries and pulse points, wherever an artery comes close to the skin, 2 times daily
3. Apply 2-4 drops Harmony over areas of poor circulation, 1-3 times daily as needed
4. Take 1/4 tsp of cayenne pepper with a full glass of pure water daily. Avoid using at bedtime.

Phlebitis (Inflammation of Veins)

(See also EDEMA)

Phlebitis refers to inflammation of a blood vein, usually due to a thrombus or blood clot. Symptoms include pain and tenderness along the course of the vein, discoloration of the skin, inflammatory swelling, joint pain, and acute edema below the inflamed site.

Natural progesterone is an effective anti-inflammatory.

FIRST RECOMMENDATIONS:
Aroma Life, juniper berry, cypress, wintergreen, tangerine, copaiba

Other Single Oils:
German chamomile, geranium, lavender, clove, nutmeg, helichrysum

Other Blends:
Longevity

Phlebitis Blend:
. 10 drops tangerine
. 5 drops cypress
. 4 drops juniper berry
. 7 drops lemon

EO APPLICATION METHODS:
Topical:
  NEAT, 2-4 drops on location 2-4 times daily
  COMPRESS, cold on location 2-4 times daily

DIETARY SUPPLEMENTATION:
Longevity Softgels

TOPICAL TREATMENT:
Progessence, Prenolone+

Varicose Veins (Spider Veins)

The blue color of varicose veins is coagulated blood in the surrounding tissue from hemorrhaging of capillaries around the veins. This blood has to be dissolved and re-absorbed.

Helichrysum helps dissolve the coagulated blood in the surrounding tissue.

FIRST RECOMMENDATIONS:
Helichrysum, Aroma Life, wintergreen

Other Single Oils:
Cypress, geranium, clove, peppermint, lemon, lavender

Other Blends:
Citrus Fresh, Aroma Siez

Varicose vein blend:
- 3-4 drops geranium
- 1 drop wintergreen
- 1 drop cypress
- 1 drop helichrysum

EO APPLICATION METHODS:
Topical:
  NEAT, apply 2-4 drops on location, massaging toward the heart, 3-6 times daily

Nightly Varicose Vein Regimen (legs):
A. Apply 1-3 drops varicose vein blend, neat, on location. Rub very gently towards heart with smooth strokes along the vein, then up and over the vein until the oil is absorbed.
B. Apply 6 drops tangerine and 6 drops cypress to the area. Gently massage until absorbed.
C. Do the lymphatic pump procedure described in Chapter 22.
D. Follow with a soft massage of the whole leg using 10-15 drops of Aroma Life, diluted 50:50
E. Wrap and elevate the leg. It is best to do this at night before retiring and to gradually elevate the foot off the bed, an inch more each night, until it is 4 inches higher than the head.
F. Wear support hose during the daytime. It may take up to a year to achieve desired results.

DIETARY SUPPLEMENTATION:
MultiGreens, Super B, Longevity Softgels, Omega Blue Softgels

TOPICAL TREATMENT:

OrthoEase, Acne-prone Essential Beauty Serum, Thieves Spray

COLD SORES (Herpes Simplex Type 1)

(See CANKER SORES)

Cold sores are also known as *Herpes labialis.* Diets high in the amino acid lysine can reduce the incidence of herpes. Conversely, the amino acid arginine can worsen herpes outbreaks.

Studies have shown neat applications of melissa to be effective against Herpes Simplex type I and Herpes Labialis. The healing period was shortened, the spread of infection prevented, and symptoms such as itching, tingling and burning were lessened.[19,20]

Peppermint and tea tree oils have also been studied for positive effects on the pain of herpes.[21,22]

FIRST RECOMMENDATIONS:

Peppermint, ravansara, Thieves, Inner Defense softgels

Other Single Oils:

Melissa, tea tree, niaouli, lavender, sandalwood, mountain savory, oregano, thyme

Other Blends:

Melrose, Purification

EO APPLICATION METHODS:
Topical:

NEAT, apply one drop as soon as a cold sore starts. Repeat 5-10 times daily. DILUTE 50:50, dilution in V6 Oil Complex will help to reduce discomfort or drying of the skin when applying essential oils to an open sore.

DIETARY SUPPLEMENTATION:

ImmuPro, Super C, MultiGreens, ICP/ComforTone/ Essentialzyme, JuvaTone, JuvaPower/Spice

TOPICAL TREATMENTS:

Thieves Antiseptic Spray

COLDS

(See also INFECTION, SINUS INFECTIONS, THROAT INFECTIONS, and LUNG INFECTIONS)

The best treatment for a cold or flu is prevention. Because many essential oils have strong antimicrobial properties, they can be diffused to prevent the spread of airborne bacteria and viruses. Antiviral essential oils (such as ravensara, hyssop, rosemary, tea tree, clove, oregano and thyme) and blends (such as Thieves, Inner Defense, Purification, R.C., Raven, and Sacred Mountain are very effective as preventative aids in avoiding colds as well as in helping the body defenses fight colds, once an infection has started. ImmuPro tablets are a powerful immune stimulant that can also increase infection resistance.

FIRST RECOMMENDATIONS:

Ravansara, blue cypress, Raven, Thieves, Inner Defense softgels, ImmuPro

Other Single Oils:

Peppermint, thyme, laurus nobilis, oregano, *Eucalyptus radiata*, tea tree, rosemary, mountain savory

Other Blends:

Melrose, Australian Blue, Purification, ImmuPower, Sacred Mountain, R.C., Breath Again Roll-on

Cold blend #1:
- 2 drops lemon
- 4 drops *Eucalyptus radiata*
- 5 drops rosemary
- 4 drops peppermint
- 3 drops cypress

Cold blend #2:
- 5 drops rosemary
- 4 drops R.C.
- 4 drops frankincense
- 1 drops oregano
- 2 drops peppermint

19. Dimitrova et al., "effect of Melissa officinalis L. extracts," Acta Microbiol Bulg 1993;29-:65-72.

20. Koytchev R, et al., "Balm mint extract (Lo-701) for topical treatment of recurring herpes labialis," Phytomedicine 1999 Oct;6(4):225-30.

21. Davies SJ, Harding LM, Baranowski AP, "A novel treatment of postherpetic neuralgia using peppermint oil," Clin J Pain 2002 May-Jun;18(3):200-2

22. Carson CF et al., "Melaleuca alternifolia (tea tree) oil gel (6%) for the treatment of recurrent herpes labialis," J Antimicrob Chemother 2001 Sep;48(3):450-1.

EO APPLICATION METHODS:
Inhalation:
   DIRECT, 3-5 times daily, or as needed
   VAPOR, 2-3 times daily, as needed
Ingestion:
   SYRUP, 3-6 times daily
Oral:
   GARGLE, 3-6 times daily
Topical:
   DILUTE 50:50, massage 1-3 drops on each
   of the following areas: forehead, nose,
   cheeks, lower throat, chest and upper back,
   1-3 times daily
   VITA FLEX, massage 1-3 drops on Vita
   Flex points on the feet, 1-2 times daily
   RAINDROP Technique, 1-2 times weekly
   BATH SALTS, (see below)

Bath blend for relief of cold symptoms:
- 2 drops Eucalyptus radiata
- 6 drops frankincense
- 3 drops laurus nobilis
- 6 drops spruce
- 15 drops ravensara
- 8 drops wintergreen

Stir above essential oils into 1/2 cup Epsom salt or baking soda, then add the mixture to hot bath water while tub is filling. Soak in hot bath until water cools.

DIETARY SUPPLEMENTATION:
   ImmuPro, Thieves Lozenges, Super C, Super
   C Chewables, Longevity Softgels, Exodus,
   ImmuneTune, True Source Multivitamins

Oral Treatment:
Thieves Antiseptic Spray

Congestive Cough

FIRST RECOMMENDATIONS:
Eucalyptus globulus, peppermint, R.C.,
Breath Again Roll-on, Raven

Other Single Oils:
Goldenrod, *Eucalyptus radiata*, niaouli, ledum,
spruce, ravensara, cedarwood, marjoram,
hyssop, copaiba

Other Blends:
Thieves, Inner Defense, Melrose, Peace &
Calming, Idaho balsam fir

EO APPLICATION METHODS:
Ingestion:
   SYRUP, 2-4 times daily
Inhalation:
   DIRECT, 3-6 times daily, as needed
   VAPOR, 1-3 times daily, as needed
Oral:
   GARGLE, 4-6 times daily
Topical:
   COMPRESS, warm, 1-2 times daily over
   chest, over throat and on upper back
DIETARY SUPPLEMENTATION:
ImmuPro, Super C, Super C Chewables, Exodus,
Thieves lozenges, Thieves Antiseptic Spray

Excess Mucus

(See MUCUS)

Head Cold / Sinus Congestion

(See also SINUS INFECTIONS)

FIRST RECOMMENDATIONS:
Eucalyptus globulus, *Eucalyptus radiata*,
Raven, R.C., Breath Again Roll-on

Other Single Oils:
Frankincense, pine, Idaho balsam fir,
peppermint, rosemary, ravensara,
wintergreen, lemon

Other Blends:
Melrose, Christmas Spirit

EO APPLICATION METHODS:
Inhalation:
   DIRECT, 3-5 times daily, or as needed
   VAPOR, 2-3 times daily, as needed
Ingestion:
   SYRUP, 3-6 times daily
Oral:
   GARGLE, 3-6 times daily
Topical:
   DILUTE 50:50, massage 1-3 drops on each
   of the following areas: forehead, nose,
   cheeks, lower throat, chest and upper
   back, 1-3 times daily
   VITA FLEX, massage 1-3 drops on Vita
   Flex points on the feet, 1-2 times daily
   RAINDROP Technique, 1-2 times weekly
   BATH SALTS, daily

COLITIS

Ulcerative Colitis

Also known as ileitis or proctitis, ulcerative colitis is marked by the inflammation of the top layers of the lining of the large intestine (colon) It is different from both irritable bowel syndrome (which has no inflammation) and Crohn's disease (which occurs deeper in the colon wall).

The inflammation and ulcerous sores that are characteristic of ulcerative colitis occur most frequently in the lower colon and rectum and occasionally throughout the entire colon.

Symptoms include: fatigue, nausea, weight loss, loss of appetite, bloody diarrhea, loss of body fluids and nutrients, frequent fevers, abdominal cramps, arthritis, liver disease, skin rashes

FIRST RECOMMENDATIONS:

Spearmint, wintergreen, DiGize, Digest & Cleanse Softgels

Other Single Oils:

Peppermint, tarragon, anise, fennel, orange

EO APPLICATION METHODS:

Ingestion:
  CAPSULE, 00 size, 2-3 times daily
  SYRUP, 3-4 times daily
Topical:
  DILUTE 50:50, massage 4-6 drops over lower abdomen area 2-4 times daily

OTHER DIETARY SUPPLEMENTATION:

ICP/ComforTone/Essentialzyme, Polyzyme, Detoxzyme, , Life 5

Viral Colitis

In cases where colitis is caused by a virus rather than a bacteria, the following is recommended:

FIRST RECOMMENDATIONS:

Lemongrass, clove, Melrose, Digest & Cleanse Softgels

Other Single Oils:

Blue cypress, melissa, oregano, cumin, tea tree, tarragon, niaouli, thyme, Roman chamomile, German chamomile, rosemary, peppermint, cinnamon

Other Blends:

Thieves, Inner Defense softgels, Longevity, Purification

EO APPLICATION METHODS:

Ingestion:
  CAPSULE, 00 size, 2-3 times daily
Topical:
  DILUTE 50:50, massage 4-6 drops over colon area 2-4 times daily
  VITA FLEX, 1-3 drops on colon Vita Flex points
  RAINDROP Technique, 1-2 times weekly
  COMPRESS, warm, diluted 20:80, using equal parts helichrysum and Di-Gize over colon area
Retention:
  RECTAL, use the formula below in a rectal implant 3 times weekly

Viral colitis retention blend:

- 2 drops oregano
- 2 drops thyme
- 3 drops niaouli
- 2 drops German chamomile
- 2 drops clove
- 2 drops peppermint

Mix above oils with 1 tablespoon V6 Advanced Oil Complex

OTHER DIETARY SUPPLEMENTATION:

Polyzyme, Essentialzyme, RoyaldophiIus, Longevity Softgels, Life 5

Colitis Regimen:

Take Polyzyme, along with ComforTone. Wait about 2 weeks or more before adding ICP. Start with a small amount of the ICP and increase slowly. If any discomfort is experienced, reduce the amount taken.

COMA

FIRST RECOMMENDATIONS:

Trauma Life, frankincense, Regenolone cream

Other Single Oils:

Valerian, vetiver, sandalwood, blue cypress, black pepper, peppermint, Idaho balsam fir, copaiba

Other Blends:

Hope, Valor, Valor Roll-on, Surrender, Brain Power

EO APPLICATION METHODS:
Inhalation:
DIFFUSION, 15 minutes, 4-7 times daily
Topical:
DILUTE 50:50, 3-5 drops on temples,
neck and shoulders

OTHER TOPICAL TREATMENTS:
Progessence cream, NeuroGen cream

CONFUSION

FIRST RECOMMENDATIONS:
Brain Power, cardamom, Mineral Essence

Other Single Oils:
Peppermint, lemon, rosemary, basil

Other Blends:
Clarity, M-Grain, Gathering

OTHER DIETARY SUPPLEMENTATION:
Mega Cal, Super B, Omega Blue Softgels,
Digest & Cleanse Softgels

CONNECTIVE TISSUE TRAUMA
(Ligaments, Tendons, Cartilage)

(See also MUSCLES)

Tendonitis, (often called Tennis Elbow and Golfer's Elbow), is a torn or inflamed tendon. Tenosynovitis, sometimes called "Trigger Finger," is an inflamed tendon being restricted by its sheath (particularly in thumbs and fingers). Repetitive use or infection may be the cause.

Mega Cal and BLM provide critical nutrients for connective tissue repair. Sulfurzyme, an outstanding source of organic sulfur, equalizes water pressure inside the cells and reduces pain.

PanAway reduces pain and lemongrass promotes the repair of connective tissue. Lavender with lemongrass, and marjoram with lemongrass work well together for inflamed tendons. Deep Relief Roll-on is a convenient way to apply a blend of oils that is both pain relieving and anti-inflammatory.

When selecting oils for injuries, think through the cause and type of injury and select appropriate oils. For instance, tendonitis could encompass

muscle damage, nerve damage, ligament strain/tear, inflammation, infection, and possibly an emotion. Therefore, select an oil or oils for each potential cause and apply in rotation or prepare a blend to address multiple causes. The emotional distress may be anger or guilt.

The oils in Ortho Sport and Ortho Ease Massage Oils reduce pain and promote healing.

EO APPLICATION METHODS:
Topical:
NEAT or DILUTE 50:50 as required. Gently massage 4-6 drops on affected areas 2-4 times daily. For swelling, elevate and apply ice packs
COMPRESS, cold, 2-4 times daily

DIETARY SUPPLEMENTATION:
Mega Cal, Super B, Super C, MultiGreens, Mineral Essence, Sulfurzyme (capsules or powder)

Topical Treatments:
Ortho Ease, Regenolone, NeuroGen

Cartilage Injury (knee, elbow , etc.)

FIRST RECOMMENDATIONS:
Wintergreen, copaiba, Cartilage blend (below)

Other Single Oils:
Peppermint, Idaho balsam fir, Douglas fir, white fir, marjoram

Cartilage blend:
• 9 drops lemongrass
• 10 drops marjoram
• 12 drops wintergreen

EO APPLICATION METHODS:
Topical:
NEAT or DILUTE 50:50 as required. Gently massage 4-6 drops on affected areas 2-4 times daily. For swelling, elevate and apply ice packs
COMPRESS, cold, 2-4 times daily

DIETARY SUPPLEMENTATION:
Mega Cal, Super B, Super C, MultiGreens, Mineral Essence, Sulfurzyme (capsules or powder)

Topical Treatments:
Ortho Ease, Regenolone, NeuroGen

Knee

Ligament Sprain or Tear

NOTE: For sprains, use cold packs. For any serious sprain or constant skeletal pain, always consult a health care professional. Any time there is tissue damage, there is always inflammation. Reduce this first.

FIRST RECOMMENDATIONS:
PanAway, peppermint, BLM

Other Single Oils:
Helichrysum, lavender, elemi, basil

Other Blends:
Relieve It, Aroma Siez, Deep Relief Roll-on

Sprain blend:
- 5 drops lemongrass
- 15 drops Aroma Siez

EO APPLICATION METHODS:
Topical:
NEAT or DILUTE 50:50 as required. Gently massage 4-6 drops on affected areas 2-4 times daily. For swelling, elevate and apply ice packs
COMPRESS, cold, 2-4 times daily

DIETARY SUPPLEMENTATION:
Mega Cal, Super B, Super C, MultiGreens, Mineral Essence, Sulfurzyme (capsules or powder)

Topical Treatments: Ortho Ease, Regenolone cream, NeuroGen cream

Tendonitis

FIRST RECOMMENDATIONS:
Marjoram, copaiba, Tendonitis blend #1(below), Regenolone Cream

Other Single Oils:
Lavender

Tendonitis blend #1:
- 4 drops vetiver
- 4 drops valerian
- 8 drops wintergreen

Tendonitis blend #2 (for pain relief):
- 10 drops rosemary
- 10 drops *Eucalyptus radiata*
- 10 drops peppermint

EO APPLICATION METHODS:
Topical:
NEAT or DILUTE 50:50 as required. Gently massage 4-6 drops on affected areas 2-4 times daily. For swelling, elevate and apply ice packs
COMPRESS, cold, 2-4 times daily

DIETARY SUPPLEMENTATION:
Mega Cal, Super B, Super C, MultiGreens, Mineral Essence, Sulfurzyme (capsules or powder). BLM

Other Topical Treatments:
NeuroGen

CONSTIPATION

(See DIGESTION PROBLEMS)

CONVULSIONS

(See also BRAIN DISORDERS)

Monitor diet. Discontinue sugar and dairy products, fried and processed foods.

FIRST RECOMMENDATIONS:
Brain Power, Valor, Valor Roll-on

EO APPLICATION METHODS:
Inhalation:
DIRECT, 4-6 times daily
DIFFUSION, 20 minutes, 2-3 times daily
Topical:
NEAT, apply 2-4 drops at base of skull, across the neck and top of spine (C1-C6 vertebrae) and on bottom of feet (for relief only)

CORNS

(See FOOT PROBLEMS)

COUGHS

(See COLDS, THROAT INFECTIONS and LUNG INFECTIONS)

CRAMPS (Abdominal)

(See DIGESTIVE PROBLEMS)

CRAMPS (Muscle)

(See MUSCLES)

CROHN'S DISEASE

(See also COLITIS, DIGESTION PROBLEMS, DIVERTICULITIS/DIVERTICULOSIS

Crohn's disease creates inflammation, sores, and ulcers on the intestinal wall. These sores occur deeper than ulcerative colitis. Moreover, unlike other forms of colitis, Crohn's disease can also occur in other areas of the body including the large intestine, appendix, stomach, and mouth.

Symptoms include:
• Abdominal cramping
• Lower right abdominal pain
• Diarrhea
• A general sense of feeling ill

Attacks may occur once or twice a day for life. If the disease continues for years, it can cause deterioration of bowel function, leaky gut syndrome, poor absorption of nutrients, loss of appetite and weight, intestinal obstruction, severe bleeding, and increased susceptibility to intestinal cancer.

Most researchers believe that Crohn's disease is caused by an overreacting immune system and is actually an autoimmune disease (where the immune system mistakenly attacks the body's own tissues). MSM has been extensively researched for its ability to treat many autoimmune diseases, and is the subject of research by University of Oregon researcher Stanley Jacobs. (MSM is a key ingredient in Sulfurzyme).

FIRST RECOMMENDATIONS:
Peppermint, copaiba, Omega Blue Softgels

Other Single Oils:
Ginger, nutmeg, wintergreen, German chamomille

Other Blends:
Di-Gize, PanAway

EO APPLICATION METHODS:
Ingestion:
CAPSULE, 00 size, 3 times daily
RICE MILK, 2-4 times daily
Topical:
RAINDROP Technique, 1-2 times weekly, using ImmuPower

DIETARY SUPPLEMENTATION:
Sulfurzyme, Polyzyme, AlkaLime, ICP/ComforTone/Essentialzyme, MultiGreens, Digest & Cleanse Softgels, Life 5, Ningxia Red, Balance Complete

Regimen for Crohn's disease:

Each phase lasts 3 days and should be added to the previous phases.

Phase I: Polyzyme: 1-2 capsules, 3 times daily.
Phase II: Take the Polyzyme in yogurt or liquid acidophilus, and charcoal tablets. Do not use ICP, ComforTone, or Essentialzyme yet.

Phase III: Drink 6 oz. raw juice (cherry, prune, celery, carrot or Ningxia Red) twice a day.

Phase IV: Take 2 scoops Balance Complete in water or juice twice a day.

Phase V: (Start only if no sign of bleeding).

• ComforTone (1 capsule morning and night) until stools loosen.
• ICP: Start with 1 level tsp., 2 times daily and gradually increase.

- Essentialzyme: Start 1 tablet, 3 times daily. If irritation occurs, discontinue for a few days and start again.

CUSHING'S DISEASE

(See ADRENAL GLAND IMBALANCE)

CUTS

(See WOUNDS, SCRAPES AND CUTS)

CYST (Ganglion)

FIRST RECOMMENDATIONS:
Oregano, thyme

EO APPLICATION METHODS:
Topical:
NEAT, 2 drops oregano first day, 2 drops thyme second day, apply on location as often as needed

CYSTITIS

(See URINARY TRACT/BLADDER INFECTION)

DANDRUFF

(See HAIR AND SCALP PROBLEMS)

DECONGESTANTS

(See MUCUS)

DENTAL PROBLEMS

(See ORAL CARE and Chapter 16: Oral Health Care)

DEPRESSION

(See also INSOMNIA)

Diffusing or directly inhaling essential oils can have an immediate positive impact on mood. Olfaction is the only sense that can have direct effects on the limbic region of the brain (see chart on page 2). Studies at the University of Vienna[23]
have shown that some essential oils and their primary constituents (cineol) can stimulate blood flow and activity in the emotional regions of the brain.

Clinical studies at the Department of Psychiatry at the Mie University of Medicine showed that lemon not only reduced depression but reduced stress when inhaled.[24]

FIRST RECOMMENDATIONS:
Cedarwood, lemon, Omega Blue Softgels

Other Single Oils:
Jasmine absolute, frankincense, peppermint, ylang ylang, rosemary

Other Blends:
Valor, Valor Roll-on, Passion, Hope, Joy

EO APPLICATION METHODS:
Inhalation:
DIFFUSION, 20 minutes, 3 times daily
DIRECT, 4-6 times daily

DIETARY SUPPLEMENTATION:
MultiGreens, Life 5, Super B, Mineral Essence, Balance Complete

Postpartum Depression

FIRST RECOMMENDATIONS:
Progessence cream, Prenolone cream

Single Oils:
Vetiver, lemon, clary sage, cedarwood, sandalwood, St. John's wort

Blends:
Trauma Life, Peace & Calming, Transformation, Dragon Time

EO APPLICATION METHODS:
Inhalation:
DIFFUSION, 20 minutes, 3 times daily
DIRECT, 4-6 times daily
Topical:
NEAT, 2-4 drops on temples and/or back of neck 2-4 times daily, as needed

DERMATITIS

(see Eczema/Dermatitis in SKIN DISORDERS)

23. Nasel et al., Functional imaging of effects of fragrances on the human brain after prolonged inhalation, *Chem Senses,* 1995 Jun;20(3):349-50.

24. Komori, Fujiward, Tanida, Nomura, Yokoyama "Effects of citrus fragrance on immune function and depressive states". *Neuroimmunomodulation.* 1995 May-Jun;2(3):174-80.

DIABETES (Blood Sugar Imbalance)

Diabetes is the leading cause of cardiovascular disease and premature death in westernized countries today. Diabetes causes low energy and persistently high blood glucose.

Type I Diabetes usually manifests by age 30 and is often considered to be genetic. Type II Diabetes generally manifests later in life and may have a nutritional origin.

Chromium has been shown to be helpful in helping the body metabolize sugars properly.

FIRST RECOMMENDATIONS:
Coriander, fennel, dill, dried wolfberries

Other Single Oils:
Clove, cinnamon, lemongrass

Blends:
EndoFlex, Di-Gize

EO APPLICATION METHODS:
Ingestion:
CAPSULE, 0 size, 3 times daily

DIETARY SUPPLEMENTATION:
Chromium picolinate, MultiGreens, Stevia, Mega Cal, Balance Complete, Essentialzyme, Carbozyme, True Source Multivitamins

Wolfberry balances the pancreas and is a detoxifier and cleanser. Diabetes is not common in certain regions of China, where wolfberry is consumed regularly.

The Stevia leaf extract is one of the most health-restoring plants known. It is a natural sweetener, has no calories, and does not have the harmful side effects of processed sugar or sugar substitutes. Substituting stevia for sugar helps rebuild glucose tolerance and normalize blood sugar fluctuations.

An East Indian herbal formula was shown in a *Journal of the National Medical Association* study to possess hypoglycemic activity. The herbs are: *Cinnamomum tamale, Pterocarpus marsupeum, Momordica charantia, Azardichta indica, Tinospora cordifolia, Aegle marmelose, Gymnema sylvestre, Syzygium cumini, Trigonella foenum graecum,* and *Ficus racemosa.*

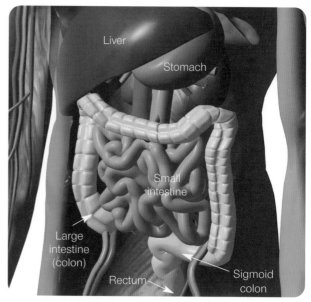

Gastrointestinal system

DIGESTION PROBLEMS

(See also Food Allergies under ALLERGIES)

Any of the following indicate that the digestive system is not digesting properly:
- Rumbling or gurgling sounds in the abdomen.
- Heartburn (may be a possible indication of candida).
- Constipation and/or diarrhea.
- Constant hunger or fatigue after eating.
- Food intolerance or food allergies.
- Intestinal parasites.

Poor bowel function is linked to enzyme deficiency, low fiber, insufficient liquid, bad diet, and stress.

Why Constipation Can Produce Problems Later in Life

The reason constipation creates diverticulosis is due to the fact that the muscles of the colon must strain to move an overly-hard stool, which puts excess pressure on the colon. Eventually weak spots in the colon walls form, resulting in the creation of abnormal pouches called diverticula.

These pouches can also be created by parasites which burrow and embed in the lining of the colon wall and lay eggs there. It's always wise to consider treating for parasites when diverticula are present.

Constipation

The principle causes of constipation are inadequate fluid intake and low fiber consumption. Constipation can eventually lead to diverticulosis and diverticulitis, conditions common among older people. Certain essential oils have demonstrated their ability to improve colon health through supporting intestinal flora, stimulating intestinal motility and peristalsis, fighting infections and eliminating parasites.

(see also DIVERTICULOSIS and DIVERTICULITIS)

FIRST RECOMMENDATIONS:
Digest & Cleanse Softgels, ICP, Comfortone, peppermint

Other Single Oils:
Ginger, fennel, tarragon, anise seed.

Other Blends:
Di-Gize

EO APPLICATION METHODS:
Ingestion:
CAPSULE, 00 size, 2-3 times daily
RICE MILK, 2-4 times daily

OTHER DIETARY SUPPLEMENTATION:
Prune juice, Aloe vera juice, Mega Cal, Balance Complete, Essentialzyme, Polyzyme, Longevity Softgels, Life 5

Regimen:
- Essentialzyme: 3 to 6 capsules, 3 times daily
- ComforTone: Start with 1 capsule and increase next day to 2 capsules. Continue to increase 1 capsule each day until bowels start moving.
- ICP: One week after beginning ComforTone, start with 1 Tbsp., 2 times daily and then increase to 3 times daily, up to 2 Tbsp., 3 times daily.
- 3 scoops Balance Complete/day or as needed
- Drink at least 1/2 cup unsweetened cherry juice, prune juice, pineapple juice, or other raw fruit and vegetable juices, each morning.
- Drink 8 glasses of pure water daily.

Cramps (Stomach)

FIRST RECOMMENDATIONS:
Ginger, peppermint, Digest & Cleanse Softgels, Life 5

Other Single Oils:
Rosemary

EO APPLICATION METHODS:
Ingestion:
CAPSULE, 0 size, 2 times daily
RICE MILK, 1-3 times daily
Topical:
DILUTE 50:50, apply 6-10 drops over stomach area 2 times daily
COMPRESS, warm, 1-2 times daily
VITA FLEX, 1-3 drops on stomach Vita Flex points of feet

Diarrhea

FIRST RECOMMENDATIONS:
Life 5, peppermint, Di-Gize, nutmeg

Other Single Oils:
Ginger, oregano, mountain savory, clove, lemon

Other Blends:
Thieves

Diarrhea detox blend:
- 4 drops lemon
- 3 drops mountain savory
- 2 drops wintergreen

EO APPLICATION METHODS:
Ingestion:
CAPSULE, 0 size, 2 times daily
RICE MILK, 1-3 times daily
Topical:
DILUTE 50:50, apply 6-10 drops over stomach area 2 times daily
COMPRESS, warm, 1-2 times daily
VITA FLEX, 1-3 drops on stomach Vita Flex points of feet

OTHER DIETARY SUPPLEMENTATION:
ComforTone, Essentialzyme, Super Cal Inner Defense softgels

A maintenance dosage of ComforTone has helped to protect travelers going to other countries from diarrhea and other digestive discomforts.

Nutmeg has been shown to have powerful action against diarrhea in a number of medical studies.[25,26]

Gas, Flatulence

(See also FLATULENCE)

FIRST RECOMMENDATIONS:
Tarragon, Detoxzyme, Digest & Cleanse Softgels

Other Single Oils:
Peppermint, nutmeg, anise, fennel

Other Blends:
Di-Gize, Longevity

EO APPLICATION METHODS:
Ingestion:
CAPSULE, 0 size, 2 times daily

DIETARY SUPPLEMENTATION:
Essentialzyme, Polyzyme, Life 5, Carbozyme

Giardia

(See FOOD POISONING)

FIRST RECOMMENDATION:
Basil

EO APPLICATION METHODS:
Take 4 drops basil oil diluted 50:50 in a capsule every 2 hours.

Heartburn

Lemon juice is one of the best remedies for heartburn. Mix the juice of 1/2 squeezed lemon in 8 oz. water and sip slowly upon awakening each morning.

By ingesting lemon juice and/or essential oils the stomach stops excreting digestive acids. Therefore alleviating heartburn or other stomach ailments.

Do NOT take peppermint for heartburn.

FIRST RECOMMENDATIONS:
Spearmint, Alkalime, Essentialzyme

Other Single Oils:
Ginger, lemon

Heartburn blend:
- 2 drops basil
- 1 drop Idaho tansy
- 8 drops sage
- 3 drops sandalwood

EO APPLICATION METHODS:
Ingestion:
CAPSULE, 0 size, 2 times daily
Topical:
DILUTE 50:50, apply 6-10 drops over stomach area twice daily
COMPRESS, warm, 1-2 times daily
VITA FLEX, 1-3 drops on stomach Vita Flex points of feet

OTHER DIETARY SUPPLEMENTATION:
ICP, ComforTone, Polyzyme, Detoxzyme

Hiccups

(See HICCUPS as a main heading)

Indigestion (Bloating)

FIRST RECOMMENDATIONS:
Essentialzyme, Carbozyme, wintergreen, Digest & Cleanse Softgels

Other Single Oils:
Peppermint, nutmeg, fennel, ginger, cumin, spearmint, grapefruit, copaiba

Other Blends:
Di-Gize, Longevity

EO APPLICATION METHODS:
Ingestion:
CAPSULE, 0 size, 2 times daily
RICE MILK, 1-3 times daily, as needed
Topical:
DILUTE 50:50, apply 6-10 drops over stomach area twice daily
VITA FLEX, 1-3 drops on stomach Vita Flex points of feet

25. Weiss HJ, et al., "The effect of salicylates on the hemostatic properties of platelets in man," *J Clin Invest* 1968 Sep;47(9):2169-80.

26. Fawell WN, Thompson G, "Nutmeg for diarrhea of medullary carcinoma of thyroid," *N Eng J Med* 1973 Jul 12;289(2):108-9.

DIETARY SUPPLEMENTATION:
ICP/ComforTone/Essentialzyme, Polyzyme, Carbozyme

Two to four capsules of Polyzyme, Essentialzyme or Detoxzyme taken before eating helps with digestion and upset stomach. When heaviness is felt in the stomach, Polyzyme is a beneficial companion to Di-Gize.

Nausea

(See NAUSEA as a main heading)

Ulcers, Stomach

Ulcers may be caused by *Helicobacter pylori* bacteria. Several gastroduodenal diseases include gastritis and gastric or peptic ulcers.

FIRST RECOMMENDATIONS:
Lemongrass, copaiba, Digest & Cleanse Softgels, Inner Defense softgels

Other Single Oils:
Lemon myrtle, German chamomile, oregano, thyme

Other Blends:
Thieves, Di-Gize

EO Application Methods:
Ingestion:
CAPSULE, 0 size, 1 capsule
3 times a day for 20 days

DIPTHERIA

An acute infectious disease caused by toxigenic strains of *Corynebacterium diphtheriae,* acquired by contact with an infected person or carrier. It is usually confined to the upper respiratory tract, and characterized by the formation of a tough false membrane attached firmly to the underlying tissue that will bleed if forcibly removed. In the most serious infections the membrane begins in the tonsil area and may spread to the uvula, soft palate and pharyngeal wall, followed by the larynx, trachea, and bronchial tree where it may cause life-threatening bronchial obstructions.

FIRST RECOMMENDATIONS:
Niaouli, *Eucalyptus radiata,* Inner Defense softgels,

Other Single Oils:
Oregano, thyme, clove

Other Blends:
Thieves, Melrose

EO APPLICATION METHODS:
Inhalation:
DIRECT, 6-8 times daily
Ingestion:
CAPSULE, 00 size, 2 times daily

DIETARY SUPPLEMENTATION:
Essentialzyme

DISINFECTANT

(See ANTISEPTIC)

DIVERTICULOSIS / DIVERTICULITIS

(See COLITIS, CROHN'S DISEASE)

Diverticulosis is one of the most common conditions in the U.S. It is caused by a lack of fiber in the diet. Diverticulosis is characterized by small, abnormal pouches (diverticula) that bulge out through weak spots in the wall of the intestine. It is estimated that half of all Americans from age 60 to 80 have diverticulosis.

Symptoms:
• Cramping
• Bloating
• Constipation

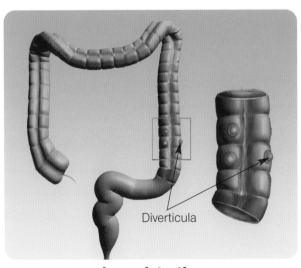

Diverticula

Large Intestine

One of the easiest ways to resolve this condition is by increasing fiber intake to 20-30 grams daily. Also, peppermint oil can stimulate contractions in the colon.

While diverticulosis involves the condition of merely having colon abnormalities, diverticulitis occurs when these abnormalities or diverticula become infected or inflamed. Diverticulitis is present in 10 to 25 percent of people with diverticulosis.

Symptoms:
- Tenderness on lower left side of abdomen
- Fever and chills
- Constipation
- Cramping

Many of these symptoms are similar to those of irritable bowel syndrome.

(See also IRRITABLE BOWEL SYNDROME)

FIRST RECOMMENDATIONS:
Oregano, Thieves, Inner Defense softgels, Digest & Cleanse Softgels, Essentialzyme

Other Single Oils:
Patchouli, anise, tarragon, rosemary, fennel, peppermint, mountain savory, thyme, nutmeg, clove

Other Blends:
Di-Gize. Melrose

Diverticulitis Blend:
- 15 drops Di-Gize
- 5 drops Melrose

EO APPLICATION METHODS:
Ingestion:
CAPSULE, enteric coated, 0 size, 2-3 times daily
SYRUP, 2-3 times daily
Topical:
DILUTE 50:50, 3-5 drops on lower abdomen 2 times daily
VITA FLEX, 2-4 drops on intestinal Vita Flex points on feet, 2-3 times daily
COMPRESS, warm, 2 times daily

Retention:
RECTAL, nightly before retiring, retain overnight

DIETARY SUPPLEMENTATION:
ICP/ComforTone/Essentialzyme, Balance Complete

DIZZINESS

FIRST RECOMMENDATIONS:
Peppermint, cedarwood, Aroma Life

Other Single Oils:
Tangerine, basil, cardamom, niaouli, sandalwood, frankincense

Other Blends:
Clarity, Brain Power

EO APPLICATION METHODS:
Inhalation:
DIRECT, 1-2 minutes, as needed
Topical:
NEAT, 1-3 drops on temples, back of neck and shoulders, as needed
VITA FLEX, 1-3 drops on brain Vita Flex points of feet, as needed

DIETARY SUPPLEMENTATION:
MultiGreens, True Source Multivitamins

If blood circulation is a factor, see CIRCULATION DISORDERS.

DYSENTERY

(See also Giardia under DIGESTION PROBLEMS)

FIRST RECOMMENDATIONS:
Thieves, Inner Defense softgels, Detoxzyme, oregano

Other Single Oils:
Lemon, mountain savory, peppermint

Other Blends:
Di-Gize

Dysentery Blend:
Mix 5 drops Thieves with 5 drops of peppermint

EO APPLICATION METHODS:

Ingestion:

CAPSULE, 00 size, 3 times daily

OTHER DIETARY SUPPLEMENTATION:

Polyzyme, ImmuPro,
ICP/ComforTone/Essentialzyme

EAR PROBLEMS

Ear Ache

FIRST RECOMMENDATIONS:

Niaouli, wintergreen, manuka, Melrose

Other Single Oils:

Thyme, lavender, tea tree, rosemary,
helichrysum, Roman chamomile, ravensara,
peppermint, *Eucalyptus radiata*

Other Blends:

Purification, PanAway, Immupower

Other:

Thieves Antiseptic Spray

EO APPLICATION METHODS:

Topical:

DILUTE 50:50 in warm olive or fractionated
coconut oil. Apply 2 drops to a cotton swab.
Using the swab, apply traces to the skin
around the opening of the ear, but not in it.
Put 2-3 drops of the diluted essential oil on a
piece of cotton and place it carefully over the
ear opening. Leave in overnight. Additional
relief may be obtained by placing a warm
compress over the ear
VITA FLEX, massage 1-2 drops on ear lobes
and on ear Vita Flex points of the feet.

Oral:

GARGLE, up to 8 x daily.

CAUTION: Never put essential oils directly
into the ear canal. Ear pain can be very serious.
Always seek medical attention if pain persists.

DIETARY SUPPLEMENTATION:

ImmuPro, Super C

Other:

Gargle up to 8 x daily with Fresh Essence Plus
mouthwash or spray Thieves Antiseptic Spray
into the throat up to 5 x daily.

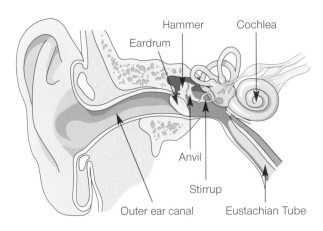

Ear

Ear Infection (without pain)

FIRST RECOMMENDATION:

Thieves

Single Oils:

Thyme, wintergreen

Other Blends:

Melrose

EO APPLICATION METHODS:

Oral:

GARGLE, up to 8 x daily. Also spray
Thieves Antiseptic Spray into back of
throat cavity up to 5 x daily.

Topical:

Dilute 50:50 in warm olive oil. Apply 2
drops to a cotton swab. Using the swab,
apply traces to the skin AROUND the
opening of the ear, but not in it. Put 2-3
drops of the diluted essential oil on a piece
of cotton and place it carefully over the ear
opening. Leave in overnight.

CAUTION: <u>Never</u> put essential oils directly
into the ear. Ear pain can be very serious. Always
seek medical attention if pain persists.

ECZEMA

(See Eczema/Psoriasis in SKIN DISORDERS)

Case History

It was reported that a man had a heart bypass using a vein removed from his leg. The leg swelled up from fluid retention and could be moved around like jelly. The leg was first massaged from the foot up with 4 drops cypress mixed into Cel-Lite Magic Massage Oil. The massage was repeated with 4 drops each of fennel and geranium mixed into the same massage oil. After 20 minutes of massaging the swelling had dissipated.

EDEMA (Swelling)

(See also KIDNEY DISORDERS, HORMONAL EDEMA, PHLEBITIS)

Swelling--particularly around the ankles--is noticeable when fluids accumulate in the tissue. This puffiness under the skin and around the ankles is more apparent at the end of the day when fluids settle to the lowest part of the body. A potassium deficiency can make swelling worse, so the first recourse is to increase potassium intake.

FIRST RECOMMENDATIONS:
Juniper berry, tangerine, geranium

Using juniper berry essential oil helps flush the kidneys to better eliminate excess water.

Other Single Oils:
German chamomile, wintergreen, peppermint, lavender, grapefruit, helichrysum

Other Blends:
Aroma Life, EndoFlex, DiTone

General Edema Blend:
- 10 drops wintergreen
- 6 drops fennel
- 4 drops juniper berry
- 3 drops patchouli
- 8 drops tangerine

EO APPLICATION METHODS:
Topical:
DILUTE 50:50, massage 3-5 drops into affected area 2-3 times daily
COMPRESS, cold, 1-2 times daily
VITA FLEX, massage 1-3 drops on bladder Vita Flex point on foot

Ingestion:
CAPSULE, 0 size, 2 times daily

Morning and Evening Edema regimen:
Morning blend:
- 10 drops tangerine
- 10 drops cypress

Evening blend:
- 8 drops geranium
- 5 drops cypress
- 5 drops helichrysum or grapefruit

Dilute each blend 60-40 in vegetable or massage oil and rub 15-20 drops on legs working from the feet up to the thighs. Do this for one week

DIETARY SUPPLEMENTATION:
Digest & Cleanse Softgels, Super C, K & B, Life 5, Mega Cal, Balance Complete

EMOTIONAL TRAUMA

The effect of heavy emotional trauma can disrupt the stomach and digestive system. (See DIGESTION)

FIRST RECOMMENDATIONS:
Trauma Life, Peace & Calming, White Angelica, frankincense, lavender, valerian

Other Single Oils:
Idaho balsam fir, lemon, German chamomile, citrus hystrix, rose, galbanum

Other Blends:
Present Time, Valor, Valor Roll-on, Release, Sacred Mountain, Christmas Spirit, 3 Wise Men, Tranquil Roll-on, RutaVaLa

Emotional pain relief blend:
- 12 drops Idaho balsam fir
- 8 drops lavender
- 6 drops marjoram
- 3 drops spearmint
- 2 drops peppermint

EO APPLICATION METHODS:
Inhalation:
DIRECT, 3-4 times daily, as needed
Topical:
NEAT, apply 1-2 drops to crown of head and forehead as needed. Best if applied in a quiet, darkened room
VITA FLEX, massage 1-3 drops on heart Vita Flex points, 2-3 times daily

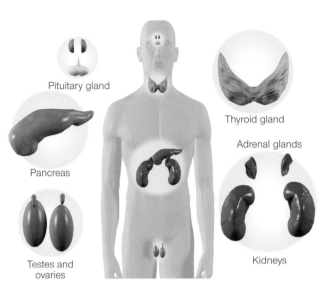

Pituitary gland

Thyroid gland

Adrenal glands

Pancreas

Testes and ovaries

Kidneys

Endocrine System

Ingestion:
SYRUP, 1-2 times daily

DIETARY SUPPLEMENTATION:
JuvaPower/Spice

Additional regimens:
A. Place 1-3 drops of Release over the thymus and rub in gently. Apply up to 3 times daily as needed.

B. Blend equal parts frankincense and Valor and apply 1-2 drops neat on temples, forehead, crown and back of neck before retiring. Use for 3 nights.

(See also Chapter 24: Emotional Response with Essential Oils)

ENDOCRINE SYSTEM

The endocrine system encompasses the hormone-producing glands of the body. These glands cluster around blood vessels and release their hormones directly into the bloodstream. The pituitary gland exerts a wide range of control over the hormonal (endocrine) system and is often called the master gland. Other glands include the pancreas, adrenals, thyroid and parathyroid, ovaries, and testes. The limbic system lies along the margin of the cerebral cortex (brain) and is the hormone-producing system of the brain. It includes the amygdala, hippocampus, pineal, pituitary, thalamus, and hypothalamus. (See chart on page 2)

Essential oils increase circulation to the brain.

This better enables the pituitary and other glands to secrete neural transmitters and hormones that support the endocrine and immune systems.

The thyroid is one of the most important glands for regulating the body systems. The hypothalamus plays an even more important role, since it not only regulates the thyroid, but the adrenals and the pituitary gland as well.

(See also THYROID PROBLEMS)

(See also ADRENAL GLAND IMBALANCE)

(See also MALE HORMONE IMBALANCE)

(See also MENSTRUAL CONDITIONS)

EPILEPSY

Note: Epileptics should consult their health care professional before using essential oils. Use extreme caution with high ketone oils such as basil, rosemary, sage and Idaho tansy.

FIRST RECOMMENDATIONS:
Frankincense, blue tansy, lavender

Other Single Oils:
Clary sage, sandalwood, cedarwood

Blends:
Valor, Valor Roll-on, Brain Power

EO APPLICATION METHODS:
Inhalation:
DIRECT, 4 times per day as needed.
Topical:
DILUTE 50:50, apply 1-3 drops on back of neck and behind ears 2-3 times daily
VITA FLEX, massage 2-4 drops on brain Vita Flex points on feet, 2-3 times daily

DIETARY SUPPLEMENTATION:
ICP/Comfortone/Essentialzyme, Ningxia Red, Dried wolfberries, Juva Power

(See also SEIZURES, BRAIN DISORDERS)

EPSTEIN-BARR VIRUS

Also known as Chronic Fatigue Syndrome, the Epstein-Barr virus is a type of herpes virus that also causes mononucleosis.

Symptoms include indigestion, upper and lower gas, poor assimilation, poor electrolyte balance, allergic reaction to foods and other substances, emotional mood swings, fatigue, irritability, and a lack of motivation, discipline, and creativity.

Hypoglycemia is a precursor and can render the body susceptible to the Epstein-Barr virus. Treat the hypoglycemia, and the symptoms of the Epstein-Barr virus may begin to disappear.

FIRST RECOMMENDATIONS:
Thieves, Inner Defense softgels, thyme, clove, Life 5, True Source Multivitamins

Other Single Oils:
Sandalwood, grapefruit, nutmeg, blue tansy, mountain savory, oregano, tea tree, rosemary

Other Blends:
ImmuPower, EndoFlex, Longevity, Di-Gize, Exodus II

EO APPLICATION METHODS:
Ingestion:
CAPSULE, 00 size, 3 times daily
Topical:
RAINDROP Technique, weekly with ImmuPower
Inhalation:
DIRECT, 4-5 times daily

OTHER DIETARY SUPPLEMENTATION:
Super C Chewable, ImmuPro, Thyromin, ImmuneTune, Detoxyme, Digest & Cleanse Softgels, ICP, Comfortone, Essentialzyme, True Source Multivitamins, Life 5

(See also HYPOGLYCEMIA, FATIGUE, THYROID PROBLEMS, ADRENAL GLAND IMBALANCE)

Mononucleosis

Infectious mononucleosis is a disease caused by the Epstein-Barr virus (EBV) which is a type of herpes virus. Symptoms usually last four weeks or more. The spleen enlarges and may even rupture in severe cases.

FIRST RECOMMENDATIONS:
Mountain savory, blue cypress, Raven

Other Single Oils:
Ravensara, niaouli, hyssop, thyme, frankincense

Other Blends:
Thieves, Inner Defense softgels, R.C., Breath Again Roll-on

Mononucleosis blend:
- 3 drops Thieves
- 3 drops thyme
- 3 drops mountain savory
- 2 drops ravensara

EO APPLICATION METHODS:
Ingestion:
CAPSULE, 00 size, 1 capsule twice daily
Topical:
RAINDROP Technique twice a week
VITA FLEX, massage 3-6 drops on bottom of feet twice daily

DIETARY SUPPLEMENTATION:
ImmuPro, Super C Chewable, Longevity Softgels, ICP/Comfortone/Essentialzyme, True Source Multivitamins, Life 5

EXPECTORANT

(See MUCUS)

EYE DISORDERS

In 1997 Dr. Terry Friedmann, MD, eliminated his need for glasses after applying sandalwood and juniper on the areas around his eyes--above the eyebrows and on the cheeks (being careful never to get oil into eyes.) He also used the supplements of Chelex, MultiGreens, ICP/Comfortone/ Essentialzyme, and JuvaTone for a complete colon and liver cleanse.

CAUTION: NEVER put any essential oils in the eyes or on eyelids.

Age-Related Macular Degeneration (AMD)

AMD is one of the most common causes of blindness among people over 60 years of age. In fact 30% of all people over 70 years of age suffer to some degree from this disease. The most common form of the disease is DRY in which macular cells degenerate irreversibly. The WET form of the disease is marked by abnormal blood vessel growth that results in macula-damaging blood leaks. The disease results in a steady loss of central vision until eyesight is totally impaired.

Eye

For dry AMD, the best prevention will be foods rich in antioxidants and carotenoids. The Ningxia wolfberry, the highest known antioxidant food, is also extremely high in lutein, which is vital for preserving eye health. Other foods rich in carotenoids that are also powerful antioxidants include blueberries and spinach.

Clove oil, the highest known antioxidant nutrient, may be a good nutritional defense for WET AMD only. For DRY AMD lemon oil may be helpful as a dietary supplement.

FIRST RECOMMENDATIONS:
Dried Wolfberries, Ningxia Red, Omega Blue Softgels

Single Oils:
Lemon (DRY AMD only) as a dietary supplement, Clove (WET AMD only) as a dietary supplement

Other Blends:
Longevity

EO APPLICATION METHODS:
Capsule, 00 size, 1 daily

DIETARY SUPPLEMENTATION:
Longevity Softgels, Wolfberry Crisp Bar, Super C Chewable

Blocked Tear Ducts

Single Oils:
Lavender.

EO Application Methods:
1 drop lavender oil rubbed over the bridge of the nose 2 times daily has been reported to work in some cases.

Cataracts

Cataracts are a clouding of the eye lens that often comes with aging.

FIRST RECOMMENDATIONS:
Dried wolfberries, Ningxia Red

Single Oils:
Clove, lavender

Clove oil is the most powerful known antioxidant and when taken internally it can slow or prevent both cataracts and AMD.

Eye blend:
- 10 drops lemon
- 5 drops cypress
- 3 drops *Eucalyptus radiata*

EO APPLICATION METHODS:
Ingestion:
CAPSULE, 0 size 2-3 times daily
Topical:
DILUTE 20:80, apply 2-4 drops in a wide circle around the eye, being careful not to get any oil in the eye or on the eyelid, 1-3 times daily. This may also help with puffiness. Also apply on temples and eye Vita Flex points on the feet and hands (the undersides of your two largest toes and your index and middle fingers.)

NOTE: If essential oils should ever accidentally get into the eyes, dilute with V-6 Advanced Oil Complex or other pure vegetable oil. NEVER rinse with water.

DIETARY SUPPLEMENTATION:
Alpha lipoic acid, JuvaPower/Spice, Omega Blue Softgels, ImmuPro, AD&E, Ningxia Red

Blurred Vision

(See AMD, Cataracts)

Pink Eye

FIRST RECOMMENDATIONS:
Tea Tree, manuka, lavender

EO APPLICATION METHODS:
Inhalation:
DIFFUSER, at night while sleeping
Topical:
DILUTE 20:80, apply 2-4 drops in a wide
circle around the eye, being careful not
to get any oil in the eye or on the eyelid,
1-3 times daily. This may also help with
puffiness. Also apply on temples and
eye Vita Flex points on the feet and
hands (the undersides of your two largest
toes and your index and middle fingers.)

NOTE: If essential oils should ever accidentally
get into the eyes, dilute with V-6 Advanced Oil
Complex or other pure vegetable oil. NEVER
rinse with water.

DIETARY SUPPLEMENTATION:
Alpha lipoic acid, JuvaPower/Spice, Omega
Blue Softgels, ImmuPro, AD&E

FAINTING

(See SHOCK)

FIRST RECOMMENDATION:
Brain Power, spearmint

Other Single Oils:
Melissa, peppermint, sandalwood, cardamom

Other Blends:
Clarity, Trauma Life

EO APPLICATION METHODS:
Inhalation:
DIRECT, 1-2 times as needed

FATIGUE

(See also DIABETES, FUNGAL
INFECTIONS, EPSTEIN-BARR VIRUS,
HEART HEALTH, THYROID PROBLEMS,
ADRENAL GLAND IMBALANCE)

Hormone imbalances may play a large role in
fatigue as well as latent viral infections (Herpes
virus and/or Epstein-Barr Virus). Also mineral
deficiencies (especially magnesium) can play a
large part in low energy.

Natural progesterone for women and DHEA for
men can be instrumental in helping combat the
fatigue that comes with age and declining hormone
levels. Because pregnenolone is a precursor for all
male and female hormones, both men and women
can benefit from its supplementation.

Physical Fatigue

A lack of energy can be due to a host of factors,
including poor thyroid function or adrenal
imbalance. Other factors may also play a part,
including diabetes, cancer and other conditions.

FIRST RECOMMENDATIONS:
Peppermint, nutmeg, Awaken

Other Single Oils:
Lemongrass, juniper, basil, lemon, rosemary,
black pepper, thyme, melissa, cypress

Other Blends:
Motivation, Valor, valor roll-on, En-R-Gee,
Hope, Clarity, Joy

MultiGreens is a plant-derived high-protein
energy formula that athletes use to boost
endurance. Longevity Softgels increase
energy and endurance.

Digestion and colon problems may cause
fatigue. A colon and liver cleanse unburdens the
digestive system and increases energy.

EO APPLICATION METHODS:
Inhalation:
DIRECT, 2-5 times daily
DIFFUSION, 10 minutes 3 times daily
Topical:
DILUTE 50:50, 2-4 drops on temples, in
clavicle notch (over thyroid), and behind
ears, 2-4 times daily as needed

DIETARY SUPPLEMENTATION:
MultiGreens, Power Meal, True Source
Multivitamins, Longevity Softgels, Super B,
Dried wolfberries, Digest & Cleanse Softgels,
Life 5, ImmuPro (only at bedtime)

Mental Fatigue

FIRST RECOMMENDATIONS:
Peppermint, spearmint, En-R-Gee

Other Single Oils:
Black pepper, sage, nutmeg, pine

Other Blends:
Clarity, Envision, Valor, Motivation

EO APPLICATION METHODS:
Topical:
DILUTE 50:50, 2-4 drops at base of throat, temples, back of neck, as needed
VITA FLEX, massage 1-3 drops on relevant Vita Flex points on feet 1-3 times daily
Inhalation:
DIRECT, 2-4 times daily
Ingestion:
SYRUP, 1-3 times daily

DIETARY SUPPLEMENTATION:
Power Meal, Balance Complete, MultiGreens, Mineral Essence, Longevity Softgels, Ningxia Red

FERTILITY ISSUES
(See INFERTILITY)

FEVER
(See INFECTION)

Fevers are one of the most powerful healing responses orchestrated by the human body, and are especially valuable in fighting infectious diseases. However, if fever raises body temperature excessively (over 104° F) then neurological damage can occur.

Reducing fever is best accomplished by using anti-inflammatory essential oils, internally and topically.

FIRST RECOMMENDATIONS:
Wintergreen, copaiba

Other Single Oils:
Peppermint, *Eucalyptus globulus*, nutmeg, German chamomille, Idaho balsam fir

Other Blends:
ImmuPower, Melrose

EO APPLICATION METHODS:
Topical:
DILUTE 50:50, apply 2-3 drops to forehead, temples and back of neck.

Ingestion:
RICE MILK, sip slowly, 1-2 times as needed
CAPSULE, 00 size, 1-2 capsules, as needed
SYRUP, dissolve 1 tsp of the syrup/essential oil mixture in an 8 oz glass of cool water and sip slowly.
Inhalation:
DIRECT, 3-4 times as needed

DIETARY SUPPLEMENTATION:
Super C Chewable, ImmuPro, ImmuneTune, Exodus, Longevity Softgels

Topical Treatments:
Cinnamint Lip Balm (for dry lips)

FIBRILLATION
(See CARDIOVASCULAR CONDITIONS

FIBROIDS
(See MENSTRUAL CONDITIONS)

Fibroids are fairly common benign tumors of the female pelvis that are composed of smooth muscle cells and fibrous connective tissue. Fibroids are not cancerous and neither develop into cancer nor increase a women's cancer risk in the uterus.

Fibroids can have a diameter as small as 1 mm or as large as 8 inches. They can develop in clusters or alone as a single knot or nodule.

Fibroids frequently occur in premenopausal women and are seldom seen in young women who have not begun menstruation. Fibroids usually stabilize or even regress in women who have been through menopause.

FIRST RECOMMENDATIONS:
Cistus, lavender

Other Single Oils:
Frankincense, Idaho tansy, oregano, pine, helichrysum

Other Blends:
Valor, valor roll-on, EndoFlex, Cel-Lite Magic

EO APPLICATION METHODS:
Ingestion:
CAPSULE, 0 size, 2 times daily
Topical:
COMPRESS, warm on lower abdomen, daily

DIETARY SUPPLEMENTATION:
MultiGreens, Power Meal, Balance Complete, Prenolone, PD 80/20, Essentialzyme, Life 5

FIBROMYALGIA

Fibromyalgia is an autoimmune disorder of soft tissues. (By contrast, arthritis occurs in the joints.) Symptoms include general body pain, in some parts worse than others, usually brought on by short periods of exercise.

The pain is ubiquitous and continuous. It interrupts sleep patterns so that the fourth stage of sleep is never attained, and thus the body cannot rejuvenate and heal. Fibromyalgia is an acid condition in which the liver is toxic (see LIVER DISORDERS).

The best natural treatments for fibromyalgia are omega-3 fats such as flax seed, proteolytic enzymes such as bromelain and pancreatin, and MSM.

According to UCLA researcher, Ronald Lawrence, M.D. Ph.D., supplementation with MSM often offers a breakthrough in the treatment of fibromyalgia.

FIRST RECOMMENDATIONS:
Frankincense gum resin, wintergreen, copaiba, Sulfurzyme, Essentialzyme

Other Single Oils:
German chamomile, nutmeg, Idaho balsam fir

Other Blends:
PanAway, Relieve It, ImmuPower, Ortho Ease, Deep Relief Roll-on

Fibromyalgia blend #1:
- 8 drops Idaho balsam fir
- 6 drops white fir
- 4 drops wintergreen
- 2 drops spruce

Fibromyalgia blend #2:
- 10 drops PanAway
- 8 drops wintergreen
- 8 drops marjoram
- 6 drops spruce

EO APPLICATION METHODS:
Topical:
DILUTE 50:50, gently massage 2-4 drops on pain locations

COMPRESS, warm, on location, 3 x weekly
BODY MASSAGE, weekly
Raindrop, adding Immune blend, weekly
Ingestion:
CAPSULE, 0 size, 2 times daily

OTHER DIETARY SUPPLEMENTATION:
Myrrh gum resin, Polyzyme, Super C Chewable, MultiGreens, ImmuneTune, ICP/Comfortone/Essentialzyme, Super Cal, Life 5

Topical Treatment:
Regenolone

Fibromyalgia Regimen:

1. Start cleansing by using ICP/Comfortone/Essentialzyme.
2. Use 2 Tbsp. Sulfurzyme daily
3. Eat less acidic-ash foods and more alkaline-ash foods such as wheat sprouts or barley sprouts. See Appendix B. The following is a list of alkalinizing supplements:
   - MultiGreens: up to 4 times daily.
   - Super C: 4-6 tablets daily.
   - ImmuneTune: 2-6 times daily.
   - Mineral Essence: 2-3 droppers, 2 times daily in water or cold apple juice will supply the trace minerals needed without increasing the acid condition.
   - Super Cal or Mega Cal: 2-4 capsules daily, or as needed
   - ImmuPower: Apply 4-6 drops along the spine and back along with Raindrop Technique (See chapter 21 on RAINDROP TECHNIQUE).

FLATULENCE (GAS)

(See DIGESTIVE PROBLEMS)

Flatulence (gas) can be caused by a lack of digestive enzymes and the consumption of indigestible starches that promote bifidobacteria production in the colon. Although increasing bifidobacteria production can lead to gas, it is highly beneficial to long term health, as the increase of beneficial flora crowds out disease-causing microorganisms such as *Clostridium perfringens*. Consumption of FOS (fructooligosaccharides), an indigestible sugar, can create short term flatulence even as it drastically improves bifidobacteria production in the small and large intestine and increases mineral absorption.

DIETARY SUPPLEMENTATION:
Carbozyme, Detoxzyme, Dried wolfberries, ICP/ComforTone/Essentialzyme

FLU (Influenza)

(See INFLUENZA)

FOOD POISONING

(See also ALLERGIES, Giardia under DIGESTION PROBLEMS)

FIRST RECOMENDATIONS:
Polyzyme, cumin, Thieves, Inner Defense softgels

Other Single Oils:
Oregano, thyme, clove, ginger

Other Blends:
Di-Gize

EO APPLICATION METHODS:
Ingestion:
CAPSULE, 00 size, 2 capsules, 2-3 times per day

DIETARY SUPPLEMENTATION:
ComforTone, Digest & Cleanse Softgels, Detoxzyme, Essentialzyme

FOOT PROBLEMS

Athlete's Foot

(see FUNGAL INFECTIONS)

Blisters on Feet

(see BLISTERS and BOILS)

Bunions

Bunions are caused from bursitis at the base of a toe. (See BURSITIS)

Bunion Blend:
- 6 drops *Eucalyptus radiata*
- 3 drops lemon
- 4 drops raven
- 1 drop wintergreen

EO APPLICATION METHODS:
Topical:
NEAT or DILUTE 50:50, as needed. Apply 2-4 drops over bunion area 2-3 times daily

Corns

Blend for corns:
- 2 drops myrrh
- 2 drops blue cypress
- 7 drops oregano
- 4 drops basil

EO APPLICATION METHODS:
Topical:
NEAT, 1 drop directly on the corn 2-3 times daily

Sore Feet

FIRST RECOMMENDATION:
Sore Feet Blend:
- 5 drops wintergreen
- 3 drops peppermint
- 1 drop sandalwood
- 2 drops German chamomille
- 2 drops orange

Single Oils:
Peppermint, white fir, lavender, patchouli, myrrh, frankincense, sandalwood, vetiver

Other Blends:
Melrose, PanAway, Relieve It

EO APPLICATION METHODS:
Topical:
DILUTE 50:50, massage 6-9 drops onto each foot at night
COMPRESS, warm, for added effect and penetration
BATH SALTS, mix 10 drops essential oils in 1 Tbsp. Epsom salts and add to hot water in a basin large enough for footbath

Topical Treatment:
OrthoEase Massage Oil

FRIGIDITY

(See SEXUAL DYSFUNCTIONS)

Using Raindrop Technique to Purge Pathogenic Fungi

Pathogenic microorganisms have a tendency to hibernate along the spinal cord and in the lymphatic system. The body has the ability to hold them in a suspended state for long periods of time. When the immune system becomes compromised from stress, fatigue or other factors, they can be released and manifest illness and disease.

Oregano, thyme, or hyssop along the spine using Raindrop Technique may help to drive the dormant fungi out of the spinal fluid.

Additionally, lymphatic pump therapy will revitalize a sluggish lymphatic system to better combat pathogenic fungi. (see Chapter 22)

FUNGAL INFECTIONS

Fungi and yeast feed on decomposing or dead tissues. They exist everywhere: inside our stomachs, on our skin, and out on the lawn. When kept under control, the yeast and fungi populating our bodies are harmless and digest what our bodies cannot or do not use.

When we feed the naturally-occurring fungi in our bodies too many simple sugars, the fungal populations are more likely to grow out of control. This condition is known as systemic candidiasis and is marked by fungi invading the blood, gastrointestinal tract, and tissues.

Reducing or eliminating simple sugars from the diet is essential to combatting all fungal infections. So also is avoiding the use of antibiotics and alcohol.

Fungal cultures such as candida excrete large amounts of poisons called mycotoxins as part of their life cycles. These poisons must be detoxified by the liver and immune systems. Eventually they can wreak enormous damage on the tissues and organs and are believed to be an aggravating factor in many degenerative diseases, such as cancer, arteriosclerosis, and diabetes.

Insufficient intake of minerals and trace minerals like magnesium, potassium, and zinc may also stimulate candida and fungal overgrowth in the body.

Symptoms of Systemic Fungal Infection:

- Fatigue/low energy
- Overweight
- Low resistance to illness
- Allergies
- Unbalanced blood sugar
- Headaches
- Irritability
- Mood swings
- Indigestion
- Colitis and ulcers
- Diarrhea/constipation
- Urinary tract infections
- Rectal or vaginal itch

Athlete's Foot

(See RINGWORM in this section).

Tinea pedis or athlete's foot is a fungal infection of the skin that infects the feet. (it is identical to ringworm which infects the skin in the rest of the body). This fungus thrives in the warm, moist environment to which many feet are subjected.

The best remedy is to keep feet cool and dry and avoid wearing tight-fitting shoes or heavy natural (ie. cotton) socks. Wear sandals, shoes, and socks woven from a light, breathable fabric.

It is especially important to control this fungus infection during showering or bathing, since the moist, warm environment favors the growth of the *Tinea* culture responsible for athlete's foot. Antifungal essential oils such as tea tree and Melrose can be added to bath salts or Epsom salts and used in specially designed shower heads to create a mild, antifungal shower.

FIRST RECOMMENDATIONS:

Niaouli, peppermint and athlete's foot blend (below)

Athlete's Foot Blend:

- 8 drops tea tree
- 4 drops peppermint
- 2 drops mountain savory

Other Single Oils:

Tea tree, *Melaleuca ericifolia*, blue cypress, lemongrass (always dilute), lavender, thyme, mountain savory, melissa

Other Blends:

Melrose, Thieves, Purification, ClaraDerm

EO APPLICATION METHODS:

Topical:

NEAT or DILUTE 50:50 as needed.
Apply 5-7 drops to affected areas between toes and around toenails
BATH SALTS, daily

Topical Treatments:

Thieves Antiseptic Spray, Ortho Ease Massage Oil, Fresh Essence Plus Mouthwash (used on the feet)

Candida Albicans (Candidiasis)

Two of the most powerful weapons for fighting intestinal fungal infections such as candida are FOS (fructooligosaccharides) and *L. acidophilus* cultures.

FOS has been clinically documented in dozens of peer-reviewed studies for its ability to build up the healthy intestinal flora in the colon and combat the overgrowth of negative bacteria and fungi (See Appendix O).

Acidophilus cultures have also been shown to combat fungus overgrowth in the gastrointestinal tract.

FIRST RECOMMENDATIONS:

Lemongrass, cumin, geranium, Candida Blend (below), Life 5

Candida Blend:

- 5 drops lemongrass
- 4 drops thyme
- 4 drops tea tree
- 2 drops manuka

(NOTE: this blend is not recommended for those with estrogen sensitive cancers.)

Other Single Oils:

Tea tree, niaouli, ravensara, thyme, manuka, peppermint, lavender, rosemary, palmarosa

Other Blends:

Melrose, Raven, R.C., ImmuPower, Breath Again Roll-on

Combating Ringworm

Using antifungal essential oils while bathing or showering is especially important because fungal infections thrive in moist, warm environments. Essential oils like tea tree or Melrose can easily be added to bath salts or Epsom salts to combat fungal infections.

There are specially designed shower heads that can be filled with bath salts and essential oils. As the water passes over the mixture, it disperses the essential oils and salts into the shower spray, creating an antifungal spa.

EO APPLICATION METHODS:

Topical:

Dilute 50:50 or 20:80, as needed, massage 3-4 drops on thymus (at clavical notch, center of collarbone at base of throat) to stimulate the immune system. Also apply 3-6 drops on bottoms of the feet and on the chest. Also apply 5-10 drops on stomach. Do these applications 2 times daily.
VITA FLEX, massage 2-4 drops on relevant Vita Flex points of feet 2-4 times daily.
BATH SALTS, daily

Ingestion:

CAPSULE, 0 size, 2-3 times daily between meals
RICE MILK, 3 times daily between meals

Dietary Supplementation:

Essentialzyme, ImmuPro, ImmuneTune, MultiGreens, Digest & Cleanse Softgels, Detoxyme, Super C Chewable

Ringworm and Skin Candida

The ringworm fungus infects the skin causing scaly round itchy patches. It is infectious and can be spread from an animal or human host alike. Skin candida is a fungal infection that can erupt almost anywhere on the skin. It shows up in various places, such as behind the knees, inside the elbows, behind the ears, on temple area, and between the breasts.

FIRST RECOMMENDATIONS:

Melaleuca ericifolia, geranium, Thieves Antiseptic Spray

Other Single Oils:

Tea tree, niaouli (MQV), blue cypress, lavender, rosemary, rosewood, manuka, lemongrass, lemon myrtle

Blends:

Melrose, Raven, R.C., Ortho Ease, Breath Again Roll-on

Ringworm blend:

- 3 drops tea tree
- 3 drops spearmint
- 1 drop peppermint
- 1 drop rosemary

Skin Candida blend:

- 2 drops manuka
- 10 drops tea tree
- 1 drop oregano
- 4 drops lavender

EO APPLICATION METHODS:

Topical:

DILUTE 50:50, massage 2-4 drops over affected area, 2-4 times daily. In severe cases, use 35 percent food-grade hydrogen peroxide to clean infected areas before applying essential oils. Saturate a gauze with essential oils and apply to affected area and wrap to hold in place.

Topical Treatment:

Ortho Sport, Massage Oil

Thrush

Thrush is a fungal infection of the mouth and throat marked by creamy, curd-like patches in the oral cavity. Even though it appears in the mouth, thrush is usually a sign of systemic fungal overgrowth throughout the body. Thrush can usually be treated locally through the use of antifungal essential oils such as clove, cinnamon, rosemary CT cineol, peppermint, and rosewood.

FIRST RECOMMENDATIONS:

Clove, Melrose

Single Oils:

Cinnamon, peppermint, rosemary cineol, geranium, rosewood, orange, lavender

Blends:

Thieves, Inner Defense, Purification

EO APPLICATION METHODS:

Oral:

GARGLE, 3-5 times daily

Topical:

Dilute 50:50 or 20:80, as needed, massage 3-4 drops on thymus (at clavical notch, center of collarbone at base of throat) to stimulate the immune system. Also apply 3-6 drops on bottoms of the feet and on the chest. Also apply 5-10 drops on stomach. Do these applications 2 times daily

VITA FLEX, massage 2-4 drops on relevant Vita Flex points of feet, 2-4 times daily

Ingestion:

CAPSULE, 0 size, 2-3 times daily between meals

RICE MILK, 3 times daily between meals

NOTE: These applications are for adults, not infants. In cases of infants with thrush, consult a medical professional first.

Oral Hygiene:

Thieves Lozenges, Fresh Essence Plus Mouthwash, Thieves Antiseptic Spray

Vaginal Yeast Infection

Essential oils like tea tree have been documented to have highly antifungal activity. Positive results have been obtained on vaginal yeast infections using these oils in douches.

FIRST RECOMMENDATIONS:

Tea tree, Fresh Essence Plus mouthwash (used in a tampon), Vaginal yeast infection blend (below)

Vaginal Yeast Infection Blend:

- 7 drops tea tree
- 2 drops lemongrass
- 5 drops mountain savory

Other Single Oils:

Lavender, rosemary, manuka, geranium, peppermint, mountain savory, thyme

Other Blends:

Melrose, Purification, R.C., Aroma Siez, Breath Again Roll-on

EO APPLICATION METHODS:

Retention:
TAMPON, dilted 40:60, nightly for 5-10 days, as needed

Ingestion:
CAPSULE, 00 size, 3 times daily

GALLBLADDER INFECTION

The gallbladder stores bile created by the liver and releases it through the biliary ducts into the duodenum to promote digestion. Bile is extremely important for fat digestion and the absorption of vitamins such as A, D, and E.

When bile flow is obstructed due to gallstones or inflamed due to infection, serious consequences can ensue, including poor digestion, jaundice, and severe abdominal pain.

FIRST RECOMMENDATIONS:
Thieves, Inner Defense, rosemary, Gall Bladder Blend (below)

Gall Bladder Blend:
• 2 drops oregano
• 1 drop Roman chamomille
• 1 drop lavender
• 1 drop rosemary
• 1 drop tangerine
• 2 drops juniper berry

Other Single Oils:
Lemon, carrot seed, juniper berry, German chamomile, oregano, cumin

Other Blends:
JuvaFlex, Juva Cleanse, PanAway

EO APPLICATION METHODS:

Ingestion:
CAPSULE, 00 size, 1 capsule 3 times daily

Topical:
NEAT, apply 6-10 drops over gallbladder area, 2-3 times daily
COMPRESS, warm, 2-3 times daily
VITA FLEX, massage 1-3 drops on liver Vita Flex points of the feet, 2-3 times daily

DIETARY SUPPLEMENTATION:
Sulfurzyme, JuvaTone, Essentialzyme, Polyzyme, Longevity Softgels, Life 5

GALLSTONES

When bile contains excessive cholesterol, bilirubin, or bile salts, gallstones can form. Stones made from hardened cholesterol account for the vast majority of gallstones, while stones made from bilirubin, the brownish pigment in bile, constitute only about 20 percent of gallstones.

Gallstones can block both bile flow and the passage of pancreatic enzymes. This can result in inflammation in the gallbladder (cholecystitis) or pancreas (pancreatitis) and jaundice. In some cases, gallstones can be life-threatening, depending on where they are lodged.

Several Japanese studies show that limonene (a key constituent in orange, lemon, and tangerine oils) can effectively dissolve gallstone with no negative side effects.

FIRST RECOMMENDATIONS:
Lemon, Citrus Fresh, orange

Other Single Oils:
Grapefruit, mandarin, tangerine, juniper, nutmeg, rosemary

Other Blends:
JuvaFlex, Juva Cleanse

EO APPLICATION METHODS:

Ingestion:
Capsule: 0 size, 2 times daily for 2 weeks

Topical:
DILUTE 50:50, massage 6-10 drops over gallbladder twice daily
COMPRESS, 2-3 times daily
VITA FLEX, massage 1-3 drops on liver Vita Flex points of feet, 2-3 times daily

GANGRENE

NOTE: as with all serious medical conditions, consult your health care professional immediately if you suspect gangrene.

Gangrene is the death or decay of living tissue caused by a lack of blood supply. A shortage of blood can result from a blood clot, arteriosclerosis, frostbite, diabetes, infection, or some other obstruction in the arterial blood supply. Gas gangrene (also known as acute or moist gangrene) occurs when tissues are infected with *Clostridium* bacteria. Unless the limb is amputated or treated with antibiotics, the gangrene can be fatal.

The part of the body affected with gangrene displays the following symptoms:

- Coldness
- Dark in color
- Looks rotten/decomposed
- Putrid smell

Other symptoms include:
- Fever
- Anemia

Dr. René Gattefossé suffered gas gangrene as a result of burns from a chemical explosion at the turn of the century. He successfully engineered his own recovery solely with the use of pure lavender oil.

FIRST RECOMMENDATIONS:
Thyme, peppermint, NeuroGen cream

Other Single Oils:
Oregano, rosemary, lavender, mountain savory, cistus, blue cypress

Blends:
Exodus II, Thieves, ImmuPower, Melrose

EO APPLICATION METHODS:
Topical:
DILUTE 20:80, apply 2-4 drops on affected area, 3-5 times daily
COMPRESS, warm, 3 times daily, every other day

DIETARY SUPPLEMENTATION:
Super C, Inner Defense softgels

Other Topical Treatment:
Regenolone cream

GASTRITIS

(See DIGESTIVE PROBLEMS)

Gastritis occurs when the stomach's mucosal lining becomes inflamed and the cells become eroded. This can lead to bleeding ulcers and severe digestive disturbances. Gastritis may be caused by excess acid production in the stomach, alcohol consumption, stress, and fungal or bacterial infections.

Symptoms of gastritis:
- Weight loss
- Abdominal pain
- Cramping

FIRST RECOMMENDATIONS:
AlkaLime, Polyzyme

Other Dietary Supplementation:
Essentialzyme, Life 5, Digest & Cleanse Softgels, Balance Complete

Supplementation regimen for gastritis:
- Alkalime: 1/2 tsp. each morning
- Polyzyme: 3-4 capsules, 3 times daily
- ComforTone and ICP: Begin after 2 weeks of using the products listed above.
- Mega Cal: 1 Tbsp. each morning in 8 oz. warm water

GINGIVITIS

(See ORAL CARE, and Chapter 16: Oral Health Care)

Essential oils are one of the best treatments against gum diseases such as gingivitis and pyorrhea. Clove oil, for example, is used as dental disinfectant; and the active principle in clove oil, eugenol, is one of the best-studied germ-killers available.

GOUT

Gout is a disease marked by abrupt, temporary bouts of joint pain and swelling that are most evident in the joint of the big toe. It can also affect the wrist, elbow, knee, ankle, hand, and foot. As the disease progresses, pain and swelling in the joints becomes more frequent and chronic, with deposits called tophi appearing over many joints, including the elbows and on ears.

Gout is characterized by accumulation of uric acid crystals in the joints caused by excess uric acid in the blood. Uric acid is a byproduct of the breakdown of protein that is normally excreted by the kidneys into the urine. To reduce uric acid concentrations, it is necessary to support the kidneys, adrenal, and immune functions. It is also necessary to detoxify by cleansing and drinking plenty of fluids.

Excess alcohol, allergy-producing foods, or strict diets can cause outbreaks of gout. Foods rich in purines, such as wine, anchovies, and animal liver, can also cause gout.

FIRST RECOMMENDATIONS:
  Juniper berry, lemon, Gout blend (below)

Gout Blend:
  • 10 drops lemon
  • 4 drops juniper berry
  • 2 drops Roman chamomile
  • 3 drops tea tree

EO APPLICATION METHODS:
  Ingestion:
    CAPSULE, 0 size, 3 times daily for 10 days, then rest 4 days, repeat as needed
    RICE MILK, 3 times daily
  Topical:
    NEAT, gently massage 1-3 drops on affected joints 2-3 times daily

DIETARY SUPPLEMENTATION:
  MultiGreens, ICP/Comfortone/Essentialzyme

Topical Treatment:
  Ortho Ease Massage Oil (for pain)

(See also KIDNEY DISORDERS)
(for pain, see JOINT STIFFNESS & PAIN)

GRAVE'S DISEASE

(See THYROID PROBLEMS)

GUM DISEASE

(See ORAL CARE, and Chapter 16: Oral Health Care)

HAIR AND SCALP PROBLEMS

(See also HEAD LICE)

Sulfur is the single most important mineral for maintaining the strength and integrity of the hair and hair follicle.

FIRST RECOMMENDATIONS:
  Lavender, cedarwood (dry scalp), peppermint (oily scalp), Sulfurzyme

Other Single Oils:
  Rosemary, clary sage, sage, basil, juniper, ylang ylang, sandalwood, lemon, cypress, rosewood

  Rosemary adds body and conditions the hair.

Blends:
Dry Scalp Blend
  • 6 drops cedarwood
  • 2 drops sandalwood or geranium
  • 2 drops patchouli

Oily Scalp Blend:
  • 6 drops pepperminti
  • 2 drops lavender
  • 4 drops lemon

EO APPLICATION METHODS:
  Topical:
    DILUTE 20:80, massage 1 tsp into the scalp vigorously and thoroughly for 2-3 minutes; leave on scalp for 60-90 minutes. (An excellent time to do this would be during an exercise routine). Mix 2-4 drops of essential oils with 1-2 teaspoons of shampoo to wash hair after exercising.

    A rinse to help restore the acid mantle of the scalp:
    • 1 drop rosemary
    • 1 tsp. pure apple cider vinegar
    • 8 oz. water.

    Use as a final rinse on hair. Rub 1 or 2 drops on as hairdressing or on hairbrush to prevent static electricity.

OTHER DIETARY SUPPLEMENTATION:
  True Source Multivitamins, Balance Complete, Sulferzyme

Topical Treatment:
  Lavender Volume Hair and Scalp Wash, Lemon Sage Clarifying Hair and Scalp Wash, Rosewood Moisturizing Hair and Scalp Wash

Dandruff

Dandruff may be caused by allergies, parasites (fungal), and/or chemicals. The mineral selenium has been shown to help prevent dandruff.

Melaleuca alternifolia (tea tree) has been shown to be effective in treating dandruff and other fungal infections.[27]

FIRST RECOMMENDATIONS:
  Tea tree, cedarwood, selenium

---

27. "Antifungal activity of the essential oil of *Melaleuca alternifolia* (tea ree oil) against pathogenic fungi in vitro." Skin Pharmacol. 1996;9(6):388-94.

Other Single Oils:

Rosemary, peppermint

Other Blends:

Citrus Fresh, Melrose

Dandruff blend:
- 5 drops lemon
- 2 drops lavender
- 1 drops rosemary
- 2 drops peppermint

EO APPLICATION METHODS:

Topical:

DILUTE 50:50, massage 1 tsp into the scalp vigorously and thoroughly for 2-3 minutes; leave on scalp for 15 minutes. Mix 2-4 drops of essential oils with 1 teaspoons of shampoo to wash hair afterward.

Topical treatment:

Lavender Volume Hair and Scalp Wash, Lemon-Sage Clarifying Hair and Scalp Wash, Rosewood Hair and Scalp Wash

Hair Loss

Hair loss is caused by hormonal imbalances (such as increase in testosterone), or inflammatory conditions (as in the case of alopecia areata).

Essential oils are excellent for cleansing, nourishing, and strengthening the hair follicle and shaft. Rosemary (cineol chemotype) encourages hair growth.

FIRST RECOMMENDATIONS:

Hair Loss Prevention Blends (below)

Hair loss prevention blend #1:
- 10 drops cedarwood
- 8 drops rosemary
- 10 drops sandalwood
- 10 drops lavender

Hair loss prevention blend #2:
- 3 drops rosemary
- 5 drops lavender
- 4 drops cypress
- 2 drops clary sage
- 2 drops juniper

Add 10 drops of either of the above blends to 1 tsp. of fractionated coconut oil and massage into the scalp where it is balding; then rub gently into

the remainder of the scalp. This works best when done at night. It may help to alternate blends.

Other Single Oils:

Lavender, rosemary, cedarwood, sandalwood, clary sage

EO APPLICATION METHODS:

Topical:

DILUTE 50:50, massage 1 tsp. into the scalp vigorously and thoroughly for 2-3 minutes; leave on scalp for 15 minutes. (An excellent time to do this would be during an exercise routine). Mix 2-4 drops of essential oils with 1-2 teaspoons of shampoo to wash hair afterward.

DIETARY SUPPLEMENTATION:

Sulfurzyme, True Source Multivitamins, Balance Complete

(See also ALOPECIA AREATA)

HALITOSIS (Bad Breath)

(See also DIGESTION PROBLEMS, ORAL CARE and Candida in FUNGAL INFECTIONS)

Persistent bad breath or gum disease, may be a sign of poor digestion, candida/yeast infestation, or other health problems.

FIRST RECOMMENDATIONS:

Bad Breath Blends (below)

Bad Breath Blend #1:
- 3 drops peppermint
- 2 drops lemon
- 2 drops clove
- 1 drop tea tree oil

Bad Breath Blend #2:
- 4 drops spearmint
- 2 drops mandarin
- 2 drops cinnamon

Blends Application:

DILUTE 50:50 and swab 4-8 drops inside cheeks and on tongue, gums and teeth, as needed.

Single Oils:

Peppermint, spearmint, clove, mandarin, cinnamon, rosemary, wintergreen

Other Blends:

Thieves, Melrose, Purification

Dilute the above essential oil blend in 2 tsp. blue agave nectar and 4 oz. of hot water. Gargle as needed.

EO APPLICATION METHODS:

Oral:

GARGLE, 2-4 times daily as needed
TONGUE, 2-4 times daily as needed

Ingestion:

CAPSULE, 0 size, 3 times daily

Oral Treatment:

Dentarome Ultra Toothpaste, Thieves Antiseptic Spray, Thieves Lozenges

(See also DIGESTION PROBLEMS and ORAL CARE).

(See also Candida in FUNGAL INFECTIONS)

HASHIMOTO'S THYROIDITIS

(See THYROID PROBLEMS)

HEAD LICE

The most common remedy for lice (pediculosis) and their eggs (nits) is lindane (gamma benzene hexachloride) a highly toxic polychlorinated chemical that is structurally very similar to hazardous banned pesticides such as DDT and chlordane. It is so dangerous that Dr. Guy Sansfacon, head of the Quebec Poison Control Centre in Canada, has requested that lindane be banned.

Essential oils represent a safe and effective alternative. A 1996 study by researchers in Iceland showed the effectiveness against headlice of the essential oils of anise seed, cinnamon leaf, thyme, tea tree, peppermint, and nutmeg in shampoo and rinse solutions.[28]

FIRST RECOMMENDATIONS:

Tea tree, Head Lice blend (below)

Head lice blend:

- 4 drops thyme
- 2 drops lavender
- 2 drops geranium

Other Single Oils:

Lavender, peppermint, thyme, geranium, nutmeg, rosemary, cinnamon leaf

EO APPLICATION METHODS:

Topical:

DILUTE 50:50, 1 tsp. applied to scalp. Massage into entire scalp, cover with disposable shower cap and leave for at least 1/2 hour. Then shampoo and rise well. Use the rinse below.

Head Lice Rinse

1 cup Fresh Essence Plus mouthwash massaged into hair and scalp. Retain for 10 minutes before rinsing out.

HEADACHE

(See also STRESS, HYPOGLYCEMIA, LIVER DISORDERS, MENSTRUAL CONDITIONS)

Headaches are usually caused by hormone imbalances, circulatory problems, stress, sugar imbalance (hypoglycemia), structural (spinal) misalignments, and blood pressure concerns

Placebo-controlled double-blind crossover studies at the Christian-Albrechts University in Kiel, Germany, found that essential oils were just as effective in blocking pain from tension-type headaches as acetominophen (ie., Tylenol).[29, 30]

Essential oils also promote circulation, reduce muscle spasms, and decrease inflammatory response.

FIRST RECOMMENDATIONS:

Peppermint, wintergreen, PanAway

Other Single Oils:

Roman chamomile, German chamomile, lavender, spearmint, valerian, clove, rosemary, *Eucalyptus globulus,* copaiba

Other Blends:

M-Grain, Brain Power, Clarity, Relieve It, Deep Relief Roll-on

General Headache Blend #1:

- 4 drops wintergreen
- 2 drops lavender
- 3 drops German chamomille

28. Veal L, "The potential effectiveness of essential oils as a treatment for headlice, Pediculus humanus capitis," *Complement Ther Nurs Midwifery* 1996 Aug;2(4):97-101.

29. Gobel H, et al., *Effectiveness of Oleum menthae piperitae and paracetamol in therapy of headache of the tension type.* Nervenarzt. 1996 Aug; 67(8): 672-81.

30. Gobel H, Schmidt G, Soyka D. *Effect of peppermint and eucalyptus oil preparations on neurophysiological and experimental algesimetric headache parameters.* Cephalalgia. 1994 Jun; 14(3): 228-34; discussion 182.

- 1 drop clove
- 2 drops copaiba

General Headache Blend #2:
- 4 drops *Eucalyptus globulus*
- 6 drops peppermint
- 2 drops myrrh

EO APPLICATION METHODS:
Inhalation:
DIFFUSION, 15 minutes 3-5 times daily
DIRECT, 3-8 times daily as needed
Topical:
DILUTE 50:50, apply 1-3 drops on back of neck, behind ears, on temples, on forehead, and under nose. Be careful to keep away from eyes and eyelids.
Oral:
TONGUE, place a drop on the tongue then push against the roof of the mouth

Dietary Supplementation:
MultiGreens, Power Meal, Balance Complete, Essentialzyme, Polyzyme

Topical Treatment:
Prenolone, Prenolone+, Progessence

Migraine (Vascular-type Headache)

The vast majority of migraine headaches may be due to colon congestion or poor digestion. The combination of ICP/ Comfortone/Essentialzyme is most important for cleansing the colon. Eye strain and decreased vision can accompany migraine headaches. Dried woflberries contain large amounts of lutein, which is vital for healthy vision.

FIRST RECOMMENDATIONS:
M-Grain, wintergreen

Other Single Oils:
Helichrysum, basil, rosemary, peppermint, lavender, marjoram, German chamomile, *Eucalyptus globulus,* copaiba

Other Blends:
PanAway, Clarity

M-Grain is specially formulated for migraine headaches.

EO APPLICATION METHODS:
Topical:
NEAT, Apply 1-2 drops to temples, at base of neck, in center of forehead, and at nostril openings. Also massage on thumbs and big toes
Inhalation:
DIRECT, as needed

DIETARY SUPPLEMENTATION:
Magnesium, Mega Cal, Polyzyme, Balance Complete, Dried wolfberries, ICP/Comfortone/Essentialzyme

Sinus Headache

(See also SINUS INFECTION)

FIRST RECOMMENDATIONS:
Eucalyptus radiata, peppermint, R.C., Breath Again Roll-on, Sinus Headache blend (below)

Sinus Headach Blend:
- 5 drops tea tree
- 9 drops rosemary
- 2 drops *Eucalyptus globulus*
- 2 drops lavender
- 3 drops peppermint
- 4 drops geranium

Other Single Oils:
Rosemary, tea tree, *Eucalyptus globulus*, lavender, geranium

Other Blends:
Melrose, Purification

EO APPLICATION METHODS:
Inhalation:
DIFFUSION, 10 min. 2-5 times daily and at night
DIRECT, 2-5 times daily as needed

Dietary Supplementation:
Super C Chewable, True Source Multivitamins, ImmuPro

Tension Headache

(See also STRESS)

FIRST RECOMMENDATIONS:
PanAway, peppermint, lavender, Roman chamomille

Other Single Oils:
Valerian, cardamom, tangerine, jasmine absolute, palmarosa, geranium, frankincense

Other Blends:
Valor, Aroma Siez, M-Grain, Peace & Calming, Hope, Sacred Mountain, Trauma Life, RutaVaLa, Tranquil Roll-on, Valor Roll-on

EO APPLICATION METHODS:
Topical:
DILUTE 50:50, apply 1-2 drops around the hairline, on the back of the neck, and across the forehead. Be careful not to use too much, as it will burn if any oil drips near eyes. If this should occur, dilute with a pure vegetable oil. Never with water.

DIETARY SUPPLEMENTATION:
Mega Cal, Polyzyme, Balance Complete, Dried wolfberries, magnesium ICP/Comfortone/Essentialzyme

HEARING IMPAIRMENT

FIRST RECOMMENDATION:
Helichrysum

Other Single Oils:
Juniper, geranium, peppermint, lavender, basil

EO APPLICATION METHODS:
Topical:
NEAT, (1) apply 1 drop essential oil on a cotton ball, then place it carefully in the opening of the ear canal. Retain overnight. <u>Do NOT place oils directly in the ear canal.</u>
NEAT, (2) massage 1-2 drops on each ear lobe, behind the ears, and down the jaw line (along the Eustachian tube).

Hearing Vita Flex Regimen
- Apply 1-2 drops neat helichrysum to the area OUTSIDE the opening to the ear canal with fingertip or cotton swab. <u>Do NOT put oil inside the ear canal</u>
- After applying the helichrysum, hold ear lobes firmly and pull in circular motion 10 times to help stimulate absorption and circulation in the ear canal.

Tinnitus (ringing in the ears)

FIRST RECOMMENDATIONS:
Helichrysum

Other Single Oils:
Juniper, geranium, peppermint, lavender, basil

EO APPLICATION METHODS:
Topical:
NEAT, massage 1-2 drops on temples and forehead and back of neck. Additionally, apply 1 drop each on tips of toes and fingers, so that the oils get into the Vita Flex pathways.
VITA FLEX, Do the hearing Vita Flex regimen described above

(See also EAR PROBLEMS)

HEART ATTACK

(See Heart Attack under CARDIOVASCULAR CONDITIONS)

HEART HEALTH

Heart Vita Flex

The foot Vita Flex point related to the heart is on the sole of the left foot, below the ring toe (fourth toe) and approx. 1" below the base of the toe. Massaging this point is as effective as massaging the hand and arm points together (see below).

The hand Vita Flex point related to the heart is in the palm of the left hand, one inch below the ring finger joint (at the lifeline). A secondary heart point is on the inside of the lower end of the upper left arm, approximately 2 inches up the arm from the funny bone (elbow), not on the muscle but up under the muscle. Have another person use thumbs and firmly press these two points alternately for 3 minutes, in a kind of pumping action. Work all 3 points when possible. Start with the foot first; then go to the hand and arm.

Heart Tonic-Stimulant

FIRST RECOMMENDATIONS:
Rosemary, peppermint

Other Single Oils:
Goldenrod, anise seed, mandarin, thyme, marjoram

Blends:
Aroma Life, Peace & Calming

EO APPLICATION METHODS:
Topical:
NEAT, massage 1-3 drops over heart area
1-3 times daily
VITA FLEX, massage 1 drop each of 2 or
3 of the recommended oils on heart Vita
Flex points on foot, hand, and arm, as needed
Inhalation:
DIRECT, as often as needed to bring calm

(See also CARDIOVASCULAR
CONDITIONS)

HEARTBURN

(See Heartburn in DIGESTION PROBLEMS)

HEAVY METALS

(See also METAL TOXICITY, Aluminum)

We absorb heavy metals from air, water, food, skin care products, mercury fillings in teeth, etc. These chemicals lodge in the fatty tissues of the body, which, in turn, give off toxic gases that may cause allergic symptoms. Cleansing the body of these heavy metals is extremely important to have a healthy immune function, especially if one has amalgam fillings.

Drink at least 64 ounces of distilled water daily to flush toxins and chemicals out of the body.

(See CIRCULATION PROBLEMS)

FIRST RECOMMENDATIONS:
MultiGreens, chlorella, Comfortone, Mega Cal

OTHER DIETARY SUPPLEMENTATION:
JuvaPower/Spice, Super C, Mineral Essence, Life 5, ICP/Comfortone/ Essentialzyme

(See also CHEMICAL SENSITIVITY REACTION)

HEMATOMA

(See also BLOOD CLOTS)

A hematoma is a tumor-like mass of coagulated blood, caused by a break in the blood vessel or capillary wall. Essential oils, such as helichrysum or geranium, are excellent for balancing blood viscosity and dissolving clots. Clove oil and citrus rind oils, such as lemon and grapefruit, exert a blood-thinning effect that can help speed the dissolution of the clot.

Those who bruise easily are usually low in vitamin C, which may be caused by insufficient intake or poor absorption.

FIRST RECOMMENDATIONS:
Geranium, helichrysum, clove, wintergreen, Aroma Life, lemon

Other Single Oils:
Cypress, cistus, lemon, grapefruit, nutmeg

Other Blends:
PanAway, Longevity

EO APPLICATION METHODS:
Topical:
DILUTE 50:50, on location
4-6 times daily
COMPRESS, warm, 15 min., 2 times daily
Massage equal parts lemon, lavender and helichrysum on location, with or without hot packs
Ingestion:
CAPSULE, 00 size, 2 times daily between meals (this works especially well with helichrysum and cistus
RICE MILK, 2 times daily

DIETARY SUPPLEMENTATION:
Super C Chewable, Mineral Essence, Omega Blue Softgels, Longevity Softgels, Dried wolfberries, Ningxia Red

HEMORRHAGES

(See also CIRCULATION DISORDERS, LIVER DISORDERS)

Some essential oils, when topically applied or used on pressure bandages, are excellent for slowing bleeding and initiating healing.

FIRST RECOMMENDATIONS:
Geranium, cistus

Other Single Oils:
Helichrysum, cypress, lavender, myrrh

EO APPLICATION METHODS:
Topical:
COMPRESS, cold, as needed
NEAT, 1-2 drops on location for small wounds

DIETARY SUPPLEMENTATION:
Juva Power/Spice, True Source Multivitamins

HEMORRHOIDS

FIRST RECOMMENDATIONS:
Basil, wintergreen, Essentialzyme

Other Single Oils:
Cypress, cistus, helichrysum, myrrh, lemon, spikenard, peppermint

Other Blends:
Aroma Siez, Aroma Life, PanAway

Hemorrhoid blend #1:
- 4 drops of basil
- 1 drop of wintergreen
- 1 drop of cypress
- 1 drop of helichrysum

Hemorrhoid blend #2:
- 3 drops cypress
- 2 drops helichrysum
- 10 drops myrtle

EO APPLICATION METHODS:
Retention:
RECTAL, once every other day for 6 days.
Topical:
DILUTE 50:50, apply 3-5 drops on location. This may sting, but usually brings relief with one or two applications.

OTHER DIETARY SUPPLEMENTATION:
Polyzyme, MultiGreens, Longevity Softgels, Mega Cal, Digest & Cleanse Softgels, ICP.Comfortone, Essentialzyme

Cleanse using the Enzyme Cleanse in Chapter 25.

Topical Treatment:
Cel-Lite Magic

HEPATITIS

(See HEPATITIS in LIVER DISORDERS)

HERPES SIMPLEX

(See SEXUALLY TRANSMITTED DISEASES for Herpes Type II, COLD SORES for Herpes Type I, and CHICKEN POX for Herpes Zoster)

HICCUPS

Hiccups are usually caused by irritated nerves of the diaphragm, possibly caused from a full stomach or indigestion.

One technique for stopping hiccups that often works when others fail is to stimulate the Vita Flex point for hiccups by placing one drop of cypress and one drop of tarragon on the end of the index finger; then place that finger against the esophagus in the clavicle notch in the center, and curl inward and down, like you're curling down inside the throat, and release.

Tarragon or cypress either topically applied or taken as a dietary supplement may relax intestinal spasms, nervous digestion, and hiccups.

FIRST RECOMMENDATIONS:
Tarragon, cypress, spearmint

EO APPLICATION METHODS:
topical:
DILUTE 50:50, apply 3-5 drops to chest and stomach areas.
Ingestion:
CAPSULE, 0 size, 1 capsule 2 times daily
RICE MILK, 2-4 times daily

(See also DIGESTIVE PROBLEMS)

HIGH BLOOD PRESSURE (Hypertension)

(See also CARDIOVASCULAR CONDITIONS)

FIRST RECOMMENDATIONS:
Omega Blue Softgels, dried wolfberies, clove

Other Single Oils:
Lavender, marjoram, ylang ylang, cypress

Other Blends:
Aroma Life, Peace & Calming, Citrus Fresh, Humility

EO APPLICATION METHODS:
Topical:
DILUTE 20:80, full body massage daily
Inhalation:
DIFFUSION, 20 minutes, 3 times daily
Ingestion:
CAPSULE, 00 size, 1-2 times daily

Additional essential oil regimens:
1. For 3 minutes, massage 1-2 drops each of Aroma Life and ylang ylang on the heart Vita Flex point and over the heart and carotid arteries along the neck. Blood pressure will begin to drop within 5 to 20 minutes. Monitor the pressure and reapply as required.
2. Inhalation of jasmine reduces anxiety in some people and thereby lowers blood pressure.

OTHER DIETARY SUPPLEMENTATION:
CardiaCare, ImmuPro, ImmuneTune, Super B, Mineral Essence, Super Cal, Balance Complete, Mega Cal

Supplementation regimen:
1. Increase intake of magnesium which acts as a smooth-muscle relaxant and acts as a natural calcium channel blocker for the heart, lowering blood pressure and dilating the heart blood vessels. Mineral Essence and Mega Cal are good sources of magnesium.
2. Take 20 mg daily of vitamin B3 (niacin) an excellent vasodilator (found in Super B).
3. Use therapeutic-grade Hawthorne berry extracts. Hawthorne berry (contained in HRT tincture) provides powerful cardiovascular support.
4. Do a colon and liver cleanse.

HIVES

Hives is a generalized itching or dermatitis that can be due allergies, damaged liver, chemicals, or other factors.

FIRST RECOMMENDATIONS:
German chamomille, wintergreen, Ravensara

Other Single Oils:
Peppermint, myrrh, *Eucalyptus radiata,* tea tree

EO APPLICATION METHODS:
Topical:
DILUTE 50:50, 2-4 drops on location as needed
COMPRESS, cold, as needed

DIETARY SUPPLEMENTATION:
Super Cal, Mega Cal, Mineral Essence, True Source Multivitamins

Topical Treatment:
Tender Tush Ointment

(See also ITCHING in SKIN DISORDERS and LIVER DISORDERS)

HORMONAL EDEMA (Cyclic)

(See also EDEMA, MENSTRUAL CONDITIONS)

This type of edema usually fluctuates with the female menstrual cycle. First line therapy would be to utilize a progesterone hormone cream (Progessence), but before starting any hormone therapy, see your health care provider or lab for your hormone profile.

FIRST RECOMMENDATIONS:
Progessence cream, Prenolone

Single Oils:
Clary sage, lemongrass

Blends:
Dragon Time, Sclaraderm

OTHER DIETARY SUPPLEMENTATION:
PD 80/20

HORMONE IMBALANCE

(See MENSTRUAL CONDITIONS)

HOT FLASHES

(See MENSTRUAL CONDITIONS)

HUNTINGTON'S CHOREA

(See NEUROLOGICAL DISEASES)

HYPERACTIVITY

(see also ATTENTION DEFICITE DISORDER)

FIRST RECOMMENDATIONS:
Valerian, cedarwood

Other Single Oils:
Lavender, vetiver, Roman chamomile, peppermint

EO APPLICATION METHODS:
Inhalation:
 DIRECT, 5 times daily for up to 30 days,
 then off 5 days, then repeat if necessary
Topical:
 NEAT, 2-4 drops on toes and balls of feet,
 as needed

HYPERTENSION

(See HIGH BLOOD PRESSURE)

HYPOGLYCEMIA

Hypoglycemia may also be caused by low thyroid function (See THYROID).

Excessive consumption of sugar or honey will also cause reactive hypoglycemia, in which a rapid rise in blood sugar is followed by a steep drop to abnormally low levels.

In some cases, hypoglycemia may be a precursor to candida, allergies, chronic fatigue syndrome, depression, and chemical sensitivities.

Signs of hypoglycemia (low blood sugar) include:
- Fatigue, drowsiness, and sleepiness after meals.
- Headache or dizziness if periods between meals are too long.
- Craving for sweets.
- Allergic reaction to foods.
- Palpitations, tremors, sweats, rapid heart beat.
- Inattentiveness, mood swings, irritability, anxiety, nervousness, inability to cope with stress, and feelings of emotional depression,
- Lack of motivation, discipline, and creativity.
- Hunger that cannot be satisfied.

Often people with some of these symptoms are misdiagnosed as suffering either chronic fatigue or neurosis. Instead, they may be hypoglycemic.

To treat chronic hypoglycemia, it may be necessary to first treat the underlying candida or yeast overgrowth (See FUNGAL INFECTIONS).

Essential oils may reduce hypoglycemic symptoms by helping to normalize sugar cravings and supporting and stabilizing sugar metabolism in the body.

FIRST RECOMMENDATIONS:
 MultiGreens, Dried wolfberries, Cinnamon
 Bark powder

Single Oils:
 Lavender, cinnamon, coriander, dill, fennel
EO APPLICATION METHODS:
Ingestion:
 CAPSULE, 00 size, 1 times daily
 (coriander, dill and fennel work
 best through ingestion)
Inhalation:
 DIRECT, 2-5 times daily as needed
DIETARY SUPPLEMENTATION:
 Ningxia Red, Life 5, Digest & Cleanse
 Softgels, True Source Multivitamins,
 Blue Agave Nectar

HYSTERECTOMY

(See Hysterectomy in MENSTRUAL CONDITIONS)

IMPOTENCE

(See also SEXUAL DYSFUNCTIONS, INFERTILITY)

Impotence (the inability to perform sexually) can be caused by physical limitations (an accident or injury) or psychological factors (inhibitions, trauma, stress, etc). In males, impotence is often linked to problems with the prostate or prostate surgery

(See also PROSTATE PROBLEMS)

If impotence is related to psychological trauma or unresolved emotional issues, it may be necessary to deal with these issues before any meaningful progress can be made.

(See also TRAUMA)

There is an extensive historical basis for the ability of fragrance to amplify desire and create a mood that can overcome frigidity or impotence. In fact, aromas such as rose and jasmine have been used since antiquity to attract the opposite sex and create a romantic atmosphere.

Modern research has shown that the fragrance of some essential oils can stimulate the emotional center of the brain. This may explain why essential oils have the potential to help people overcome impotence based on emotional factors or inhibitions.

Male Impotence

FIRST RECOMMENDATIONS:
Ylang ylang, ProGen, EndoGize

Other Single Oils:
Frankincense, myrrh, ginger, nutmeg, jasmine absolute

Blends:
Valor, Valor Roll-on

EO APPLICATION METHODS:
Inhalation:
DIFFUSION, 15 min, twice daily
DIRECT, as needed
Topical:
NEAT, 2-3 drops to Vita Flex points on feet or lower abdomen. Do NOT apply on sensitive skin in crotch area.

Female Impotence

(See also Female Frigidity under SEXUAL DYSFUNCTION)

FIRST RECOMMENDATIONS:
Progessence Cream, Clary sage, SclarEssence, EndoGize

Other Single Oils:
lemongrass, jasmine absolute, rose, frankincense

Other Blends:
Lady Sclareol, Joy, Valor, Valor Roll-on

EO APPLICATION METHODS:
Inhalation:
DIFFUSION, 15 min, twice daily
DIRECT, as needed
Topical:
NEAT, 2-3 drops to Vita Flex points on feet or lower abdomen. Do NOT apply on sensitive skin in crotch area.

DIETARY SUPPLEMENTATION:
PD 80/20, Prenolone cream

INDIGESTION

(See DIGESTIVE PROBLEMS)

> ### To Kill Airborne Viruses and Bacteria
>
> Periodically alternate diffusing ImmuPower and Thieves.
>
> Topically apply 1 drop *Melaleuca alternifolia* and 1 drop rosemary to stem infection.
>
> **Single Oils:** Tea Tree, cinnamon, clove, thyme, oregano, ravensara, or frankincense.
>
> **Blends:** Thieves, Melrose, Purification

INFECTION (Bacterial and Viral)

Diffusing essential oils is one of the best ways to prevent the spread of airborne bacteria and viruses. Many essential oils, such as oregano, mountain savory, and rosemary, exert highly antimicrobial effects and can effectively eliminate many kinds of pathogens.

Viruses and bacteria have a tendency to hibernate along the spine. The body may hold a virus in a suspended state for long periods of time. When the immune system is compromised, these viruses may be released and then manifest into illness. Raindrop Technique along the spine helps reduce inflammation and kill the microorganism.

Oregano and thyme are generally used first for the Raindrop application. However, other oils may also be used and may be more desirable for some people. ImmuPower, R.C., and Purification all work well in the Raindrop application method.

Mountain savory, ravensara, and thyme applied during Raindrop Technique on the spine may be beneficial for many infections, particularly chest-related.

(See also COLDS, LUNG-, SINUS-, and THROAT INFECTION)

FIRST RECOMMENDATIONS:
Thieves, Inner Defense, niaouli, oregano, thyme

Other Single Oils:
Mountain savory, rosemary, lemongrass, clove, rosewood, tea tree, geranium, manuka

Other Blends:

Purification, Melrose, R.C., ImmuPower, Exodus II, Breath Again Roll-on

EO APPLICATION METHODS:

Inhalation:

DIFFUSION: 15 minutes, 4-7 time daily

DIRECT: 3-6 times daily, as needed

Topical:

DILUTE 20:80, 4-6 drops on location 2-3 times daily

RAINDROP Technique, 1-2 times weekly

Ingestion:

CAPSULE, 00 size, 1 capsule twice daily

DIETARY SUPPLEMENTATION:

Super C Chewable, Exodus, Dried wolfberries, Ningxia Red, Longevity sofgels, MultiGreens, ImmuPro, Omega Blue Softgels, Life 5

INFERTILITY

Women

Natural progesterone creams when use from the middle to the end of the cycle (starting on the day after ovulation, usually day 15 or later) may improve fertility Some essential oils have hormone-like qualities that can support or improve fertility processes.

FIRST RECOMMENDATIONS:

Progessence cream, SclarEssence, clary sage

Other Single Oils:

Sage, anise, fennel, blue yarrow, geranium

Other Blends:

Dragon Time, Acceptance, Mister, SclarEssence, Lady Sclareol

EO APPLICATION METHODS:

Ingestion:

CAPSULE, 0 size, 2 times daily

Topical:

NEAT or Dilute 50:50, as desired, 2-4 drops on the lower back and lower abdomen areas 2-3 timess daily

VITA FLEX, 2-4 drops on the reproductive Vita Flex points of hands and feet (inside of wrists, around the front of the ankles in line with the anklebone, on the lower sides of the anklebone, and along the Achilles tendon.) 1-3 times daily.

OTHER DIETARY SUPPLEMENTATION:

PD 80/20, MultiGreens, Mineral Essence, Super Cal, Thyromin, EndoGize

Use MultiGreens, 3-8 capsules, 2-3 times daily

Other Topical Treatments:

Prenolone cream

Rub daily 1/2 tsp Progessence or Prenolone on lower back area and the lower bowel area near the pubic bone.

Men

FIRST RECOMMENDATIONS:

Protec, ProGen, EndoGize

Single Oils:

Sage, Frankincense

Other Blends:

Mister

EO APPLICATION METHODS:

Topical:

NEAT or Dilute 50:50, as desired, 2-4 drops on the reproductive Vita Flex points of hands and feet (inside of wrists, around the front of the ankles in line with the anklebone, on the lower sides of the anklebone, and along the Achilles tendon.) 1-3 times daily.

Protec/Progen Application:

Take 2-4 ProGen capsules daily to nourish the reproductive system.

Also, rub 4-6 drops Protec on the lower adomen near the pubic bone and in the area between the scrotum and the rectum. (Alternatively, use 1 tablespoon of Protec in overnight rectal retention.)

INFLAMMATION

(See also MUSCLES)

Inflammation can be caused by a variety of conditions, including bacterial infection, poor diet, chemicals, hormonal imbalance, and physical injury.

Certain essential oils have been documented to be excellent for reducing inflammation. German chamomile contains azulene, a blue compound with highly anti-inflammatory properties. Wintergreen is also highly anti-inflammatory. Other oils with anti-inflammatory properties include peppermint, tea tree and clove.

Some oils are better suited for certain types of inflammation. For example:

- Myrrh and lavender work well for inflammation due to tissue/capillary damage, and bruising.

- German chamomile and tea tree are helpful with inflammation due to bacterial infection.

- Ravensara, hyssop, and thyme are appropriate for inflammation caused by viral infection.

FIRST RECOMMENDATIONS:

ImmuPro, wintergreen, German chamomille, myrrh, ravensara, copaiba

Other Single Oils:

Clove, nutmeg, lavender, thyme, Roman chamomile, hyssop, peppermint, tea tree

Blends:

Purification, PanAway, Aroma Siez, Melrose, Relieve It, Deep Relief Roll-on

Anti-inflammation blend #1:
- 6 drops wintergreen
- 6 drops tea tree
- 4 drops German chamomile
- 2 drops peppermint
- 2 drops lemongrass

Anti-inflammation blend #2:
- 6 drops myrrh
- 6 drops *Eucalyptus globulus*
- 4 drops clove
- 3 drops wintergreen
- 1 drop peppermint

EO APPLICATION METHODS:
Topical:
DILUTE 50:50, 2-4 drops on inflamed area, 2 times daily
COMPRESS, cold, 1-3 times daily as needed
Ingestion:
CAPSULE, 0 size, 2 times daily

Topical Treatment:
Ortho Ease

INFLUENZA

(See also COLDS, INFECTION)

FIRST RECOMMENDATIONS:
Ravansara, ImmuPro

Single Oils:
Blue cypress, mountain savory, oregano, *Eucalyptus radiata*, peppermint, clove, tea tree

Blends:
ImmuPower, Di-Gize, Exodus II, Thieves, Inner Defense, ParaFree, Essentialzyme, Polyzyme

EO APPLICATION METHODS:
Ingestion:
RICE MILK, 2-4 times daily
CAPSULE, 00 size, 1 capsule 3 times daily
Inhalation:
DIRECT, 2-4 times daily
Topical:
DILUTE 50:50, 2-4 drops on chest, stomach or lower back, as needed, 2- times daily
RAINDROP Technique, 1-2 times weekly
COMPRESS, warm, over lower abdomen, 1-2 times daily
BATH SALTS, (see below)

Influenza Recipe for bath
- 2 drops Eucalyptus radiata
- 6 drops frankincense
- 3 drops blue cypress
- 6 drops spruce
- 15 drops ravensara
- 1 drop wintergreen

Stir above essential oils thoroughly into 1/4 cup Epsom salt or baking soda, then add salt/oil mixture to hot bath water while tub is filling. Soak in hot bath until water cools.

Dietary Supplementation:
Essentialzyme, Polyzyme, ParaFree, Digest & Cleanse Softgels, Exodus

INSECT BITES

(See INSECT REPELLENT)

Because of their outstanding antiseptic and oil-soluble properties, essential oils are ideal for treating most kinds of insect bites. Essential oils such as lavender and peppermint reduce insect-bite-induced itching and infection.

FIRST RECOMMENDATIONS:

Purification, Melrose, citronella

Other Single oils:

Lavender, *Eucalyptus globulus*, tea tree, peppermint, rosemary, copaiba

Other Blends:

PanAway

Blend for stings and bites:

- 2 drops thyme
- 10 drops lavender
- 4 drops *Eucalyptus radiata*
- 3 drops German chamomile

EO APPLICATION METHODS:

Topical:

Neat or Dilute 50:50, apply 1-2 drops on bite location 2-4 times daily

Bee Stings

FIRST RECOMMENDATION:

Melrose

Other Single Oils:

Lavender, Idaho tansy, peppermint, wintergreen

Blends:

Purification, PanAway

Bee Sting blend:

- 2 drops lavender
- 1 drop peppermint
- 1 drop German chamomile
- 1 drop wintergreen

Bee Sting Regimen:

- Flick or scrape stinger out with credit card or knife, taking care not to squeeze the venom sack.
- Apply 1-2 drops Bee Sting Blend on location. Repeat every 15 minutes for 1 hour.
- Apply any of the recommended blends 2-3 times daily until redness abates.

Black Widow Spider Bite

Seek emergency care immediately.

Brown Recluse Spider Bite

The bite of this spider causes a painful redness and blistering which progresses to a gangrenous slough of the affected area. Seek immediate medical attention.

Blends:

Purification, Thieves, Inner Defense, Pan Away

Spider Bite blend:

- 1 drop lavander
- 1 drop wintergreen
- 1 drop Melrose

EO APPLICATION METHODS:

Topical:

NEAT, 1 drop of any of the above blends every 10 minutes until you reach professional medical treatment.

Chigger and Tick Bites

It is important that ticks and chiggers be removed before treating their bites. Sometimes chiggers can be removed or killed by covering the bite with clear fingernail polish. A common method for removing ticks is to touch them gently with a recently blown out match head. The heat often causes ticks to let go so they can be brushed off.

Essential oils may work to help remove ticks and chiggers. Mix thyme or oregano in a 50:50 dilution and apply 1-2 drops over the bite area. The phenols in these oils will usually cause them to let go and squirm to get away from the oil. When they do, they can be brushed off and killed.

After the tick/chiggers are removed, treat the bite with topical application of oils listed below:

FIRST RECOMMENDATIONS:

Tea tree, peppermint

Other Single Oils:

Lavender, rosemary

Blends:

Melrose, Thieves, Inner Defense, R.C., Breath Again Roll-on

EO APPLICATION METHODS:

Topical:

NEAT, 1-6 drops, depending on size of affected area, 3-5 times daily

Using Essential Oils As Insect Repellents

Mosquito-repellent: Lemon, peppermint, *Eucalyptus radiata*, lemongrass.

Moth repellent: Patchouli.

Horse-fly repellent: Idaho tansy floral water.

Aphids repellent: Mix 10 drops spearmint and 15 drops orange essential oils in 2 quarts salt water, shake well, and spray on plants.

Cockroach repellent: Mix 10 drops peppermint and 5 drops cypress in 1/2 cup salt water. Shake well and spray where roaches live.

Silverfish repellent: *Eucalyptus radiata*, citriadora

To repel insects, essential oils can be diffused or put on cotton balls or cedar chips (for use in closets or drawers).

INSECT REPELLENT

FIRST RECOMMENDATION:
Citronella

Other Single Oils:
Peppermint, lavender, tea tree, geranium, Idaho tansy, lemon, rosemary, lemongrass, thyme, spearmint

Blends:
Purification, Melrose

Insect Repellent blend:
- 6 drops peppermint
- 6 drops tea tree
- 9 drops *citronella*

EO APPLICATION METHODS:
Topical:
DILUTE 20:80, apply to exposed skin as needed

INSOMNIA

(see also DEPRESSION, THYROID PROBLEMS)

After age 40, sleep quality and quantity deteriorates noticeably as melatonin production in the brain declines. Supplemental melatonin (found in ImmuPro) has been researched to

To Relax Before Sleep:

Rub Peace & Calming or Dream Catcher across the shoulders along with a little lavender or Roman chamomile if needed.

Put 1 drop of Harmony on energy meridians to help balance the energy flow in the body. (1 drop on stomach, navel, thymus, throat, forehead, and crown of head).

Apply 2-3 drops valerian to the brain Vita Flex points on each foot.

dramatically improve sleep/wake cycles and combat age-related insomnia.

Insomnia may also be caused by bowel or liver toxicity, poor heart function, negative memories and trauma, depression, mineral deficiencies, hormone imbalance, or underactive thyroid.

The fragrance of many essential oils can exert a powerful calming effect on the mind through their influence on the limbic region of the brain. Historically, lavender sachets or pillows were used.

FIRST RECOMMENDATIONS:
ImmuPro, valerian, RutaVaLa, Tranquil Roll-on

Other Single Oils:
Lavender, cedarwood, orange, Roman chamomile, mandarin, citrus hystrix

Other Blends:
Peace & Calming, Harmony, Dream Catcher, Valor, Valor Roll-on, Gentle Baby, Trauma Life

Insomnia Blend:
- 12 drops orange
- 8 drops lavender
- 4 drops citrus hystrix
- 3 drops valerian
- 2 drops Roman chamomile

EO APPLICATION METHODS:
Inhalation:
DIFFUSION, 30-60 min. at bedtime. Or apply 1-3 drops on a cotton ball and place on or near your pillow.
Topical:
NEAT, apply 1-3 drops to shoulders, stomach and on bottoms of feet.
BATH SALTS, just before retiring at night

Ingestion:
CAPSULE, 00 size, of lavender oil diluted 50:50 one hour before bedtime.

DIETARY SUPPLEMENTATION:
Mega Cal, PD80:20, PowerMeal, Life 5, dried wolfberries, Omega Blue Softgels

Topical Treatment:
Progessence cream, Prenolone cream

IRRITABLE BOWEL SYNDROME

(See DIGESTIVE PROBLEMS)

Irritable bowel syndrome (IBS) is a common disorder of the intestines marked by the following symptoms:

- Cramps
- Gas and bloating
- Constipation
- Diarrhea and loose stools

IBS may be caused by a combination of stress and a high-fat diet. Fatty foods worsen symptoms by increasing the intensity of the contractions in the colon, thereby increasing symptoms. Chocolate and milk products, in particular, seem to have the most negative effect on IBS sufferers.

IBS is not the same as colitis, mucous colitis, spastic colon, and spastic bowel. Unlike colitis, IBS does not involve any inflammation and is actually called a "functional disorder" because it presents no obvious, outward signs of disease.

A number of medical studies have documented that peppermint oil (in enteric-coated capsules) is beneficial in treating irritable bowel syndrome and decreases pain.[31,32,33]

FIRST RECOMMENDATIONS:
Digest & Cleanse Softgels, tarragon, peppermint, Life 5

Single Oils:
Wintergreen, anise, fennel

Blends:
Di-Gize

EO APPLICATION METHODS:
Ingestion:
CAPSULE, 0 size, 3 times daily
RICE MILK, 2-4 times daily
SYRUP, 2-4 times daily

DIETARY SUPPLEMENTATION:
Polyzyme, Essentialzyme, Detoxzyme, Omega Blue Softgels

ITCHING

(See SKIN DISORDERS or FUNGAL INFECTIONS)

JAUNDICE

(See LIVER DISORDERS)

JOINT STIFFNESS/PAIN

(See also PAIN, ARTHRITIS and CONNECTIVE TISSUE)

FIRST RECOMMENDATIONS:
PanAway, wintergreen, copaiba, Sulfurzyme, Deep Relief Roll-on

Other Single Oils:
Spruce, Douglas fir, elemi, Idaho balsam fir, German chamomille, peppermint, pine

Other Blends:
Aroma Siez, Aroma Life, Relieve It

Joint Pain blend #1:
- 10 drops black pepper
- 2 drops rosemary
- 5 drops marjoram
- 5 drops lavender

Joint Pain blend #2:
- 7 drops fir
- 4 drops wintergreen
- 2 drops blue chamomile
- 3 drops vetiver

EO APPLICATION METHODS:
Topical:
DILUTE 50:50, massage 3-6 drops on location, repeat as needed to control pain

31. Weydert JA, et al., "Systematic review of treatments for recurrent abdominal pain," *Pediatrics* 2003 Jan;111(1):e1-11.

32. Logan AC, Beaulne TM, "The treatment of small intestinal bacterial overgrowth with enteric-caoated peppermint oil: a case report," *Altern Med Rev,* 2002 Oct;7(5):410-7.

33. Sagduyu K, "Peppermint oil for irritable bowel syndrome," *Psychosomatics* 2002 Nov-Dec;43(6):508-9.

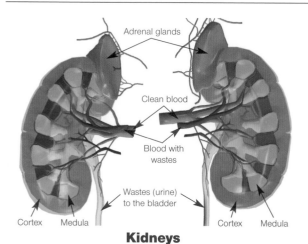

Kidneys

VITA FLEX, apply to appropriate Vita Flex points on the feet. Repeat as needed

DIETARY SUPPLEMENTATION:
Myrrh or Frankincense gum resin (ingest 2 crystals twice a day), Omega Blue Softgels

Topical Treatment:
Regenolone, Ortho Ease

KIDNEY DISORDERS

(See also HIGH BLOOD PRESSURE)

The kidneys remove waste products from the blood, and helps control blood pressure. The kidneys filter over 200 quarts of blood each day and remove over 2 quarts of waste products and water which flow into the bladder as urine through tubes called ureters.

Strong kidneys are essential for good health. Inefficient or damaged kidneys can result in wastes accumulating in the blood and causing serious damage.

High blood pressure can be a cause and a result of chronic kidney failure, since kidneys are central to blood regulation (see BLOOD PRESSURE, HIGH).

Symptoms of poor kidney function:
- Infrequent or inefficient urinations
- Swelling, especially around the ankles
- Labored breathing due to fluid accumulation in chest

A Simple Way To Strengthen the Kidneys

- Take 3 droppers K & B Tincture in 4 oz. distilled water, 3 times daily.

- Drink 8 oz. water with about 10 percent unsweetened cranberry juice and the fresh juice of 1/2 lemon.

- Drink plenty of other liquids, preferably distilled water.

Diuretic (To Increase Urine Flow)

FIRST RECOMMENDATIONS:
Juniper berry, geranium

Other Single Oils:
Grapefruit, lemon

EO APPLICATION METHODS:
Ingestion:
CAPSULE, 0 size, 3 times daily
Topical:
DILUTE 50:50, massage 6-8 drops over kidney area on back, 1-2 times daily
COMPRESS, warm, 1-2 times daily

DIETARY SUPPLEMENTATION:
K & B Tincture, Digest & Cleanse Softgels

Edema (Swelling)

(See EDEMA, WATER RETENTION)

Kidney Inflammation/Infection (Nephritis)

(See also URINARY TRACT/BLADDER INFECTION)

Kidney inflammation can be caused by structural defects, poor diet, or bacterial infection from *Escherichia coli, Staphylococcus aureus, Enterobacter,* and *Klebsiellabacteri.*

Abnormal proteins trapped in the glomeruli can also cause inflammation and damage to these tiny filtering units. This is called *glomerulonephritis.* This disease can be acute (flaring up in a few days), or chronic (taking months or years to develop). The mildest forms may not show any symptoms except through a urine test. At more advanced stages, urine appears smokey (as small amounts of blood

Detoxifing the Kidneys

The Chinese Wolfberry has been used in China for centuries as a kidney tonic and detoxifier. Essential oils can also assist in the detoxification due to their unique lipid-soluble properties.

Blend:
*   2 drops German chamomille
*   2 drops juniper berry
*   1 drop fennel

Dilute the above oils with 5 drops V6 and place in a gel capsule. Take twice daily. Also apply neat as a compress over kidneys.

Supplements:
K & B tincture, MultiGreens, Sulfurzyme.

are passed) and eventually red as more blood is excreted—the signs of impending kidney failure. As with all serious conditions, you should immediately consult a health care professional if you suspect a kidney infection of any kind.

Symptoms include:
*   Feeling of discomfort in lower back
*   Drowsiness
*   Nauseous
*   Smokey or red-colored urine

Damage to the glomeruli (tiny filtering units in the kidneys) caused by bacterial infections is called *pyelonephritis*. To reduce infection, drink a gallon of water mixed with 8 oz. of unsweetened cranberry juice daily and use the following products:

FIRST RECOMMENDATIONS:
Geranium, thyme, Mineral Essence, Thieves, Inner Defense softgels

Other Single Oils:
Cumin, lemongrass, rosemary, anise

Blends:
Melrose, Purification, Longevity

EO APPLICATION METHODS:
Ingestion:
CAPSULE, 00 size, 2 times daily for 10 days
RICE MILK, 2-4 times daily
Topical:
COMPRESS, cold, 1-2 times daily over kidney area

VITA FLEX, massage 1-3 drops on kidney Vita Flex points on feet

DIETARY SUPPLEMENTATION:
K & B tincture, Digest + Cleanse, Super C chewable, Life 5

Kidney Stones

(See also PAIN, URINARY TRACT/BLADDER INFECTION)

CAUTION: Kidney stones can create intense pain and dangerous infection. You should always consult a qualified health professional before beginning any treatment for kidney stones.

A kidney stone is a solid piece of material that forms in the kidney from mineral or protein-breakdown products in the urine. Occasionally, larger stones can become trapped in a ureter, bladder, or urethra, which can block urine flow causing intense pain.

There are four types of kidney stones: Stones made from calcium (the most common type), stones made from magnesium and ammonia (a struvite stone), stones made from uric acid, and stones made from cystine (the most rare).

Some of the symptoms of kidney stones include:
*   Persistent, penetrating pain in side or lower back
*   Blood in the urine
*   Fainting

It is important to drink plenty of water *(at least 6 eight-ounce glasses daily)* to help pass a kidney stone.

FIRST RECOMMENDATIONS:
Wintergreen, lemon

Other Single Oils:
Geranium, juniper berry, orange

EO APPLICATION METHODS:
Topical:
COMPRESS, warm, use 6-10 drops of above blend, over kidney area 1-2 times daily
VITA FLEX, massage 2-3 drops on kidney Vita Flex points of feet
Ingestion:
CAPSULE, 00 size, 2 times daily
RICE MILK, 2-4 times daily

DIETARY SUPPLEMENTATION:
K & B, Polyzyme, Essentialzyme, Detoxzyme, apple cider vinegar

Do NOT take Vitamin C.

Ureter Infection

The ureter is the duct from the kidney to the bladder.

See URINARY TRACT/BLADDER INFECTION)

KNEE CARTILAGE INJURY

(See CONNECTIVE TISSUE)

LEUKEMIA

(See CANCER)

LEG ULCERS

(See SKIN DISORDERS)

LIGAMENTS

(See CONNECTIVE TISSUE)

LIVER DISORDERS

(See also GALL BLADDER INFECTION, GALLSTONES)

The liver is one of the most important organs in the body, playing a major role in detoxifying the body. When the liver is damaged, frequently due to excess alcohol consumption, viral hepatitis, or poor diet, an excess of toxins can build up in the blood and tissues that can result in degenerative disease and death.

Symptoms of a stressed or diseased liver include:
- Jaundice (abnormal yellow color of the skin). This may be the only visible sign of liver disease.
- Nausea
- Loss of appetite
- Dark-colored urine
- Yellowish or grey-colored bowel movements

liver

- Abdominal pain or ascites, an unusual swelling of the abdomen caused by an accumulation of fluid
- Itching, dermatitis, or hives
- Disturbed sleep caused by the build up of unfiltered toxins in blood
- General fatigue and loss of energy
- Lack of sex drive

Toxic Liver

FIRST RECOMMENDATIONS:
Milk thistle extract, orange, JuvaCleanse

Other Single Oils:
Ledum, citrus hystrix, celery seed, lemon, cardamom, geranium, carrot seed, German chamomile, rosemary

Other Blends:
JuvaFlex, Release

Liver Support blend:
- 2 drops German chamomile
- 3 drops celery seed
- 10 drops orange
- 5 drops rosemary

EO APPLICATION METHODS:
Ingestion:
  CAPSULE, 0 size, 2 times daily
  RICE MILK, 2-4 times daily
Topical:
  COMPRESS, warm, over the liver 1-2 times daily

How to Protect Your Liver

- Use supplements such as schizandra, milk thistle, and N-acetyl cysteine
- Avoid alcoholic beverages.
- Avoid unnecessary use of prescription drugs. Even some common over-the-counter pain relievers can have toxic effects on the liver in moderately high doses.
- Consume a diet high in selenium.
- Avoid mixing pharmaceutic drugs. Be especially cautious in mixing prescription drugs with alcohol.
- Avoid exposure to industrial chemicals whenever possible.
- Eat a healthy diet.
- The Chinese wolfberry (Ningxia variety) is widely used in China as a liver tonic and detoxifier.

VITA FLEX, massage 1-3 drops on liver Vita Flex point of foot, 1-2 times daily
RAINDROP Technique, 1-2 times weekly

DIETARY SUPPLEMENTATION:

JuvaTone, JuvaPower/Spice, Longevity Softgels, Sulfurzyme, Digest & Cleanse Softgels, ICP/Comfortone/Essentialzyme, Life 5, dried wolfberries, True Source Multivitamins

Hepatitis

Viral hepatitis is a serious, life-threatening disease of the liver which can result in scarring (cirrhosis) and eventual organ destruction and death. A qualified health professional should be seen immediately if you suspect hepatitis.

There are several different kinds of hepatitis: Hepatitis A (spread by contaminated food, water, or feces) and Hepatitis B and C (spread by contaminated blood or semen).

A 2003 study conducted by Roger Lewis, MD at the Young Life Research Clinic in Provo, Utah evaluated the efficacy of helichrysum, ledum, and celery seed in treating cases of advanced Hepatitis C. In one case a 20 year old male diagnosed with Hepatitis C had a viral count of 13,200. After taking two capsules (approx. 750 mg each) of a blend of helichrysum, ledum, and celery seed (JuvaCleanse) per day for one month with no other intervention, the patient's viral count dropped more than 80 percent to 2,580.

Symptoms include jaundice, weakness, loss of appetite, nausea, brownish or tea colored urine, abdominal discomfort, fever and whitish bowel movements.

FIRST RECOMMENDATIONS:

Milk thistle extract, JuvaCleanse, German chamomile (Also cleansing with ICP/ComforTone/Essentialzyme. See Chapter 25: Cleansing and Diets)

Other Single Oils:

Ledum, celery seed, ravensara, peppermint, myrrh, wintergreen

Other Blends:

JuvaFlex, PanAway

EO APPLICATION METHODS:

Ingestion:
CAPSULE, 0 size, 3 times daily
RICE MILK, 2-4 times daily

Topical:
DILUTE 50:50, apply 1-3 drops on carotid arteries (on right and left side of throat just under jaw bone on either side), 2-5 times daily. (Carotid arteries are an excellent place to apply oils for fast absorption.)
COMPRESS, warm, over liver 1-2 times daily
VITA FLEX, massage 1-3 drops on liver Vita Flex point of foot, 1-3 times daily
RAINDROP Technique 2-3 times weekly

Dietary Supplementation:

JuvaPower/Spice, MultiGreens, JuvaTone, ImmuPro, Polyzyme, Detoxyme, Life 5, True Source Multivitamins

NOTE: Avoid grapefruit juice and any medications that stress the liver.

Daily Hepatitis regimen:
- Begin with colon cleanse using ICP/ComforTone/Essentialzyme. After 3 days add JuvaTone, 1-2 tablets 3 times daily
- ImmuPro: Chew 4 tablets at night, 1-2 tablets morning and afternoon.
- MultiGreens: 1-3 capsules, 3 times daily
- True Source multivitamins: 1 packet, 2-3 times daily

LIVER CANCER

(See CANCER)

LIVER SPOTS (Senile Lentigenes)

(See also SKIN DISORDERS)

FIRST RECOMMENDATION:
  Liver Spot Blend:
  • 20 drops avocado oil
  • 6 drops sandalwood
  • 4 drops blue cypress
  • 4 drops lavender
  • 4 drops nutmeg

Apply 2-4 drops of the above blend over affected area 3 times daily for 2 weeks

LOU GEHRIG'S DISEASE (ALS)

(See NEUROLOGICAL DISORDERS)

LUMBAGO (LOWER BACK PAIN)

(See SPINE INJURIES AND PAIN)

LUNG INFECTIONS

(See also COLDS, SINUS INFECTION, THROAT INFECTIONS)

Bronchitis

(See also ASTHMA)

Bronchitis is characterized by inflammation of the bronchial tube lining accompanied by a heavy mucus discharge. Bronchitis can be caused by an infection or exposure to dust, chemicals, air pollution, or cigarette smoke.

When bronchitis occurs regularly over a long periods (i.e. 3 months out of the year for several years) it is known as chronic bronchitis. It can eventually lead to emphysema.

Symptoms:
• Persistent, hacking cough
• Mucus discharge from the lungs
• Difficulty breathing

Avoiding air pollution is an easy way to reduce bronchitis symptoms. In cases where bronchitis is caused by a bacteria or virus, the inhalation of high antimicrobial essential oils may help combat the infection. Heavy mucus may increase after eating foods containing processed sugar or flour.

FIRST RECOMMENDATIONS:
  Eucalyptus globulus, R.C., Thieves, myrtle, Breath Again Roll-on

Other Single Oils:
  Rosemary, *Eucalyptus radiata*, thyme, wintergreen, pine, oregano, tea tree, Idaho balsam fir, bay laurel, copaiba

Other Blends:
  Raven, Melrose, Purification, PanAway

Bronchitis blend:
  • 2 drops wintergreen
  • 4 drops myrrh
  • 5 drops clove
  • 6 drops ravensara

NOTE: Essential oil blends work especially well in respiratory applications.

EO APPLICATION METHODS:
  Topical:
    DILUTE according to application code (Appendix E). Apply 2-6 drops to neck and chest as needed.
    COMPRESS, warm, on neck, chest and upper back areas 1-3 times daily
    VITA FLEX, on lung points of feet, 2-4 times daily
  Oral:
    GARGLE, hourly, or as needed
  Inhalation:
    DIRECT, 5-10 times daily as needed
    DIFFUSION, 15 minutes, 3-10 times daily as needed. Alternate oils/blends each time. Also diffuse at night during sleep
    VAPOR, 2-4 times daily as needed
  Retention:
    RECTAL, using any of the recommended blends, combine 20 drops with 1 tablespoon olive oil. Insert into rectum with bulb syringe and retain throughout the night. Repeat nightly for 2-3 days.

DIETARY SUPPLEMENTATION:
  Super C, ImmuPro, ImmuneTune, Fresh

Essence Plus, Life 5, Longevity Softgels, Digest & Cleanse Softgels, Inner Defense softgels

Oral Care:
Thieves Antiseptic Spray, Thieves Lozenges, Fresh Essence Plus mouthwash

Pneumonia

(See also THROAT INFECTION)

FIRST RECOMMENDATIONS:
R.C., Thieves, Inner Defense softgels, oregano, tea tree, Breath Again Roll-on

Other Single Oils:
Thyme, ravensara, *Eucalyptus globulus*, *Eucalyptus radiata*, mountain savory, clove

Other Blends:
Raven, Aroma Siez, Melrose

Pneumonia Blend:
- 10 drops *Eucalyptus globulus*
- 8 drops ravensara
- 2 drops oregano
- 2 drops peppermint

EO APPLICATION METHODS:
Topical:
Dilute according to application code (Appendix E). Apply 2-6 drops to neck and chest as needed.
COMPRESS, warm, on neck, chest and lungs
VITA FLEX, on lung points of feet, 2-4 times daily
Oral:
GARGLE, hourly, or as needed
Inhalation:
DIRECT, 5-10 times daily as needed
DIFFUSION, 15 minutes, 3-10 times daily as needed. Alternate oils/blends each time. Also diffuse at night during sleep
VAPOR, 2-4 times daily as needed
Retention:
RECTAL, using any of the recommend blends, combine 20 drops with 1 tablespoon olive oil. Insert into rectum with bulb syringe and retain throughout the night. Repeat nightly for 5-6 days.

DIETARY SUPPLEMENTATION:
Super C, Longevity Softgels, MultiGreens, ImmuPro, Digest & Cleanse Softgels, Life 5

Whooping Cough

NOTE: Because whooping cough usually affects children, always dilute essential oils in V6 Oil Complex or other cold-pressed vegetable oil before topically applying. Start with low concentrations until response is observed. Diffuse intermittently and observe reaction.

This is a contagious disease affecting the respiratory system particularly in children. Lungs become infected, as the air passages become clogged with thick mucus. Over the course of several days, the condition worsens, resulting in long coughing bouts (up to 1 minute). The continual coughing makes breathing difficult and labored.

FIRST RECOMMENDATIONS:
Nutmeg, peppermint, R.C., Breath Again Roll-on

Other Single Oils:
Rosemary, lavender, basil, wintergreen, thyme, oregano, tea tree

Other Blends:
Thieves, Melrose, Raven

EO APPLICATION METHODS:
Topical:
DILUTE 20:80, apply 2-4 drops to neck and chest as needed.
COMPRESS, warm, on neck, chest and upper back areas 1-3 times daily
VITA FLEX, on lung points of feet, 2-3 times daily
Inhalation:
DIRECT, 5-10 times daily as needed
DIFFUSION, 15 minutes, 3-10 times daily as needed. Alternate oils/blends each time. Also diffuse at night during sleep.
VAPOR, 2-4 times daily as needed

DIE TARY SUPPLEMENTATION:
Super C, Longevity Softgels, MultiGreens, ImmuPro, Sulfurzyme, Digest & Cleanse softgels, Inner Defense softgels

Oral Care:

Thieves Antiseptic Spray, Fresh Essence Plus mouthwash, Thieves lozenges

LUPUS

Lupus is an autoimmune disease that has several different varieties:

- *Lupus vulgaris* is characterized by lesions that form on skin. Brownish lesions may form on the face and become ulcerous and form scars.

- Discoid *Lupus erythematosus* is characterized by scaly red patches on the skin and oval or butterfly-shaped lesions on the face. It is milder than the systemic type.

- Systemic *Lupus erythematosus* is more serious—and more common—than discoid lupus. It inflames the connective tissue in any part of the body, including the joints, muscles, skin, blood vessels, membranes surrounding the lungs and heart, and occasionally the kidneys and brain.

Because lupus is an autoimmune disease, it has been successfully treated using MSM, a form of organic sulfur, found in Sulfurzyme.

FIRST RECOMMENDATIONS:

Myrrh, wintergreen, Sulfurzyme, Essentialzyme, basil

Other Single Oils:

Eucalyptus globulus, thyme, nutmeg

Other Blends:

Valor, Valor Roll-on, PanAway, R.C., Breath Again Roll-on

Lupus blend:

- 3 drops myrrh
- 4 drops *Eucalyptus globulus*
- 10 drops lavender

EO APPLICATION METHODS:

Ingestion:
CAPSULE, 0 size, 5 drops oil, 2 times daily
Topical:
BODY MASSAGE, once every other day
RAINDROP Technique, 1-2 times weekly

Lupus daily regimen:
1. BATH SALTS, using Lupus Blend, above, add 30 drops to 1/2 cup Epsom salt or baking soda and add to hot bath. Soak for 30 minutes.
2. VITA FLEX: Massage PanAway on bottoms of the feet; follow two hours later with foot massage using Thieves.
3. Topical: Massage 10-15 drops basil over liver and on feet 2-3 times daily.
4. SULFURZYME: 1-2 Tbsp powder or 5 capsules 1-2 times daily
5. IMMUNETUNE: 2-4 capsules 2 times daily
6. ESSENTIALZYME: 2-6 tablets, 2 times daily
7. MULTIGREENS: 2-4 capsules, 2 times daily

DIETARY SUPPLEMENTATION:

Polyzyme, ImmuneTune, MultiGreens

LYME DISEASE AND ROCKY MOUNTAIN SPOTTED FEVER

Viral infection caused by the bite of an infected tick. Lyme disease is caused by the microorganism *Borrelia burgdorferi*.

FIRST RECOMMENDATIONS:

Blue cypress, melissa, oregano, Inner Defense softgels

Other Singles:

Thyme, clove, niaouli

Other Blends:

PanAway, Melrose, Thieves, Exodus II

EO APPLICATION METHODS:
Ingestion:
CAPSULE, 00 size, 3 times daily

DIETARY SUPPLEMENTATION:
Power Meal, Polyzyme, ImmuPro

(See also TICK BITES in INSECT BITES)

(See also RHEUMATOID ARTHRITIS)

LYMPHATIC SYSTEM

Essential oils have long been known to aid in stimulating and detoxifying the lymphatic system.

FIRST RECOMMENDATIONS:

Hyssop, myrrh, ImmuPro

Lymphatic System Blend:
- 3 drops cypress
- 1 drop orange
- 2 drops grapefruit

Other Single Oils:
Myrtle, grapefruit, lemongrass, tangerine, orange, tangerine, rosemary, cypress, bay laurel

Other Blends:
Di-Gize, Aroma Life, En-R-Gee, Citrus Fresh

EO APPLICATION METHODS:
Ingestion:
CAPSULE, 0 size, 5 drops, twice daily
Topical:
DILUTE 50:50, massage 2-4 drops on sore lymph glands and under arms, 2-3 times daily
RAINDROP Technique weekly or as needed
COMPRESS, warm, over affected areas 1- 2 times daily

Massage oils over lymph gland areas, then apply Cel-Lite Magic and grapefruit or cypress oil, which helps detoxify chemicals stored in body fat.

DIETARY SUPPLEMENTATION:
Super C, Longevity Softgels, MultiGreens, ImmuPro, Digest & Cleanse Softgels, Life 5

Topical Treatment:
Cel-Lite Magic Massage Oil

LYMPHOMA

(See CANCER)

M.C.T. (Mixed Connective Tissue Disease)

(see LUPUS)

M.C.T. is an autoimmune disease similar to lupus in which the connective tissue in the body becomes inflamed and painful. This condition is usually due to poor assimilation of protein and mineral deficiencies.

FIRST RECOMMENDATION:
Sulfurzyme

MCT Blend (for aches & discomfort)
- 10 drops basil
- 8 drops wintergreen
- 6 drops cypress
- 3 drops peppermint

Other Single Oils:
Rosemary, nutmeg, clove, basil, marjoram, peppermint, wintergreen

Other Blends:
Valor, Valor Roll-on

EO APPLICATION METHODS:
Topical:
DILUTE 50:50, massage 4-8 drops on affected location 2-3 times daily
VITA FLEX, massage 1-3 drops on liver Vita Flex points of the feet
RAINDROP Technique, weekly or as needed.
MCT/Lupus regimen:
Rub 2-4 drops of ImmuPower over the liver and on liver Vita Flex Points on the bottom of the right foot 2-3 times daily. This has been reported to help lupus, which is similar to M.C.T.

OTHER DIETARY SUPPLEMENTATION:
MultiGreens, ImmuneTune, Mega Cal, Omega Blue Softgels

MALARIA

(See also FEVER, ANEMIA, INSECT BITES, INSECT REPELLANT)

Malaria is a serious disease contracted from several species of *Anopheles* mosquitoes. While malaria is largely confined to the continents of Asia and Africa, an increasing number of cases have arisen in North and South America. If not treated, malaria can be fatal.

Symptoms:
- Fever
- Chills
- Anemia

The best defense against malaria is to use insect repellents effective against *Anopheles* mosquitoes. Once a person has contracted the disease, one of the few natural aids to healing the disease is natural quinine. Essential oils such as niaouli can help amplify immune response.

FIRST RECOMMENDATIONS:
Natural quinine

Single Oils:
Lemon, niaouli, thyme

Topical/Oral Treatment:
Thieves Antiseptic Spray

EO APPLICATION METHODS:
Ingestion:
Mix 3-6 drops lemon oil in 1 tsp blue agave syrup and 8 oz. water, shake, and sip regularly to build immune system.

MALE HORMONE IMBALANCE

As men age, their DHEA and testosterone levels decline. Conversely, levels of dihydrotestosterone (DHT) increase, contributing to prostate enlargement and hair loss. Because pregnenolone is the master hormone from which all hormones are created, men can directly benefit from transdermal pregnenolone creams as a way of jump-starting sagging DHEA levels. Herbs such as saw palmetto and *Pygeum africanum* can prevent the conversion of testosterone into DHT, thereby reducing prostate enlargement and slowing hair loss.

FIRST RECOMMENDATIONS:
Prenolone Plus, ProGen, DHEA supplements, frankincense, EndoGize

Other Single Oils:
Rosemary, sage, fennel, geranium, blue yarrow

Other Blends:
Mister

EO APPLICATION METHODS:
Ingestion:
CAPSULE, 0 size, once a day

DIETARY SUPPLEMENTATION:
Saw palmetto, True Source Multivitamins

MEASLES

Measles, also called rubeola, is a highly contagious - but rare - respiratory infection caused by a virus. It causes a total-body skin rash and flu-like symptoms, including a fever, cough, and runny nose.

Since measles is caused by a virus, symptoms typically go away on their own without medical treatment once the virus has run its course. A person with measles should get plenty of fluids and rest, and avoid spreading the infection to others.

The first symptoms of the infection are sometimes a hacking cough, runny nose, high fever, and watery red eyes. Another indicator is Koplik's spots, small red spots with blue-white centers inside the mouth.

The measles rash typically has a red or reddish brown blotchy appearance, and first usually shows up on the forehead, then spreads downward over the face, neck, and body, then down to the feet.

FIRST RECOMMENDATIONS:
German chamomile, ravansara, ImmuPro

Measles blend:
- 10 drops lavender
- 10 drops German chamomile
- 5 drops ravensara
- 5 drops tea tree

Other Single Oils:
Lavender, Roman chamomile, tea tree, clove, thyme, niaouli

Other Blends:
Thieves, Melrose

EO APPLICATION METHODS:
Ingestion:
CAPSULE, 0 size, 5 drops oil, 2-3 times daily
Topical:
DILUTE 50:50, apply on spots, 3-5 x daily or as needed
BATH SALTS, soak at least 30 minutes in bath daily
Mix 6-9 drops of any of the above essential oils in 8 oz. water, shake well, and use to sponge down patient 1-2 times daily

OTHER DIETARY SUPPLEMENTATION:
Super C, Longevity Softgels, Life 5, Digest & Cleanse Softgels, Inner Defense softgels

MEMORY

(See BRAIN DISORDERS)

MENOPAUSE

(See Menopause under MENSTURAL CONDITIONS)

MENSTRUAL CONDITIONS

(See Chapter 11: Topical Hormone Products)

Natural hormones such as natural progesterone and pregnenolone are the most effective treatment for menstrual difficulties and irregularities. The most effective method of administration is transdermal delivery in a cream. Just 20 mg applied to the skin twice a day is equivalent to 1000 mg taken internally.

As women reach menopause, progesterone production declines and a state of estrogen dominance often arises. The most commonly prescribed drugs are conjugated estrogens (from horse urine) or synthetic medroxyprogesterone. The molecules in these synthetic hormones are foreign to the human body and can dramatically increase the risk for ovarian and breast cancer with time.

Endometriosis

This occurs when the uterine lining develops on the outer wall of the uterus, ovaries, fallopian tubes, vagina, intestines, or on the abdominal wall. These fragments cannot escape like the normal uterine lining, which is shed during menstruation. Because of this, fibrous cysts often form around the misplaced uterine tissue. Symptoms can include abdominal or back pain during menstruation or pain that often increases after the period is over. Other symptoms may include heavy periods and pain during intercourse.

FIRST RECOMMONDATIONS:
Melrose, clary sage

Other Single Oils:
Fennel

Other Blends:
Thieves

DIETARY SUPPLEMENTATION:
ImmuPro, Super C Chewable, PD 80/20

Topical Treatment:
Prenolone, Prenolone+, Progessence

Regimen:
• Colon and liver cleanse:
   ICP/ComforTone/Essentialzyme.
• Hot compress of Melrose on the stomach.
• Apply Thieves to bottom of the feet.

Excessive Bleeding

FIRST RECOMMENDATIONS:
Excessive Bleeding blend:
• 10 drops geranium
• 5 drops helichrysum
• 5 drops cistus

EO APPLICATION METHODS:
Topical:
DILUTE 50:50, apply 4-6 drops to forehead, crown of head, soles of feet, lower abdomen and lower back, 1-3 times daily
COMPRESS, warm, daily on lower back and abdomen
1/10 tsp. cayenne in 8 oz. warm water may help regulate bleeding during periods.

Hysterectomy

(See Menopause, below)

FIRST RECOMMENDATIONS:
Clary sage, Progessence cream

Other Single Oils:
Sage

Other Blends:
Dragon Time, Lady Sclareol, SclarEssence

OTHER DIETARY SUPPLEMENTATION:
PD 80/20.

Other Topical Treatment:
Progessence cream, Prenolone + cream

Irregular Periods

FIRST RECOMMENDATIONS
Period regulator blend #1:
• 5 drops peppermint
• 9 drops fleabane
• 16 drops clary sage
• 11 drops sage
• 5 drops jasmine absolute

Period regulator blend #2:
• 10 drops chamomile
• 10 drops fennel

EO APPLICATION METHODS:
Topical:
DILUTE 50:50, apply 4-6 drops to forehead, crown of head, soles of feet, lower abdomen, and lower back 1-3 times daily
VITA FLEX, massage 3-6 drops on reproductive Vita Flex points of feet, 2-3 times daily
COMPRESS, warm, daily, on lower back or lower abdomen

Menopause

As women age, their levels of progesterone decline and contribute to osteoporosis, increased risk of breast and uterine cancers, mood swings, depression, and many other conditions. Estrogen levels can also decline and increase women's risk of heart disease. Between ages 45 and 55, these hormones decline to a point where menstruation ceases. Replacing these declining levels using topically applied progesterone or pregnenolone creams may be the most effective way to replace and boost declining hormone levels. Pregnenolone may be especially effective, as it is the precursor hormone from which the body creates both progesterone and estrogens.

FIRST RECOMMENDATIONS:
Clary sage, Progessence cream, SclarEssence

Other Single Oils:
Geranium

Other Blends:
Mister, Dragon Time, Lady Sclareol, Transformation

EO APPLICATION METHODS:
Topical:
DILUTE 50:50, apply 4-6 drops to forehead, crown of head, soles of feet, lower abdomen and lower back 1-3 times daily
VITA FLEX, massage 3-6 drops on reproductive Vita Flex points of feet
COMPRESS, warm, daily, on lower back or lower abdomen

DIETARY SUPPLEMENTATION:
PD80:20

Topical Treatments:
Prenolone, Prenolone+, NeuroGen

Menstrual Cramps

FIRST RECOMMENDATIONS:
Valerian, hops, Dragon Time, lavender

Other Single Oils:
Clary sage, basil, rosemary, sage, lavender, Roman chamomile, cypress, tarragon, vetiver

Other Blends:
EndoFlex

Menstrual cramp relief blend:
- 10 drops Dragon Time
- 5 drops hops (*Humulus iupulus*)

EO APPLICATION METHODS:
Topical:
COMPRESS, warm, over uterus area, 2-3 times weekly
VITA FLEX, massage 2-4 drops on reproductive Vita Flex points on feet (around ankles), also on lower back and stomach
Ingestion:
CAPSULE, 0 size, twice daily for 2 weeks prior to menses

DIETARY SUPPLEMENTATION:
PD 80/20, MultiGreen, True Source Multivitamins

Topical Treatment:
Prenolone, Prenolone+

When migraine headaches accompany periods, a colon and liver cleanse may reduce symptoms.

Premenstrual Syndrome (PMS)

PMS is one of the most common hormone-related conditions in otherwise healthy women. Women can experience a wide range of symptoms for 10 to 14 days before menstruation, and even 2 to 3 days into menstruation. These symptoms include mood swings, fatigue, headaches, breast tenderness, abdominal bloating, anxiety, depression, confusion, memory loss, sugar cravings, cramps, low back pain, irritability, weight gain, acne, and oily skin and hair. Causes are hormonal, nutritional, and psychological. The stress of the Western culture can also be a cause.

FIRST RECOMMENDATIONS:
SclarEssence, Dragon Time, rose, hops, Progessence

Other Single Oils:
Clary sage, sage, anise, fennel, ylang ylang, neroli, bergamot

Other Blends:
Mister, EndoFlex, Acceptance, Aroma Siez, Lady Sclareol, Transformation

EO APPLICATION METHODS:
Inhalation:
DIRECT, 3-6 times daily
Topical:
DILUTE 50:50, apply 4-6 drops to forehead, crown of head, soles of feet, lower abdomen and lower back 1-3 times daily
VITA FLEX, massage 2-4 drops on reproductive Vita Flex points of feet
COMPRESS, warm, daily, on lower back or lower abdomen
Oral:
TONGUE, 1 drop of EndoFlex on the tongue and then hold the tongue against the roof of the mouth, 2-4 times daily

DIETARY SUPPLEMENTATION:
True Source Multivitamins, MultiGreens, Super B, Sulfurzyme, Mineral Essence, ImmuneTune, PD 80/20, Thyromin, EndoGize

Topical Treatment:
Prenolone, Prenolone Plus,

MENTAL FATIGUE

(See Mental Fatigue in FATIGUE heading)

METAL TOXICITY (Aluminum)

(See also HEAVY METALS)

Aluminum is a very toxic metal that can cause serious neurological damage in the human body—even in minute amounts. Aluminum has been implicated in Alzheimer's disease.

People unwittingly ingest aluminum from their cookware, beverage cans, and antacids. Even deodorants have aluminum compounds. The first step toward reducing aluminum toxicity in the body is to avoid these types of aluminum-based products.

FIRST RECOMMENDATIONS:
Chlorella, clove, JuvaCleanse

Other Single Oils:
Helichrysum, *Citrus hystrix*

EO APPLICATION METHODS:
Ingestion:
CAPSULE, 00 size, 2 times daily
Topical:
RAINDROP Technique, weekly

DIETARY SUPPLEMENTATION:
Chelex, JuvaTone, Mega Cal, ComforTone

MONONUCLEOSIS (Infectious)

(See EPSTEIN-BARR VIRUS)

MORNING SICKNESS

(See NAUSEA or MENSTRUAL CONDITIONS)

MOTION SICKNESS

(See NAUSEA)

MUCUS (Excess)

Many oils are natural expectorants, helping tissues discharge mucus, soft and hard plaque and toxins.

FIRST RECOMMENDATIONS:
Eucalyptus globulus, rosemary, R.C., Breath Again Roll-on

Other Single Oils:
Lavender, lemon, cypress, peppermint, tea tree, pine, thyme

Other Blends:
Di-Gize, Raven, 3 Wise Men, Purification

Expectorant blend:
• 3 drops lemon
• 3 drops Eucalyptus globulus
• 2 drops pine
Note: some studies conclude that the expectorant effect of essential oils is obtained faster and stronger through inhalation than through ingestion.

EO APPLICATION METHODS:
Inhalation:
DIRECT, 3-5 times daily
DIFFUSION, 20 minutes 3 times daily

Ingestion:
  CAPSULE, 0 size, 1 capsule twice a day
Topical:
  DILUTE 50:50, apply 2-4 drops on the T4 and T5 thoracic vertebrae (at the neck-to shoulder intersection), 3-5 times daily
  VITA FLEX, massage on relevant Vita Flex points on the feet 2-4 times daily

MULTIPLE SCLEROSIS (MS)

(See NEUROLOGICAL DISEASES)

MUMPS (Infectious Parotitis)

(See FEVER)

An acute, contagious, viral disease marked by painful swelling and inflammation of the salivary glands. The causative agent is a paromyxovirus, spread by direct contact, airborne droplets and urine.

FIRST RECOMMENDATIONS:
  Raven, R.C., manuka, Breath Again Roll-on

Other Single Oils:
  Thyme, tea tree, ravansara, melissa, myrrh, blue cypress, wintergreen.

Other Blends:
  Thieves, Exodus II

EO APPLICATION METHODS:
  Topical:
    DILUTE 50:50, 2-4 drops behind the ears 4 times daily
    COMPRESS, warm, 1-3 times daily around throat and jaw
    RAINDROP Technique 1-2 times weekly
  Ingestion:
    CAPSULE, 00 size, 1 capsule twice a day

DIETARY SUPPLEMENTATION:
  ImmuPro, Super C, Exodus, Inner Defense softgels

> ### For Tired, Fatigued Muscles
>
> Tired muscles may be lacking in minerals such as calcium and magnesium. Mega Cal and Mineral Essence are excellent sources of both trace and macro minerals and good for all muscle conditions.

MUSCLES

Bruised Muscles

(see BRUISING)

To avoid excess blood clotting in a bruised muscle or tissue and increase circulation:

FIRST RECOMMENDATIONS:
  Geranium, helichrysum, lavender, Aroma Siez

Other Single Oils:
  German chamomile, wintergreen, peppermint

Other Blends:
  Aroma Life, PanAway, Peace & Calming, Ortho Ease

EO APPLICATION METHODS:
  Topical:
    DILUTE 50:50, apply 2-4 drops to bruised area 3 times daily.

Sequence of application for bruise treatment:

- When a bruise displays black and blue discoloration and pain, start with helichrysum, geranium, or wintergreen.

- Once the pain and inflammation decrease, use cypress, then basil and Aroma Siez to enhance the muscle relaxation.

- Follow with peppermint to stimulate the nerves and reduce inflammation. Finish with cold packs.

DIETARY SUPPLEMENTATION:
  Mega Cal, Mineral Essence, dried wolfberries

> ### General Rules
>
> When selecting oils for injuries, think through the cause and type of injury and select oils for each segment. For instance, whiplash could encompass muscle damage, nerve damage, ligament damage, inflammation, bone injury, and possibly emotion. Select oils for each perceived problem and apply.

Muscle Spasms (Cramps and Charley Horses)

Magnesium and calcium deficiency may contribute to muscle cramps.

FIRST RECOMMENDATIONS:
Aroma Siez, wintergreen, ravansara, Mega Cal

Other Single Oils:
Rosemary, fennel, marjoram, basil, elemi, nutmeg, copaiba

Other Blends:
PanAway, Relieve It

Blend for muscle spasms:
- 2 drops ravensara
- 5 drops Aroma Siez
- 2 drops black pepper

EO APPLICATION METHODS:
Topical:
DILUTE 50:50, massage 2-4 drops on cramped muscle 3 times daily. It is usually helpful to alternate cold and hot packs when applying the above essential oil blend to muscles that are in spasm.

DIETARY SUPPLEMENTATION:
Mega Cal, Mineral Essence, BLM, Omega Blue Softgels, Life 5

Topical Treatment:
Ortho Sport, Ortho Ease

Inflammation Due to Injury

Tissue damage is usually accompanied by inflammation. Reduce inflammation by massaging with anti-inflammatory oils to minimize further tissue damage and speed healing.

FIRST RECOMMENDATIONS:
Wintergreen, PanAway, German chamomille, nutmeg

Other Single oils:
Peppermint, lavender, myrrh, marjoram, clove, thyme, copaiba

Other Blends:
Aroma Siez, Deep Relief Roll-on

Muscle Injury blend:
- 10 drops German chamomille
- 8 drops lavender
- 6 drops marjoram
- 3 drops blue yarrow
- 2 drops peppermint

EO APPLICATION METHODS:
Topical:
DILUTE 50:50, massage 2-4 drops on inflamed muscle 3 times daily

DIETARY SUPPLEMENTATION:
Mineral Essence, Mega Cal, Sulfurzyme, MultiGreens, Life 5

Inflammation Due to Infection

FIRST RECOMMENDATIONS:
Ravensara, thyme

Other Single Oils:
Hyssop, niaouli, blue cypress

EO APPLICATION
Topical:
DILUTE 50:50, massage 2-4 drops on inflamed muscle 3 times daily COMPRESS, cold, 1-3 times daily

DIETARY SUPPLEMENTATION:
Longevity Softgels, ImmuPro, BLM

Sore Muscles

FIRST RECOMMENDATIONS:
Rosemary, PanAway, Deep Relief Roll-on

Other Single Oils:
Wintergreen, black pepper, ginger, spruce, pine, marjoram, peppermint,

Other Blends:
Aroma Siez, Peace & Calming, M-Grain

Sore muscle blend #1:
- 2 drops rosemary
- 4 drops marjoram
- 4 drops lavender
- 5 drops wintergreen

Sore muscle blend #2:
- 5 drops pine
- 4 drops rosemary
- 4 drops ginger
- 1 drop valerian

EO APPLICATION METHODS:
Topical:
DILUTE 50:50, massage 4-6 drops into sore muscle 3 times daily.
COMPRESS, warm, 1-3 times daily

DIETARY SUPPLEMENTATION:
Mega Cal, Mineral Essence, Power Meal, Sulfurzyme

Muscle Weakness

FIRST RECOMMENDATIONS:
Idaho balsam fir, BLM, Power Meal

Other Singles:
Ravensara, Douglas fir, juniper, nutmeg, white fir

Other Blends:
En-R-Gee

EO APPLICATION METHODS:
Topical:
DILUTE 50:50, massage 4-6 drops into weak muscle 3 times daily

OTHER DIETARY SUPPLEMENTATION:
MultiGreens, Balance Complete, Protein Complete, Mega Cal, Juva Power/Spice

MUSCULAR DYSTROPHY

(See also Muscle Weakness under MUSCLES)

FIRST RECOMMENDATIONS:
PanAway, Sulfurzyme, Essentialzyme

Single Oils:
Pine, lavender, marjoram, lemongrass, vetiver, Idaho balsam fir

Other Blends:
Aroma Siez, Relieve It

EO APPLICATION METHODS:
Topical:
DILUTE 50:50, massage 4-6 drops along spine 3 times daily

DIETARY SUPPLEMENTATION:
Polyzyme, Power Meal, MultiGreens, Mineral Essence

Topical Treatment:
Ortho Ease, Ortho Sport

NAILS (Brittle or Weak)

Poor or weak nails, often containing ridges, indicate a sulfur deficiency.

FIRST RECOMMENDATIONS:
Sulfurzyme, myrrh, lemon

Other Single Oil:
Frankincense

Other Blend:
Citrus Fresh

EO APPLICATION METHODS:
Topical:
NEAT, 1-3 drops on nails and at base of nails, daily for 30 days.

OTHER DIETARY SUPPLEMENTATION:
Mega Cal, Mineral Essence

Nail strengthening blend:
• 4 drops Wheat Germ Oil
• 2 drops frankincense
• 2 drops myrrh
• 2 drops lemon

Apply 1 drop of the above blend on each nail 2-3 daily for 30 days.

NARCOLEPSY

A chronic ailment consisting of uncontrollable, recurrent attacks of drowsiness and sleep during daytime. May be aggravated by hypothalamus dysregulation or thyroid hormone deficiency.

(see also THYROID PROBLEMS)

FIRST RECOMMENDATIONS:
Peppermint, lemon, Brain Power

Other Single Oils:
Fleabane, rosemary, black pepper

Other Blends:
Clarity

EO APPLICATION METHODS:
Inhalation:
DIRECT, 4-8 times daily as needed
Topical:
DILUTE 50:50, apply 1-2 drops on temples, behind ears, back of neck, on forehead, and under nostrils, as needed

DIETARY SUPPLEMENTATION:
Mineral Essence, MultiGreens, Thyromin

NAUSEA

Patchouli oil contains compounds that are extremely effective in preventing vomiting due to their ability to reduce the gastrointestinal muscle contractions associated with vomiting.[34] Peppermint has also been found to be effective in many kinds of stomach upset, including nausea.

FIRST RECOMMENDATIONS:
Peppermint, patchouli, Life 5

Other Single Oils:
Ginger, nutmeg, wintergreen, Idaho tansy

Other Blends:
Di-Gize

EO APPLICATION METHODS:
Topical:
DILUTE 50:50, massage 1-3 drops behind each ear (mastoids) and over navel 2-3 times hourly.
COMPRESS, warm, over stomach, as needed
Inhalation:
DIRECT, 4-6 times hourly as needed
Oral:
TONGUE, 1-4 times as needed

DIETARY SUPPLEMENTATION:
Polyzyme, Essentialzyme, Life 5, Digest & Cleanse Softgels

Morning Sickness

FIRST RECOMMENDATIONS:
Di-Gize, spearmint

Other Single Oils:
Peppermint, ginger

EO APPLICATION METHODS:
Topical:
DILUTE 50:50, massage 1-3 drops behind each ear (mastoids) and over navel 2-3 times hourly
COMPRESS, warm, over stomach, as needed

Inhalation:
DIRECT, 4-6 times hourly as needed
Oral:
TONGUE, 1-4 times as needed

DIETARY SUPPLEMENTATION:
Polyzyme, Essentialzyme, Life 5

Motion Sickness

FIRST RECOMMENDATIONS:
Peppermint

Other Single Oils:
Lavender, ginger, spearmint, patchouli

Other Blend:
Valor, Valor Roll-on

EO APPLICATION METHODS:
Topical:
DILUTE 50:50, massage 1-3 drops behind each ear (mastoids) and over navel 2-3 times hourly
COMPRESS, warm, over stomach, as needed
Inhalation:
DIRECT, 4-6 times hourly as needed
Oral:
TONGUE, 1-4 times as needed
Ingestion:
RICE MILK, 1-2 times as needed

Motion Sickness Preventative:
• 2 drops peppermint
• 2 drops ginger
• 5 drops V6 Oil Complex

Rub 6-10 drops of the above blend on chest and stomach 1 hour before traveling.

DIETARY SUPPLEMENTATION:
Polyzyme, Essentialzyme

NERVE DISORDERS

(See also NEUROLOGICAL DISEASES)

Nerve disorders usually involve peripheral or surface nerves and include neuritis, neuropathy, neuralgia, Bell's palsy, and carpal tunnel syndrome. In contrast, neurological diseases are

---

34. Yang, Kinoshita, Koyama, Takahashi, Tai, Nunoura, "Anti-emetic principles of Pogostemon cablin" (Blanco) 1999 *Watanabe Phytomedicine* Vol. 6(2), pp 89-93.

usually associated with deep neurological disturbances in the brain, and these conditions include ALS (Lou Gehrig's disease), MS, and Parkinson's Disease.

Mega Cal used with Omega Blue Softgels helps provide calcium, magnesium and natural lipids necessary to maintain nerve signal transmissions along neurological pathways.

Sulfur deficiency is often present in nerve problems. Sulfur requires calcium and vitamins B and C for the body to metabolize. Super B, Super C, and Sulfurzyme work well together to help repair nerve damage and the myelin sheath.

CAUTION: Never use hot packs for neurological problems. Always use cold packs to reduce pain and inflammation. In other words, reduce the temperature of the damaged site.

Bell's Palsy

A type of neuritis, marked by paralysis on one side of the face and inability to open or close the eyelid.

FIRST RECOMMENDATIONS:
Peppermint, rosemary

Other Single Oils:
Helichrysum, pine

Other Blends:
Aroma Siez, PanAway, Relieve It

EO APPLICATION METHODS:
Topical:
NEAT, massage 1-3 drops on the facial nerve, which is in front and behind the ear and any areas of pain 3-5 times daily until symptoms end.

DIETARY SUPPLEMENTATION:
MultiGreens, Sulfurzyme, Mega Cal, Omega Blue Softgels

Carpal Tunnel Syndrome

Nerves pass through a tunnel formed by wrist bones (known as carpals) and a tough membrane on the underside of the wrist that binds the bones together. The tunnel is rigid, so if the tissues within it swell for some reason, they press and

pinch the nerves creating a painful condition known as carpal tunnel syndrome. This condition is primarily sports-related or due to activities that involve strenuous or repeated use of wrists. A similar but less common condition can occur in the ankle (tarsal tunnel syndrome), or elbow.

FIRST RECOMMENDATIONS:
Wintergreen, marjoram, NeuroGen

Other Single Oils:
Peppermint, basil, cypress, lemongrass

Other Blends:
PanAway, Relieve It

Carpal tunnel blend:
- 5 drops wintergreen
- 3 drops cypress
- 1 drop peppermint
- 2 drops marjoram
- 3 drops myrrh

EO APPLICATION METHODS:
Topical:
NEAT or DILUTE 50:50 as required, apply 2-4 drops to affected area 3-5 times daily COMPRESS, cold, on location 2-3 times daily

DIETARY SUPPLEMENTATION:
Sulfurzyme, Mega Cal, Mineral Essence

Topical Treatments:
Regenolone, NeuroGen, Ortho Ease

Neuralgia

Neuralgia is pain from a damaged nerve. It can occur in the face, spine, or elsewhere. This reoccuring pain can be traced along a nerve pathway. Carpal tunnel syndrome is a specific type of neuralgia. The primary symptom is temporary sharp pain in the peripheral nerve(s).

FIRST RECOMMENDATIONS:
PanAway, peppermint, wintergreen, Regenolone cream

Other Single Oils:
Marjoram, helichrysum, nutmeg, tea tree, Roman chamomile, rosemary

Other Blends:
Relieve It, Peace & Calming, Deep Relief Roll-on

EO APPLICATION METHODS:
Topical:
NEAT or DILUTE 50:50 as required, apply 2-4 drops to affected area 3-5 times daily
COMPRESS, cold, on location 2-3 times daily

DIETARY SUPPLEMENTATION:
Sulfurzyme, Super B, PD 80-20, Omega Blue Softgels

Topical Treatment:
NeuroGen, Ortho Ease, Prenolone Plus

Neuritis

Neuritis is a painful inflammation of the peripheral nerves.

It is usually caused by prolonged exposure to cold temperature, heavy-metal poisoning, diabetes, vitamin deficiencies (beriberi and pellagra), and infectious diseases such as typhoid fever and malaria.

Symptoms:
• Pain
• Burning
• Numbness or tingling
• Muscle weakness or paralysis

FIRST RECOMMENDATIONS:
PanAway, lavender, nutmeg, copaiba

Other Single Oils:
Lavender, juniper, wintergreen, thyme, blue yarrow, clove

Other Blends:
Valor, Valor Roll-on, Aroma Siez, Deep Relief Roll-on

EO APPLICATIONS:
Topical:
NEAT or DILUTE 50:50 as required, apply 2-4 drops to affected area 3-5 times daily
COMPRESS, cold, on location 2-3 times daily
Inhalation:
DIRECT, Peace & Calming, 2-4 times daily

DIETARY SUPPLEMENTATION:
Sulfurzyme, Super B, PD 80-20, Omega Blue Softgels

Topical Treatment:
Regenolone, NeuroGen, Prenolone Plus

Neuropathy

Neuropathy refers to actual damage to the peripheral nerves, usually from an auto-immune condition.

Damage to these peripheral nerves (other than spinal or those in the brain), generally starts as tingling in hands and feet and slowly spreads along limbs to the trunk.

Numbness, sensitive skin, neuralgic pain, weakening of muscle power can all develop in varying degrees. Most common causes include complications from diabetes (diabetic neuropathy), alcoholism, vitamin B12 deficiency, tumors, too many pain killers, exposure and absorption of chemicals, metallics, pesticides, and many other causes.

B vitamins and minerals such as magnesium, calcium, potassium, and organic sulfur are important in repairing nerve damage and quenching pain from inflamed nerves.

Fleabane may boost production of pregnenolone and human growth hormone. Pregnenolone aids in repairing damage to the myelin sheath.[35] Juniper also may help in supporting nerve repair.

If paralysis is a problem, a regeneration of up to 60 percent may be possible. If, however, the nerve damage is too severe, treatment may not help. If the damage starts to reverse, there will be pain. Apply a few drops of PanAway neat on location.

Symptoms:
• Tingling or numbness
• Gangrene

FIRST RECOMMENDATIONS:
Frankincense, lavender, Super B, cedarwood, PanAway, Omega Blue Softgels, Sulfurzyme

Other Single Oils:
Peppermint, Roman chamomille, geranium, blue yarrow, goldenrod, helichrysum, fleabane, nutmeg

35. Baulieu E, Schumacher M, Progesterone as a neuroactive neurosteriod, with special reference to the effect of progesterone on myelination, *Steroids* 2000 Oct-Nov;65(10-11):605-12.

Other Blends:
Aroma Siez, Peace & Calming

Neuropathy blend #1:
- 3 drops frankincense
- 3 drops geranium
- 3 drops lavender

Neuropathy blend #2:
- 3 drops geranium
- 3 drops fleabane
- 3 drops cedarwood
- 2 drops peppermint

EO APPLICATION METHODS:
Topical:
NEAT or DILUTE 50:50 as required, apply 2-4 drops to affected area 3-5 times daily
COMPRESS, cold, on location 2-3 times daily
Inhalation:
DIRECT, Peace & Calming, 2-4 times daily

OTHER DIETARY SUPPLEMENTATION:
Super B, Longevity Softgels, Mineral Essence, Mega Cal, Super C, MultiGreens

Topical Treatment:
NeuroGen cream, Prenolone Plus cream, PD 80/20

NERVOUS FATIGUE

(See FATIGUE)

NERVOUS SYSTEM (Autonomic)

The autonomic nervous system controls involuntary activities such as heartbeat, breathing, digestion, glandular activity, and contraction and dilation of blood vessels.

The autonomic nervous system is composed of two parts that balance and complement each other: the parasympathetic and sympathetic nervous systems.

The sympathetic nervous system has stimulatory effects and is responsible for secreting stress hormones such as adrenaline and noradrenaline.

The parasympathetic nervous system has relaxing effects and is responsible for secreting acetylcholine which slows the heart and speeds digestion.

To Stimulate Parasympathetic Nervous System

FIRST RECOMMENDATIONS:
Rose, valerian, Peace & Calming

Other Single Oils:
Lavender, patchouli, marjoram, ylang ylang

Other Blends:
Valor, Valor Roll-on

EO APPLICATION METHODS:
Inhalation:
DIRECT, 1-2 times daily, as needed
Ingestion:
CAPSULE, 0 size, 1 capsule 2 times daily
Topical:
RAINDROP Technique, biweekly

OTHER DIETARY SUPPLEMENTATION:
Ningxia Red, Mega Cal, Sulfurzyme

To Stimulate Sympathetic Nervous System

FIRST RECOMMENDATIONS:
Peppermint, rosemary, black pepper

Other Single Oils:
Fennel, ginger, *Eucalyptus radiata*

Other Blends:
Clarity, Brain Power

EO APPLICATION METHODS:
Inhalation:
DIRECT, 1-2 times daily, as needed
Ingestion:
CAPSULE, 0 size, 1 capsule twice daily
Topical:
RAINDROP Technique, biweekly

OTHER DIETARY SUPPLEMENTATION:
Super B, Super C, Mineral Essence

NEURALGIA, NEURITIS, NEUROPATHY

(See NERVE DISORDERS)

NEUROLOGICAL DISEASES

(See also NERVE DISORDERS)

CAUTION: Never use hot packs for neurological problems. Always use cold packs to reduce pain and inflammation. In other words, reduce the temperature of the damaged site.

ALS (Lou Gehrig's Disease)

Lou Gehrig's Disease is another name for Amyotrophic Lateral Sclerosis (ALS), a degenerative nerve disorder. ALS affects the nerve fibers in the spinal cord which control voluntary movement. Muscles require continuous stimulation by their associated nerves to maintain their tone. Removal or deadening of these nerves results in muscular atrophy. The lack of control forces the muscles to spasm, resulting in twitching and cramps. The sensory pathways are unaffected so feeling is never lost in the afflicted muscles.

Juniper may support nerve function. Frankincense may help clear the emotions of fear and anger, which is common with people who have these neurological diseases. When these diseases are contracted, people often become suicidal.

Hope, Joy, Gathering, and Forgiveness will help work through the psychological and emotional aspects of the disease.

FIRST RECOMMENDATIONS:
Rosemary, frankincense, Omega Blue Softgels

Other Single Oils:
Helichrysum, sage, juniper, clove, cardamom.

Other Blends:
Hope, Joy, Gathering, Brain Power, Clarity, Forgiveness

ALS blend:
- 3 drops rosemary
- 1 drop helichrysum
- 1 drop ylang ylang
- 2 drop clove

EO APPLICATION METHODS:
Inhalation:
DIRECT, 3-4 times daily
DIFFUSION, 30 minutes, 2-3 times daily

Topical:
DILUTE 50:50, 1-3 drops on brain reflex points on forehead, temples and mastoids (just behind ears). Use a direct pressure application, massaging 6-10 drops of diluted oil from the base of the skull down the neck and down the spine. Put a few drops of the oil on a loofah brush and rub along the spine vigorously. (Always use a natural bristle brush, since the oils may dissolve plastic bristles.)
RAINDROP Technique, 3 times monthly

OTHER DIETARY SUPPLEMENTATION:
Sulfurzyme, MultiGreens, Mega Cal, Super C, Super B, Longevity Softgels, Omega Blue softgels

Sulfur deficiency is often prevalent in neurological diseases. Sulfur requires calcium and Vitamin C for the body to metabolize. Super B and Sulfurzyme work well together to help repair nerve damage and the myelin sheath.

Topical Treatment:
NeuroGen cream, Prenolone + cream, PD 80/20

Huntington's Chorea

Huntington's Chorea is a degenerative nerve disease that generally becomes manifest in middle age. It is marked by uncontrollable body movements, which are followed—and occasionally preceded—by mental deterioration.

NOTE: Huntington's Chorea should not be confused with Sydenham's chorea (often called St. Vitus Dance, chorea minor, or juvenile chorea) which affects children, especially females, usually appearing between the ages of 7 and 14. The jerking symptoms eventually disappear.

FIRST RECOMMENDATIONS:
Peppermint, Omega Blue Softgels, Power Meal, True Source Multivitamins

Other Single Oil:
Juniper, basil

Other Blend:
Aroma Siez

Nerve blend:
- 2 drops peppermint
- 5 drops juniper
- 1 drops basil
- 3 drops Aroma Siez

EO APPLICATION METHODS:
Inhalation:
DIRECT, 3-4 times daily
DIFFUSION, 30 minutes, 2-3 times daily
Topical:
DILUTE 50:50, 1-3 drops on brain reflex points on forehead, temples and mastoids (just behind ears). Use a direct pressure application, massaging 6-10 drops of diluted oil from the base of the skull down the neck and down the spine. Put a few drops of the oil on a loofah brush and rub along the spine vigorously. (Always use a natural bristle brush, since the oils may dissolve plastic bristles.)
RAINDROP Technique, 3 times monthly,

DIETARY SUPPLEMENTATION:
Sulfurzyme, MultiGreens, Power Meal, Super C, Super B, Mega Cal, Omega Blue softgels, True Source Multivitamins

Multiple Sclerosis (MS)

Multiple Sclerosis is a progressive, disabling disease of the nervous system (brain and spinal cord) in which inflammation occurs in the central nervous system. Eventually, the myelin sheaths protecting the nerves are destroyed, resulting in a slowing or blocking of nerve transmission.

MS is an autoimmune disease, in which the body's own immune system attacks the nerves. Some researchers believe that MS is triggered by a virus, while others make a case that it has a strong genetic or environmental component.

Symptoms:
- Muscle weakness in extremities
- Deteriorating coordination and balance
- Numbness or prickling sensations
- Poor attention or memory
- Speech impediments
- Incontinence
- Tremors
- Dizziness
- Hearing loss

Maintaining MS Status Quo

One of the simplest ways to keep MS symptoms from becoming more severe is to keep the body cool and avoiding any locations or physical activities which heat the body (including hot showers or exercise). Cold baths and relaxed swimming are two of the best activities for relieving symptoms.

Applying heat is the worst thing to do for MS. If an MS patient is experiencing increasingly severe symptoms, lower their body temperature (by up to 3 degrees F) by laying them on a table, covering them with a sheet, ice, shower curtain, and blankets (in that order). Work the feet with oils and watch for benefits.

FIRST RECOMMENDATIONS:
PanAway, Omega Blue Softgels, Regenolone cream

Other Single Oils:
Juniper, wintergreen, frankincense, rosemary, basil, helichrysum, peppermint, thyme, marjoram,

Other Blends:
Valor, Valor Roll-on, Aroma Siez

MS Recipe:
- 2 drops helichrysum
- 4 drops wintergreen
- 4 drops rosemary
- 2 drops basil

EO APPLICATION METHODS:
Inhalation:
DIRECT, 3-4 times daily
DIFFUSION, 30 minutes, 2-3 times daily
Topical:
DILUTE 50:50, 1-3 drops on brain reflex points on forehead, temples and mastoids (just behind ears). Use a direct pressure application, massaging 6-10 drops of diluted oil from the base of the skull down the neck and down the spine. Put a few drops of the oil on a loofah brush and rub along the spine vigorously. (Always use a natural bristle brush, since the oils may dissolve plastic bristles.)
RAINDROP Technique, 3 times monthly, but use a cold compress instead of a warm one.

MS Regimen (to be performed daily):

1. Layer neat applications of 4-6 drops of helichrysum, wintergreen, rosemary and peppermint, Raindrop-style, along the spine. Lightly massage oils in the direction of the MS paralysis. For example, if it is in the lower part of the spine, massage down; if it is in the upper part of the spine, massage up. Follow the application with 30 minutes of cold packs (change cold packs as needed).

2. Apply 4-6 drops Valor on the spine. If the MS affects the legs, rub down the spine; if it affects the neck, rub up the spine.

3. Apply 2-3 drops each of cypress and marjoram to the back of the neck then cover with 2-3 drops of Aroma Siez.

To give additional emotional support to the person with MS symptoms, use Acceptance and Awaken. Be patient. Overcoming MS is a long-term endeavor.

OTHER DIETARY SUPPLEMENTATION:
Sulfurzyme, MultiGreens, Power Meal, Mega Cal, Super C, Super B, Ningxia Red

Parkinson's Disease

Parkinson's Disease involves the deterioration of specific nerve centers in the brain and affects more men than women by a ratio of 3:2. The main symptom is tremors, an involuntary shaking of hands, head, or both. Other symptoms include rigidity, slowed movement, and loss of balance. In many cases these are accompanied by a continuous rubbing together of thumb and forefinger, stooped posture, mask-like face, trouble swallowing, depression, and difficulty performing simple tasks. These symptoms may all be seen at different stages of the disease. The tremors are most severe when the affected part of the body is not in use. There is no pain or other sensation, other than a decreased ability to move. Symptoms appear slowly, in no particular order and may end before they interfere with normal activities. Restoring dopamine levels in the brain can reduce symptoms of Parkinson's. Sulfurzyme provides a source of organic sulfur, a vital nutrient for nerve and myelin sheath formation.

FIRST RECOMMENDATIONS:
NeuroGen cream, Sulfurzyme, Omega Blue Softgels

Other Single Oils:
Lavender, peppermint, cedarwood, myrrh, basil

Other Blends:
Peace & Calming, Valor, Valor Roll-on, Brain Power

EO APPLICATION METHODS:
Inhalation:
DIRECT, 3-4 times daily
DIFFUSION, 30 minutes, 2-3 times daily
Topical:
DILUTE 50:50, 1-3 drops on brain reflex points on forehead, temples and mastoids (just behind ears). Use a direct pressure application, massaging 6-8 drops of diluted oil from the base of the skull down the neck and down the spine. Put a few drops of the oil on a loofah brush and rub along the spine vigorously. (Always use a natural bristle brush, since the oils may dissolve plastic bristles.)
RAINDROP Technique, 3 times monthly

CAUTION: *Never use hot packs for neurological problems. Always use cold packs to reduce pain and inflammation. In other words, reduce the temperature of the affected area.*

OTHER DIETARY SUPPLEMENTATION:
Super B, PD80:20, BLM

NOSE PROBLEMS

(See also sinus INFECTIONS)

Nosebleeds

Nosebleeds usually are not serious. However, if bleeding does not stop in a short time or is excessive or frequent, consult your doctor.

FIRST RECOMMENDATIONS:
Helichrysum, geranium

Other Single Oils:
Lavender, cypress

Nosebleed blend:
- 3 drops helichrysum or geranium
- 2 drops lavender
- 2 drops cypress

EO APPLICATION METHODS:
Topical:
NEAT, apply 2-4 drops to the bridge and sides of nose and back of neck. Repeat as needed.

Nosebleed regimen:
Put 1 drop geranium on a tissue paper and wrap the paper around a chip of ice about the size of a thumb nail, push it up under the top lip in the center to the base of the nose. Hold from the outside with lip pressure. This usually will stop bleeding in a very short time.

Dry Nose

FIRST RECOMMENDATIONS:
Myrrh, lavender

Single Oils:
Lemon, peppermint

Dry nose blend:
• 2 drops lavender
• 1 drop myrrh

EO APPLICATION METHODS:
Inhalation:
DIRECT, 3-5 times daily as needed
DIFFUSION, 20 minutes 3 times daily and before retiring
Topical:
DILUTE 50:50, apply 1-2 drops to nostril walls with cotton swab twice daily

Nasal Irrigation Regimen:
Rosemary and tea tree oils can be used in a saline solution for very effective nasal irrigation that clears and decongests sinuses. As recommended by Daniel Pénoël, MD, the saline solution is prepared as follows:

• 10 drops rosemary
• 6 drops tea tree
• 8 tablespoons ultra fine salt

The essential oils are mixed thoroughly in the fine salt and stored in a sealed container. For each nasal irrigation session, 1 teaspoon of this salt mixture is dissolved into 1 1/2 cups distilled water.

This oils/salt/water solution is then placed in the tank of an oral irrigator to irrigate the nasal cavities, which is done while bending over a sink. This application has brought surprisingly positive results in treating latent sinusitus and other nasal congestion problems.

Olfactory Loss (Loss of Smell)

FIRST RECOMMENDATIONS:
Peppermint, thyme, R.C., Breath Again Roll-on

Other Single Oils:
Myrtle, *Eucalyptus globulus*

EO APPLICATION METHODS:
Inhalation:
DIRECT, 3-5 times daily, or as needed

Polyps (Nasal)

FIRST RECOMMENDATION:
Citronella

Other Blend:
Purification

EO APPLICATION METHODS:
Topical:
DILUTE 50:50, carefully apply 1 drop on location inside the nostrils with a cotton swab 1-3 times daily

OBESITY

(see DEPRESSION)

Hormone treatments using natural progesterone (for women) and testosterone (for men) may be one of the most powerful treatments for obesity. In women, progesterone levels drop dramatically after menopause and this can result in substantial weight gain, particularly around the hips and thighs. Using transdermal creams to replace declining progesterone can result in substantial declines in body fat.

Diffusing or directly inhaling essential oils can have an immediate positive impact on moods and appetites. Olfaction is the only sense that can have direct effect on the limbic region of the brain. Studies at the University of Vienna have shown that some essential oils and their primary constituents can stimulate blood flow and activity in the emotional centers of the brain.[36]

36. Nasel, C. et al. "Functional imaging of effects of fragrances on the human brain after prolonged inhalation." Chemical Senses. 1994;19(4):359-6

Fragrance influences the satiety center in the brain in such a manner that frequent inhalation of pleasing aromas can significantly reduce appetite. Dr. Alan Hirsch, in his landmark studies, showed dramatic weight loss in research subjects using aromas from peppermint oil and vanilla absolute to curb food cravings.[37]

FIRST RECOMMENDATIONS:
Peppermint, vanilla absolute, Roman chamomille

Other Single Oils:
Nutmeg, clove, grapefruit

Other Blends:
Valor, Valor Roll-on, Juva Cleanse

EO APPLICATION METHODS:
Inhalation:
DIRECT, 5-20 times daily or as often as needed

DIETARY SUPPLEMENTATION:
ThermaBurn, Juva Power, Omega Blue Softgels, Balance Complete, Digest & Cleanse Softgels

Topical Treatments:
Progessence, Prenolone, Prenolone+

ORAL CARE (Teeth and Gums)

(See also Chapter 16: Oral Health Care and HALITOSIS)

Poor oral hygiene has not only been linked to bad breath (halitosis) but also cardiovascular disease. Some of the same bacteria that populate the mouth have now been implicated in arteriosclerosis.

Essential oils make excellent oral antiseptics, analgesics and anti-inflammatories. Clove essential oil has been used in mainstream dentistry for decades to numb the gums and help prevent infections. Similarly menthol (found in peppermint oil), methyl salycilate (found in wintergreen oil), thymol (found in thyme essential oil) and eucalyptol (found in eucalyptus and rosemary essential oils) are approved OTC drug products for combating gingivitis and periodontal disease.

Dental Visits

Prior to visiting the dentist, rub one drop each of helichrysum, clove and PanAway on gums and jaw. Clove may interfere with bonding of crowns so keep it off the teeth if this procedure is planned.

Oral Infection Control

FIRST RECOMMENDATIONS:
Clove, tea tree

Other Single Oils:
Wintergreen, helichrysum, *Eucalyptus radiata*, thyme, oregano

Other Blends:
PanAway, Thieves

EO APPLICATION METHODS:
Topical:
DILUTE 50:50, apply 1-2 drops on gums and around teeth. Repeat as needed. Just before a tooth extraction, rub 1-2 drops of helichrysum, Thieves and R.C. around the gum area. Rubbing R.C. on gums may also help to bring back feeling after numbness from anesthesia.

Oral Treatments:
Dentarome Ultra Toothpaste, Thieves Lozenges, Thieves Antiseptic Spray, Fresh Essence Plus mouthwash

Gingivitis & Periodontitis

Periodontal diseases are infections of the gum and bone that hold the teeth in place. Gingivitis affects the upper areas of the gum, where it bonds to the visible enamel, while periodontitis is a more internal infection affecting the gum at the root level of the tooth. In advanced stages, these diseases can lead to painful chewing problems and even tooth loss. Oils such as peppermint, wintergreen, clove, thyme, and eucalyptus can kill bacteria and effectively combat a variety of gum infections.

FIRST RECOMMENDATIONS:
Clove, tea tree, thyme, Thieves

---

37. Hirsch AR. Inhalation of Odorants for Weight Reduction, *Int J Obes*, 1994, page 306

Other Single Oils:

Mountain savory, peppermint, wintergreen, thyme, oregano, *Eucalyptus globulus*

Other Blends:

Exodus II, PanAway

EO APPLICATION METHODS:

Oral:

GARGLE, up to 10 times daily as needed

DIETARY SUPPLEMENTATION:

Super C, Super C Chewable, Longevity Softgels, Omega Blue Softgels, Inner Defense softgels

Oral Treatments:

Dentarome Ultra Toothpaste, Fresh Essence Plus mouthwash, Thieves Lozenges, Thieves Antiseptic Spray, Thieves Dental Floss

Bleeding Gums

FIRST RECOMMENDATIONS:

Clove, geranium, wintergreen

Other Single Oils:

Cinnamon, peppermint, mountain savory, myrrh

Other Blends:

Thieves, Melrose, PanAway

Blend for combating gum bleeding:

• 2 drops myrrh
• 2 drops thyme
• 1 drop Thieves
• 1 drop geranium

EO APPLICATION METHODS:

Oral:

GARGLE, 3-10 times daily, as needed

Topical:

DILUTE 50:50, apply 1-2 drops on gums 2-3 times daily

Oral Hygiene Regimen:

Brush teeth and gums after every meal with Dentarome Ultra toothpaste.

Mouth Ulcers

(See also CANKER SORES)

FIRST RECOMMENDATIONS:

Tea tree, thyme, Thieves

Other Single Oils:

Myrrh, oregano

Other Blends:

Exodus II

EO APPLICATION METHODS:

Oral:

GARGLE, 3-10 times daily, as needed

Topical:

DILUTE 50:50, apply 1-2 drops on gums 2 times daily

Oral Hygiene:

Dentarome Ultra Toothpaste, Thieves lozenges, Thieves Antiseptic Spray, Fresh Essence Plus mouthwash

Gargle with Thieves Antiseptic Spray. Add 1-2 drops of Thieves, clove, and Exodus II to strengthen therapeutic action.

Teeth Grinding

(See also Chapter 24: Emotional Response with Essential Oils)

FIRST RECOMMENDATIONS:

Valerian, ImmuPro, Peace & Calming

Other Single Oils:

Lavender, Roman chamomile

EO APPLICATION METHODS:

Inhalation:

DIRECT, 1-3 times daily and before retiring
DIFFUSION, 30 minutes twice a day and before retiring

Topical:

NEAT, massage 1-3 drops each of lavender and valerian on bottoms of feet each night before retiring

Other Dietary Supplementation:

Mineral Essence, Mega Cal

Toothache and Teething Pain

FIRST RECOMMENDATIONS:

Clove, PanAway

Other Single Oils:

Wintergreen, German chamomile, tea tree, Idaho tansy

Other Blends:
Thieves, Exodus

EO APPLICATION METHODS:
Topical:
DILUTE 50:50, apply on affected tooth and gum area as needed
Oral:
GARGLE, 4-6 times daily or as needed

Oral Hygiene:
Thieves Antiseptic Spray, Dentarome Ultra toothpaste, Fresh Essence Plus mouthwash

NOTE: All essential oils should be diluted 20:80 before being used orally on small children.

OSTEOPOROSIS (Bone Deterioration)

(See also BONE PROBLEMS)

Osteoporosis is primarily caused by four main factors:

- Progesterone Deficiency
- Lack of Magnesium and boron in diet
- Lack of Vitamin D in diet
- Lack of dietary calcium

Natural progesterone is the single most effective way to increase bone density in women over age 40. Clinical studies by John Lee, MD, showed dramatic increases in bone density using just 20 mg of daily topically-applied progesterone

Calcium, magnesium, and boron are a few of the most important minerals for bone health and are usually lacking or deficient in most modern diets. Magnesium is especially important to bone strength, but most Americans consume only a fraction of the daily 400 mg daily value needed for bone health. Calcium and magnesium may not be adequately metabolized when consumed because of poor intestinal flora and excess phytates in the diet (a problem with vegetarians). Phytates occur in many nuts, grains, and seeds including rice. Enzymes like phytase are essential for increasing calcium absorption by liberating calcium from insoluble phytate complexes.

Lack of vitamin D (cholecalciferol) has become epidemic among older people and has contributed to a lack of absorption of calcium in the diet.

FIRST RECOMMENDATIONS:
Wintergreen, Idaho balsam fir, thyme, PanAway

Other Single Oils:
Elemi, spruce, pine, cypress, peppermint, marjoram, rosemary, basil

Other Blends:
Aroma Siez, Purification, Melrose, Sacred Mountain, Relieve It

EO APPLICATION METHODS:
Topical:
DILUTE 50:50, massage 6-10 drops on spine (or area affected) 2-3 times daily

DIETARY SUPPLEMENTATION:
Polyzyme, Essentialzyme, Super Cal, MegaCal, BLM, AlkaLime, Mineral Essence, Sulfurzyme, Thyromin

Topical Treatments:
Prenolone, Prenolone+, Progessence, EndoBalance

Mega Cal, AlkaLime, and Mineral Essence are all excellent sources of calcium and magnesium which is essential for strong bones. Mineral Essence is an excellent source of magnesium and other trace minerals.

Especially avoid consuming carbonated drinks which can leach calcium out of the body due to their phosphoric acid content.

Studies show that the majority of women that do resistance training 3-4 times a week do not develop osteoporosis.

OVARIAN AND UTERINE CYSTS

(See also MENSTRUAL CONDITIONS)

FIRST RECOMMENDATIONS:
Lemongrass, geranium, Progessence cream

Female Cyst blend #1:
- 9 drops frankincense
- 5 drops clary sage

Female Cyst blend #2:
- 4 drops frankincense
- 4 drops geranium
- 2 drops oregano

Other Single Oils:
Frankincense, tea tree

Other Blends:
DragonTime, SclarEssence

EO APPLICATION METHODS:
Retention:
TAMPON, nightly for 4 nights.
NOTE: if irritation occurs, discontinue use for 3 days before resuming use.

Topical:
COMPRESS, warm, on location, as needed
VITA FLEX, massage 1-3 drops on the reproductive Vita Flex points, located around the anklebone, on either side of the foot. Work from the ankle bone down to the arch of the foot.

DIETARY SUPPLEMENTATION:
PD80:20, EndoGize

Topical Treatments:
Prenolone, Prenolone+, Progessence

PAIN

(See also ARTHRITIS, HEADACHE)

One of the most effective essential oils for blocking pain is peppermint. A study in 1994 showed that peppermint oil is extremely effective in blocking calcium channels and substance P, important factors in the transmission of pain signals.[38] Other essential oils also have unique

---

How to Use Essential Oils for Pain Control

PanAway is powerful for pain reduction. When applied on location or to the Vita Flex points on the feet, it can act within seconds. Alternate with Relieve It. These 2 blends are a powerful combination for deep-tissue pain as well as bone-related pain.

How MSM Works to Control Pain

When fluid pressure inside cells is higher than outside, pain is experienced. The MSM found in Sulfurzyme equalizes fluid pressure inside cells by affecting the protein envelope of the cell so that water transfers freely in and out.

---

pain-relieving properties, including helichrysum, Idaho balsam fir, and Douglas fir.

MSM, a source of organic sulfur, has also been proven to be extremely effective for alleviating pain, especially tissue and joint pain. The subject of a best-selling book by Dr. Ronald Lawrence and Dr. Stanley Jacobs, MSM is redefining the treatment of pain, especially associated with arthritis and fibromyalgia. Sulfurzyme is an excellent source of MSM.

Natural pregnenolone can also blunt pain.

Bone-Related Pain

FIRST RECOMMENDATIONS:
Wintergreen, Idaho balsam fir, copaiba, PanAway

Other Single Oils:
Spruce, pine, peppermint, helichrysum

Other Blends:
Relieve It, Deep Relief Roll-on

EO APPLICATION METHODS:
Topical:
DILUTE 50:50, 2-4 drops on location as needed
VITA FLEX, apply to relevant points on feet, repeat as needed

DIETARY SUPPLEMENTATION:
Sulfurzyme, Mega Cal, BLM

Topical Treatment:
Ortho Ease, Regenolone, NeuroGen

Chronic Pain

To pinpoint the most effective essential oil for quenching pain, it may be necessary to try each of the essential oils in these categories in order to find the one that is most effective for your particular pain situation.

FIRST RECOMMENDATIONS:
Peppermint, wintergreen, clove, PanAway

Other Single Oils:
Helichrysum, spruce, elemi, oregano, Douglas fir, Idaho balsam fir, copaiba

---

38. "Effect of Peppermint and Eucalyptus Oil Preparations on Neurophysiological and experimental algesimetric headache parameters" 1994 Germany Gobel, Schmidt, Soyka Cephalalgia Jun;14(3):228-34; discussion 182.

Other Blends:
Relieve It, Aroma Siez, Release, Sacred Mountain

EO APPLICATION METHODS:
Topical:
DILUTE 50:50, 2-4 drops on location as needed
COMPRESS, warm, on location as needed

DIETARY SUPPLEMENTATION:
Sulfurzyme, Super Cal, Mega Cal, BLM

Topical Treatment:
Regenolone, Ortho Ease

Emotional Pain

(See Emotional Trauma)

Inflammation Pain

(see INFLAMMATION)

Joint Pain:

(See JOINT STIFFNESS and ARTHRITIS)

Muscle-related Pain

(See MUSCLES)

PANCREATITIS

Pancreatitis is an inflammation of the pancreas that can be either acute or chronic. Acute pancreatitis can be caused by a sudden blockage in the main pancreatic duct, which results in enzymes becoming backed-up and literally digesting the pancreas unless remedied. Chronic pancreatitis occurs more gradually, with attacks recurring over weeks or months.

Symptoms:
• abdominal pain
• muscle aches
• vomiting
• abdominal swelling
• sudden hypertension
• jaundice
• rapid weight loss
• fever.

In the case of acute pancreatitis, a total fast for at least 4-5 days is one of the safest and most effective methods of treatment. In the case of infection, fasting should be combined with immune stimulation by using Exodus combined with Vitamin C and B-complex vitamins.

FIRST RECOMMENDATIONS:
Essentialzyme, Polyzyme, orange

Other Single Oils:
Geranium, peppermint, oregano, vetiver, mountain savory

Other Blends:
Exodus II, Thieves, ImmuPower,

EO Application Methods:
Retention:
RECTAL, 3 times per week
Topical:
RAINDROP Technique, once a week
Ingestion:
CAPSULE, 0 size, 1 capsule 3 times per week

OTHER DIETARY SUPPLEMENTATION:
Exodus, MultiGreens, Super B, Digest & Cleanse Softgels, Omega Blue Softgels, Super C

PARASYMPATHETIC NERVOUS SYSTEM

(See NERVOUS SYSTEM-AUTONOMIC)

PARASITES, Intestinal

(See also FOOD POISONING)

Many types of parasites use up nutrients, while giving off toxins. This can leave the body depleted, nutritionally deficient, and susceptible to infectious disease.

Occasionally parasites can lie dormant in the body and then become active due to ingestion of a particular food or drink. This can result in the appearance and disappearance of symptoms even though parasites are always present.

The parasite, *Cryptosporidium parrum,* may be present in many municipal or tap waters. To remove, water must be distilled or filtered using a .3 micron filter.

Using Di-Gize and ParaFree Softgels For Parasite Control

The essential oil blend Di-Gize is excellent for parasite removal.

Di-Gize: Add 6 drops to 1 tsp. V6 Oil Complex or 4 oz. rice/soy milk and take as a dietary supplement twice a day. Di-Gize can also be diluted in massage oil and applied over abdomen. Or take 15 drops in a capsule 3 times a day for 7 days.

ParaFree Softgels: Take 5 soft gels 2-3 times daily for 21 days, then rest for 7 days. Repeat up to three times to achieve desired results.

Symptoms:
- Fatigue
- Weakness
- Diarrhea
- Gas and bloating
- Cramping
- Nausea
- Irregular bowel movements.

The first step to controlling parasites is beginning a fasting and/or cleansing program. A colon cleanse is particularly important.

FIRST RECOMMENDATIONS:
Lemongrass, ParaFree Softgels, Digest & Cleanse Softgels, cumin, Thieves, Inner Defense, Life 5, Essentialzyme

Other Single Oils:
Tarragon, anise, Idaho tansy, basil, peppermint, ginger, cumin, niaouli, nutmeg, tea tree, rosemary

Other Blends:
Di-Gize, JuvaFlex, JuvaCleanse

EO APPLICATION METHODS:
Ingestion:
CAPSULE, 00 size, 3 times per week
RICE MILK, 1-3 times daily
Topical:
COMPRESS, warm, over intestinal area, 2 times weekly
VITA FLEX, daily massage up to 6 drops to the instep area on both feet (small intestine and colon Vita Flex points)

Blend for parasite-killing retention blend:
- 4 drops ginger
- 4 drops Di-Gize
- 16 drops V6 Oil Complex

Retention:
RECTAL, use above blend nightly for 7 nights, then rest for 7 nights. Repeat this cycle 3 times to eliminate all stages of parasite development.

OTHER DIETARY SUPPLEMENTATION:
Polyzyme, ICP/Comfortone/Essentialzyme

PERIODONTAL DISEASE

(See ORAL CARE)

PH BALANCE

(See Chapter 26) (See ACIDOSIS)

PHLEBITIS

(See Phlebitis under CIRCULATION DISORDERS. Also see EDEMA)

PINKEYE

(See EYE DISORDERS)

PLAQUE

(See CARDIOVASCULAR CONDITIONS)

PLEURISY

(See also LUNG INFECTIONS)

Inflammation of the pleura, or outer membranes covering the lungs and the thoracic cavity.

FIRST RECOMMENDATIONS:
Wintergreen, PanAway, Sulfurzyme

Other Single Oils:
Myrrh, copaiba, German chamomille

EO APPLICATION METHODS:
Topical:
DILUTE 20:80, massage 5-7 drops on neck and chest 2-3 times daily

COMPRESS, warm, on neck, chest and upper back areas, daily

VITA FLEX, 1-3 drops on lung Vita Flex points of feet daily

RAINDROP Technique, 1-2 times weekly

DIETARY SUPPLEMENTATION:

ImmuneTune, Super C, Omega Blue Softgels

PNEUMONIA

(See LUNG INFECTIONS)

POLIO

Polio (Poliomylitis) is an acute infectious disease usually manifested in epidemics and caused by a virus. It creates an inflammation of the gray matter of the spinal cord. It is characterized by fever, sore throat, headache, and vomiting, sometimes stiffness of the neck and back. If it develops into the major illness, it can involve paralysis and atrophy of groups of muscles ending in contraction and permanent deformity.

FIRST RECOMMENDATIONS:

Ravansara, blue cypress, wintergreen

Single Oils:

Frankincense, tea tree, melissa, peppermint, sandalwood

Other Blends:

Polio blend:

- 6 drops lemon
- 10 drops ravensara
- 7 drops frankincense
- 10 drops wintergreen
- 8 drops blue cypress
- 15 drops myrrh

EO APPLICATION METHODS:

Ingestion:

CAPSULE, 0 size, 2 times daily

DIETARY SUPPLEMENTATION:

ImmuPro, Life 5

PREGNANCY

(See also BREASTFEEDING, Postpartum Depression in DEPRESSION, and Diaper Rash and Stretch Marks in SKIN DISORDERS)

CAUTION: Essential Oils and Pregnancy

Some essential oils should be avoided during pregnancy because they contain biochemicals that could disrupt normal pregnancy development in a variety of ways. For this reason, they should be avoided by pregnant women until after delivery. These include: basil, calamus, clary sage, fennel, hyssop, nutmeg, rosemary, sage, tansy, tarragon.

Some of these oils, such as fennel, may help to accelerate labor once it has begun. Always consult a health professional before using essential oils other than the ones recommended here during pregnancy.

Essential oils can be invaluable companions during pregnancy. Oils like lavender and myrrh may help reduce stretch marks and improve the elasticity of the skin. Geranium and Gentle Baby blend have similar effects and can be massaged on the perineum (tissue between vagina and rectum) to lower the risk of tearing or the need for an episiotomy (an incision in the perineum) during birth.

FIRST RECOMMENDATIONS:

Gentle Baby, lavender, myrrh, rose

Other Single Oils:

Geranium, German chamomille, neroli, sandalwood, rosewood

Other Blends:

Forgiveness, Valor, Valor Roll-on

EO APPLICATION METHODS:

Topical:

DILUTE 50:50, massage 2-4 drops on reproductive Vita Flex points on sides of ankles. Also massage 4-6 drops on lower stomach and lower back.

Inhalation:

DIFFUSION, diffuse Gentle Baby, Joy or Valor to reduce stress before and after the birth. (Expectant fathers will also find this helps to reduce anxiety while waiting for delivery.)

Topical Care:

Clara Derm Spray, Tender Tush Ointment

Labor Blend, only for use after labor has started:

- 4 drops helichrysum
- 2 drops fennel
- 2 drops peppermint
- 5 drops ylang ylang
- 2 drops clary sage

DILUTE above oils 50:50, massage 2-4 drops on reproductive Vita Flex points on sides of ankles. Apply ONLY after labor has started. Also massage 4-6 drops on lower stomach and lower back.

PROSTATE PROBLEMS

Natural progesterone is one of the best natural remedies for prostate inflammation (BPH) that can obstruct urinary flow and lead to impotence. Transdermal creams are the most effective means of hormone delivery.

Scientists are tracing the higher incidence of hormone-dependent cancers including cancer of the breast, prostate and testes to exposure to endocrine disrupters in the environment.[39] Petrochemical contamination from DDT, PCB, pesticides, the phylate DBP, and synthetic steroids in meat, are all implicated in interfering with hormone receptors, rendering them unable to function properly, eventually leading to cancer.

For prostate problems, peppermint acts as an anti-inflammatory to the prostate. Saw palmetto, Pygeum africanum, and pumpkin seed oil also help reduce prostate swelling.[40]

FIRST RECOMMENDATIONS:
ProGen, Progessence cream, pumpkin seed oil

Other Single Oils:
Myrrh, Idaho balsam fir, thyme, wintergreen, copaiba

Other Blends:
Mister, EndoFlex, Australian Blue

EO APPLICATION METHODS:
Topical:
DILUTE 20:80, apply 2-4 drops between the rectum and scrotum twice daily. Mister works especially well here

VITA FLEX, massage 4-6 drops on Vita Flex reproductive points on the feet 2 times daily
Retention:
RECTAL, nightly for 7 days; rest 7 days, then repeat

OTHER DIETARY SUPPLEMENTATION:
Longevity Softgels, PD 80/20, True Source Multivitamins

Zinc helps reduce prostate swelling. ProGen, and True Source Multivitamins are good sources of zinc.

Other Topical Treatments:
Prenolone, Prenolone +

Benign Prostate Hyperplasia (BPH)

Almost all males over age 50 have some degree of prostate hyperplasia, a condition which worsens with age. BPH can severely restrict urine flow and result in frequent, small urinations.

Three herbs which are extremely effective for treating this condition are saw palmetto, pumpkin seed oil, and *Pygeum africanum*. The mineral zinc is also important for normal prostate function and prostate health. The hormone-like activity of some essential oils can support a nutritional regimen to reduce BPH swelling.

FIRST RECOMMENDATIONS:
ProGen, saw palmetto, pumpkin seed oil, Progessence cream

Other Single Oils:
Frankincense, myrrh, Idaho balsam fir, blue cypress

Other Blends:
Mister, EndoFlex, Australian Blue, Protec

EO APPLICATION METHODS:
Topical:
DILUTE 50:50, 1-3 drops between the rectum and scrotum 1-3 times daily
VITA FLEX, 1-3 drops on reproductive Vita Flex points on feet, 2 times daily
Ingestion:
CAPSULE, 00 size, 1 capsule 3 times daily
RICE MILK, 2-4 times daily

---

39. Skakkebaek NE, "Endocrine disrupters and testicular dysgenesis syndrome," *Horm Res* 2002;57 Suppl 2:43.

40. Zhang X, et al., "Effect of the extracts of pumpkin seeds on the urodynamics of rabbits: an experimental study," *J Tongji Med Univ* 1994;14(4):235-8.

Retention:
RECTAL, 3 times per week, at night

BPH Specific Regimen:
The following regimen reduced PSA (prostate specific antigen) counts 70 percent in 2 months: PSA counts typically rise when BPH occurs.

BPH blend:
- 10 drops frankincense
- 5 drops myrrh
- 3 drops sage

Use the above blend for the following three applications simultaneously:
1. Mix the above amounts of essential oils with 1 tablespoon olive oil and use 3 times weekly as overnight rectal retention enema.
2. Massage 1-3 drops neat on Vita Flex reproductive points on both feet daily
3. Dilute above blend 50:50 with V6 Oil Complex and apply 2-4 drops topically between the rectum and the scrotum daily.

OTHER DIETARY SUPPLEMENTATION:
True Source Multivitamins, Longevity Softgels, Mineral Essence

Topical Treatments:
Prenolone, Prenolone +

Prostate Cancer

(See Prostate Cancer in CANCER)

Prostatitis

Prostatitis is an inflammation of the prostate that can present symptoms similar to benign prostate hyperplasia: frequent urinations, restricted flow, etc.

FIRST RECOMMENDATIONS:
Peppermint, German chamomille, wintergreen

Other Single Oils:
Rosemary, myrtle, thyme, tsuga, blue cypress

Other Blends:
Australian Blue, Mister, Aroma Siez, Di-Gize

EO APPLICATION METHODS:
Ingestion:
CAPSULE, 0 size, twice daily
Retention:
RECTAL, 3 times per week, at night

Topical:
DILUTE 20:80, apply 1-3 drops to the area between the rectum and the scrotum daily
VITA FLEX, massage 4-6 drops on reproductive foot Vita Flex points daily

DIETARY SUPPLEMENTATION:
ProGen, True Source Multivitamins, Longevity Softgels, ImmuPro, Mineral Essence

Topical Treatment:
Prenolone, Prenolone+, Progessence

PSORIASIS

(See SKIN DISORDERS)

PYORRHEA

(See ORAL CARE)

Essential oils are one of the best treatments against gum diseases such as gingivitis and pyorrhea. Clove oil, for example, is used as a dental disinfectant; and the active principle in clove oil, eugenol, is one of the best-studied germ-killers available.

RADIATION DAMAGE

Many cancer treatments use radiation therapy that can severely damage both the skin and vital organs. Using gentle, antioxidant essential oils topically, as well as proper nutrients internally, is helpful in minimizing radiation damage.

FIRST RECOMMENDATIONS:
Sandalwood, hyssop, and (internal only) oregano

Other Single Oils:
Peppermint, frankincense, Idaho balsam fir, blue cypress

Other Blend:
Longevity

EO APPLICATION METHODS:
Ingestion:
CAPSULE, 00 size, 2 times daily
Topical:
DILUTE 50:50, massage 2-4 drops on affected area 1-2 times daily

DIETARY SUPPLEMENTATION:
Super C, Power Meal, ImmuPro, Dried wolfberries, Ningxia Red, Longevity Softgels, Omega Blue softgels

RESTLESS LEG SYNDROME

(See also ATTENTION DEFICIT SYNDROME)

FIRST RECOMMENDATIONS:
ImmuPro, valerian, wintergeen, Peace & Calming

Other Single Oils:
Basil, marjoram, lavender, cypress, Roman chamomile

Other Blends:
Aroma Siez, Tranquil Roll-on

EO APPLICATION METHODS:
Inhalation:
DIRECT, 6-8 times daily as needed
DIFFUSION, 20 minutes, 4 times daily
Topical:
VITA FLEX Daily, before retiring
RAINDROP Technique, weekly

OTHER DIETARY SUPPLEMENTATION:
Mineral Essence, MultiGreens, Mega Cal, Omega Blue softgels

RHEUMATIC FEVER

Rheumatic fever results from a *Streptococcus* infection that primarily strikes children (usually before age 14). It can lead to inflammation that damages the heart muscle and valve.

Rheumatic fever is caused by the same genus of bacteria that causes strep throat and scarlet fever. Diffusing essential oils can help reduce the likelihood of contracting the disease. Essential oils such as mountain savory, rosemary, tea tree, thyme, and oregano, have powerful antimicrobial effects.

In cases where a person is already infected, the use of essential oils in the Raindrop Technique may be appropriate.

FIRST RECOMMENDATIONS:
Oregano, clove, tea tree, Thieves, Inner Defense softgels

Other Single Oils:
Mountain savory, peppermint, thyme, rosemary, black pepper

Other Blends:
Melrose, Exodus II

EO APPLICATION METHODS:
Inhalation:
DIFFUSION, 1 hour, 3 times daily
Topical:
DILUTE 50:50, massage 3-5 drops on bottoms of feet and on carotid artery spots under ear lobes
RAINDROP Technique, once weekly

DIETARY SUPPLEMENTATION:
Exodus, ImmuPro, ImmuneTune, Super C, Sulfurzyme, HRT, Longevity softgels

RINGWORM

(See Ringworm or Athlete's Foot in FUNGAL INFECTIONS)

SALMONELLA

(See FOOD POISONING and INFECTION)

SCABIES

(See also LICE in SKIN DISORDERS)

Scabies are caused by eight-legged insects known as itch mites—tiny parasites that burrow into the skin, usually in the fingers and genital areas. The most common variety, *Sarcoptes scabiei,* can quickly infest other people. Although it only lives six weeks, it continually lays eggs once it digs into the skin.

The most common remedy for scabies and lice is lindane (gamma benzene hexachloride) a highly toxic polychlorinated chemical that is structurally very similar to hazardous banned pesticides such as DDT and chlordane. It is so dangerous that Dr. Guy Sansfacon, head of the Quebec Poison Control Centre in Canada, has requested that lindane be banned.

Natural plant-derived essential oils have the same activity as commercial pesticides but are far safer. Essential oils have been studied for their ability to not only repel insects, but also kill them and their eggs as well. Because many oils are nontoxic to humans, they make excellent treatments to combat scabies infestations.

FIRST RECOMMENDATIONS:
Citronella, peppermint

Other Single Oils:
Palmarosa, lavandin, *Eucalyptus globulus*, black pepper, ginger

Other Blends:
Purification, Melrose

EO APPLICATION METHODS:
Topical:
NEAT, or Dilute 50:50 if needed, apply 2-4 drops on location, 3 times daily

To treat hair or scalp, add 3-5 drops of essential oil to 1 tsp. of shampoo and massage into wet hair. Leave for 5 minutes, then rinse.

SCAR TISSUE

Some essential oils may be valuable for reducing or minimizing the formation of scar tissue:

FIRST RECOMMENDATIONS:
Helichrysum, lavender, Gentle Baby

Other Single Oils:
Cypress, elemi, blue yarrow, rose, cistus, myrrh, sandalwood

Scar prevention blend:
• 2 drops helichrysum
• 3 drops lavender
• 4 drops myrrh
• 1 drops sandalwood

EO APPLICATION METHODS:
Topical:
NEAT, gently apply 2-6 drops over wound or cut daily until healed

DIETARY SUPPLEMENTATION:
Super C, Sulfurzyme, Power Meal

Topical Application:
Tender Tush Ointment

SCIATICA

(See SPINE INJURIES and PAIN)

SCHIZOPHRENIA

(See NEUROLOGICAL DISORDERS)

A neurological disease that involves identity confusion. Onset is typically between the late teens and early 30's. Abnormal neurological findings may show a broad range of dysfunction including slow reaction time, poor coordination, abnormalities in eye tracking, and impaired sensory gating. Typically schizophrenia involves dysfunction in one or more areas such as interpersonal relations, work, education, or self-care. Some cases are believed to be caused by viral infection.

FIRST RECOMMENDATIONS:
Clarity, peppermint, frankincense

Single Oils:
Cardamom, cedarwood, vetiver, melissa, rosemary, valerian

Other Blends:
Brain Power, Valor, Valor Roll-on, M-Grain

EO APPLICATION METHODS:
Inhalation:
DIRECT, 4-6 times daily
Topical:
RAINDROP Technique, once weekly

DIETARY SUPPLEMENTATION:
Mineral Essence, Mega Cal, Dried wolfberries, Ningxia Red

SCLERODERMA

Also known as systemic sclerosis, scleroderma is a non-infectious, chronic, autoimmune disease of the connective tissue. Caused by an overproduction of collagen, the disease can involve either the skin or internal organs and can be life-threatening. Scleroderma is far more common among women than men.

FIRST RECOMMENDATIONS:
Wintergreen, German chamomille

Other Single Oils:
Frankincense, copaiba lavender, patchouli, sandalwood, myrrh

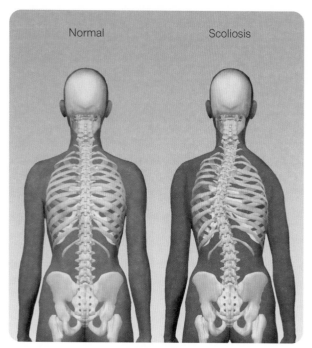

Scoliosis

Other Blends:
Melrose, Aroma Siez

Scleroderma blend #1:
- 2 drops German chamomile
- 1 drops lavender
- 1 drops patchouli

Scleroderma blend #2:
- 2 drops sandalwood
- 3 drops myrrh

EO APPLICATION METHODS:
Topical:
DILUTE 50:50, massage 4-6 drops on location 3 times daily. Alternate between blend #1 and blend #2 (above) each day

DIETARY SUPPLEMENTATION:
PD 80/20, ICP/Comfortone/Essentialzyme, JuvaTone, JuvaPower/Spice, Thyromin, Mineral Essence, Power Meal, Sulfurzyme, Detoxyme, Longevity Softgels

Topical Treatment:
Prenolone

SCOLIOSIS

(See SPINE INJURIES and Chapter 21: Raindrop Technique)

Scoliosis is an abnormal lateral or side-to-side curvature or twist in the spine. It is different from hyperkyphosis (hunchback) or hyperlordosis (swayback) which involve excessive front-to-back accentuation of existing spine curvatures.

While a few cases of scoliosis can be attributed to congenital deformities (such as MS, cerebral palsy, Down's syndrome, or Marfan's syndrome), the vast majority of scoliosis types are of unknown origin.

Some medical professionals believe that scoliosis may be caused by persistent muscle spasms that pull the vertebrae of the spine out of alignment. Others feel - and there is a growing body of research documenting this hypothesis - that it begins with hard-to-detect inflammation along the spine caused by latent viruses. (See citations in Chapter 21.)

Symptoms:
- When bending forward, the left side of the back is higher or lower than the right side (the patient must be viewed from the rear).

- One hip may appear to be higher or more prominent than the other.

- Uneven shoulders or scapulas (shoulder blades).

- When the arms are hanging loosely, the distance between the left arm and left side is different than the distance between the right arm and right side.

The Raindrop Technique is proving to be an effective therapy for helping to straighten spines misaligned due to scoliosis.

FIRST RECOMMENDATION:
Raindrop Technique (see Chapter 21)

Other Single Oils:
Oregano, thyme, basil, wintergreen, cypress, marjoram, peppermint

Other Blends:
Aroma Siez, PanAway, Valor, Valor Roll-on

EO APPLICATION METHODS:
Topical:
RAINDROP Technique, 2-3 times monthly DILUTE 50:50 and apply 3-6 drops along the spine daily or as needed, as a supplement to Raindrop Technique

DIETARY SUPPLEMENTATION:
Mineral Essence, Mega Cal, Power Meal, Sulfurzyme, BLM

Topical Treatments:
Ortho Ease, Ortho Sport

SCURVY

A condition due to deficiency of vitamin C in the diet and marked by weakness, anemia, spongy gums, bleeding of the gums and nose, and a hardening of the muscles of the calves and legs.

FIRST RECOMMENDATIONS:
Super C, Super C Chewable

OTHER DIETARY SUPPLEMENTATION:
Power Meal, Balance Complete, Dried wolfberries, Ningxia Red, True Source Multivitamins

SEIZURES

(See also BRAIN DISORDERS or EPILEPSY)

Many seizures can be treated by removing all forms of sugar, artificial colors, and flavors from diet. Avoid using personal care products with ammonia-based compounds, such as quaterniums and polyquaterniums.

FIRST RECOMMENDATIONS:
Peppermint, R.C., Valor, Valor Roll-on, Breath Again Roll-on

Other Single Oils:
Frankincense, sandalwood, melissa, jasmine absolute, basil

Other Blends:
Valor, Valor Roll-on, Aroma Siez, Exodus II, Peace & Calming

EO APPLICATION METHODS:
Topical:
DILUTE 50:50, massage 10 drops into scalp 3 times daily to help reduce risk of seizure. Supplement with inhalation therapy below
Inhalation:
DIRECT, 3-5 times daily

Seizure regimen (do all the following):
- Massage 4-6 drops Valor on bottoms of feet daily

- Diffuse Peace & Calming for 30 minutes 3-4 times daily
- Massage 4-6 drops Joy over heart daily
- Do a Raindrop Technique on spine twice monthly

DIETARY SUPPLEMENTS:
Blue Agave Nectar and Stevia (in place of sugars), Mineral Essence, True Source Multivitamins, MultiGreens, Super B, Longevity Softgels, Power Meal, Sulfurzyme, Omega Blue Softgels, Balance Complete

SEXUAL DYSFUNCTION

(See also IMPOTENCE)

Lack of Libido - Women

FIRST RECOMMENDATIONS:
EndoGize, clary sage, nutmeg,

Other Single Oils:
Geranium, ylang ylang, jasmine absolute, rose

Blends:
Sensation, Lady Sclareol, SclarEssence, Joy

CAUTION: Except for jasmine absolute, the above oils can be inhaled or taken orally as dietary supplements. Because they are chemically processed, all absolutes—including jasmine absolute—may be used in inhalation therapy, but must NEVER be ingested.

- Ylang Ylang helps balance sexual emotion and sex drive problems. Its aromatic influence elevates sexual energy and enhances relationships.
- Clary sage can help with lack of sexual desire particularly with women by regulating and balancing hormones.
- Nutmeg supports the nervous system to help overcome frigidity.

(See also FRIGIDITY)

EO APPLICATION METHODS:
Inhalation:
DIRECT, 3-5 times daily
Topical:
DILUTE 50:50, massage 4-6 drops on neck, shoulders and lower abdomen, 1-3 times daily

OTHER DIETARY SUPPLEMENTATION:
MultiGreens, Sulfurzyme, PD 80/20

Sulfurzyme provides MSM (sulfur), which can harmonize libido.

Topical Treatment:
Progessence, Prenolone, Prenolone+

Lack of Libido - Men

FIRST RECOMMENDATIONS:
Valor, Valor Roll-on, pine

Other Single Oils:
Myrrh, black pepper, ylang ylang, ginger, nutmeg

Other Blends:
Brain Power, Transformation

EO APPLICATION METHODS:
Inhalation:
DIRECT, 3-5 times daily
Topical:
DILUTE 50:50, massage 4-6 drops on neck, shoulders and lower abdomen, 1-3 times daily

DIETARY SUPPLEMENTATION:
MultiGreens, ProGen, Sulfurzyme, EndoGize

(Sulfurzyme provides MSM, which can harmonize libido)

Topical Treatment:
Prenolone, Prenolone+

Female Frigidity

FIRST RECOMMENDATIONS:
Jasmine absolute, rose, ylang ylang

Other Blends:
Joy, Valor, Valor Roll-on

EO APPLICATION METHODS:
Inhalation:
DIRECT, 3-5 times daily
Topical:
DILUTE 50:50, massage 4-6 drops on neck, shoulders and lower abdomen, 1-3 times daily

Topical Treatment:
Progessence, Prenolone, Prenolone+, NeuroGen

Excessive Sexual Desire (both sexes)

FIRST RECOMMENDATIONS:
Marjoram, valerian

Other Single Oils:
Lavender

Other Blends:
Peace & Calming, Acceptance, Surrender

EO APPLICATION METHODS:
Inhalation:
DIRECT, 3-5 times daily
Topical:
DILUTE 50:50, massage 4-6 drops on neck, shoulders and lower abdomen, 1-3 times daily

DIETARY SUPPLEMENTATION:
Mineral Essence, Super B, PD 80/20, Mega Cal, ImmuPro

SEXUALLY TRANSMITTED DISEASES

(See also INFECTIONS)

Herpes Simplex Type II

The Herpes Simplex Virus Type 2, is transmitted by sexual contact and results in sores or lesions. Four to seven days after contact with an infected partner, tingling, burning, or persistent itching usually heralds an outbreak. One or two days later, small pimple-like bumps appear over reddened skin. The itching and tingling continue, and the pimples turn into painful blisters, which burst, bleeding with a yellowish pus. Five to seven days after the first tingling, scabs form, and healing begins.

Antiviral essential oils have generally been very effective in treating herpes lesions and reducing their onset. Oils such as tea tree, melissa, and rosemary have been successfully used for this purpose by Daniel Pénoël, M.D. in his clinical practice. A study at the University of Buenos Aires found that sandalwood essential oil inhibited the replication of Herpes Simplex viruses-1 and -2.[41]

Those with herpes should avoid diets high in the amino acid L-arginine, substituting instead L-lysine. Lysine retards the growth of the virus. Foods such as amaranth and plain yogurt are good sources of lysine.

---

41. Benencia F, et al. "Antiviral activity of sandalwood oil against herpes simplex viruses-1 and -2." *Phytomedicine*. 1999;6(2):119-23

FIRST RECOMMENDATIONS:

Ravansara, manuka, tea tree, melissa, L-lysine supplement

Other Single Oils:

Sandalwood, blue cypress, cumin, rosemary

Other Blends:

Melrose, Thieves, Exodus II

Herpes blend #1 (topical):

- 4 drops manuka
- 2 drops tea tree
- 1 drop ravansara

Herpes blend #2 (vaginal):

- 2 drops sage
- 4 drops manuka
- 3 drops ravensara
- 1 drop lavender

EO APPLICATION METHODS:

Topical:

NEAT, apply Herpes blend #1 (above) on lesion as soon as it appears. Apply 1-2 drops of neat oil 2-3 times daily, alternating between the above herpes blend and Melrose each day. RAINDROP Technique, 1-2 treatments

Retention:

TAMPON, for vaginal treatment of herpes, use Herpes blend #2 (above), diluted 20:80 in tampon/ pad application nightly. If tampon/pad stings after 5 minutes, remove and change dilution rate to 10:90.

DIETARY SUPPLEMENTATION:

ImmuPro, ImmuneTune, Sulfurzyme, Super C Chewable, ICP/Comfortone/Essentialzyme

Topical Treatment:

Thieves Antiseptic Spray

Genital Warts

Genital warts are a form of viral infection caused by the human papillomavirus (HPV), of which there are more than 60 different types.

One type of HPV virus is among the most common sexually transmitted diseases. Up to 24 million Americans may be currently infected with HPV, usually spread through sexual contact. HPV lives only in genital tissue. HPV can later lead to cervical cancer in women.

FIRST RECOMMENDATIONS:

Melissa, manuka, ravansara, tea tree, Melrose

Other Single Oils:

Idaho tansy, niaouli, *Melaleuca ericifolia*, lavender

Other Blends:

Thieves, ImmuPower

EO APPLICATION METHODS:

Topical:

NEAT or DILUTE 50:50, 1-3 drops 2 times daily for 10 days

Retention:

TAMPON, nightly

Topical Treatment:

Thieves Antiseptic Spray

Gonorrhea and Syphilis

NOTE: Seek immediate professional medical attention if you suspect you may have either of these diseases.

FIRST RECOMMENDATIONS:

Oregano, Thieves, Inner Defense softgels

Other Single Oils:

Melissa, thyme, mountain savory, cinnamon

Other Blends:

Melrose, Exodus II

EO APPLICATION METHODS:

Ingestion:

CAPSULE, 00 size, 1 capsule 2 times daily for 15 days

DIETARY SUPPLEMENTATION:

Exodus, ImmuPro, Life 5

Topical Treatment:

Thieves Antiseptic Spray

SHINGLES (Herpes Zoster)

(See same topic under CHICKEN POX)

SHOCK

Shock can be described as a state of profound depression of the vital processes associated with reduced blood volume and pressure. The blood rushes to the vital organs after trauma.

It may be caused by the sudden stimulation of the nerves and convulsive contraction of the muscles caused by the discharge of electricity. Other causes include sudden trauma, terror, surprise, horror, or disgust.

Symptoms or signs:
- Irregular breathing
- Low blood pressure
- Dilated pupils
- Cold and sweaty skin
- Weak and rapid pulse
- Dry mouth
- Muscle weakness
- Dizziness or fainting

Any injury that results in the sudden loss of substantial amounts of fluids can trigger shock.

Shock can also be caused by allergic reactions (anaphylactic shock), infections in the blood (septic shock), or emotional trauma (neurogenic shock).

Shock should be treated by covering the victim with a blanket and elevating the victim's feet unless there is a head or upper torso injury. Inhaling essential oils can also help—especially in cases of emotional shock.

FIRST RECOMMENDATIONS:
Peppermint, Idaho balsam fir, Trauma Life

Other Single Oils:
Cardamom, frankincense, basil, rosemary, sandalwood

Other Blends:
Clarity, 3 Wise Men, Valor, Valor Roll-on, Harmony, Present Time

EO APPLICATION METHODS:
Inhalation:
DIRECT, 1-2 drops, as needed
Topical:
DILUTE 50:50, rub 1-2 drops on temples, back of neck, and under nose.

NOTE: When applying essential oil to the temples be careful not to get the oil too close to the eyes.

SINUS INFECTIONS

(See also COLDS and THROAT INFECTIONS)

Nasopharyngitis

Inflammation of the mucous membranes of the back of the nasal cavity where it connects to the throat and the eustachian tubes.

FIRST RECOMMENDATIONS:
Peppermint, ravansara, tea tree, Nasal Irrigation Regimen (see box on next page)

Other Single Oils:
Thyme, rosemary, blue cypress, *Melaleuca ericifolia*, manuka, *Eucalyptus radiata*

Other Blends:
Raven, R.C., Exodus II, Thieves, Inner Defense, Breath Again Roll-on

EO APPLICATION METHODS:
Topical:
DILUTE 50:50, apply just under jawbone on right and left sides, 4-8 times daily
Inhalation:
DIRECT, 4-8 times daily
Oral:
GARGLE, 2-5 times daily
Many have found it effective to place one drop of Thieves or tea tree at the very back of the tongue and hold it in the mouth, mixing with saliva for several minutes, then swallowing. This can be very effective if started at the very first indication of infection and repeated 3-4 times for the first hour, then once an hour until symptoms subside.

DIETARY SUPPLEMENTATION:
Super C, Super C Chewable, ImmuPro, Exodus

Oral Care:
Dentarome Ultra, Thieves lozenges, Fresh Essence Plus mouthwash, Thieves antiseptic spray

SPECIAL NOTE: In most sinus infections, including nasopharyngitis, rhinitis, sinus congestion and sinusitis, the nasal irrigation regimen above can be extremely effective.

Nasal Irrigation Regimen:

Rosemary and tea tree oils can be used in a saline solution for very effective nasal irrigation that clears and decongests sinuses. As recommended by Daniel Pénoël, MD, the saline solution is prepared as follows:

- 10 drops rosemary
- 6 drops tea tree
- 8 tablespoons very fine salt (salt flower)

The essential oils are mixed thoroughly in the fine salt and kept in a sealed container. For each nasal irrigation session, 1 teaspoon of this salt mixture is dissolved into 1 1/2 cups distilled water. This oils/salt/water solution is then placed in the tank of an oral irrigator to irrigate the nasal cavities, which is done while bending over a sink. This application has brought surprisingly positive results in treating latent sinusitus and other nasal congestion problems.[42]

Sinus Congestion

FIRST RECOMMENDATIONS:
Peppermint, R.C., *Eucalyptus radiata*, ravansara, Breath Again Roll-on, Nasal Irrigation Regimen (see above)

Other Single Oils:
Idaho balsam fir, thyme, *Melaleuca ericifolia*, tea tree, fennel, rosemary

Other Blends:
Di-Gize, Raven, Thieves, Exodus II

EO APPLICATION METHODS:
Inhalation:
DIRECT, 3-8 times daily, or as needed
VAPOR, 2-5 times daily, as needed
Ingestion:
SYRUP, 3-6 times daily
Oral:
GARGLE, 3-6 times daily
Topical:
DILUTE 50:50, massage 1-3 drops on each of the following areas: forehead, nose, cheeks, lower throat, chest and upper back, 1-3 times daily

VITA FLEX, massage 1-3 drops on Vita Flex points on the feet, 2-4 times daily
RAINDROP Technique, 1-2 times weekly
BATH SALTS, daily

DIETARY SUPPLEMENTATION:
Super C, Super C Chewable, ImmuPro, Exodus

Oral Care:
Dentarome Ultra, Thieves lozenges, Fresh Essence Plus mouthwash, Thieves antiseptic spray, Thieves lozenges

Sinusitis/Rhinitis

Essential oils, such as *Eucalyptus radiata* and ravensara strengthen the respiratory system, open the pulmonary tract, and fight respiratory infection.

FIRST RECOMMENDATIONS:
Tea tree, peppermint, R.C., *Eucalyptus radiata*, ravansara, Breath Again Roll-on, Nasal Irrigation Regimen (see above)

Other Single Oils:
Idaho balsam fir, thyme, *Melaleuca ericifolia*, fennel, rosemary

Other Blends:
Melrose, Raven, Thieves, Exodus II

EO APPLICATION METHODS:
Inhalation:
DIRECT, 3-8 times daily, or as needed
VAPOR, 2-5 times daily, as needed
Ingestion:
SYRUP, 3-6 times daily
Oral:
GARGLE, 3-6 times daily
Topical:
NEAT, massage 1-3 drops on each of the following areas (being careful not to get oils in or near eyes/eyelids) : forehead, nose, cheeks, lower throat, chest and upper back, 3-5 times daily
VITA FLEX, massage 1-3 drops on Vita Flex points on the feet, 2-4 times daily
RAINDROP Technique, 1-2 times weekly
BATH SALTS, daily
Use Nasal Irrigation Regimen: (see Rhinitis)

---

42. Pénoël, Daniel, MD. and Rose Marie, *Natural Home Health Care Using Essential Oils*, Essential Science Publishing, 1998. pp. 166-167

DIETARY SUPPLEMENTATION:

Super C, Super C Chewable, ImmuPro, Exodus, Inner Defense softgels

Oral Care:

Dentarome Ultra, Thieves lozenges, Fresh Essence Plus mouthwash, Thieves antiseptic spray, Thieves lozenges

SKIN DISORDERS

(See also BLISTERS and BOILS, LIVER DISORDERS and MENSTRUAL CONDITIONS)

Essential oils can have powerful antioxidant and antibacterial benefits for the skin. Essential oils used on the skin typically should be combined with a vegetable carrier oil to (a) slow evaporation allowing more time for the oils to penetrate and protect the skin; (b) maintain the lipid barrier of the skin because most essential oils will tend to dry the skin; and (c) enhances the effect of the essential oils--certain essential oils work synergistically with quality vegetable oils.

Many skin conditions may be related to dysfunctions of the liver. It may be necessary to cleanse, stimulate, and condition the liver and colon for 30 to 90 days before the skin begins to improve.

Abscesses/Boils

Skin abscesses are small pockets of pus that collect under the skin. They are usually caused by a bacterial or fungal infection.

A number of essential oils may reduce inflammation and combat infection, helping to bring abscesses/boils to a head, so they can close and heal.

FIRST RECOMMENDATIONS:

Oregano, clove, tea tree

Other Single Oils:

Frankincense, peppermint, lavender, rosemary, thyme, lemongrass, mountain savory, palmarosa, patchouli, ravensara

---

Tips for Clearing Up Acne

- Eliminate dairy products, fried foods, chemical additives, and sugar from diet.

- Avoid use of makeup or chlorinated water.

- Avoid contact with plastics which may exude estrogenic chemicals.

- Topically apply essential oils such as tea tree to problem areas. Tea tree was shown to be equal to benzoyl peroxide in the treatment of acne, according research published in the *Medical Journal of Australia*.[44]

- Begin a cleansing program with the Cleansing Trio and Sulfurzyme.

Other Blends:

Melrose, Purification, Exodus II, Thieves, Inner Defense, Sacred Mountain

EO APPLICATION METHODS:
Topical:

DILUTE 50:50, apply on location 3-6 times daily

DIETARY SUPPLEMENTATION:
JuvaTone, ICP/Comfortone/Essentialzyme, ImmuPro, Digest & Cleanse Softgels, Longevity softgels, Life 5

Acne

(See also Clogged Pores in this section)

Acne results from an excess accumulation of dirt and sebum (oil produced by the hair follicle) in the follicles and pores of the skin. As the pores and hair follicles become congested, bacteria begins to feed on the sebum. This leads to inflammation and infection and the formation of a pimple or a blackhead around the hair follicle.

One of the most common forms of acne, *Acne vulgaris,* occurs primarily in adolescents due to hormone imbalances which stimulate the creation of sebum.

Acne in adults can be also be caused by hormone balances, as well as the use of chlorinated com-

---

43. Toyoda M, Morohashi M, "Pathenogenesis of acne," *Med Electron Microse* 2001 Mar;34(1):29-40.

44. Bassett IB, et al. "A comparative study of tea-tree oil versus benzoyl peroxide in the treatment of acne." *Med J Aust.* 1990;153(8):455-8.

pounds, endocrine system imbalances, or poor dietary practices. Heavy or greasy makeup can also contribute to acne.

Stress may also play a role. According to research conducted by Dr. Toyoda in Japan, acne and other skin problems are a direct result of physical and emotional stress.[43]

Essential oils are outstanding for treating acne because of their ability to dissolve sebum, kill bacteria, and preserve the acid mantle of the skin.

FIRST RECOMMENDATIONS:
Tea tree, manuka, niaouli, Essential Beauty Serum for Acne-Prone skin, ART Foaming Cleanser, ART Toner, Mint Satin Facial Scrub

Other Single Oils:
Geranium, vetiver, lavender, patchouli, German or Roman chamomile, rosewood, cedarwood, *Eucalyptus radiata*, orange, clove

Other Blends:
Melrose, Purification

EO APPLICATION METHODS:
Topical:
NEAT or DILUTE 50:50 as required. Gently massage 3-5 drops into oily areas 1-3 times daily. Alternate oils daily for maximum effect

DIETARY SUPPLEMENTATION:
Mineral Essence, MultiGreens, ICP/Comfortone/ Essentialzyme, Dried wolfberries, Omega Blue Softgels, Digest & Cleanse Softgels, Balance Complete

To resolve acne caused by hormonal imbalance: Progessence cream or Prenolone cream

Other Topical Treatment:
Ortho Ease, Melaleuca-Geranium Bar Soap

Burns

(See BURNS)

Chapped, Dry, or Cracked Skin

(See also Eczema in this section)

FIRST RECOMMENDATIONS:
Myrrh, sandalwood, ART Night Reconstructor, Essential Beauty Serum for Dry Skin

Other Single Oils:
Neroli, rose, cedarwood, Roman chamomille, palmarosa, geranium, lavender, spikenard, rosewood

Chapped skin blend:
- 1 drop rosewood
- 1 drop patchouli
- 1 drop geranium

Dry skin blend:
- 1 drop rose
- 1 drop Roman chamomile
- 1 drop sandalwood

EO APPLICATION METHODS:
Topical:
DILUTE 20:80 in a natural, unperfumed lotion base (V6 or avocado oil) or other high grade emollient oil, apply on location as often as needed

Topical Treatment:
Tender Tush Ointment, Sandalwood Moisturizing Cream, Rose Ointment

Lip Treatment:
Cinnamint Lip Balm

Combine 3-5 drops of essential oils with 1 tsp of Sensation or Genesis Body lotion to create a very effective lotion for rehydrating the skin of chapped hands and maintaining the natural pH balance of the skin.

Bath and shower gels, such as Dragon Time, Evening Peace, Morning Start, and Sensation, are formulated to help balance the acid mantle of the skin. The AromaSilk Bar Soaps are rich in moisturizers.

Clogged Pores

FIRST RECOMMENDATIONS:
Lemon, tea tree, ART Foaming Cleanser, Essential Beauty Serum for Oily Skin

Other Single Oils:
Orange, geranium

Other Blends:
Purification

EO APPLICATION METHODS:
Topical:
NEAT, apply 2-4 drops to affected area and gently remove with cotton ball

Topical Treatment:
ART Toner, AromaSilk Bar Soaps

Satin Facial Scrub - Mint is a gentle exfoliator designed to clarify skin and reduce acne. (If its texture is too abrasive for your skin, mix it with Orange Blossom Facial Wash. This is excellent for those with severe or mild acne.)

Spread scrub over face and let dry for perhaps 5 minutes to draw out impurities, pulling and toning the skin at the same time. Put a hot towel over face for greater penetration. Wash off with warm water by gently patting skin with warm face cloth. If you do not have time to let the mask dry, gently massage in a circular motion for 30 seconds, then rinse. Afterwards, apply Sandalwood Moisture Cream. This also works well underneath foundation makeup.

Diaper Rash

FIRST RECOMMENDATIONS:
Tender Tush Ointment

Other Single Oils:
Lavender, helichrysum, German chamomile cypress

Other Blends:
Gentle Baby, Clara Derm spray

EO APPLICATION METHODS:
Topical:
DILUTE 50:50, apply on location 2-4 times daily

Other Topical Treatment:
Lavaderm Cooling Mist

Eczema / Dermatitis

(See also Chapped Skin, Psoriasis in this section)

Eczema and dermatitis are both inflammations of the skin and are most often due to allergies, but also can be a sign of liver disease (See LIVER DISORDERS).

Dermatitis usually results from external factors, such as sunburn or contact with poison ivy, or metals (wristwatch, earrings, jewelry, etc.). Eczema usually results from internal factors,

---

> **Essential oils that help the skin**
>
> **To rejuvenate and heal:**
> • Rosewood
>
> **To prevent and retard wrinkles:**
> • Lavender, spikenard, and myrrh
>
> **To regenerate:**
> • Geranium, helichrysum, and spikenard
>
> **To restore skin elasticity**
> • Rosewood, lavender
> • Ylang ylang with lavender
>
> **To combat premature aging of the skin**
> Mix the following recipe into 1 tablespoon of high grade, unperfumed skin lotion and apply on location twice daily.
>
> • 6 drops rosewood
> • 4 drops geranium
> • 3 drops lavender
> • 2 drops frankincense

such as irritant chemicals, soaps and shampoos, or allergies (gluten, lactose, etc.). In both dermatitis and eczema, skin becomes red, flaky and itchy. Small blisters may form and if broken by scratching, can become infected.

FIRST RECOMMENDATIONS:
Lavender, German chamomille, myrrh, Detoxyme

Other Single Oils:
Citrus hystrix, celery seed, cistus, blue cypress, Roman chamomile, geranium, rosewood

Other Blends:
JuvaCleanse, Purification, Melrose, Australian Blue

EO APPLICATION METHODS:
Topical:
DILUTE 50:50, apply as needed on location

OTHER DIETARY SUPPLEMENTATION:
ICP/Comfortone/Essentialzyme, JuvaTone, Rose Ointment, Juva Power, Polyzyme

Fungal Skin Infection

(See FUNGAL INFECTIONS)

FIRST RECOMMENDATIONS:
Tea tree, lemongrass

Other Single Oils:
Oregano, niaouli, lavender, *Melaleuca ericifolia*

Other Blends:
Melrose, Clara Derm spray

Antifungal skin blend:
- 10 drops patchouli
- 4 drops niaouli
- 2 drops tea tree
- 5 drops lemongrass

EO APPLICATION METHODS:
Topical:
DILUTE 50:50, apply 2-4 drops on location, 3-5 times daily

Dietary Supplementation:
Life 5, Omega Blue Softgels, Digest & Cleanse Softgels, ICP/Comfortone/Essentialzyme, Mineral Essence

Itching

Itching can be due to dry skin, impaired liver function, insects, allergies, or over-exposure to chemicals or sunlight.

FIRST RECOMMENDATIONS:
Peppermint, patchouli, Tender Tush ointment

Other Single Oils:
Oregano, lavender, wintergreen, nutmeg, German chamomile

Other Blends:
Aroma Siez, Purification

EO APPLICATION METHODS:
Topical:
DILUTE 50:50, Apply 2-6 drops on location as needed

DIETARY SUPPLEMENTATION:
Omega Blue Softgels, Digest & Cleanse Softgels, Life 5, Juva Flex, JuvaTone, Comfor-Tone

Topical Treatment:
LavaDerm Spray, ClaraDerm Spray

Melanoma

(See CANCERS)

Moles

To remove moles: Apply 1-2 drops of oregano neat, directly on the mole, 2-3 times daily.

Poison Oak - Poison Ivy

(See also Eczema, Itching in this section)

FIRST RECOMMENDATIONS:
Peppermint, wintergreen, Melrose, PanAway

Other Single Oils:
Eucalyptus dives, German chamomile, Roman chamomille, rose, lemon, Idaho tansy, tea tree, rosemary, basil, lemongrass

Other Blends:
Purification, R.C., JuvaCleanse, Breath Again Roll-on

EO APPLICATION METHODS:
Topical:
DILUTE 50:50, apply 4-6 drops to affected areas twice daily
COMPRESS, Cold, apply on affected area, twice daily

DIETARY SUPPLEMENTATION:
Omega Blue Softgels

Topical Treatment:
Rose Ointment, Sandalwood Moisturizing cream

Psoriasis

(See also Eczema in this section)

Psoriasis is a non-infectious skin disorder that is marked by skin patches or flaking skin that can occur in limited areas (such as the scalp) or that can cover up to 80-90 percent of the body.

The overly rapid growth of skin cells is the primary cause of psoriasis. In some cases, skin cells grow four times faster than normal, resulting in the formation of silvery layers that flake off.

Treating Psoriasis with pH Balance

Psoriasis, eczema, dermatitis, dry skin, allergies, and similar problems indicate an excessive acidic pH in the body. The more acid in the blood and skin, the less therapeutic effect the oils will have. People who have a negative reaction to oils are usually highly acidic. An alkaline balance must be maintained in the blood and skin for the oils to work the best. AlkaLime and MultiGreens are both helpful for this balancing. (See FUNGUS)

Symptoms:
• Occurs on elbows, chest, knees, and scalp.
• Slightly elevated reddish lesions covered with silver-white scales.
• The disease can be limited to one small patch or can cover the entire body.
• Rashes subside after exposure to sunlight.
• Rashes recur over a period of years.

FIRST RECOMMENDATIONS:
Roman chamomille, tea tree, Melrose

Other Single Oils:
Patchouli, helichrysum, rose, German chamomile, lavender

Other Blends:
Gentle Baby, JuvaFlex, JuvaCleanse

Psoriasis blend:
• 2 drops patchouli
• 2 drops Roman chamomile
• 2 drops lavender
• 2 drops tea tree

EO APPLICATION METHODS:
Topical:
NEAT, apply 2-4 drops to affected area twice daily. 6-10 drops can be added to 1 tsp of regular skin lotion and applied daily or as needed
COMPRESS, warm, 3 times weekly
Ingestion:
CAPSULE, 0 size, 1 per day

DIETARY SUPPLEMENTATION:
ICP/Comfortone/Essentialzyme, Life 5, Balance Complete, AlkaLime, JuvaTone, JuvaPower, Sulfurzyme

Topical Treatment:
Tender Tush Ointment, Rose Ointment

Sagging Skin

FIRST RECOMMENDATIONS:
ART Toner, Boswellia Wrinkle Cream

Single Oils:
Lavender, helichrysum, patchouli, cypress, tangerine, sandalwood

Skin firming blend (morning):
• 3 drops tangerine
• 3 drops cypress

Skin firming blend (evening):
• 8 drops patchouli
• 5 drops cypress
• 5 drops geranium
• 1 drop sandalwood

EO APPLICATION METHODS:
Topical:
Neat or DILUTE 50:50, massage 4-6 drops on affected area twice daily. Use morning blend before dressing in the morning; evening blend before bed at night.

Topical Treatment:
Cel-Lite Magic

NOTE: Strength training with weights can help tighten sagging skin.

Skin Ulcers

FIRST RECOMMENDATIONS:
Lavender, clove, myrrh, Melrose

Other Single Oils:
Rosewood, helichrysum, Roman chamomile, patchouli

Other Blends:
Thieves, Purification, Relieve It

EO APPLICATION METHODS:
Topical:
Neat or DILUTE 50:50, massage 4-6 drops on affected areas 2 times daily

DIETARY SUPPLEMENTATION:
Super C, ICP/Comfortone/Essentialzyme

Topical Treatment:
Tender Tush Ointment

Stretch Marks

Stretch marks are most commonly associated with pregnancy, but can also occur during growth spurts and periods of weight gain.

FIRST RECOMMENDATIONS:
Lavender, myrrh, Gentle Baby

Other Single Oils:
Frankincense, elemi, spikenard, geranium

EO APPLICATION METHODS:
Topical:
Neat or DILUTE 50:50, apply on affected areas 2 times daily

DIETARY SUPPLEMENTATION:
Sulfurzyme

Topical Treatment:
Tender Tush Ointment, Rose Ointment, A.R.T. Day Activator, A.R.T. Night Reconstructor

Vitiligo

A skin disorder marked by patches of skin devoid of skin pigmentation.

FIRST RECOMMENDATIONS:
Sandalwood, myrrh, vetiver

EO APPLICATION METHODS:
Topical:
NEAT, apply 2-4 drops on location, 2 times daily

Wrinkles

FIRST RECOMMENDATIONS:
ART Day Activator, ART Night Reconstructor, Boswellia Wrinkle Cream, Wolfberry Eye Cream, Omega Blue Softgels

Other Single Oils:
Frankincense, helichrysum, cypress, rose, lavender, patchouli, sage, geranium, rosewood, sandalwood, neroli, palmarosa, spikenard

Other Blends:
Gentle Baby, Sensation

Wrinkle-reducing blend:
- 5 drops sandalwood
- 4 drops geranium
- 3 drops lavender
- 6 drops frankincense

Essential Oils and Skin Care

Tea tree, manuka and lemongrass can help clear acne and balance oily skin conditions. Lemongrass is the predominant ingredient in Morning Start Bath and Shower Gel, which can be used to balance the pH of the skin, decongest the lymphatics and stimulate circulation.

EO APPLICATION METHODS:
Topical:
DILUTE 50:50 in high grade, unperfumed body lotion or an emollient vegetable oil and apply on location as needed
NOTE: Be careful not to get lotion or oils near the eyes.

DIETARY SUPPLEMENTATION:
Mega Cal, Longevity Softgels, Dried Ningxia wolfberries, Ningxia Red, True Source Multivitamins

Other Topical Treatment:
A.R.T. Foaming Cleanser, ART Purifying Toner, Rose Ointment, NeuroGen, Sandalwood Moisture Cream

Rose Ointment was developed to feed and rehydrate the skin and to supply nutrients necessary to slow down the aging process. Moreover, it contains no synthetic chemicals which can cause skin irritation.

SLEEP DISORDERS

(See also APNEA, INSOMNIA, LIVER DISORDERS)

Melatonin is the most powerful natural remedy for restoring both quality and quantity of sleep. It improves the length of the time the body sustains deep, Stage 4 sleep, when the immune system and growth hormone production reaches its maximum. ImmuPro not only contains melatonin, but mineral and polysaccharide complexes to restore natural sleep rhythm and eliminate insomnia.

Valerian has been shown to be effective in calming the mind, enabling one to fall asleep easier.

FIRST RECOMMENDATIONS:
Valerian, RutaVaLa, Tranquil Roll-on, ImmuPro, Peace & Calming

Other Single Oils:
Lavender, goldenrod, Roman chamomile, orange, mandarin

Other Blends:
Surrender, Trauma Life, Hope, Humility

EO APPLICATION METHODS:
Ingestion:
CAPSULE, 0 size, 1 per day, 1 hour before bedtime
Inhalation:
DIRECT, 1-3 times before bed
DIFFUSER: 30 minutes before bed
Topical:
BATH SALTS, daily, just before bedtime

DIETARY SUPPLEMENTATION:
Essentialzyme, Mega Cal, Mineral Essence, Omega Blue Softgels, Life 5

SMOKING CESSATION

(See also ADDICTIONS)

FIRST RECOMMENDATIONS:
Cinnamon, clove, vanilla absolute

Other Single Oils:
Nutmeg, peppermint, Roman chamomille, clary sage

Other Blends:
Harmony, JuvaCleanse, Peace & Calming, Thieves

EO APPLICATION METHODS:
Inhalation:
DIRECT, whenever the urge for a cigarette arises
DIFFUSION, 30 minutes, 3 times a day as needed

DIETARY SUPPLEMENTATION:
ICP/Comfortone/Essentialzyme, Life 5, JuvaTone, JuvaPower/Spice

Cleanse colon and liver with ICP/Comfortone/Essentialzyme and JuvaTone.

JuvaTone, JuvaPower/Spice detoxify the liver, which in turn helps to reduce cravings for nicotine and caffeine, Take 3 tablets of JuvaTone 3 times daily and two tablespoons JuvaPower/Spice daily.

SNAKE BITES

CAUTION: Get medical attention immediately if you have been bitten by a poisonous snake.

FIRST RECOMMENDATIONS:
Clove, Thieves Antiseptic Spray

EO APPLICATION METHODS:
Topical:
DILUTE 50:50, Apply 2-3 drops on location every 15 minutes until professional medical help is available

SNORING

(See also APNEA)

Rub 4-6 drops thyme diluted 50:50 on the soles of both feet at bedtime.

SORE THROAT

(See COLDS or THROAT INFECTION)

SPASTIC COLON

(See DIGESTION PROBLEMS)

SPINA BIFIDA

Spina bifida (SB) is a defect in which the spinal cord of the fetus fails to close during the first month of pregnancy. This results in varying degrees of permanent nerve damage, paralysis in lower limbs, and incomplete brain development.

SB has three different variations:

- The most severe form is Myelomeningocele. The spinal cord and its protective sheath (known as the meninges) protrude from an opening in the spine.

- The next most severe form is Meningocele. Only the meninges protrude from the opening in the spine

- The mildest form is Occulta. It is characterized by malformed vertebrae. Symptoms of this disease range from bowel and bladder dysfunctions to excess build up in the brain of cerebrospinal fluid.

The easiest way to prevent SB is with folic acid supplementation (at least 400 mcg daily, found in Super B) by all women of child-bearing age.

To Prevent:

Dietary Supplementation:
True Source Multivitamins, Super B, Omega Blue Softgels, Balance Complete

To Reduce Symptoms:

Single Oils:
Mountain savory, helichrysum, thyme, tea tree

Blends:
Melrose, Exodus II

EO APPLICATION METHODS:
Topical:
RAINDROP, weekly
COMPRESS, warm, 2 times weekly

SPINE INJURIES AND PAIN

According to numerous chiropractors, the Raindrop Technique using therapeutic-grade essential oils is revolutionizing the treatment of many types of back pain, spine inflammation, and vertebral misalignments. (See chapter 21: RAINDROP TECHNIQUE)

The following essential oils, blends, and supplements are used for supporting the structural integrity of the spine and reducing discomfort:

FIRST RECOMMENDATIONS:
Wintergreen, marjoram, Idaho balsam fir, Aroma Siez

Other Single Oils:
Douglas fir, spruce, peppermint, basil, copaiba

Other Blends:
Valor, Valor Roll-on, PanAway

EO APPLICATION METHODS:
Topical:
DILUTE 50:50, 6-10 drops on location twice a day or as needed
COMPRESS, warm, 1-2 times daily (if not inflamed)
RAINDROP TECHNIQUE, 3 times a month for one month

DIETARY SUPPLEMENTS:
Mega Cal, Super Cal, Longevity Softgels, BLM

Backache

(See also MUSCLES)

FIRST RECOMMENDATIONS:
Aroma Siez, marjoram, peppermint

Other Single Oils:
Lavender, wintergreen, German chamomile, basil, copaiba

Backache blend:
• 2 drops marjoram
• 3 drops lavender
• 5 drops wintergreen

EO APPLICATION METHODS:
Topical:
NEAT, apply 2-4 drops to aching area 1-3 times daily as needed
COMPRESS: warm, if there is no inflammation; cold, if there is inflammation, 1-2 times daily
RAINDROP, weekly for 3 weeks
Topical Treatment:
Regenolone, Ortho Ease

Herniated Disk / Disk Deterioration

For this situation, it is best to consult a specialist.

For temporary relief until medical attention can be given:

FIRST RECOMMENDATIONS:
Helichrysum, wintergreen, PanAway

Other Single Oils:
Basil, thyme, Idaho balsam fir, spruce, vetiver, valerian

Other Blends:
Relieve It, Aroma Siez, Deep Relief Roll-on

EO APPLICATION METHODS:
Topical:
DILUTE 50:50, apply on location for pain relief
COMPRESS: Cold, on location as needed
RAINDROP, weekly (after medical attention). Stimulate vertebrae with the "pointer technique"

How to Make Your Own High-Powered Massage Oil

Add either of these formulas to 4 oz. of vegetable or massage oil to create a custom muscle-toning formula.

Massage Oil #1:
- 10 drops wintergreen
- 10 drops balsam fir
- 10 drops marjoram
- 8 drops elemi
- 8 drops vetiver
- 5 drops helichrysum
- 5 drops cypress
- 5 drops peppermint

Massage Oil #2:
- 20 drops wintergreen
- 15 drops marjoram
- 10 drops juniper
- 10 drops cypress
- 6 drops spruce

Dietary Supplementation:
Sulfurzyme, BLM, MegaCal, Omega Blue Softgels

Topical Treatments:
Regenolone, Ortho Sport

Lumbago (Lower back pain)

Chronic lower back pain can have many causes, including a damaged or pinched nerve (neuralgia) or a congested colon.

FIRST RECOMMENDATIONS:
Marjoram, wintergreen, PanAway, Deep Relief Roll-on

Other Single Oils:
Basil, helichrysum, German chamomile, elemi, peppermint, copaiba

Chiropractors have found that by applying Valor on the bottom of the feet, spinal manipulations take 60 percent less time and work, and the results last 75 percent longer.

Pointer Technique for Nerve Damage

The "pointer technique" may also be used on the foot Vita Flex points.

If there is nerve damage, apply about 6 drops of peppermint along the spine, starting at the hips and ending at the neck, using Raindrop Technique. Starting at the bottom of the spine, use a small-nosed pointer (about the size of a pencil but with a rounded end).

Stimulate each vertebra between each rib on the vertebra knuckles all the way up on each side of the spine. Use medium pressure and a rocking motion for 1-10 seconds at each location. Then follow the same procedure once more up the center of the spine directly on each vertebra.

Other Blends:
Di-Gize, Relieve It

EO APPLICATION METHODS:
Topical:
DILUTE 50:50, 6-10 drops on location twice a day or as needed, Also apply to navel
VITA FLEX, massage 2-3 drops on stomach and intestine Vita Flex points on the feet
COMPRESS, warm, 1-2 times daily (if not inflamed)
RAINDROP TECHNIQUE, 3 times a month

DIETARY SUPPLEMENTATION:
ICP/Comfortone/Essentialzyme, Life 5, Omega Blue Softgels, MegaCal

Topical Treatments:
Regenolone, NeuroGen, Ortho Sport and Ortho Ease Massage Oils, Raindrop Technique

Neck Pain and Stiffness

FIRST RECOMMENDATIONS:
PanAway, wintergreen, peppermint, Deep Relief Roll-on

Other Single Oils:
Basil, marjoram, helichrysum, Idaho balsam fir, nutmeg, copaiba, elemi

Other Blends:
Relieve It

Neck stiffness blend:
- 5 drops PanAway
- 5 drops marjoram
- 3 drops peppermint

Neck pain blend:
- 5 drops wintergreen
- 4 drops cypress
- 7 drops basil
- 2 drops peppermint

EO APPLICATION METHODS:
  Topical:
  DILUTE 50:50, apply 4-6 drops to neck area and massage 1-3 times daily, as needed
  COMPRESS: warm, on neck area, daily or as needed (if no inflammation)

DIETARY SUPPLEMENTATION:
  Mineral Essence, MegaCal, Omega Blue Softgels, BLM

Sciatica

Sciatica is characterized by pain in the buttocks and down the back of the thigh. The pain worsens during coughing, sneezing, or extension or flexion of the back. The pain is caused by pressure on the sciatic nerve as it leaves the spine in the lower pelvic region, due to spinal misalignment, nerve inflammation or both. The sciatic nerve is the largest in the body, with branches throughout the legs and feet, and sciatica pain can be intense and immobilizing.

Acute sciatica has a sudden onset and is usually triggered by a misaligned vertebra pressing against the sciatic nerve due to accident, injury, pregnancy, or inflammation.

Symptoms:
- Lower back pain
- Swelling or stiffness in a leg
- Loss of sensation in a leg
- Muscle wasting in a leg

Sulfurzyme, Super B and Omega Blue Softgels work well together to help rebuild nerve damage and the myelin sheath.

FIRST RECOMMENDATIONS:
  PanAway, Raindrop Technique

Other Single Oils:
  Helichrysum, peppermint, nutmeg, thyme, spruce, wintergreen, basil, rosemary, clove, copaiba

Other Blends:
  Aroma Siez, Relieve It, Aroma Life

EO APPLICATION METHODS:
  Topical:
  DILUTE 50:50, 6-10 drops on location twice a day or as needed
  COMPRESS, warm,1-2 times daily (if not inflamed)
  VITA FLEX, 2-3 drops on Vita Flex points on feet, 2-4 times daily
  RAINDROP TECHNIQUE, 3 times a month
  Ingestion:
  CAPSULE, 0 size, 2 times daily

DIETARY SUPPLEMENTATION:
  Sulfurzyme, Super B, Omega Blue Softgels, Mega Cal, Mineral Essence

Topical Treatments:
  Regenolone, Ortho Sport, Ortho Ease

SPRAIN

(See also CONNECTIVE TISSUE)

FIRST RECOMMENDATIONS:
  Idaho balsam fir, wintergreen, Regenolone, Aroma Siez

Other Single Oils:
  Basil, pine, spruce, cypress, peppermint, copaiba

Other Blends:
  PanAway, Relieve It

EO APPLICATION METHODS:
  Topical:
  DILUTE 50:50, apply 4-6 drops on location 3-5 times daily
  COMPRESS, cold, on location, 2 times daily

DIETARY SUPPLEMENTATION:
  Sulfurzyme, Mineral Essence, MegaCal

Topical Treatment:
  Prenolone, Ortho Sport

STOMACHACHE

(See DIGESTIVE DISORDERS)

479

STRESS

FIRST RECOMMENDATIONS:
Lavender, Valor, Valor Roll-on, Peace & Calming, Super B, Tranquil Roll-on

Other Single Oils:
Roman chamomile, blue tansy, cedarwood, marjoram, rose, sandalwood, frankincense, valerian

Other Blends:
Trauma Life, Humility, Harmony, RutaVaLa

EO APPLICATION METHODS:
Inhalation:
DIRECT, as needed
DIFFUSION, 30 minutes 1-3 times daily
Ingestion:
CAPSULE, 0 size, 2 times a day
Topical:
DILUTE 50:50, apply on temples, neck, and shoulders twice daily, or as needed
BATH SALTS, daily

Dietary Supplementation:
Super B, Super C, MultiGreens, True Source Multivitamins, MegaCal, Omega Blue softgels

STRETCH MARKS
(See SKIN DISORDERS)

STROKE
(See BRAIN DISORDERS)

SUNBURN
(See BURNS)

SYMPATHETIC NERVOUS SYSTEM
(See NERVOUS SYSTEM-AUTONOMIC)

TACHYCARDIA
(See HEART, CARDIOVASCULAR CONDITIONS)

TENDONITIS
(See CONNECTIVE TISSUE, MUSCLES)

TEETHING PAIN
(See ORAL CARE)

TEETH GRINDING
(See ORAL CARE)

THROAT INFECTIONS
(See also COLDS, INFECTION, LUNG INFECTIONS, ORAL CARE)

Cough

FIRST RECOMMENDATIONS:
R.C., *Eucalyptus globulus*, peppermint, tea tree, Breath Again Roll-on

Other Single Oils:
Eucalyptus radiata, lemon, oregano, frankincense, ravensara, thyme, myrrh, cedarwood, mountain savory

Other Blends:
R.C., Thieves, Melrose, Raven, Purification, Breath Again Roll-on

Cough blend:
• 3 drops oregano
• 10 drops *Eucalyptus globulus*

EO APPLICATION METHODS:
Inhalation:
DIRECT, 3-6 times daily
VAPOR, 2-3 times daily
Ingestion:
Rice Milk, 2-4 times daily. It is beneficial to heat the rice milk and sip slowly for more soothing relief.
SYRUP, 3-5 times daily
Oral:
TONGUE, 2-6 times daily or as often as needed
GARGLE, 4-8 times daily
Topical:
DILUTE 50:50, apply 1-3 drops to throat, chest and back of neck 2-4 times daily
VITA FLEX, apply 1-3 drops to lung Vita Flex points, 1-3 times daily
RAINDROP TECHNIQUE, weekly

DIETARY SUPPLEMENTATION:
Super C, Exodus, Longevity Softgels, MultiGreens, ImmuPro, Omega Blue Softgels

NOTE: Mountain savory, ravensara, and thyme applied by Raindrop Technique on the spine are beneficial for any and all chest-related infections.

Topical Treatment:
Thieves Antiseptic Spray

Dry Cough

Dry Cough Tea recipe
- 2 drops lemon
- 3 drops *Eucalyptus radiata*
- 1 tsp blue agave or maple syrup
- 4 oz. heated distilled water

Sip slowly. Repeat as often as needed for relief.

Topical Treatment:
Thieves Antiseptic Spray in oral cavity as needed

Laryngitis

Put 2 drops Melrose and 1 drop lemon in 1/2 tsp. blue agave or maple syrup. Hold in back of mouth for 1-2 minutes, then swallow. Repeat as needed.

Topical Treatment:
Thieves Antiseptic Spray in oral cavity as needed

Sore Throat

FIRST RECOMMENDATIONS:
Tea tree, ravansara, Thieves lozenges

Other Single Oils:
Cypress, *Eucalyptus radiata,* lemon, frankincense, thyme, oregano, peppermint, myrrh, wintergreen

Other Blends:
Thieves, Melrose, Raven

Sore throat blend #1:
- 2 drops thyme
- 2 drops cypress
- 1 drop *Eucalyptus radiata*
- 1 drop peppermint
- 1 drop myrrh

Sore throat blend #2:
- 2 drops *Eucalyptus globulus*
- 5 drops lemon
- 2 drops wintergreen

EO APPLICATION METHODS:
Inhalation:
DIRECT, 3-6 times daily
VAPOR, 2-3 times daily
Ingestion:
RICE MILK, 2-4 times daily. It is beneficial to heat the rice milk and sip slowly for more soothing relief.
SYRUP, 3-5 times daily
Oral:
TONGUE, 2-6 times daily or as often as needed
GARGLE, 4-8 times daily
Topical:
DILUTE 50:50, apply 1-3 drops to throat, chest and back of neck 2-4 times daily
COMPRESS, warm, on throat and chest area 2-3 times daily
VITA FLEX, apply 1-3 drops to lung Vita Flex points, 1-3 times daily
RAINDROP Technique, weekly

Other Oral Treatment:
Fresh Essence Plus Mouthwash, Thieves Antisteptic spray

DIETARY SUPPLEMENTATION:
Super C, Super C Chewable, ImmuPro, Exodus, Longevity Softgels, Omega Blue softgels

Strep Throat

FIRST RECOMMENDATIONS:
Inner Defense softgels, Oregano, thyme, Thieves, Thieves Antiseptic Spray, Thieves lozenges, Raindrop Technique

Other Single Oils:
Eucalyptus globulus, frankincense, myrrh, mountain savory, clove, cinammon

Other Blends:
Exodus II, Melrose, Raven

Strep throat blend:
- 1 drops cinnamon
- 6 drops lavender
- 2 drops oregano

EO APPLICATION METHODS:
Inhalation:
DIRECT, 3-6 times daily
VAPOR, 2-3 times daily

Ingestion:
RICE MILK, 2-4 times daily. It is beneficial to heat the rice milk and sip slowly for more soothing relief.
SYRUP, 3-5 times daily

Oral:
TONGUE, 2-6 times daily or as often as needed
GARGLE, 4-8 times daily

Topical:
DILUTE 50:50, apply 1-3 drops to throat, chest and back of neck 2-4 times daily
COMPRESS, warm, on chest area 2-3 times daily
VITA FLEX, apply 1-3 drops to lung Vita Flex points, 1-3 times daily
RAINDROP Technique, weekly

DIETARY SUPPLEMENTATION:

ImmuPro, Super C, Longevity Softgels, Super C Chewable, MultiGreens, Exodus, ICP/ComforTone/Essentialzyme, Omega Blue softgels, True Source Multivitamins

Regimen for strep throat:
- ImmuPro: 2-4 tablets at bedtime
- Longevity Softgels: 2-4 capsules daily
- Super C: 2-3 tablets, 2 times daily
- Use Raindrop Technique with ImmuPower and/or Exodus II along sides of spine, weekly
- Spray throat with Thieves Antiseptic Spray every 2 hours

Tonsillitis

The tonsils are infection-fighting lymphatic tissues (immune cells) that surround the throat. When these become infected with streptococcal bacteria they become inflamed, causing a condition known as tonsillitis.

It became popular in the 1960's and 1970's to have the tonsils removed when they became infected. However, tonsillectomies have become much less frequent as researchers have discovered the important role tonsils play in protecting and fighting infectious diseases and optimizing immune response.

The pharyngeal tonsils located at the back of the throat (known as the adenoids) can also become infected—a condition known as adenitis.

FIRST RECOMMENDATIONS:
Clove, tea tree, Thieves, Inner Defense softgels

Single Oils:
Goldenrod, oregano, mountain savory, ravensara, thyme

Blends:
Melrose, Exodus II, ImmuPower

Topical Treatment:
Thieves Antiseptic Spray

EO APPLICATION METHODS:
Ingestion:
RICE MILK, 2-4 times daily. It is beneficial to heat the rice milk and sip slowly for more soothing relief.
SYRUP, 3-5 times daily

Oral:
TONGUE, 2-6 times daily or as often as needed
GARGLE, 4-8 times daily

Topical:
DILUTE 50:50, apply 1-3 drops to throat, chest and back of neck 2-4 times daily
COMPRESS, warm, on chest area 2-3 times daily
VITA FLEX, apply 1-3 drops to lung Vita Flex points, 1-3 times daily
RAINDROP Technique, weekly

DIETARY SUPPLEMENTATION:
Super C Chewable

THRUSH

(See FUNGAL INFECTIONS)

THYROID PROBLEMS

Located at the base of the neck just below the Adam's apple, the thyroid is the energy gland of the human body. It produces T3 and T4 thyroid hormones that control the body's metabolism. The thyroid also controls other vital functions such as digestion, circulation, immune function, hormone balance, and emotions.

The thyroid gland is actually controlled by the pituitary gland which signals the thyroid when to produce thyroid hormone. The pituitary gland, in turn, is directed by chemical signals sent by the hypothalamus gland which monitors hormone levels in the blood stream.

A lack of thyroid hormone does not necessarily mean that the thyroid is not functioning properly. In some instances, the pituitary may be malfunctioning because of its failure to release sufficient TSH (thyroid stimulating hormone) to spur the thyroid to make thyroid hormone.

Other cases of thyroid hormone deficiency may be due to the hypothalamus failing to release sufficient TRH (thyrotropin releasing hormone).

In cases where thyroid hormone deficiency is caused by a malfunctioning pituitary or hypothalamus, better results may be achieved by using supplements or essential oils that stimulate the pituitary or hypothalamus, such as Cedarwood.

People with type A blood have more of a tendency to have weak thyroid function.

Hyperthyroid (Graves Disease)

When the thyroid becomes overactive and produces excess thyroid hormone, the following symptoms occur:

Symptoms of hyperthyroidism:
• Anxiety
• Restlessness
• Insomnia
• Premature gray hair
• Diabetes mellitus
• Arthritis
• Vitiligo (loss of skin pigment)

Graves disease, unlike Hashimoto's disease, is an autoimmune disease which results in an excess of thyroid hormone production.

MSM has been studied for its ability to reverse many kinds of autoimmune diseases. MSM is a key component of Sulfurzyme.

FIRST RECOMMENDATIONS:
Sulfurzyme, wintergreen, German chamomillle

Other Single Oils:
Myrrh, spruce, blue tansy, lemongrass

Other Blends:
EndoFlex

OTHER DIETARY SUPPLEMENTATION:
MultiGreens, Mineral Essence, Mega Cal, Omega Blue softgels

Hypothyroid (Hashimoto's Disease)

(see also HYPOGLYCEMIA)

This condition occurs when the thyroid is underactive and produces insufficient thyroid hormone. Approximately 40 percent of the U.S. population suffers from milder forms of this disorder to some degree, and these people tend to also suffer from hypoglycemia (low blood sugar). In its severe form it is referred to as Hashimoto's disease.

Hashimoto's disease, like Graves disease, is an autoimmune condition. It affects the thyroid differently, however, limiting its ability to produce thyroid hormone.

The following symptoms occur:
• Fatigue
• Yeast infections (Candida)
• Lack of energy
• Reduced immune function
• Poor resistance to disease
• Recurring infections

FIRST RECOMMENDATIONS:
Lemongrass, spearmint, Thyromin

Other Single Oils:
Ledum, myrtle, peppermint, myrrh, clove

Other Blends:
EndoFlex

EO APPLICATION METHODS:
Topical:
DILUTE 50:50, apply 3-5 drops over the thyroid (lower front of the neck on both sides of the trachea), 1-3 times daily
VITA FLEX, apply 1-3 drops on the thyroid Vita Flex points of the feet (located on the inside edge of the ball of the foot, just below the base of the big toe.)
Ingestion:
CAPSULE, 00 size, 1 capsule twice a day

DIETARY SUPPLEMENTATION:
MultiGreens, Sulfurzyme

TINNITIS (Ringing in Ears)

(See HEARING IMPAIRMENT)

TOOTHACHE

(See ORAL CARE)

TONSILLITIS

(See COLDS AND THROAT INFECTIONS)

TOXEMIA

(See INFECTION)

When toxins or bacteria begin to accumulate in the bloodstream, a condition called toxemia is created.

FIRST RECOMMENDATIONS:
Orange, Citrus Fresh

Other Single Oils:
Clove, tangerine, lemon, cypress

Other Blends:
Inner Child, Purification

EO APPLICATION METHODS:
Ingestion:
CAPSULE, 0 size, 1 capsule 3 times a day

DIETARY SUPPLEMENTATION:
ICP/ComforTone/Essentialzyme, Exodus, Super C

NOTE: Best results are achieved by eliminating all sugar, white flour, breads, pasta, and fried foods.

TRAUMA (EMOTIONAL)

(See also Emotional Pain under PAIN and SHOCK)

Emotional trauma can be generated from events that involve loss, abuse, bereavement, accidents, or misfortunes. Essential oils, through their ability to tap the emotional and memory center of the brain, may facilitate the processing and release of emotional trauma in a way that minimizes psychological turmoil.

FIRST RECOMMENDATIONS:
Trauma Life, Peace & Calming

Blends:
Hope, Forgiveness, Release, Envision, Valor, Valor Roll-on

EO APPLICATION METHODS:
Topical:
DILUTE 50:50, massage 2-4 drops to temples, forehead, crown and shoulders 1-3 times daily
Inhalation:
DIRECT, 1-3 times daily as needed

DIETARY SUPPLEMENTATION:
Super C, Mineral Essence, Mega Cal, Omega Blue Softgels, Balance Complete, Ningxia Red

TUBERCULOSIS

(See also LUNG INFECTION)

Tuberculosis (TB) is a highly contagious lung disease caused by *Mycobacterium tuberculosis*. The germs are spread via coughs, sneezes, and physical contact. The most worrisome aspect of this disease is it latency. Those infected may harbor the germ for years, yet display no outward or visible signs of infection. However, when the immune system becomes challenged or downregulated due to stress, candida, diabetes, corticosteroid use, or other factors, the bacteria can become reactivated and develop into full-blown TB.

Prior to the 1940's, tuberculosis was one of the leading causes of the death in the United States. After the introduction of anti-TB drugs following World War II, incidences of the disease dwindled. However, the incidence of TB has recently staged a surprising resurgence, with the number of TB cases increasing dramatically since 1984. In 1993 over 25,000 cases of TB were reported.

Because many essential oils have broad-spectrum antimicrobial properties, they can be diffused to prevent the spread of airborne bacteria like *Mycobacterium tuberculosis*. Essential oils and blends such as Thieves, Purification, Raven, R.C., and Sacred Mountain are extremely effective for killing this type of germ.

Many essential oils have also been shown to be immune-stimulating. Lemon oil has been shown to increase lymphocyte production—a pivotal part of the immune system.

FIRST RECOMMENDATIONS:
Inner Defense softgels, Thieves, Raindrop Technique

Other Single Oils:
Oregano, thyme, ravensara, rosemary, cinnamon, *Eucalyptus radiata*, clove, mountain savory, peppermint, spearmint, myrtle, Idaho balsam fir

Other Blends:
Raven, Melrose, R.C., ImmuPower, Purification, Sacred Mountain, Breath Again Roll-on

EO APPLICATION METHODS:
Inhalation:
DIFFUSION, 1 hour, twice a day and at night.
DIRECT, 3-5 times daily
Topical:
DILUTE 50:50, apply 6-10 drops on chest and upper back 1-3 times daily
COMPRESS, warm, on chest and upper back, twice daily
Ingestion:
CAPSULE, 00 size, 1 capsule 3 times daily for 10 days

DIETARY SUPPLEMENTATION:
ImmuPro, Super C Chewable, Longevity Softgels, MultiGreens, ICP/Comfortone/ Essentialzyme

Tuberculosis-specific regimen:

1. Alternate diffusing Raven and R.C. as often as possible during the day

2. Mix the following in 2 Tbsp. of V-6 Oil Complex. Insert into rectum with bulb syringe and retain overnight. Do this nightly for 7 nights; rest for 4 nights; then repeat.
   • 2 drops oregano
   • 4 drops myrrh
   • 5 drops clove
   • 6 drops ravensara
   • 15 drops frankincense

3. Take one Inner Defense softgel 3 times daily for 5 days.

4. Rub 4-6 drops Thieves on the bottom of the feet nightly

5. Rub Melrose up the spine daily and apply as a compress on back and chest twice a day.

6. Use Raindrop Technique 2-4 times/month.

TUMORS

(See CANCER)

TYPHOID FEVER

Typhoid fever is an infectious disease caused by a bacteria known as *Salmonella typhi*. Usually contracted through infected food or water, typhoid is common in lesser-developed countries.

Some people infected with typhoid fever display no visible symptoms of disease, while others become seriously ill. Both people who recover from typhoid fever and those who remain symptomless are carriers for the disease, and can infect others through the bacteria they shed in their feces.

To avoid contracting typhoid fever—especially when traveling overseas—it is essential to drink purified or distilled water and to thoroughly cook foods. Fresh vegetables can be carriers of the bacteria, especially if they have been irrigated with water that has come into contact with human waste.

Symptoms:
• Sustained, high fever (101° to 104° F).
• Stomach pains
• Headache
• Rash of reddish spots
• Impaired appetite
• Weakness

FIRST RECOMMENDATIONS:
Clove, thyme, Thieves, Inner Defense softgels

Other Single Oils:
Ravensara, cinnamon, cassia, peppermint, black pepper, mountain savory, oregano, tea tree

Other Blends:
Melrose

EO APPLICATION METHODS:

Topical:

DILUTE 50:50, massage 4-6 drops on lower abdomen, 2-4 times daily

Ingestion:

CAPSULE, 00 size, 1 capsule 2 times daily for 10 days

DIETARY SUPPLEMENTATION:

ImmuPro

ULCERS (Stomach)

(See DIGESTIVE PROBLEMS)

URINARY TRACT/BLADDER INFECTION

(See also KIDNEY DISORDERS)

Infections and inflammation of the urinary tract are caused by bacteria that travel up the urethra. This disorder is more common in women than men because of the woman's shorter urethra. If the infection travels up the ureters and reaches the kidneys, kidney infection can result.

Symptoms:

- Frequent urge to urinate with only a small amount of urine coming out
- Strong smelling urine
- Blood in urine
- Burning or stinging during urination

Bladder infection (known as cystitis) is marked by the following symptoms:

- Tenderness or chronic pain in bladder and pelvic area
- Frequent urge to urinate
- Pain intensity fluctuates as bladder fills or empties
- Symptoms worsen during menstruation

FIRST RECOMMENDATIONS:

Tea tree, juniper berry, oregano

Other Single Oils:

Mountain savory, thyme, cistus, rosemary, clove

Other Blends:

Di-Gize, EndoFlex, R.C., Breath Again Roll-on, Melrose, Purification, Inspiration, Thieves

EO APPLICATION METHODS:

Ingestion:

CAPSULE, 0 size, 1 capsule 3 times daily

Topical:

COMPRESS, warm, over bladder, 1-2 times daily

DIETARY SUPPLEMENTATION:

K&B tincture, ImmuPro, AlkaLime

Use K&B tincture (2-3 droppers in distilled water) 3-6 times daily. K & B Tincture helps strengthen and tone weak bladder, kidneys, and urinary tract (see KIDNEY DISORDERS).

Take 1 tsp. of AlkaLime daily, in water only, 1 hour before or after meal.

Another useful remedy is to take 1 tsp. baking soda, dissolve in 8 oz. of pure water and drink 4 x daily until symptoms subside.

UTERINE CANCER

(See CANCER)

VAGINAL YEAST INFECTION

(See FUNGAL INFECTIONS or ANTISEPTIC)

Vaginal yeast infections are usually caused from overgrowth of fungi like *Candida albicans*. These naturally-occurring intestinal yeast and fungi are normally kept under control by the immune system, but when excess sucrose is consumed or antibiotics are used, these organisms convert from relatively harmless yeast into an invasive, harmful fungus that secretes toxins as part of its life cycle.

Vaginal yeast infections are just one symptom of systemic fungal infestation. While the yeast infection can be treated locally, the underlying problem of systemic candidiasis may still remain unless specific dietary and health practices are used.

FIRST RECOMMENDATIONS:

Tea tree, mountain savory, Melrose

Other Single Oils:

Myrrh, oregano, thyme, niaouli

Other Blends:

3 Wise Men, Inspiration, Clara Derm spray

EO APPLICATION METHODS:
Retention:

TAMPON, dilute 80-20, apply 3 times a week

Alternate approach: use a tampon soaked in Fresh Essence Plus overnight 3 times a week.

VARICOSE VEINS (SPIDER VEINS)

(See CIRCULATION DISORDERS)

VASCULAR CLEANSING

(See HEAVY METALS and CIRCULATION DISORDERS)

VITILIGO

(See SKIN DISORDERS)

WARTS (GENITAL)

(See SEXUALLY TRANSMITTED DISEASES)

WEST NILE VIRUS

(See INSECT BITES)

WHOOPING COUGH

(See COLDS, FLU, or INFECTION)

WOUNDS, SCRAPES, OR CUTS

(See SKIN DISORDERS and ANTISEPTIC)

When selecting oils for surface injuries, treat the whole person, not just the cut. Think through the cause and type of injury and select oils for each aspect of the trauma. For instance, a wound could encompass muscle damage, nerve damage, ligament damage, inflammation, infection, bone injury, fever, and possibly an emotion. Therefore, select an oil or blend that treats each of these.

FIRST RECOMMENDATIONS:
Lavender, tea tree, Melrose, Thieves Antiseptic spray

Single Oils:
Rosemary, *Eucalyptus globulus,* cypress, wintergreen, thyme, oregano, German chamomile, lavandin, mountain savory, peppermint

Other Blends:
Thieves, Purification, 3 Wise Men

Topical Treatment:
LavaDerm Spray

Bruise and scrape blend
(may be used on infants and children):
• 1 drop clove
• 4 drops lavender

Infected cuts blend:
• 7 drops geranium
• 5 drops peppermint
• 10 drops tea tree
• 4 drops thyme

EO APPLICATION METHODS:
Topical:

DILUTE 50:50, apply 2-6 drops on location, 1-4 times daily as needed

NOTE: Peppermint may sting when applied to an open wound. To reduce discomfort, dilute with lavender oil or mix in a sealing ointment before applying. When applied to a wound or cut that has a scab, a diluted peppermint blend will soothe, cool, and reduce inflammation in damaged tissue.

To reduce bleeding

FIRST RECOMMENDATIONS:
Geranium, helichrysum, cistus

Other Single Oils:
Cypress, lemon, rose

Other Blends:
PanAway

Wound compress blend:
• 5 drops geranium
• 5 drops lemon
• 5 drops German chamomile

EO APPLICATION METHODS:
Topical:

COMPRESS, cold, 1-2 times until bleeding stops

To reduce scarring

FIRST RECOMMENDATIONS:
Lavender, Gentle Baby

Other Single Oils:
Frankincense, lemongrass, geranium, helichrysum, myrrh

Other Blends:
Scar Prevention blend:
- 10 drops geranium
- 6 drops lavender
- 8 drops lemongrass
- 4 drops patchouli

EO APPLICATION METHODS:
Topical:
DILUTE 50:50, apply 2-4 drops on wound, 2-5 times daily

To promote healing

FIRST RECOMMENDATIONS:
Tea tree, sandalwood, Melrose

Other Single Oils:
Lavender, patchouli, niaouli, neroli, myrrh, helichrysum, Idaho tansy

Other Blends:
Purification

EO APPLICATION METHODS:
Topical:
DILUTE 50:50, apply 2-4 drops on wound 2-5 times daily.

To disinfect

FIRST RECOMMENDATIONS:
Thieves, tea tree, oregano

Other Single Oils:
Thyme, mountain savory

Other Blends:
Melrose, Purification

EO APPLICATION METHODS:
Topical:
DILUTE 50:50, apply 2-4 drops on wound 2-5 times daily.

Topical Treatment:
Thieves Antiseptic Spray

First-Aid Spray

- 5 drops lavender
- 3 drops *Melaleuca alternifolia*
- 2 drops cypress

Mix above oils thoroughly in 1/2 teaspoon of salt. Add this to 8 ounces of distilled water and shake vigorously. Put in a spray bottle. Spray minor cuts and wounds before applying bandage. Repeat 2-3 times daily for 3 days. Complete the healing process by applying a drop or two of tea tree oil to the wound daily for the next few days.

WORMS

(See PARASITES)

WRINKLES

(See this heading under SKIN DISORDERS)

YEAST INFECTION

(See HORMONES, VAGINAL YEAST INFECTION, or ANTISEPTIC)

Melaleuca alternifolia (Tea tree oil)

During World War II, melaleuca was found to have very strong antibacterial properties and worked well in preventing infection in open wounds. Melrose is a blend containing two types of melaleuca oil, plus rosemary and clove, making it an exceptional antiseptic and tissue regenerator.

Notes

SECTION **9**

Melaleuca

BIBLIOGRAPHY

Achanzar WE et al. "Cadmium-induced malignant transformation of human prostate epithelial cells." *Cancer Res.* 2001 Jan 15;61(2):455-8.

Al-Awadi FM, et al. "Studies on the activity of individual plants of an antidiabetic plant mixture." *Acta Diabetol Lat.* 1987;24(1):37-41.

Alderman G, and Elmer H., "Inhibition of Growth and Aflatoxin Production of Aspergillus Parasiticus by Citrus Oils. Z. Leb." *Unt-Forsch* 1976: 353-58.

Aqel MB. "Relaxant effect of the volatile oil of Rosmarinus officinalis on tracheal smooth muscle." *J Ethnopharmacol.* 1991;33(1-2):57-62.

Aruna K., and Sivaramakrishnan V., "Anticarcinogenic Effects of Essential Oils from Cumin, Poppy, and Basil." *Phytotherapy Research* 1996, 577-79.

Aruna, K. and V.M. Sivaramakrishnan. "Anticarcinogenic Effects of the Essential Oils from Cumin, Poppy and Basil." Food Chem Toxicol. 1992;30(11):953-56.

Azizan A, et al. "Mutagenicity and antimutagenicity testing of six chemicals associated with the pungent properties of specific spices as revealed by the Ames Salmonella/microsomal assay." Arch Environ Contam Toxicol. 1995;28(2):248-58.

Barja de Quiroga G, et al. Antioxidant defences and peroxidation in liver and brain of aged rats. Biochemical Journal 272 (1990), 247-250.

Bassett IB, et al. "A comparative study of tea-tree oil versus benzoylperoxide in the treatment of acne." Med J Aust. 1990;153(8):455-8.

Becker, M.D., Robert O. The Body Electric. New York: Wm. Morrow, 1985.

Belaiche, M.D., Paul. Traité de Phytothérapie Et D'Aromathérapie. Paris: Maloine, 1979.

Belvi, Viktor. Aromatherapy. New York: Avon Books, 1993.

Benencia F, et al. "Antiviral activity of sandalwood oil against herpes simplex viruses-1 and -2." Phytomedicine. 1999;6(2):119-23

Bernacchi F et al., In vivo cytogenetic effects of natural humic acid. Mutagenesis. 1996 Sep;11(5):467-9.

Bernardis LL, et al. "The lateral hypothalamic area revisited: ingestive behavior." Neurosci Biobehav Rev. 20(2):189-287 (1996).

Bilgrami KS, et al. "Inhibition of aflatoxin production & growth of Aspergillus flavus by eugenol & onion & garlic extracts." Indian J Med Res. 1992;96:171-5.

Bourre et al., Function of dietary polyunsaturated fatty acids in the nervous system. Prostoglandins, leukotrienes, and essential fatty acids 48 (1993): 5-15.

Bradshaw RH, et al. "Effects of lavender straw on stress and travel sickness in pigs." J Altern Complement Med. 1998;4(3):271-5.

Brodal A. Neurological Anatomy in Relation to Clinical Medicine. New York: Oxford University Press, 1981.

Buchbauer G, et al. "Aromatherapy: evidence for sedative effects of the essential oil of lavender after inhalation." Z Naturforsch [C]. 1991;46(11-12):1067-72.

Burrows, Stanley. Healing for the Age of Enlightenment. Kailua, Hawaii, 1976.

Cai and Wu .Compounds from Syzygium aromaticum possessing growth inhibitory activity against oral pathogens. J Nat Prod. 1996 Oct;59(10):987-90.

Calabrese V, Oxidative stress and antioxidants at skin biosurface: a novel antioxidant from lemon oil capable of inhibiting oxidative damage to the skin. Drugs Exp Clin Res. 1999;25(6):281-7.

Cao G et al., Increases in human plasma antioxidant capacity after consumption of controlled diets high in fruit and vegetables. Am J Clin Nutr. 1998 Nov;68(5):1081-7.

Cao G, et al, Antioxidant capacity in different tissues of young and old rats. Proceedings of the society for Experimental Biology and Medicine 211(1996), 359-365.

Cao G, et al. Automated assay of oxygen radical absorbance capacity with the COBAS FARA II. Clin Chem. 1995 Dec;41(12 Pt 1):1738-44.

Carson CF, et al. "Antimicrobial activity of the major components of the essential oil of Melaleuca alternifolia." J Appl Bacteriol. 1995;78(3):264-9.

Carson et al. Antimicrobial activity of the major components of the essential oil of Melaleuca alternifolia. J Appl Bacteriol. 1995 Mar;78(3):264-9.

Chao et al., Seventy-four Essential Oils Against Streptococcus pneumoniae. Unpublished research, 1998.

Chao, et al., Screening for Inhibitory Activity of Essential Oils on Selected Bacteria, Fungi, and Viruses. Journal of Essential Oil Research, 1997.

Chopra, M.D., Deepak. Quantum Healing. New York: Bantam Books, 1989.

Compendium of Olfactory Research. Edited by Avery N. Gilbert. Dubuque, IA: Kendall Hunt Publishing, 1995.

Concha JM, et al. 1998 William J. Stickel Bronze Award. "Antifungal activity of Melaleuca alternifolia (tea-tree) oil against various pathogenic organisms." J Am Podiatr Med Assoc. 1998;88(10): 489-92

Cornwell S, et al. "Lavender oil and perineal repair." Mod Midwife 1995;5(3):31-3.

Covello et. al. Determination of eugenol in the essence of "Eugenia caryophyllata". Titration in non-aqueous solvent and comparison with other methods of analysis. Boll Chim Farm. 1966 Nov;105(11):799-806.

Cozzi R et al., Desmutagenic activity of natural humic acids: inhibition of mitomycin C and maleic hydrazide mutagenicity. Mutat Res. 1993 Mar;299(1):37-44.

Cox et al. The mode of antimicrobial action of the essential oil of Melaleuca alternifolia (tea tree oil). J Appl Microbiol. 2000 Jan;88(1):170-5.

Crowell P. Prevention and therapy of cancer by dietary monoterpenes. J Nutr. 1999 Mar;129(3):775S-778S.

Dakhil MA, Morsy TA. The larvicidal activities of the peel oils of three citrus fruits against Culex pipiens. J Egypt Soc Parasitol. 1999 Aug;29(2):347-52.Dalvi et al. Effect of peppermint oil on gastric emptying in man: a preliminary study using a radiolabelled solid test meal.Indian J Physiol Pharmacol. 1991 Jul;35(3):212-4.

Darom, David. Beautiful Plants of the Bible. Israel: Palphot, Ltd.

Deans SG, et al, Natural antioxidants from aromatic and medicinal plants. In Role of Free Radicals in Biological Systems, pp. 159-165 (1993a) [J Feher, A Blazovics, B Matkovics and M Mezes, editors]. Budapest: Akademiai Kiado.

Delaveau P, et al. "Neuro-depressive properties of essential oil of lavender." C R Seances Soc Biol Fil. 1989;183(4):342-8.

Dember WN, et al., Olfactory Stimulation and Sustained Attention, Compendium of Olfactory, (Avery N. Gilbert, Editor) pp. 39-46.

Didry N, et al. "Activity of thymol, carvacrol, cinnamaldehyde and eugenol on oral bacteria." Pharm Acta Helv. 1994;69(1):25-8.

Diego MA, et al. "Aromatherapy positively affects mood, EEG patterns of alertness and math computations." Int J Neurosci. 1998 Dec;96(3-4):217-24.

Dolara P, et al. "Analgesic effects of myrrh." Nature. 1996 Jan 4;379(6560):29.

Doss, Besada. The Story of Abu Simbel. Essex, England: Longman Group UK Limited, 1973.

Dunn C, et al. "Sensing an improvement: an experimental study to evaluate the use of aromatherapy, massage and periods of rest in an intensive care unit." J Adv Nurs. 1995;21(1):34-40.

Dwivedi C, et al. "Chemopreventive effects of sandalwood oil on skin papillomas in mice." Eur J Cancer Prev. 1997;6(4):399-401.

Elisabetsky et al. Anticonvulsant properties of linalool in glutamate-related seizure models. Phytomedicine. 1999 May;6(2):107-13.

Elkins Rita, "Blue/Green Algae." Pleasant Grove, UT. 1995.

Elson CE, et al. "Impact of lemongrass oil, an essential oil, on serum cholesterol." Lipids. 1989;24(8):677-9.

Fang, H.J., et al. "Studies on the chemical components and anti-tumour action of the volatile oils from Pelargonium graveoleus." Yao Hsueh Hsueh Pao. 1989;24(5):366-71.

Faoagali JL, et al. "Antimicrobial effects of melaleuca oil." Burns. 1998;24(4):383. No abstract available.

Farag et. al. Acute hepatic damage in rats impairs metharbital metabolism. Pharmacology. 1987;34(4):181-91.

Farag et al., Antioxidant activity of some spice essential oils on linoleic acid oxidation in aqueous media. JAOCS June 1989;66: 792-799.

Farag et al., Inhibitory effects of individual and mixed pairs of essential oils on the oxidation and hydrolysis of cottonseed oil and butter. FASC, 1989; 40: 275-279.

Farag et al., Safety evaluation of thyme and clove essential oils as natural antioxidants. Afr J Agr Sci. 1991;18: 169-175,

Farag, Ph.D., Radwan S. "Safety Evaluation of Thyme and Clove Essential Oils as Natural Antioxidants." African Journal of Agricultural Sciences, Vol. 18, No. 1. Gisa, Egypt: Cairo University, 1991.

Fleming, T., Ed. PDR for Herbal Medicines, Medical Economics Company, Inc., Montvale, NJ (1998).

Fyfe L, et al. "Inhibition of Listeria monocytogenes and Salmonella enteriditis by combinations of plant oils and derivatives of benzoic acid: the development of synergistic antimicrobial combinations." Int J Antimicrob Agents. 1997;9(3):195-9.

Garrison, Omar. Tantra: The Yoga of Sex. New York: Harmony Books, 1964.

Gattefossé, René-Maurice. Gattefossé's Aromatherapy. Saffron Walden, UK: C.W. Daniel & Co., 1993.

Ghelardini et al. Local anaesthetic activity of the essential oil of Lavandula angustifolia. Planta Med. 1999 Dec;65(8):700-3

Gobel et al. Effect of peppermint and eucalyptus oil preparations on neurophysiological and experimental algesimetric headache parameters. Cephalalgia. 1994 Jun;14(3):228-34; 182.

Gobel H, et al. "Effect of peppermint and eucalyptus oil preparations on neurophysiological and experimental algesimetric headache parameters." Cephalalgia. 1994; 14(3):228-34.

Grassmann J, Schneider D, Weiser D, Elstner EF. Antioxidative effects of lemon oil and its components on copper induced oxidation of low density lipoprotein. Arzneimittelforschung. 2001 Oct;51(10):799-805.

Guenther, Ernest. The Essential Oils. Florida: Malabar, 1950.

Guillemain J, et al. "Neurodepressive effects of the essential oil of Lavandula angustifolia Mill." Ann Pharm Fr. 1989;47(6):337-43.

Gumbel, D. Principles of Holistic Therapy with Herbal Essences, Haug International, Brussels, Belgium (1993)

Halliwell B & Gutteridge JMC, Free Radicals in Biology and Medicine, 2nd Edition. (1989), Oxford: Clarendon Press.

Hakim IA, Harris RB, Ritenbaugh C. Citrus peel use is associated with reduced risk of squamous cell carcinoma of the skin. Nutr Cancer. 2000;37(2):161-8.

Hammer KA, et al. "In vitro susceptibilities of lactobacilli and organisms associated with bacterial vaginosis to Melaleuca alternifolia (tea tree) oil." Antimicrob Agents Chemother. 1999;43(1):196.

Hammer KA, et al. "Susceptibility of transient and commensal skin flora to the essential oil of Melaleuca alternifolia (tea tree oil)." Am J Infect Control. 1996;24(3):186-9.

Harmon, D, Aging: a theory based on free radical and radiation chemistry. J. Gerontology 11, (1956): 298-300.

Harmon, D, Free radical theory of aging: Effect of free radical inhibitors on the mortality rate of male LAFmice. J. Gerontology 23 (1968): 476-482.

Harmon, D, Free radical theory of aging: Effect of the amount and degree of unsaturation of dietary fat on mortality rate. J. Gerontology 26 (1971): 451-457.

Hasan HA, et al. "Inhibitory effect of spice oils on lipase and mycotoxin production." Zentralbl Mikrobiol. 1993;148(8):543-8.

Hausen BM, et al. "Comparative studies of the sensitizing capacity of drugs used in herpes simplex." Derm Beruf Umwelt. 1986;34(6):163-70.

Hay IC, et al. "Randomized trial of aromatherapy. Successful treatment for alopecia areata." Arch Dermatol. 1998; 134(11):1349-52.

Hayes AJ, Markovic B. Toxicity of Australian essential oil Backhousia citriodora (Lemon myrtle). Part 1. Antimicrobial activity and in vitro cytotoxicity. Food Chem Toxicol. 2002 Apr;40(4):535-43.

Hayflick, L. How and Why We Age. Ballantine Books, New York, 1994.

Hirsch, Alan. "Inhalation of 2 acetylpyridine for weight reduction." Chemical Senses 18:570 (1993).

Hirsch, Alan. A Scentsational Guide to Weight Loss. Rockport, MA: Element, 1997.

Hoffer BJ, Olson L, and Palmer MR Toxic effects of lead in the developing nervous system: in oculo experimental models. Environ

Health Perspect. 1987 Oct;74:169-75.

Hudak A et al., The favorable effect of humic acid based complex micro-element preparations in cadmium exposure. Orv Hetil. 1997 Jun 1;138 (22):1411-6.

Inhibition of growth and aflatoxin production of Aspergillus parasiticus by citrus oils. Z Lebensm Unters Forsch. 1976 Apr 28;160(4):353-8.

Inouye S, et al. "Antisporulating and respiration-inhibitory effects of essential oils on filamentous fungi." Mycoses. 1998;41(9-10):403-10.

Inouye S, et al., Inhibitory effect of essential oils on apical growth of Aspergillus fumigatus by vapour contact. Mycoses. 2000;43(1-2):17-23.

Inouye S, Takizawa T, Yamaguchi H. Antibacterial activity of essential oils and their major constituents against respiratory tract pathogens by gaseous contact. J Antimicrob Chemother. 2001 May;47(5):565-73.

Jayashree T, et al. "Antiaflatoxigenic activity of eugenol is due to inhibition of lipid peroxidation." Lett Appl Microbiol. 1999; 28(3):179-83.

Jones MM and Basinger MA. Restrictions on the applicability of mixed ligand chelate therapy (MLC) in acute cadmium intoxication. Res Commun Chem Pathol Pharmacol. 1979 Jun;24(3):525-31.

Juergens UR, et al. "The anti-inflammatory activity of L-menthol compared to mint oil in human monocytes in vitro: a novel perspective for its therapeutic use in inflammatory diseases." Eur J Med Res. 1998; 3(12):539-45.

Kaplan RJ & Greenwood CE, Dietary saturated fatty acids and brain function. Neurochemistry Research 23, (1989)615-626.

Kim HM, et al. "Lavender oil inhibits immediate-type allergic reaction in mice and rats." J Pharm Pharmacol. 1999;51(2):221-6.

Komori T, Fujiwara R, Tanida M, Nomura J. Application of fragrances to treatments for depression Nihon Shinkei Seishin Yakurigaku Zasshi. 1995 Feb;15(1):39-42

Kucera LS, et al. "Antiviral activities of extracts of the lemon balm plant." Ann NY Acad Sci. 1965 Jul 30;130(1):474-82.

Kulieva ZT. "Analgesic, hypotensive and cardiotonic action of the essential oil of the thyme growing in Azerbaijan." Vestn Akad Med Nauk SSSR. 1980;(9):61-3.

Lachowicz KJ, et al. "The synergistic preservative effects of the essential oils of sweet basil (Ocimum basilicum L.) against acid-tolerant food microflora." Lett Appl Microbiol. 1998;26(3):209-14.

LaDoux, M.D., Joseph. Rationalizing Thoughtless Emotions. Insight, Sept. 1989.

LaLonde RT and Xie S. Glutathione and N-acetylcysteine inactivations of mutagenic 2(5H)-furanones from the chlorination of humics in water. Chem Res Toxicol. 1993 Jul-Aug;6(4): 445-51. Nature. 1978 Sep 28;275(5678):311-3.

Lamptey MS & Walker BL, A possible dietary role for linolenic acid in the development of the young rat. Journal of Nutrition 106, (1976) 86-93.

Lantry LE, et al. "Chemopreventive effect of perillyl alcohol on 4-(methylnitrosamino)-1-(3-pyridyl)-1-butanone induced tumorigenesis in (C3H/HeJ X A/J)F1 mouse lung." J Cell Biochem Suppl. 1997;27:20-5.

Larrondo JV, et al. "Antimicrobial activity of essences from labiates." Microbios. 1995; 82(332): 171-2.

Lis-Balchin, M., et al. "Antimicrobial activity of Pelargonium essential oils added to a quiche filling as a model food system." Lett Appl Microbiol. 1998;27(4):207-10.

Lis-Balchin, M., et al. "Comparative antibacterial effects of novel Pelargonium essential oils and solvent extracts." Lett Appl Microbiol. 1998;27(3): 135-41.

Lopez-Bote et. al. Effect of dietary administration of oil extracts from rosemary and sage on lipid oxidation in broiler meat. Br Poult Sci.

1998 May;39(2):235-40.

Lorenzetti BB, et al. "Myrcene mimics the peripheral analgesic activity of lemongrass tea." J Ethnopharmacol. 1991;34(1):43-8.

Mahmood N, et al. "The anti-HIV activity and mechanisms of action of pure compounds isolated from Rosa damascena." Biochem Biophys Res Commun. 1996;229(1):73-9.

Mailhebiau, Philippe. La Nouvelle Aromathérapie. Editions. France: Jakin, 1994.

Mangena T, et al. "Comparative evaluation of the antimicrobial activities of essential oils of Artemisia afra, Pteronia incana and Rosmarinus officinalis on selected bacteria and yeast strains." Lett Appl Microbiol. 1999;28(4):291-6.

Masquelier, J. Radical Scavenging Effect of Proanthocyanidins. Paris, 1986.

Maury, Marguerite. The Secret and Life of Youth. Saffon Waldon, UK: C.W. Daniels & Co., 1995.

McGuffin, M., et al. Botanical Safety Handbook, CRC Press, Boca Raton, FL (1997)

Meeker HG, et al. "The antibacterial action of eugenol, thyme oil, and related essential oils used in dentistry." Compendium. 1988;9(1):32, 34-5, 38 passim.

Meunier, Christiane. Lavandes & Lavandins. Aix-en-Provence, France: Chaudoreille, 1985.

Michie, C.A., et al. "Frankincense and myrrh as remedies in children." J R Soc Med. 1991;84(10): 602-5.

Miltner et al. Emotional qualities of odors and their influence on the startle reflex in humans. Psychophysiology. 1994 Jan;31(1):107-10.

Miyake Y et al., Identification of coumarins from lemon fruit (Citrus limon) as inhibitors of in vitro tumor promotion and superoxide and nitric oxide generation. J Agric Food Chem. 1999 Aug;47(8):3151-7.

Modgil R, et al. "Efficacy of mint and eucalyptus leaves on the physicochemical characteristics of stored wheat against insect infestation." Nahrung. 1998;42(5):304-8.

Moleyar V, et al. "Antibacterial activity of essential oil components." Int J Food Microbiol. 1992;16(4): 337-42.

Momchilova, A. M. 330 Years of Bulgarian Rose Oil. Sofia, Bulgaria, 1994.

Montagna, F. J. HDR Herbal Desk Reference Kendall/Hunt Publishing Company, Dubuque, IA (1979).

Motomura N, Sakurai A, Yotsuya Y. Reduction of mental stress with lavender odorant. Percept Mot Skills. 2001 Dec;93(3):713-8.

Murray, M. Encyclopedia of Nutritional Supplements, Prima Publishing, Rocklin, CA (1996).

Nagababu E, et al. "The protective effects of eugenol on carbon tetrachloride induced hepatotoxicity in rats." Free Radic Res. 1995;23(6):617-27.

Naidu KA. "Eugenol--an inhibitor of lipoxygenase-dependent lipid peroxidation." Prostaglandins Leukot Essent Fatty Acids. 1995;53(5):381-3.

Nakamoto K, et al. "In vitro effectiveness of mouthrinses against Candida albicans." Int J Prosthodont. 1995;8(5):486-9.

Nasel, C. et al. "Functional imaging of effects of fragrances on the human brain after prolonged inhalation." Chemical Senses. 1994;19(4):359-64

Nenoff P, et al. "Antifungal activity of the essential oil of Melaleuca alternifolia (tea tree oil) against pathogenic fungi in vitro." Skin Pharmacol. 1996;9(6):388-94.

Neuringer M & Connor WE, N-3 fatty acids in the brain and retina: evidence for their essentiality. Nutrition Reviews 44, 285-294.

Niazi, H. The Egyptian Prescription. Cairo, Egypt: Elias Modern

Press, 1988.

Nikolaevskii VV, et al. "Effect of essential oils on the course of experimental atherosclerosis." Patol Fiziol Eksp Ter. 1990; (5):52-3.

Nishijima H, et al. "Mechanisms mediating the vasorelaxing action of eugenol, a pungent oil, on rabbit arterial tissue." Jpn J Pharmacol. 1999 Mar;79(3):327-34.

Nordenstrom, Bjorn. Biologically Closed Circuits. Sweden.

Okuyama H, Minimum requirements of n-3 and n-6 essential fatty acids for the function of the central nervous system and for the prevention of chronic disease. Proceedings of the Society for Experimental Biology and Medicine 200, (1992) 174-176.

Olson L, et al., Some toxic effects of lead, other metals and antibacterial agents on the nervous system--animal experiment models. Acta Neurol Scand Suppl. 1984;100:77-87.

Osterberg R and Mortensen K. The growth of fractal humic acids: cluster correlation and gel formation. Radiat Environ Biophys. 1994;33(3):269-76.

Panizzi L, et al. "Composition and antimicrobial properties of essential oils of four Mediterranean Lamiaceae." J Ethnopharmacol. 1993;39(3):167-70.

Pattnaik S, et al. "Antibacterial and antifungal activity of ten essential oils in vitro." Microbios. 1996;86(349):237-46.

Pedersen, M. Nutritional Herbology, A Reference Guide to Herbs, Wendell W. Whitman Company, Warsaw, IN (1998)

Pénoël, Daniel. Natural Home Health Care Using Essential Oils. Salem, UT: Essential Science Publishing, 1998.

Pénoël, M.D., Daniel and Pénoël, R.-M., Natural Home Health Care Using Essential Oils. La Drome, France: Editions Osmobiose, 1988.

Pénoël, M.D., Daniel and Pierre Franchomme. L'aromathérapie exactement. Limoges, France: Jollois, 1990.

Plato. Chronicles 156 E.

Pourgholami M.H. et.al. Evaluation of the anticonvulsant activity of the essential oil of Eugenia caryophyllata in male mice. J Ethnopharmacol. 1999 Feb;64(2):167-71.

Privitera, James. Silent Clots. Covina, CA: 1996

Ramadan W. et. al. Oil of bitter orange: new topical antifungal agent. Int J Dermatol. 1996 Jun;35(6):448-9.

Recsan Z, et al, Effect of essential oils on the lipids of the retina in the aging rat: a possible therapeutic use. J Ess Oil Res 9, (1997) 53-56.

Reddy AC, et al. "Effect of curcumin and eugenol on iron-induced hepatic toxicity in rats." Toxicology 1996;107(1):39-45.

Reddy AC, et al. "Studies on anti-inflammatory activity of spice principles and dietary n-3 polyunsaturated fatty acids on carrageenan-induced inflammation in rats." Ann Nutr Metab. 1994;38(6): 349-58.

Reddy BS, et al. "Chemoprevention of colon carcinogenesis by dietary perillyl alcohol." Cancer Res. 1997;57(3):420-5.

Restick, M.D., Richard. The Brain. New York: Random House, 1991.

Riede UN et al., Collagen stabilization induced by natural humic substances. Arch Orthop Trauma Surg. 1992;111(5):259-64.

Rompelberg CJ, et al. "Antimutagenicity of eugenol in the rodent bone marrow micronucleus test." Mutat Res. 1995;346(2):69-75.

Rompelberg CJ, et al. "Effect of short-term dietary administration of eugenol in humans" Hum Exp Toxicol. 1996;15(2):129-35.\

Rompelberg et al. Antimutagenicity of eugenol in the rodent bone marrow micronucleus test. Mutat Res. 1995 Feb;346(2):69-75.

Rotstein et al., Effects of aging on the composition and metabolism of docosahexaenoate-containing lipids of retina. Lipids. 1987 Apr;22(4):253-60.

Russin, et al. Inhibition of rat mammary carcinogenesis by monoterpenoids. Carcinogenesis. 1989 Nov;10(11):2161-4.

Ryan PB, Huet N, and MacIntosh DL. Longitudinal Investigation of Exposure to Arsenic, Cadmium, and Lead in Drinking Water. Environ Health Perspect. 2000 Aug;108(8):731-735.

Sato T et al., Adsorption of mutagens by humic acid. Sci Total Environ. 1987 Apr;62:305-10. Sato T et al., Mechanism of the desmutagenic effect of humic acid. Mutat Res. 1987 Feb;176(2):199-204.

Ryman, Daniele. Aromatherapy: The Complete Guide to Plant and Flower Essences for Health and Beauty. New York: Bantam Books, 1993.

Saeed SA, et al. "Antithrombotic activity of clove oil." JPMA J Pak Med Assoc. 1994;44(5):112-5.

Safe Shopper's Bible: A Consumer's Guide to Nontoxic Household Products, Cosmetics, and Food." Macmillan, New York, NY (1995).

Samman MA, et al. "Mint prevents shamma-induced carcinogenesis in hamster cheek pouch." Carcinogenesis. 1998;19(10):1795-801.

Schrauzer GN. Anticarcinogenic effects of selenium. Cell Mol Life Sci. 2000 Dec;57(13-14):1864-73.

Schreuder M. Private communication with Brunswick Laboratories, Warcham, MA. March 21, 2001.

Schubert J and Derr SK. Mixed ligand chelate therapy for plutonium and cadmium poisoning.

Schubert J, Riley EJ, and Tyler SA. Combined effects in toxicology-a rapid systematic testing procedure: cadmium, mercury, and lead. J Toxicol Environ Health. 1978 Sep-Nov;4(5-6):763-76.

Scott BL & Bazan NG, Membrane docosahexaenoate is supplied to the developing brain and retina by the liver. Proceedings of the National Academy of sciences USA 86, (1989) 2903-2907.

Shapiro S, et al. "The antimicrobial activity of essential oils and essential oil components towards oral bacteria." Oral Microbiol Immunol. 1994;9(4): 202-8.

Sharma JN, et al. "Suppressive effects of eugenol and ginger oil on arthritic rats." Pharmacology. 1994;49(5):314-8.

Shirota S, et al. "Tyrosinase inhibitors from crude drugs." Biol Pharm Bull. 1994; 17(2):266-9.

Siurein S A. Effects of essential oil on lipid peroxidation and lipid metabolism in patients with chronic bronchitis]. Klin Med (Mosk). 1997;75 (10):43-5.

Socci DJ, et al, Chronic antioxidant treatment improves the cognitive performance in aged rats. Brain Research 693, (1995) 88-94.

Srivastava KC. "Antiplatelet principles from a food spice clove." Prostaglandins Leukot Essent Fatty Acids. 1993;48(5):363-72.

Steinman, David and Samuel S. Epstein. "The Safe Shopper's Bible: A Consumer's Guide to Nontoxic Household Products, Cosmetics, and Food" MacMillan, New York, NY (1995)

Steinmetz et. al.,Transmission and scanning electronmicroscopy study of the action of sage and rosemary essential oils and eucalyptol on Candida albicans. Mycoses. 1988 Jan;31(1):40-51.

Stubbs CD & Smith AD, The modification of mammalian membrane polyunsturated fatty acid composition in relation to membrane fluidity and function. Biochimica et Biophysica Acta 779, (1984)89-137.

Sukumaran K, et al. "Inhibition of tumour promotion in mice by eugenol." Indian J Physiol Pharmacol. 1994;38(4):306-8.

Syed TA, et al. "Treatment of toenail onychomycosis with 2% butenafine and 5% Melaleuca alternifolia (tea tree) oil in cream." Trop Med Int Health. 1999;4(4):284-7.

Sysoev NP. "The effect of waxes from essential-oil plants on the dehydrogenase activity of the blood neutrophils in mucosal trauma of the mouth." Stomatologiia 1991;70(1):12-3.

Takacsova M, et al. "Study of the antioxidative effects of thyme, sage, juniper and oregano." Nahrung. 1995;39(3):241-3.

Tantaoui-Elaraki A, et al. "Inhibition of growth and aflatoxin production in Aspergillus parasiticus by essential oils of selected plant materials." J Environ Pathol Toxicol Oncol. 1994;13(1):67-72.

Terpstra AH, Lapre JA, de Vries HT, Beynen AC.The hypocholesterolemic effect of lemon peels, lemon pectin, and the waste stream material of lemon peels in hybrid F1B hamsters. Eur J Nutr. 2002 Feb;41(1):19-26.

The Bible. King James Version. Books from Old and New Testament.

Tisserand, R. and T. Balacs Essential Oil Safety, Churchill Livingstone, New York, NY (1996).

Tiwari BK, et al. "Evaluation of insecticidal, fumigant and repellent properties of lemongrass oil." Indian J Exp Biol. 1966;4(2):128-9.

Tovey ER, et al. "A simple washing procedure with eucalyptus oil for controlling house dust mites and their allergens in clothing and bedding." J Allergy Clin Immunol. 1997; 100(4):464-6.

Tyler, V. E. Herbs of Choice Pharmaceutical Products Press, Binghamton, NY (1994).

Tyler, V. E. The Honest Herbal, Lubrect & Cramer, Ltd., Port Jervis, NY (1995).

Ulmer et. al., [Chronic obstructive bronchitis. Effect of Gelomyrtol forte in a placebo-controlled double-blind study]. Fortschr Med. 1991 Sep 20;109(27):547-50.

Unnikrishnan MC, et al. "Tumour reducing and anticarcinogenic activity of selected spices." Cancer Lett. 1990;51(1):85-9.

Valnet, Jean. Robert Tisserand, ed. "The Practice of Aromatherapy." Healing Arts Press, Rochester, VT (1990).

Veal L. The potential effectiveness of essential oils as a treatment for headlice, Pediculus humanus capitis. Complement Ther Nurs Midwifery. 1996 Aug;2(4):97-101.

Vernet-Maury E, et al. "Basic emotions induced by odorants: a new approach based on autonomic pattern results." J Auton Nerv Syst. 1999;75 (2-3): 176-83.

Visser SA. Some biological effects of humic acids in the rat. Acta Biol Med Ger. 1973;31(4):569-81.

Visser SA. Effect of humic substances on mitochondrial respiration and oxidative phosphorylation. Sci Total Environ. 1987 Apr;62:347-54.

Wagner J, et al. "Beyond benzodiazepines: alternative pharmacologic agents for the treatment of insomnia." Ann Pharmacother. 1998;32(6):680-91.

Wahnon R, et al, Age and membrane fluidity. Mechanisms of Aging and Development 50, (1989) 249-255.

Wan J, et al. "The effect of essential oils of basil on the growth of Aeromonas hydrophila and Pseudomonas fluorescens." J Appl Microbiol. 1998;84(2):152-8.

Wang, L.G., et al. "Determination of DNA topoisomerase II activity from L1210 cells--a target for screening antitumor agents." Chung Kuo Yao Li Hsueh Pao. 1991;12(2):108-14.

Wattenberg L.W. et. al. Inhibitory effects of 5-(2-pyrazinyl)-4-methyl-1,2-dithiol-3-thione (Oltipraz) on carcinogenesis induced by benzo[a]pyrene, diethylnitrosamine and uracil mustard. Carcinogenesis. 1986 Aug;7(8):1379-81.

Weyers W, et al. "Skin absorption of volatile oils. Pharmacokinetics." Pharm Unserer Zeit. 1989; 18(3):82-6.

Wie MB, et al. "Eugenol protects neuronal cells from excitotoxic and oxidative injury in primary cortical cultures." Neurosci Lett. 1997: 4;225(2):93-6.

Yamada K, et al. "Anticonvulsive effects of inhaling lavender oil vapour." Biol Pharm Bull. 1994;17(2):359-60.

Yamamoto N, et al, Effects of dietary alpha-linolenate/linolenate balance of brain lipid composition and learning ability of rats. Journal of Lipid Research 28, (1987) 144-151.

Yamasaki K, et al. "Anti-HIV-1 activity of herbs in Labiatae." Biol Pharm Bull. 1998;21(8):829-33.

Yang, K.K. et al., "Antiemetic principles of Pogostemon cablin (Blanco) Benth." Phytomedicine 1999, 6(2): 89-93.

Youdim KA, et al. "Beneficial effects of thyme oil on age-related changes in the phospholipid C20 and C22 polyunsaturated fatty acid composition of various rat tissues." Biochim Biophys Acta. 1999;1438(1): 140-6.

Yokota H, et al., Suppressed mutagenicity of benzo[a]pyrene by the liver S9 fraction and microsomes from eugenol-treated rats. Mutat Res. 1986 Dec;172(3):231-6.

Youdim KA, Deans SG et al., Beneficial effects of thyme oil on age-related changes in the phospholipid C20 and C22 polyunsaturated fatty acid composition of various rat tissues. Biochim Biophys Acta. 1999 Apr 19;1438(1):140-6.

Youdim KA, Deans SG., Dietary supplementation of thyme (Thymus vulgaris L.) essential oil during the lifetime of the rat: its effects on the antioxidant status in liver, kidney and heart tissues. Mech Aging Dev. 1999 Sep 8;109(3):163-75.

Youdim KA, et al., Effect of thyme oil and thymol dietary supplementation on the antioxidant status and fatty acid composition of the aging rat brain. Br J Nutr. 2000 Jan;83(1):87-93.

Young, D. Gary. An Introduction to Young Living Essential Oils. Payson, UT, 2001.

Young, Robert O. Sick and Tired. Alpine, UT, 1977.

Yousef, R.T. and G.G. Tawil. "Antimicrobial activity of volatile oils." Pharmazie 1980; 35(11);798-701

Zanker KS, et al. "Evaluation of surfactant-like effects of commonly used remedies for colds." Respiration. 1980;39(3):150-7.

Zheng GQ, et al. Sesquiterpenes from clove (Eugenia caryophyllata) as potential anticarcinogenic agents. J Nat Prod. 1992 Jul;55(7):999-1003.

Clary sage

AFNOR/ISO European and World Standards for
Salvia sclarea
Gas Chromatograph profile 4.10

CONSTITUENTS	Traditional	Crushed Green
Linalyl acetate		
min %	62	56
max %	78	70.5
Linalol		
min %	6.5	13
max %	13.5	24
Sclareol		
min %	.4	.4
max %	2.6	2.6
δ-germacrene		
min %	1.5	1.2
max %	12	7.5
α-terpineol		
min %	traces	1
max %	1.2	5

Clove

AFNOR/ISO Standards for
Syzygium aromaticum
Gas Chromatograph profile 4.8

CONSTITUENTS	Min %	Max %
Eugenol	80	92
B-caryophyllene	4	17
Eugenyl acetate	.2	4

Basil

AFNOR/ISO Standards for
Basilicum ocimum
Gas Chromatograph profile 4.8

CONSTITUENTS	Min %	Max %
Methyl chavicol	75	85
1,8 cineol	1	3.5
Trans-beta ocimene	.9	2.8
Linalol	.50	.30
Methyl eugenol	.3	2.5
Terpinen-4-ol	.20	.60
Camphor	.15	.50

Cypress

AFNOR/ISO Standards for
Cupressus sempervirens
Gas Chromatograph profile 4.11

CONSTITUENTS	Min %	Max %
α-pinene	40	65
δ-3-carene	12	25
limonene	1.8	5
α-Terpenyl acetate	1	4
Myrcene	1	3.5
Cedrol	.8	7
β-pinene	.5	3
D-germacrene	.5	3
Terpinen-4-ol	.2	2

Lavender

AFNOR/ISO Standards for

Lavandula angustifolia

Gas Chromatograph profile 4.10

CONSTITUENTS	Min %	Max %
Linalol	25	38
Linalyl acetate	25	45
cis-β-ocimene	4	10
trans-β-ocimene	1.5	6
terpinen-4-ol	2	6
Lavendulyl acetate	2	—
Lavendulol	.3	—
β-phellandrene	traces	.5
α-terpineol	—	1
Octanone-3	traces	2
Camphor	traces	.5
Limonene	—	.5
1,8 cineole	—	1

Roman chamomile

AFNOR/ISO Standards for

Chamaemelum nobilis

Gas Chromatograph profile 4.10

CONSTITUENTS	Min %	Max %
Isobutyl angelate + Isoamyl methacrylate	30	45
Isoamyl angelate	12	22
Methyl allyl angelate	6	10
2-methyl butyl angelate	3	7
Isoamyl isobutyrate	3	5
Trans-pino-carveol	2	5
Isobutyl n-butyrate	2	9
α-pinene	1.5	5
Pinocarvone	1.3	4
Isobutyl methacrylate	1	3
2-methyl butyl methacrylate	.5	1.5

Eucalyptus globulus

AFNOR/ISO European and World Standards for

Eucalyptus globulus

Gas Chromatograph profile 4.11

CONSTITUENTS	Pure Essential Oil crushed raw	Pure Essential Oil traditional	Rectified Essential Oil 70%-75%	Rectified Essential Oil 80%-85%
1,8 cineol				
min %	48	58	70	80
α-Pinene				
min %	10	20	Traces	Traces
max %	20	22	20	12
Aromadendrene				
min %	6	1	—	—
max %	10	5	traces	traces
Limonene				
min %	2	1	2	2
max %	4	8	15	15
p-cymene				
min %	1	1	1	1
max %	3	5	6	10
trans-pinocarveol				
min %	1	1	traces	traces
max %	4	5	10	6
Globulol				
min %	.5	.5	—	—
max %	2.5	1.5	traces	traces

pH measures below +7.0 are considered acidic; those above +7.0 are considered alkaline. The determination of whether a food is acid or alkaline is not gauged by its pH, but the pH of its residues or metabolites.

Alfalfa Grass	+29.3	Cantaloupe	-2.5	Fructose	-9.5
Almond	+3.6	Caraway	+2.3	Garlic	+13.2
Apricot	-9.5	Carrot	+9.5	Gooseberry, Ripe	-7.7
Artichokes	+1.3	Cashews	-9.3	Grapefruit	-1.7
Asparagus	+1.1	Cauliflower	+3.1	Grapes, Ripe	-7.6
Avocado (protein)	+15.6	Cayenne Pepper	+18.8	Hazelnut	-2.0
Banana, Ripe	-10.1	Celery	+13.3	Honey	-7.6
Banana, Unripe	+4.8	Cheese, Hard	-18.1	Horseradish	+6.8
Barley Grass	+28.7	Cherry, Sour	+3.5	Juice, natural fruit	-8.7
Barley malt syrup	-9.3	Cherry, Sweet	-3.6	Juice, white sugar	
Beans, French cut	+11.2	Chia, sprouted	+28.5	sweetened fruit	-33.4
Beans, Lima	+12.0	Chicken	-18.0 to -22.0	Kamut Grass	+27.6
Beans, White	+12.1	Chives	+8.3	Ketchup	-12.4
Beef	-34.5	Coconut, fresh	+0.5	Kohlrabi	+5.1
Beer	-26.8	Coffee	-25.1	Lecithin, pure (soy)	+38.0
Beet sugar	-15.1	Comfrey	+1.5	Leeks (bulbs)	+7.2
Beet, fresh red	+11.3	Corn oil	-6.5	Lemon, fresh	+9.9
Biscuit, White	-6.5	Cranberry	-7.0	Lentils	+0.6
Blueberry	-5.3	Cream	-3.9	Lettuce	+2.2
Borage	+3.2	Cucumber, fresh	+31.5	Lettuce, Fresh cabbage	+14.1
Brazil Nuts	-0.5	Cumin	+1.1	Lettuce, Lamb's	+4.8
Bread, Rye	-2.5	Currant	-8.2	Limes	+8.2
Bread, White	-10.0	Currant, Black	-6.1	Liquor	-28.6 to -38.7
Bread, whole-grain	-4.5	Currant, Red	-2.4	Liver	-3.0
Bread, whole-meal	-6.5	Dandelion	+22.7	Macadamia Nuts	-11.7
Brussels Sprouts	-1.5	Date	-4.7	Mandarin Orange	-11.5
Buckwheat groats	+0.5	Dog grass	+22.6	Mango	-8.7
Butter	-3.9	Eggs	-18.0 to -22.0	Margarine	-7.5
Buttermilk	+1.3	Endive, fresh	+14.5	Marine Lipids	+4.7
Cabbage, Green,		Fennel	+1.3	Mayonnaise	-12.5
December harvest	+4.0	Fig juice powder	-2.4	Meats, Organ	-3.0
Cabbage, Green,		Filbert	-2.0	Milk sugar	-9.4
March harvest	+2.0	Fish, Fresh Water	-11.8	Milk, Homogenized	-1.0
Cabbage, Red	+6.3	Fish, Ocean	-20.0	Millet	+0.5
Cabbage, Savoy	+4.5	Flax seed oil	-1.3	Molasses	-14.6
Cabbage, White	+3.3	Flax seed	+3.5	Mustard	-19.2

Nut soy (Soaked, then air dried)	+26.5	Red radish	+16.7	Sunflower Seeds	-5.4
		Rhubarb stalks	+6.3	Sweeteners, artificial	-26.5
Olive Oil	+1.0	Rice syrup, brown	-8.7	Tangerine	-8.5
Onion	+3.0	Rice, brown	-12.5	Tea (Black)	-27.1
Orange	-9.2	Rose Hips	-15.5	Tofu	+3.2
Oysters	-5.0	Rutabaga	+3.1	Tomato	+13.6
Papaya	-9.4	Sesame seeds	+.5	Turbinado	-9.5
Peach	-9.7	Shave grass	+21.7	Turnip	+8.0
Peanuts	-12.8	Sorrel	+11.5	Veal	-35.0
Pear	-9.9	Soy beans, (cooked, then ground)	+12.8	Walnuts	-8.0
Peas, fresh	+5.1			Watercress	+7.7
Peas, ripe	+0.5	Soy Flour	+2.5	Watermelon	-1.0
Pineapple	-12.6	Soy Sprouts	+29.5	Wheat Germ	-11.4
Pistachios	-16.6	Soybeans, fresh	+12.0	Wheat Grass	+33.8
Plum, Italian	-4.9	Spelt	+0.5	Wheat	-10.1
Plum, yellow	-4.9	Spinach (other than March)	+13.1	Wine	-16.4
Pork	-38.0			Zucchini	+5.7
Potatoes, stored	+2.0	Spinach, March harvest	+8.0		
Primrose	+4.1	Straw grass	+21.4		
Pumpkin	-5.6	Strawberry	-5.4		
Quark	-17.3	Sugar cane juice, dried (Sucanat)	-9.6		
Radish, Sprouted	+28.4				
Radish, Summer black	+39.4	Sugar Cane, Refined (white)	-17.6		
Radish, White (spring)	+3.1				
Raspberry	-5.1	Sunflower Oil	-6.7		

Reference:
Young, Robert O. *Sick and Tired.*
Alpine, UT, 1977.

Essential Oils Certified as GRAS or Food Additives by the FDA

Anise	**GRAS**	**FA**		Juniper	**GRAS**	**FA**		Tarragon	**GRAS**	**FA**	
Angelica	**GRAS**	**FA**		Laurus nobille	**GRAS**	**FA**		Thyme	**GRAS**	**FA**	
Basil	**GRAS**	**FA**		Lavender	**GRAS**	**FA**		Tsuga	**GRAS**	**FA**	**FL**
Bergamot	**GRAS**	**FA**		Lavindin	**GRAS**	**FA**		Valerian	**GRAS**	**FA**	**FL**
Cajeput		**FA**		Lemon	**GRAS**	**FA**		Vetiver	**GRAS**	**FA**	
Cardamom		**FA**		Lemongrass	**GRAS**	**FA**		Wintergreen		**FA**	
Carrot Seed		**FA**		Lime	**GRAS**	**FA**		Yarrow		**FA**	
Cassia	**GRAS**	**FA**		Mandarin	**GRAS**	**FA**		Ylang ylang	**GRAS**	**FA**	
Cedarwood		**FA**		Marjoram	**GRAS**	**FA**					
Celery Seed	**GRAS**	**FA**		Melaleuca alternifolia		**FA**		**Blends**			
Chamomile, Roman	**GRAS**	**FA**		Mountain Savory		**FA**		Abundance	**GRAS**		
Chamomile, German	**GRAS**	**FA**		Melissa	**GRAS**	**FA**		Believe		**FA**	
Cinnamon bark & leaf	**GRAS**	**FA**		Myrrh	**GRAS**	**FA**	**FL**	Citrus Fresh	**GRAS**		
Cistus		**FA**		Myrtle	**GRAS**	**FA**		Christmas Spirit	**GRAS**		
Citronella	**GRAS**	**FA**		Neroli	**GRAS**	**FA**		Di-Gize	**GRAS**		
Citrus rinds	**GRAS**	**FA**		Nutmeg	**GRAS**	**FA**		EndoFlex	**GRAS**		
Clary Sage	**GRAS**	**FA**		Onycha (Styrax benzoin)	**GRAS**	**FA**		Gratitude		**FA**	
Clove	**GRAS**	**FA**		Orange	**GRAS**	**FA**		Joy	**GRAS**		
Copaiba	**GRAS**	**FA**		Oregano	**GRAS**	**FA**		Juva Cleanse	**GRAS**		
Coriander	**GRAS**	**FA**		Palmarosa	**GRAS**	**FA**		Juva Flex	**GRAS**		
Cumin	**GRAS**	**FA**		Patchouli	**GRAS**	**FA**	**FL**	Longevity	**GRAS**		
Dill	**GRAS**	**FA**		Pepper	**GRAS**	**FA**		Thieves	**GRAS**		
Eucalyptus globulus	**GRAS**	**FA**	**FL**	Peppermint	**GRAS**	**FA**		M-Grain	**GRAS**		
Elemi	**GRAS**	**FA**	**FL**	Petitgrain	**GRAS**	**FA**		Purification	**GRAS**		
Fennel	**GRAS**	**FA**		Pine	**GRAS**	**FA**	**FL**	Relieve It	**GRAS**		
Fir, Balsam		**FA**		Rosemary Cineol	**GRAS**	**FA**		Sacred Mountain	**GRAS**		
Frankincense	**GRAS**	**FA**	**FL**	Rose	**GRAS**	**FA**		White Angelica	**GRAS**		
Galbanum	**GRAS**	**FA**	**FL**	Rosewood		**FA**					
Geranium	**GRAS**	**FA**		Savory	**GRAS**	**FA**					
Ginger	**GRAS**	**FA**		Sage	**GRAS**	**FA**					
Goldenrod	**GRAS**			Sandalwood	**GRAS**	**FA**	**FL**				
Grapefruit	**GRAS**	**FA**		Spearmint	**GRAS**	**FA**					
Helichrysum	**GRAS**	**FA**		Spikenard		**FA**					
Hyssop	**GRAS**	**FA**		Spruce	**GRAS**	**FA**	**FL**				
Jasmine	**GRAS**	**FA**		Tangerine	**GRAS**	**FA**					

CODE:

FA	FDA-approved food additive
FL	Flavoring agent
GRAS	Generally regarded as safe

APPENDIX D
Bible References

Cedarwood

Leviticus 14:51—"And he shall take the cedar wood, and the hyssop, and the scarlet, and the living bird, and dip them in the blood of the slain bird, and in the running water, and sprinkle the house seven times:"

Leviticus 14:52—"And he shall cleanse the house with the blood of the bird, and with the running water, and with the living bird, and with the cedar wood, and with the hyssop, and with the scarlet."

Numbers 19:6—"And the priest shall take cedar wood, and hyssop, and scarlet, and cast [it] into the midst of the burning of the heifer."

Numbers 24:6—"As the valleys are they spread forth, as gardens by the river's side, as the trees of lign aloes which the Lord hath planted, [and] as cedar trees beside the waters."

2 Samuel 5:11—"And Hiram king of Tyre sent messengers to David, and cedar trees, and carpenters, and masons: and they built David an house."

2 Samuel 7:2—"That the king said unto Nathan the prophet, See now, I dwell in an house of cedar, but the ark of God dwelleth within curtains."

2 Samuel 7:7—"In all [the places] wherein I have walked with all the children of Israel spake I a word with any of the tribes of Israel, whom I commanded to feed my people Israel, saying, Why build ye not me an house of cedar?"

1 Kings 4:33—"And he spake of trees, from the cedar tree that [is] in Lebanon even unto the hyssop that springeth out of the wall: he spake also of beasts, and of fowl, and of creeping things, and of fishes."

1 Kings 5:6—"Now therefore command thou that they hew me cedar trees out of Lebanon; and my servants shall be with thy servants: and unto thee will I give hire for thy servants according to all that thou shalt appoint: for thou knowest that [there is] not among us any that can skill to hew timber like unto the Sidonians."

1 Kings 5:8—"And Hiram sent to Solomon, saying, I have considered the things which thou sentest to me for: [and] I will do all thy desire concerning timber of cedar, and concerning timber of fir."

1 Kings 5:10—"So Hiram gave Solomon cedar trees and fir trees [according to] all his desire."

1 Kings 6:9—"So he built the house, and finished it; and covered the house with beams and boards of cedar."

1 Kings 9:11—"([Now] Hiram the king of Tyre had furnished Solomon with cedar trees and fir trees, and with gold, according to all his desire,) that then king Solomon gave Hiram twenty cities in the land of Galilee."

2 Kings 19:23—"By thy messengers thou hast reproached the Lord, and hast said, With the multitude of my chariots I am come up to the height of the mountains, to the sides of Lebanon, and will cut down the tall cedar trees thereof, [and] the choice fir trees thereof: and I will enter into the lodgings of his borders, [and into] the forest of his Carmel."

1 Chronicles 22:4—"Also cedar trees in abundance: for the Zidonians and they of Tyre brought much cedar wood to David."

2 Chronicles 1:15—"And the king made silver and gold at Jerusalem [as plenteous] as stones, and cedar trees made he as the sycomore trees that [are] in the vale for abundance."

2 Chronicles 2:8—"Send me also cedar trees, fir trees, and algum trees, out of Lebanon: for I know that thy servants can skill to cut timber in Lebanon; and behold, my servants [shall be] with thy servants,"

2 Chronicles 9:27—"And the king made silver in Jerusalem as stones, and cedar trees made he as the sycomore trees that [are] in the low plains in abundance."

Ezra 3:7—"They gave money also unto the masons, and to the carpenters; and meat, and drink, and oil, unto them of Zidon, and to them of Tyre, to bring cedar trees from Lebanon to the sea of Joppa, according to the grant that they had of Cyrus king of Persia."

Isaiah 41:19—"I will plant in the wilderness the cedar, the shittah tree, and the myrtle, and the oil tree; I will set in the desert the fir tree, [and] the pine, and the box tree together:"

Ezekiel 17:3—"And say, Thus saith the Lord God; A great eagle with great wings, longwinged, full of feathers, which had divers colours, came unto Lebanon, and took the highest branch of the cedar:"

Ezekiel 17:22—"Thus saith the Lord God; I will also take of the highest branch of the high cedar, and will set [it]; I will crop off from the top of his young twigs a tender one, and will plant [it] upon an high mountain and eminent:"

Ezekiel 17:23—"In the mountain of the height of Israel will I plant it: and it shall bring forth boughs, and bear fruit, and be a goodly cedar: and under it shall dwell all fowl of every wing; in the shadow of the branches thereof shall they dwell."

Zechariah 11:2—"Howl, fir tree; for the cedar is fallen; because the mighty are spoiled: howl, O ye oaks of Bashan; for the forest of the vintage is come down."

Cinnamon

Revelation 18:13—"And cinnamon, and odours, and ointments, and frankincense, and wine, and oil, and fine flour, and wheat, and beasts, and sheep, and horses, and chariots, and slaves, and souls of men."

Fir

1 Kings 6:15—"And he built the walls of the house within with boards of cedar, both the floor of the house, and the walls of the ceiling: [and] he covered [them] on the inside with wood, and covered the floor of the house with planks of fir."

1 Kings 6:34—"And the two doors [were of] fir tree: the two leaves of the one door [were] folding, and the two leaves of the other door [were] folding."

1 Kings 9:11—"([Now] Hiram the king of Tyre had furnished Solomon with cedar trees and fir trees, and with gold, according to all his desire,) that then king Solomon gave Hiram twenty cities in the land of Galilee."

2 Kings 19:23—"By thy messengers thou hast reproached the Lord, and hast said, With the multitude of my chariots I am come up to the height of the mountains, to the sides of Lebanon, and will cut down the tall cedar trees thereof, [and] the choice fir trees thereof: and I will enter into the lodgings of his borders, [and into] the forest of his Carmel."

2 Chronicles 2:8—"Send me also cedar trees, fir trees, and algum trees, out of Lebanon: for I know that thy servants can skill to cut timber in Lebanon; and, behold, my servants [shall be] with thy servants."

2 Chronicles 3:5—"And the greater house he cieled with fir tree, which he overlaid with fine gold, and set thereon palm trees and chains."

Psalms 104:17—"Where the birds make their nests: [as for] the stork, the fir trees [are] her house."

Song Of Solomon 1:17—"The beams of our house [are] cedar, [and] our rafters of fir."

Isaiah 14:8—"Yea, the fir trees rejoice at thee, [and] the cedars of Lebanon, [saying], Since thou art laid down, no feller is come up against us."

Isaiah 37:24—"By thy servants hast thou reproached the Lord, and hast said, By the multitude of my chariots am I come up to the height of the mountains, to the sides of Lebanon; and I will cut down the tall cedars thereof, [and] the choice fir trees thereof: and I will enter into the height of his border, [and] the forest of his Carmel."

Isaiah 41:19—"I will plant in the wilderness the cedar, the shittah tree, and the myrtle, and the oil tree; I will set in the desert the fir tree, [and] the pine, and the box tree together:"

Isaiah 55:13—"Instead of the thorn shall come up the fir tree, and instead of the brier shall come up the myrtle tree: and it shall be to the Lord for a name, for an everlasting sign [that] shall not be cut off."

Isaiah 60:13—"The glory of Lebanon shall come unto thee, the fir tree, the pine tree, and the box together, to beautify the place of my sanctuary; and I will make the place of my feet glorious."

Ezekiel 27:5—"They have made all thy [ship] boards of fir trees of Senir: they have taken cedars from Lebanon to make masts for thee."

Ezekiel 31:8—"The cedars in the garden of God could not hide him: the fir trees were not like his boughs, and the chestnut trees were not like his branches; nor any tree in the garden of God was like unto him in his beauty."

Hosea 14:8—"Ephraim [shall say], What have I to do any more with idols? I have heard [him], and observed him: I [am] like a green fir tree. From me is thy fruit found."

Nahum 2:3—"The shield of his mighty men is made red, the valiant men [are] in scarlet: the chariots [shall be] with flaming torches in the day of his preparation, and the fir trees shall be terribly shaken."

Zechariah 11:2—"Howl, fir tree; for the cedar is fallen; because the mighty are spoiled: howl, O ye oaks of Bashan; for the forest of the vintage is come down."

Frankincense

Leviticus 2:15—"And thou shalt put oil upon it, and lay frankincense thereon: it [is] a meat offering."

Leviticus 2:16—"And the priest shall burn the memorial of it, [part] of the beaten corn thereof, and [part] of the oil thereof, with all the frankincense thereof: [it is] an offering made by fire unto the Lord."

Leviticus 5:11—"But if he be not able to bring two turtledoves, or two young pigeons, then he that sinned shall bring for his offering the tenth part of an ephah of fine flour for a sin offering; he shall put no oil upon it, neither shall he put [any] frankincense thereon: for it [is] a sin offering"

Leviticus 6:15—"And he shall take of it his handful, of the flour of the meat offering, and of the oil thereof, and all the frankincense which [is] upon the meat offering, and shall burn [it] upon the altar [for] a sweet savour, [even] the memorial of it, unto the Lord."

Leviticus 24:7—"And thou shalt put pure frankincense upon [each] row, that it may be on the bread for a memorial, [even] an offering made by fire unto the Lord."

Numbers 5:15—"Then shall the man bring his wife unto the priest, and he shall bring her offering for her, the tenth [part] of an ephah of barley meal; he shall pour no oil upon it, nor put frankincense thereon; for it [is] an offering of jealousy, an offering of memorial, bringing iniquity to remembrance."

1 Chronicles 9:29—"[Some] of them also [were] appointed to oversee the vessels, and all the instruments of the sanctuary, and the fine flour, and the wine, and the oil, and the frankincense, and the spices."

Nehemiah 13:5—"And he had prepared for him a great chamber, where aforetime they laid the meat offerings, the frankincense, and the vessels, and the tithes of the corn, the new wine, and the oil, which was commanded [to be given] to the Levites, and the singers, and the porters; and the offerings of the priests."

Nehemiah 13:9—"Then I commanded, and they cleansed the chambers: and thither brought I again the vessels of the house of God, with the meat offering and the frankincense."

Song Of Solomon 3:6—"Who [is] this that cometh out of the wilderness like pillars of smoke, perfumed with myrrh and frankincense, with all powders of the merchant?"

Song Of Solomon 4:6—"Until the day break, and the shadows flee away, I will get me to the mountain of myrrh, and to the hill of frankincense."

Song Of Solomon 4:14—"Spikenard and saffron; calamus and cinnamon, with all trees of frankincense; myrrh and aloes, with all the chief spices:"

Matthew 2:11—"And when they were come into the house, they saw the young child with Mary his mother, and fell down, and worshiped him: and when they had opened their treasures, they presented unto him gifts; gold, and frankincense, and myrrh."

Revelation 18:13—"And cinnamon, and odours, and ointments, and frankincense, and wine, and oil, and fine flour, and wheat, and beasts, and sheep, and horses, and chariots, and slaves, and souls of men."

Hyssop

Leviticus 14:49—"And he shall take to cleanse the house two birds, and cedar wood, and scarlet, and hyssop:"

Leviticus 14:51—"And he shall take the cedar wood, and the hyssop, and the scarlet, and the living bird, and dip them in the blood of the slain bird, and in the running water, and sprinkle the house seven times:"

Leviticus 14:52—"And he shall cleanse the house with the blood of the bird, and with the running water, and with the living bird, and with the cedar wood, and with the hyssop, and with the scarlet:"

Numbers 19:6—"And the priest shall take cedar wood, and hyssop, and scarlet, and cast [it] into the midst of the burning of the heifer."

Numbers 19:18—"And a clean person shall take hyssop, and dip [it] in the water, and sprinkle [it] upon the tent, and upon all the vessels, and upon the persons that were there, and upon him that touched a bone, or one slain, or one dead, or a grave:"

1 Kings 4:33—"And he spake of trees, from the cedar tree that [is] in Lebanon even unto the hyssop that springeth out of the wall: he spake also of beasts, and of fowl, and of creeping things, and of fishes."

Psalms 51:7—"Purge me with hyssop, and I shall be clean: wash me, and I shall be whiter than snow."

John 19:29—"Now there was set a vessel full of vinegar: and they filled a spunge with vinegar, and put [it] upon hyssop, and put [it] to his mouth."

Hebrews 9:19—"For when Moses had spoken every precept to all the people according to the law, he took the blood of calves and of goats, with water, and scarlet wool, and hyssop, and sprinkled both the book, and all the people."

Myrrh

Esther 2:12—"Now when every maid's turn was come to go in to king Ahasuerus, after that she had been twelve months, according to the manner of the women, (for so were the days of their purifications accomplished, [to wit], six months with oil of myrrh, and six months with sweet odours, and with [other] things for the purifying of the women;)"

Psalms 45:8—"All thy garments [smell] of myrrh, and aloes, [and] cassia, out of the ivory palaces, whereby they have made thee glad."

Proverbs 7:17—"I have perfumed my bed with myrrh, aloes, and cinnamon."

Song Of Solomon 1:13—"A bundle of myrrh [is] my wellbeloved unto me; he shall lie all night betwixt my breasts."

Song Of Solomon 3:6—"Who [is] this that cometh out of the wilderness like pillars of smoke, perfumed with myrrh and frankincense, with all powders of the merchant?"

Song Of Solomon 4:6—"Until the day break, and the shadows flee away, I will get me to the mountain of myrrh, and to the hill of frankincense."

Song Of Solomon 4:14—"Spikenard and saffron; calamus and cinnamon, with all trees of frankincense; myrrh and aloes, with all the chief spices:"

Song Of Solomon 5:1—"I am come into my garden, my sister, [my] spouse: I have gathered my myrrh with my spice; I have eaten my honeycomb with my honey; I have drunk my wine with my milk: eat, O friends; drink, yea, drink abundantly, O beloved."

Song Of Solomon 5:5—"I rose up to open to my beloved; and my hands dropped [with] myrrh, and my fingers [with] sweet smelling myrrh, upon the handles of the lock."

Song Of Solomon 5:13—"His cheeks [are] as a bed of spices, [as] sweet flowers: his lips [like] lilies, dropping sweet smelling myrrh."

Matthew 2:11—"And when they were come into the house, they saw the young child with Mary his mother, and fell down, and worshiped him: and when they had opened their treasures, they presented unto him gifts; gold, and frankincense, and myrrh."

Mark 15:23—"And they gave him to drink wine mingled with myrrh: but he received [it] not."

John 19:39—"And there came also Nicodemus, which at the first came to Jesus by night, and brought a mixture of myrrh and aloes, about an hundred pound [weight]."

Myrtle

Zechariah 1:8—"I saw by night, and behold a man riding upon a red horse, and he stood among the myrtle trees that [were] in the bottom; and behind him [were there] red horses, speckled, and white."

Zechariah 1:10—"And the man that stood among the myrtle trees answered and said, These [are they] whom the Lord hath sent to walk to and fro through the earth."

Zechariah 1:11—"And they answered the angel of the Lord that stood among the myrtle trees, and said, We have walked to and fro through the earth, and, behold, all the earth sitteth still, and is at rest."

Spikenard

Song of Solomon 4:14—"Spikenard and saffron; calamus and cinnamon, with all trees of frankincense, myrrh and aloes, with all chief spices."

Mark 14:3—"And being in Bethany in the house of Simon the leper, as he sat at meat, there came a woman having an alabaster box of ointment of spikenard very precious; and she brake the box, and poured [it] on his head."

John 12:3—"Then took Mary a pound of ointment of spikenard, very costly, and anointed the feet of Jesus, and wiped his feet with her hair: and the house was filled with the odour of the ointment."

APPENDIX E
Essential Oil Application Codes

Application Codes

NEAT = straight, undiluted
Dilution usually NOT required; suitable for all but the most sensitive skin. Safe for children over 2 years old.

PHOTO = Photosensitizing
Avoid using on skin exposed to direct sunlight or UV rays (i.e. sunlamps, tanning beds, etc.)

50-50 = Dilute 50-50
Dilution recommended at 50-50 (1 part essential oils to 1 part vegetable or massage oil) for topical and internal use, especially when used on sensitive areas — face, neck, genital area, underarms, etc. Keep out of reach of children.

20-80 = Dilute 20-80
Always dilute 20-80 (1 part essential oils to 4 parts vegetable or massage oil) before applying to the skin or taking internally. Keep out of reach of children.

Single Oils

Angelica . . . . PHOTO 50-50
Anise 50-50
Basil 50-50
Bergamot . . . . PHOTO 50-50
Benzoin 50-50
Cajeput 50-50
Cedar, Western Red 50-50
Cardemom 50-50
Carrot Seed . . . . NEAT
Cassia 20-80
Celery Seed . . . . NEAT
Cedarwood . . . . NEAT
Chamomile, German . . . . . PHOTO . . . . NEAT
Chamomile, Roman . . . . NEAT
Cinnamon Bark 20-80
Cistus . . . . NEAT
Citronella 50-50
Citrus Hystrix . . . . PHOTO 50-50
Clary Sage 50-50
Clove 20-80
Copaiba/Copal . . . . NEAT
Coriander 50-50
Cumin 50-50
Cypress 50-50
Davana . . . . NEAT
Dill 50-50
Elemi . . . . NEAT
Eucalyptus dives 50-50
Eucalyptus globulus 50-50
Eucalyptus polybractea 50-50

Eucalyptus radiata 50-50
Fennel . . . . NEAT
Fir, Douglas 50-50
Fir, Idaho Balsam 50-50
Fir, White 50-50
Fleabane 50-50
Frankincense 50-50
Galbanum . . . . NEAT
Geranium 50-50
Ginger 50-50
Goldenrod 50-50
Grapefruit . . . . PHOTO 50-50
Helichrysum 50-50
Hyssop 20-80
Jasmine . . . . NEAT
Juniper 50-50
Laurus nobilis 50-50
Lavandin 50-50
Lavender . . . . NEAT
Ledum . . . . NEAT
Lemon . . . . PHOTO 50-50
Lemongrass 20-80
Lime . . . . PHOTO 50-50
Mandarin 50-50
Manuka . . . . NEAT
Marjoram 50-50
Melaleuca ericifolia 50-50
Melissa . . . . NEAT
Mountain Savory 50-50
Myrrh . . . . NEAT

Myrtle **50-50**
Neroli . . . . **NEAT**
Niaouli **50-50**
Nutmeg **50-50**
Orange . . . . **PHOTO** **50-50**
Oregano **20-80**
Palmarosa **50-50**
Palo Santo **50-50**
Patchouli . . . . **NEAT**
Pepper, Black **50-50**
Peppermint **50-50**
Petitgrain . . . . **NEAT**
Pine **50-50**
Ravensara **50-50**
Rose . . . . **NEAT**
Rosemary CT cineol **50-50**
Rosemary CT verbenon **50-50**
Rosewood . . . . **NEAT**

Sage **50-50**
Sandalwood . . . . **NEAT**
Spearmint **50-50**
Spikenard . . . . **NEAT**
Spruce **50-50**
Tangerine . . . . **PHOTO** **50-50**
Tansy **50-50**
Tansy, Blue . . . . **NEAT**
Tarragon **50-50**
Tea Tree **50-50**
Thyme **20-80**
Tsuga **50-50**
Valerian Root . . . . **NEAT**
Vetiver . . . . **NEAT**
Wintergreen **50-50**
Yarrow . . . . **NEAT**
Ylang Ylang . . . . **NEAT**

Blends

Abundance **50-50**
Acceptance . . . . **NEAT**
Aroma Life . . . . **NEAT**
Aroma Siez **50-50**
Australian Blue . . . . **NEAT**
Awaken . . . . **NEAT**
Believe **50-50**
Brain Power . . . . **NEAT**
Breath Again Roll-on . . . . **NEAT**
Christmas Spirit **50-50**
Citrus Fresh **50-50**
Clarity . . . . **NEAT**
Deep Relief Roll-on . . . . **NEAT**
Di-Gize . . . . **NEAT**
Dragon Time . . . . **NEAT**
Dream Catcher . . . . **NEAT**
Egyptian Gold **50-50**
EndoFlex . . . . **NEAT**
En-R-Gee **50-50**
Envision . . . . **NEAT**
Evergreen Essence **50-50**
Exodus II **50-50**
Forgiveness . . . . **NEAT**
Gathering . . . . **NEAT**
Gentle Baby . . . . **NEAT**
GLF **20-80**
Gratitude **50-50**
Grounding . . . . **NEAT**
Harmony . . . . **NEAT**
Highest Potential **50-50**
Hope . . . . **NEAT**
Humility . . . . **NEAT**
ImmuPower **50-50**
Inner Child . . . . **NEAT**

Inspiration . . . . **NEAT**
Into The Future . . . . **NEAT**
Joy . . . . **PHOTO** **50-50**
Juva Cleanse . . . . **NEAT**
JuvaFlex **50-50**
Lady Sclareol **50-50**
Longevity **20-80**
Magnify Your Purpose . . . . **NEAT**
Melrose **50-50**
Mister . . . . **NEAT**
Motivation . . . . **NEAT**
M-Grain **50-50**
PanAway **50-50**
Peace & Calming . . . . **NEAT**
Present Time . . . . **NEAT**
Purification . . . . **NEAT**
Raven . . . . **NEAT**
R.C. **50-50**
Release **50-50**
Relieve It **50-50**
RutaVaLa . . . . **PHOTO** **50-50**
Sacred Mountain . . . . **NEAT**
SARA . . . . **NEAT**
SclarEssence **50-50**
Sensation . . . . **NEAT**
Surrender . . . . **NEAT**
Thieves **20-80**
3 Wise Men . . . . **NEAT**
Tranquil Roll-on . . . . **NEAT**
Transformation . . . . **PHOTO** **50-50**
Trauma Life . . . . **NEAT**
Valor . . . . **NEAT**
Valor Roll-on . . . . **NEAT**
White Angelica . . . . **PHOTO** . . . . . **NEAT**

ORAC Research

A test recently developed by USDA researchers at Tufts University in Boston, Massachussetts, has been able to identify the highest known antioxidant foods. Known as ORAC (oxygen radical absorbance capacity), this test is the first of its kind to measure both time and degree of free-radical inhibition.

All antioxidant capacity measures are estimated by Ferric Reducing Power and are expressed as micromole Trolox equivalent (TE) per 100 grams, accurate to plus or minus 5%

Essential Oils Antioxidant Capacity

Clove	**1,078,700**
Myrrh	**379,800**
Citronella	**312,000**
Coriander	**298,300**
Fennel	**238,400**
Clary Sage	**221,000**
German Chamomile	**218,600**
Cedarwood	**169,000**
Rose	**160,400**
Nutmeg	**158,100**
Longevity (Blend)	**151,100**
Marjoram	**139,905**
Melissa	**134,300**
Ylang Ylang	**130,000**
Palmarosa	**127,755**
Rosewood	**113,200**
Manuka	**106,200**
Wintergreen	**101,800**
Geranium	**101,000**
Ginger	**99,300**
Bay Laurel	**98,900**
Eucalyptus citriodora	**83,000**
Cumin	**82,400**
Black Pepper	**79,700**
Vetiver	**74,300**
Petitgrain	**73,600**
Blue Cypress	**73,100**
Citrus hystrix	**69,200**
Douglas Fir	**69,000**

Foods Antioxidant Capacity

Ningxia Wolfberries	**30,300**
Blueberries	**2,400**
Kale	**1,770**
Noni Juice	**1,712**
Xango Juice	**1,644**
Strawberries	**1,540**
Spinach	**1,260**
Raspberries	**1,220**
Brussels sprouts	**980**
Plums	**949**
Broccoli florets	**890**
Beets	**840**
Oranges	**750**
Red Grapes	**739**
Red Bell Peppers	**710**
Cherries	**670**
Yellow corn	**400**
Eggplant	**390**
Limu Juice	**305**
Carrots	**210**

EO list continued on next page

Blue Tansy **68,800**
Goldenrod **61,900**
Melaleuca ericifolia. **61,100**
Blue Yarrow **55,900**
Spikenard **54,800**
Basil **54,000**
Patchouli **49,400**
White Fir **47,900**
Tarragon **37,900**
Cajeput **37,600**
Peppermint **37,300**
Cardamom. **36,500**
Dill **35,600**
Celery Seed. **30,300**
Fleabane (Canadian) **26,700**
Mandarin. **26,500**
Lime **26,200**
Galbanum **26,200**
Myrtle **25,400**
Cypress **24,300**
Grapefruit **22,600**
Hyssop **20,900**
Balsam Fir. **20,500**
Niaouli. **18,600**
Thyme **15,960**
Oregano. **15,300**
Cassia. **15,170**
Sage. **14,800**
Mountain Savory **11,300**
Cinnamon Bark **10,340**
Tsuga **7,100**
Valarian **6,200**
Cistus. **3,860**
Eucalyptus globulous. **2,410**
Orange **1,890**
Lemongrass **1,780**
Helichrysum. **1,740**
Ravensara **890**
Lemon **660**
Frankincense **630**
Spearmint **540**
Lavender **360**
Rosemary **330**
Juniper. **250**
Roman chamomille **240**
Sandalwood **160**

Single Oils

Angelica	111°F
Anise	>200°F
Basil	177°F
Bergamot	149°F
Buplevere	108°F
Cajeput	116°F
Calamus	194°F
Canadian Red Cedar	145°F
Cardamom	154°F
Carrot Seed	144°F
Cassia	152°F
Cedar Leaf	142°F
Cedarwood	>200°F
Chamomile, German	>200°F
Chamomile, Mixta	144°F
Chamomile, Roman	150°F
Cinnamon Bark	179°F
Cistus	114°F
Citronella	147°F
Clary Sage	190°F
Clove	>200°F
Coriander	153°F
Cumin	142°F
Cypress	103°F
Cypress, Blue	>200°F
Davana	>200°F
Dill	150°F
Elemi	114°F
Eucalyptus Citriodora	176°F
Eucalyptus Dives	149°F
Eucalyptus Globulus	114°F
Eucalyptus Polybractea	112°F
Eucalyptus Radiata	130°F
Fennel	168°F
Fir	104°F
Fir, Idaho Balsam	118°F
Fir, Douglas	103°F
Fir, White	107°F

Fleabane	118°F
Frankincense	102°F
Galbanum	104°F
Geranium	181°F
Ginger	168°F
Goldenrod	118°F
Grapefruit	133°F
Helichrysum	150°F
Hyssop	158°F
Inula	>200°F
Jasmine	>200°F
Juniper	104°F
Laurel	142°F
Lavandin	168°F
Lavender	157°F
Ledum	147°F
Lemon	109°F
Lemongrass	181°F
Lime	109°F
Mandarin	113°F
Marjoram	149°F
Melaleuca ericifolia	127°F
Melissa	189°F
Mountain Savory	170°F
Mugwort	162°F
Myrrh	>200°F
Myrtle	100°F
Niaouli (MQV)	168°F
Nutmeg	110°F
Orange	142°F
Oregano	168°F
Palmarosa	199°F
Patchouli	>200°F
Black Pepper	112°F
Peppermint	172°F
Petitgrain	150°F
Pine	103°F
Ravensara	124°F
Rose	156°F
Rosemary	116°F

Rosemary Verbanon	103°F
Rosewood	178°F
Sage	146°F
Sage Lavender	108°F
Sandalwood	>200°F
Spearmint	149°F
Spikenard	193°F
Spruce	102°F
Tamanu	>200°F
Tangerine	115°F
Tansy, Blue	137°F
Tansy, Idaho	168°F
Tarragon	148°F
Tea Tree	157°F
Thyme	162°F
Tsuga	103°F
Valerian	112°F
Vetiver	>200°F
Wintergreen	191°F
Yarrow	172°F
Ylang Ylang	>200°F

Blends

Abundance	144°F
Acceptance	66°F
Aroma Life	142°F
Aroma Siez	157°F
Australian Blue	150°F
Awaken	164°F
Believe	129°F
Brain Power	152°F
Christmas Spirit	125°F
Citrus Fresh	125°F
Clarity	156°F
Di-Gize	163°F
Dragon Time	171°F
Dream Catcher	142°F
EndoFlex	149°F
En-R-Gee	121°F
Envision	122°F
Exodus II	165°F

Forgiveness	172°F
Gathering	142°F
Gentle Baby	170°F
Gratitude	115°F
Grounding	134°F
Harmony	144°F
Highest Potential	155°F
Hope	142°F
Humility	194°F
ImmuPower	132°F
Inner Child	131°F
Inspiriation	153°F
Into The Future	152°F
Joy	146°F
Juva Cleanse	135°F
JuvaFlex	165°F
Longevity	137°F
M-Grain	159°F
Magnify Your Purpose	163°F
Melrose	137°F
Mister	155°F
Motivation	131°F
PanAway	187°F
Peace and Calming	128°F
Present Time	142°F
Purification	132°F
Raven	127°F
R.C.	119°F
Release	209°F
Relieve It	123°F
Sacred Mountain	124°F
SARA	185°F
Sensation	181°F
Surrender	131°F
Thieves	144°F
3 Wise Men	186°F
Trauma Life	133°F
Valor	143°F
White Angelica	180°F

Key Scientific Research on Essential Oils

Scientific Research List

1. "Effect of a Diffused Essential Oil Blend on Bacterial Bioaerosols"

2. "Screening for Inhibitory Activity of Essential Oils on Selected Bacteria, Fungi, and Viruses"

3. "Antibacterial Properties of Plant Essential Oils"

4. "Influence of Some Spice Essential Oils on *Aspergillus parasiticus* Growth and Production of Aflatoxins in a Synthetic Medium"

5. "Antioxidant Activity of Some Spice Essential Oils on Linoleic Acid Oxidation in Aqueous Media"

6. "Antimicrobial Activity of Some Egyptian Spice Essential Oils"

7. "Antimicrobial Properties of Spices and Their Essential Oils"

8. "The Antimicrobial Activity of Essential Oils and Essential Oil Components Towards Oral Bacteria"

9. "Anticarcinogenic Effects of the Essential Oils From Cumin, Poppy and Basil"

10. "Effects of Essential Oil on Lipid Peroxidation and Lipid Metabolism in Patients with Chronic Bronchitis"

11. "Effect of Essential Oils on the Course of Experimental Atherosclerosis"

12. "Inhibition of Growth and Aflatoxin Production in *Aspergillus parasiticus* by Essential Oils of Selected Plant Materials"

13. "Odors and Learning"

14. "Weight Reduction through Inhalation of Odorants"

15. "Anti-inflammatory Activity of *Passiflora incarnata* L. in Rats"

16. "Medroxyprogesterone Interferes with Ovarian Steroid Protection Against Coronary Vasospasm"

17. "Methyl-Sulfonyl-Methane (M.S.M.): A Double-Blind Study of Its Use in Degenerative Arthritis"

18. "Chemopreventive Effect of Perillyl Alcohol on 4-(methylnitrosamino)-1-(3-pyridyl)-1-buta-none Induced Tumorigenesis in (C3H/HeJ X A/J)F1 Mouse Lung"

19. "Chemoprevention of Colon Carcinogenesis by Dietary Perillyl Alcohol"

ABSTRACTS

1. Effect of a Diffused Essential Oil Blend on Bacterial Bioaerosols

Author: S.C. Chao, D. G. Young, and C.J. Oberg

Journal: Journal of Essential Oil Research 10, 517-523 (Sept/Oct 1998)

Location: Weber State University, Ogden, UT

Conclusion: Diffusion of the oil blend, Thieves, can significantly reduce the number of aerosol-borne bacteria.

Abstract: A proprietary blend of oils (named Thieves) containing cinnamon, rosemary, clove, eucalyptus, and lemon was tested for its antibacterial activity against airborne *Micrococcus luteus*, *Pseudomonas aeruginosa,* and *Staphylococcus aureus*. The bacteria cultures were sprayed in an enclosed area, and Thieves was diffused for a given amount of time. There was an 82 percent reduction in *M. luteus* bioaerosol, a 96 percent reduction in the *P. aeruginosa* bioaerosol, and a 44 percent reduction in the *S. aureus* bioaerosol following 10 minutes of exposure.

2. Screening for Inhibitory Activity of Essential Oils on Selected Bacteria, Fungi, and Viruses

Author: S.C. Chao, D.G. Young, and C.J. Oberg

Journal: Journal of Essential Oil Research

Location: Weber State University, Ogden, UT

Conclusion: Many essential oils were demonstrated to have antimicrobial properties.

Abstract: 45 essential oils were tested for their inhibitory effect against bacteria, yeast, molds, and two bacteriophage. Of the oils tested, all oils showed inhibition compared to controls. Cinnamon bark and tea tree essential oils showed an inhibitory effect against all the test organisms and phage. Other oils with broad ranges of inhibition included lemongrass, mountain savory, Roman chamomile, rosewood, and spearmint.

3. Antibacterial properties of plant essential oils

Author: S. G. Deans, G. Ritchie

Journal: International Journal of Food Microbiology 5, 165-180 (1987)

Location: Scotland Agricultural College

Conclusion: Many essential oils have antibacterial properties.

Abstract: Fifty plant essential oils were tested in different concentrations for antibacterial activity against 25 genera of bacteria. The ten most antibacterial oils were: angelica, bay, cinnamon, clove, thyme, almond, marjoram, pimento, geranium, and lovage.

4. Influence of Some Spice Essential Oils on Aspergillus parasiticus Growth and Production of Aflatoxins in a Synthetic Medium

Author: R. S. Farag, Z. Y. Daw, S. H. Abo-Raya

Journal: Journal of Food Science, Vol 54, No. 1, 74-76 (1989)

Location: Cairo University, Giza, Egypt

Conclusion: Essential oils of thyme, cumin, clove, caraway, rosemary, and sage all possess antifungal properties.

Abstract: The essential oils of thyme, cumin, clove, caraway, rosemary, and sage were tested for antifungal properties. The essential oils completely inhibited growth of fungal mycelium and aflatoxin production. The oils from most effective to least effective were: thyme > cumin > clove > caraway > rosemary > sage. The basic components of these oils were determined by gas-liquid chromatography to be: thyme—thymol, cumin—cumin aldehyde, clove—eugenol, caraway—carvone, rosemary—borneol, and sage—thujone.

5. Antioxidant Activity of Some Spice Essential Oils on Linoleic Acid Oxidation in Aqueous Media

Author: R. S. Farag, A.Z.M.A. Badei, F. M. Hewedi, G.S.A. El-Baroty

Journal: JAOCS, Vol. 66, No. 6 (June 1989)

Location: Cairo University, Giza, Egypt

Conclusion: Essential oils of caraway, clove, cumin, rosemary, sage, thyme possess antioxidant activity on linoleic acid oxidation.

Abstract: Essential oils of caraway, clove, cumin, rosemary, sage and thyme were examined for antioxidant activity in linoleic acid. These oils were all found to have an antioxidant effect which increased when their concentrations were increased. The effectiveness of these essential oils on linoleic acid oxidation was in the following order: caraway, sage, cumin, rosemary, thyme, clove.

6. Antimicrobial Activity of Some Egyptian Spice Essential Oils

Author: R.S. Farag, Z. Y. Daw, F. M. Hewedi, G.S.A. El-Baroty

Journal: Journal of Food Protection, Vol. 52 (September 1989)

Location: Cairo University, Giza, Egypt

Conclusion: Essential oils of sage, rosemary, caraway, cumin, clove, and thyme were shown to have antimicrobial properties.

Abstract: Essential oils of sage, rosemary, caraway, cumin, clove, and thyme were studied for their antibacterial effects. The minimum inhibitory concentration for each essential oil was also determined. Various essential oils were inhibitory at extremely low concentrations (0.25-12 mg/ml). Gram-positive bacteria were shown to be more sensitive to the essential oils than were gram-negative. Thyme and cumin oils had stronger antimicrobial activity than the other oils. The chemical structures of compounds in the essential oils were related to the antimicrobial activity.

7. Antimicrobial Properties of Spices and Their Essential Oils

Author: L. R. Beuchat

Journal: Nat. Antimicrob. Syst. Food Preserv. 167-79 (1994)

Location: University of Georgia, Griffin, Georgia

Conclusion: Many spices and herbs possess antimicrobial properties against various bacteria, yeasts, and molds.

Abstract: Many spices and herbs possess antimicrobial actions. These include plants of the genus *Allium*, such as onions and garlic; spices such as thyme, oregano, savory, sage, cinnamon, clove, vanilla, and others. Microbes inhibited by these herbs and spices include gram-positive and gram-negative bacteria, yeasts, and molds.

8. The Antimicrobial Activity of Essential Oils and Essential Oil Components Towards Oral Bacteria

Author: S. Shapiro, A. Meier, B. Guggenheim

Journal: Oral Microbiology and Immunology 1994: 202-208 (Copyright Munksgaard 1994)

Location: University of Zurich, Switzerland

Conclusion: Essential oils of tea tree, peppermint, and sage showed potent antimicrobial action against anaerobic oral activity.

Abstract: Antimicrobial activity of some essential oils on anaerobic oral bacteria was analyzed. The most potent essential oils tested were Australian tea tree oil, peppermint oil, and sage oil. Thymol and eugenol were the most potent oil components.

9. Anticarcinogenic Effects of the Essential Oils From Cumin, Poppy and Basil

Author: K. Aruna, V. M. Sivaramakrishnan

Journal: Phytotherapy Research, Vol. 10, 577-580 (1996)

Location: Cancer Institute (W.I.A.) Adyar Madras, India

Conclusion: Essential oils of cumin, poppy, and basil all possess potent anticarcinogenic properties.

Abstract: Essential oils of cumin, poppy, and basil were assessed for anticarcinogenic properties. The activity of glutathione-S-transferase, a carcinogen-detoxifying enzyme, was increased by over 78 percent in the stomach, liver, and esophagus of Swiss mice when they were treated with cumin, poppy, and basil essential oils.

10. Effects of Essential Oil on Lipid Peroxidation and Lipid Metabolism in Patients with Chronic Bronchitis

Author: S. A. Siurin

Journal: Klinicheskaia Meditsina, 75(10):43-5 (1997)

Location: Scientific Group NII of Pulmonology, Monchegorsk, Russia.

Conclusion: Lavender essential oil aids in normalizing lipid levels.

Abstract: Essential oils were tested in 150 patients with chronic bronchitis for their effects on lipid peroxidation and lipid metabolism. Essential oils of rosemary, basil, fir, eucalyptus, and lavender were found to have antioxidant effect and lavender was found to normalize lipid levels.

11. Effect of Essential Oils on the Course of Experimental Atherosclerosis

Author: V. V. Nikolaevskii, N. S. Kononova, A. I. Pertsoviskii, I.F. Shinkarchuk

Journal: Patologicheskaia Fiziologiia i Eksperimentalnaia Terapiia (5):52-3 (Sep-Oct 1990)

Conclusion: Inhalation of lavender and monarda essential oils reduces cholesterol content in the aorta of rabbits, providing an angioprotective effect.

Abstract: Lavender, monarda, and basil essential oils were tested in rabbits for their effect on atherosclerosis. When inhaled, lavender and monarda essential oils did not affect blood cholesterol content, but reduced cholesterol content in the aorta. These oils provide a heart-protective effect.

12. Inhibition of Growth and Aflatoxin Production in Aspergillus parasiticus by Essential Oils of Selected Plant Materials

Author: A. Tantaoui-Elaraki, L. Beraoud

Journal: Journal of Environmental Pathology, Toxicology and Oncology;13(1):67-72 (1994)

Location: Hassan II Institute for Agriculture and Veterinary Medicine, Rabat-Instituts, Morocco

Conclusion: Several essential oils (cinnamon, thyme, oregano, and cumin) were shown to have strong antifungal properties.

Abstract: Essential oils of cinnamon, thyme, oregano, cumin, curcumin, ginger, lemon, and orange were tested on *Aspergillus parasiticus* for antifungal properties. The most inhibitory essential oils were cinnamon, thyme, oregano, and cumin.

13. Odors and Learning

Author: A. R. Hirsch, M.D., L. H. Johnston, M.D.

Journal: J. Neurol Orthop Med Surg 17:119-126 (1996)

Location: Smell & Taste Research Foundation, Chicago, Illinois, USA

Conclusion: Pleasant odors increased performance of individuals on cognitive tasks.

Abstract: This study assessed the effects of hedonically positive odors on performance of cognitive tasks. Results indicate that normally performing subjects completed a cognitive task an average 17 percent faster on subsequent trials when a pleasing odor was present. Further studies are desirable to determine if odors would be useful in general education and education of those with learning disabilities.

14. Weight Reduction through Inhalation of Odorants

Author: A. R. Hirsch, M.D., R. Gomez

Journal: Annals of Clinical and Laboratory Science (Official Journal of the Association of Clinical Scientists) Volume 24 September-October Number 5

Location: Smell & Taste Research Foundation, Chicago, Illinois, USA

Conclusion: Use of aroma inhalers aided study volunteers in weight loss over a 6-month period.

Abstract: To measure the role of olfaction in weight loss, odorant inhalers were given to 3,193 overweight volunteers. Study participants were instructed to inhale odorants 3 times in each nostril whenever hunger occurred. Average weight loss was 2.1 percent body weight per month. These results suggest inhalation of odorants may induce sustained weight loss over a 6-month period.

15. Anti-inflammatory Activity of Passiflora incarnata L. in Rats

Author: F. Borrelli, L. Pinto, A. A. Izzo, N. Mascolo, F. Capasso, V. Mercati, E. Toja, G. Autore

Journal: Phytotherapy Research, Vol. 10, S104-S106 (1996)

Location: University of Naples, Naples, Italy

Conclusion: *Passiflora incarnata* extract was found to have anti-inflammatory activity in rats.

Abstract: Ethanolic extract of *Passiflora incarnata* (passion flower) was tested for anti-inflammatory activity in rats. The extract significantly inhibited swelling and inflammation.

16. Medroxyprogesterone Interferes with Ovarian Steroid Protection Against Coronary Vasospasm

Author: K. Miyagawa, J. Rosch, F. Stanczyk, K. Hermsmeyer

Journal: Nature Medicine, Vol. 3 (3); (March 1997)

Location: Oregon Health Sciences University, Beaverton, Oregon

Conclusion: Progesterone was found to cause less risk of cardiovascular disease than medroxyprogesterone, a synthetic progesterone.

Abstract: Progesterone and medroxyprogesterone, a synthetic progesterone, were tested on rhesus monkeys. Medroxyprogesterone was found to cause an increased risk of cardiovascular disease compared to progesterone.

17. Methyl-Sulfonyl-Methane (M.S.M.) A Double-Blind Study of Its Use in Degenerative Arthritis

Author: R. M. Lawrence

Journal: Preliminary correspondence, not yet published

Location: UCLA School of Medicine, Los Angeles, CA

Conclusion: MSM helps patients with degenerative arthritis in pain management.

Abstract: A double-blind study was conducted on patients suffering from degenerative joint disease. After 6 weeks, patients given MSM showed an 82 percent improvement in pain on average. MSM is a safe, non-toxic method of managing pain.

18. Chemopreventive Effect of Perillyl Alcohol on 4-(methylnitrosamino)-1-(3-pyridyl)-1-butanone Induced Tumorigenesis in (C3H/HeJ X A/J)F1 Mouse Lung

Author: L. E. Lantry, Z. Zhang, F. Gao, K. A. Crist, Y. Wang, G. J. Kelloff, R. A. Lubet, M. You

Journal: Journal of Cellular Biochemistry Supplement; 27:20-5 (1997)

Location: Medical College of Ohio, Toledo, OH.

Conclusion: Perillyl alcohol possesses chemopreventive effects in a mouse lung tumor experiment.

Abstract: Perillyl alcohol, a naturally occurring monoterpene found in lavender, cherries, and mint was given to laboratory mice which were then exposed to carcinogens. Perillyl-treated mice had a 22 percent reduction in tumor incidence compared to non-treated mice. Perillyl alcohol is an effective chemopreventive compound in mouse lung tumors.

19. Chemoprevention of Colon Carcinogenesis by Dietary Perillyl Alcohol

Author: B. S. Reddy, C. X. Wang, H. Samaha, R. Lubet, V. E. Steele, G. J. Kelloff, C. V. Rao

Journal: Cancer Research 1;57(3): 420-5 (1997 Feb)

Location: American Health Foundation, Valhalla, NY

Conclusion: Perillyl alcohol is shown to have chemopreventive activity in colon cancer in lab rats.

Abstract: Perillyl alcohol, a monoterpene found in lavender, was administered to rats which were then given azoxymethane (AOM), an agent causing colon carcinogenesis. Perillyl alcohol inhibited the incidence of adenocarcinomas of the colon and small intestine as compared to the control.

Five Key Groups of Essential Oil Compounds

Hydrogen
Carbon
Oxygen

Phenylpropanoids
C6 with C3 sidechain (Phenylalanine unit)

Eugenol	Cinnamic acid
Eugenol acetate	p-courmaric acid
Anethole	gingerol
Cinnamaldehide	myristicin

Monoterpenes
C10 (2 Isoprene units)

borneol	linalol
bornyl acetate	linalyl acetate
camphene	d-/l-limponene
camphor	menthofuran
car-3-ene	menthol
carvacrol	menthone
carvone	menthyl acetate
1,8 cineol (eucalyptol)	α/β-myrcene
geranial/neral (citral)	β-ocimene
citronellal	α/β phellanderene
α/β-citronellal	α/β-pinene
cuminaldehyde	sabinene
p-cymene	piperitone
dipentene	terpinene
fenchone	thujone
geraniol	thymol
nerol	thymyl acetate
geranyl acetate	verbenone
	γ-terpinene

Sesquiterpenes
C15 (3 isoprenes units)

α/β-bisabolol	α/β-vetivol
β/δ-cadinene	α-ylangene
α/β-caryophyllene	α-zingiberene
α-copaene	ledol
α-curcumene	longifolene
eudesmol	nerolidol
farnesene	patchoulol
germacrene B + D	α/β-santalene
himachalol	α/β-santalol
himachalene	

Diterpenes
C20 (4 isoprene unite)

Sclareol
carnosol

Triterpenes
C30 (6 Isoprene units)

ginsenoside
glycyrrhizin

Sesquiterpene Content of Selected Essential Oils

Cedarwood	98%	Patchouli	71%	Spikenard	36%
Vetiver	97%	Myrrh	62%	Galbanum	11%
Sandalwood	90%	Ginger	59%	Frankincense	8%
Black Pepper	74%	German Chamomile	47%		

APPENDIX J
Glossary of Medical Actions

alopecia: baldness, loss of hair

allopathic: refers to conventional contemporary medical approaches using prescription drugs to provide symptom relief in the treatment of illness

amenorrhea: absence of menstruation

anabolism: the creation of body tissue—the opposite of catabolism—usually from other nutrients or components

anesthetic: loss of feeling or sensation; substance which causes such a loss

analgesic: remedy or agent which deadens or relieves pain

anthelmintic: substance unfriendly to worms and parasites; a vermifuge; destroys, expels intestinal worms

anodyne: stills pain and quiets disturbed feelings

antibiotic: prevents the growth of, or destroys bacteria

anticatarrhal: agent which helps remove excess catarrh (excess mucous secreted by inflamed mucous membranes) from the body

anti-emetic: agent which reduces the incidence and severity of nausea or vomiting

antihistamine: counteracts the effects of histamine (which produces capillary dilation and, in larger doses, hemoconcentration)

anti-inflammatory: reduces inflammation

antilithic: prevents the formation of a calculus or stone

antimicrobial: agent which resists or destroys pathogenic micro-organisms

antineuralgic: relieves or reduces nerve pain

antioxidant: natural or synthetic substances that help inhibit destructive oxygen- and free radical-induced deterioration (oxidation) of substances and tissues in the body.

antipruritic: relieves or prevents itching.

antipyretic: reduces fever; see febrifuge

antisclerotic: prevents the hardening of tissue

antiseptic: destroys and prevents the development of microbes

antispasmodic: prevents and eases spasms or convulsions

antitoxic: antidote or treatment that counteracts the effects of poisons and toxins

antitussive:	relieves coughs
antiviral:	inhibits the growth of virus
aperient:	mild laxative
astringent:	causes contraction of organic tissues
bechic:	anything that relieves or cures coughs; or refers to coughs
calmative:	a sedative
carcinogen:	substance or agent which produces or creates cancer
cardiotonic:	having a stimulating effect on the heart
carminative:	agent which prevents the formation of gas (flatulence) in the intestinal system typically to relieve pain due to colic or cramping.
catabolism:	the breaking down of tissue or material within the body. Digestion is a catabolic process.
cathartic:	purgative, capable of causing a violent purging or catharsis of the body
cellulite:	accumulation of toxic matter in the form of fat in the tissue
cholagogue:	stimulates the secretion and flow of bile into the duodenum
choleretic:	aids excretion of bile by the liver, so there is a greater flow of bile
cicatrisant:	agent which promotes healing by the formation of scar tissue
cutaneous:	pertaining to the skin
cytophylactic:	referring to cytophylaxis: the process of increasing the activity of leucocytes in defense of the body against infection
cytotoxic:	toxic to all cells
demulcent:	agent which protects mucous membranes and allays irritation
diuretic:	aids production of urine, promotes urination, increases flow
edema:	a painless swelling caused by fluid retention beneath the skin's surface
emetic:	induces vomiting
emmenagogue:	induces or assists menstruation
emollient:	softens and soothes skin
enteritis:	inflammation of the mucous membrane of the intestine
expectorant:	promotes the removal of mucous from the respiratory system
febrifuge:	combats fever
fungicidal:	prevents and combats fungal infection
germicidal:	destroys germs or microorganisms such as bacteria
halitosis:	offensive breath
hemostatic:	arrests bleeding
hepatic:	relating to the liver, tones and aids its function
hypertensive:	agent which raises blood pressure

hypnotic: causing sleep

hypocholesterolemia: lowering the cholesterol content of the blood

hypotensive: agent which lowers blood pressure

laxative: promotes evacuation of the bowels

lipolytic: causing lipolysis, the chemical disintegration or splitting of fats

microbe: a minute living organism, especially pathogenic bacteria, viruses, etc.

mucolytic: dissolving or breaking down mucous

narcotic: substance which induces sleep; intoxicating or poisonous in large doses

neat: term used for describing the application of essential oil without dilution in a carrier oil

nervine: strengthening and toning to the nervous and nervous system

nephritis: inflammation of the kidneys

neuralgia: a stabbing pain along a nerve pathway

neurasthenia: nervous exhaustion

olfaction: the sense of smell

ophthalmia: inflammation of the eye, a term usually applied to conjunctivitis

otitis: inflammation of the ear

pathogenic: causing or producing disease pruritis: itching

psychosomatic: the manifestation of physical symptoms resulting from a mental state

restorative: agent that helps strengthen and revive the body systems

rhinitis: inflammation of the mucous membrane of the nose

rubefacient: reddening the skin, an agent that reddens the skin by producing hyperemia

soporific: substance which induces sleep

spasmolytic: antispasmodic

stomachic: digestive aid and tonic; improving the appetite

styptic: astringent agent which stops or reduces external bleeding

sudorific: agent which causes sweating

thrombosis: the formation of a blood clot (thrombus)

topical application: refers to applying something directly to the exterior surface of the skin; not internal.

vasoconstrictor: agent which causes narrowing of the blood vessels

vasodilator: agent which causes dilation of the blood vessels

vermifuge: expels intestinal worms

vesicant: causing blistering to the skin

vulnerary: agent which helps heal wounds and sores by external application

APPENDIX K
Common and Botanical Plant Names

Botanical Name First:

Abies balsamea . . . . .Balsam Fir

Abies concolor . . . . .White Fir

Achillea millefolium . . . . .Yarrow

Acorus calamus . . . . .Calamus

Anethum graveolens . . . . .Dill

Angelica archangelica . . . . .Angelica

Aniba rosaeodora . . . . .Rosewood

Apium graveolens . . . . .Celery Seed

Artemisia dracunculus . . . . .Tarragon

Artemisia pallens . . . . .Davana

Boswellia carteri . . . . .Frankincense

Bursera graveolens . . . . .Palo Santo

Callitris intratropica . . . . .Blue cypress

Cananga odorata . . . . .Ylang Ylang

Canarium luzonicum . . . . .Elemi

Cedrus atlantica . . . . .Cedarwood

Chamaemelum nobile . . . . . .Chamomile (Roman)

Cinnamomum cassia . . . . .Cassia

Cinnamomum verum . . . . .Cinnamon Bark

Cistus ladanifer . . . . .Cistus

Citrus aurantifolia . . . . .Lime

Citrus aurantium . . . . .Neroli

Citrus aurantium . . . . .Orange

Citrus bergamia . . . . .Bergamot

Citrus limon . . . . .Lemon

Citrus nobilis . . . . .Tangerine

Citrus reticulata . . . . .Mandarin

Citrus x paradisi . . . . .Grapefruit

Commiphora myrrha . . . . .Myrrh

Conyza canadensis . . . . .Fleabane

Copaiba reticulata (langsdorfii) . . .Copaiba/Copal

Coriandrum sativum . . . . .Coriander

Cuminum cyminum . . . . .Cumin

Cupressus sempervirens . . . . .Cypress

Cymbopogon flexuosus . . . . .Lemongrass

Cymbopogon nardus . . . . .Citronella

Daucus carota . . . . .Carrot Seed

Elettaria cardamomum . . . . .Cardamom

Eucalyptus citriodora . . . . . .Eucalyptus citriodora

Eucalyptus dives . . . . .Eucalyptus dives

Eucalyptus globulus . . . . . . .Eucalyptus globulus

Eucalyptus polybractea . . .Eucalyptus polybractea

Eucalyptus radiata . . . . .Eucalyptus radiata

Ferula gummosa . . . . .Galbanum

Foeniculum vulgare . . . . .Fennel

Gaultheria procumbens . . . . .Wintergreen

Helichrysum italicum . . . . .Helichrysum

Hyssopus officinalis . . . . .Hyssop

Jasminum officinale . . . . .Jasmine

Juniperus communis . . . . .Juniper

Juniperus osteosperma . . . . .Juniper

Laurus nobilis . . . . .Bay Laurel

Lavandula angustifolia . . . . .Lavender

Lavandula x hybrida . . . . .Lavandin

Ledum groenlandicum . . . . .Ledum

Leptospermum scoparium . . . . .Manuka

Matricaria recutita . . . . . . .Chamomile (German)

Melaleuca alternifolia . . . . .Tea Tree

523

Melaleuca ericifolia . . . . .Rosalina

Melaleuca leucadendra . . . . .Cajeput

Melaleuca quinquenervia . . . . .Niaouli

Melissa officinalis . . . . .Melissa

Mentha spicata . . . . .Spearmint

Mentha piperita . . . . .Peppermint

Myristica fragrans . . . . .Nutmeg

Myrtus communis . . . . .Myrtle

Nardostachys jatamansi . . . . .Spikenard

Ocimum basilicum .Basil

Origanum compactum . . . . .Oregano

Origanum majorana . . . . .Marjoram

Pelargonium graveolens . . . . .Geranium

Picea mariana .Spruce

Pimpinella anisum . . . . .Anise

Pinus sylvestris . . . . .Pine

Piper nigrum . . . . Black Pepper

Pogostemon cablin . . . . Patchouli

Pseudotsuga menziesii . . . . .Douglas Fir

Ravensara aromatica . . . . .Ravensara

Rosa damascena . . . . .Rose

Rosmarinus officinalis CT 1,8 cineol . . . .Rosemary

Salvia officinalis . . . . .Sage

Salvia sclarea . . . . .Clary Sage

Santalum album . . . . .Sandalwood

Satureja montana . . . . .Mountain Savory

Solidago canadensis . . . . .Goldenrod

Syzygium aromaticum . . . . .Clove

Tanacetum annuum . . . . .Blue Tansy

Tanacetum vulgare . . . . .Tansy

Thuja plicata . . . . .Western Red Cedar

Thymus vulgaris CT linalol . . . . . .Thyme Linalol

Thymus vulgaris CT thymol . . . . .Thyme

Tsuga canadensis . . . . .Tsuga

Valeriana officinalis . . . . .Valerian

Vetiveria zizanioides . . . . .Vetiver

Zingiber officinale . . . . .Ginger

Common Name First:

Angelica . . . . *Angelica archangelica*

Anise . . . .*Pimpinella anisum*

Balsam Fir . . . . *Abies balsamea*

Basil . . . .*Ocimum basilicum*

Bay Laurel . . . .*Laurus nobilis*

Bergamot . . . .*Citrus bergamia*

Black Pepper . . . .*Piper nigrum*

Blue cypress . . . . *Callitris intratropica*

Blue Tansy . . . .*Tanacetum annuum*

Cajeput . . . .*Melaleuca leucadendra*

Calamus . . . . *Acorus calamus*

Cardamom . . . . *Elettaria cardamomum*

Carrot Seed . . . .*Daucus carota*

Cassia . . . .*Cinnamomum cassia*

Cedarwood . . . .*Cedrus atlantica*

Celery Seed . . . . *Apium graveolens*

Chamomile (German) . . . .*Matricaria recutita*

Chamomile (Roman) . . . . . .*Chamaemelum nobile*

Cinnamon Bark . . . .*Cinnamomum verum*

Cistus . . . .*Cistus ladanifer*

Citronella . . . .*Cymbopogon nardus*

Clary Sage . . . .*Salvia sclarea*

Clove . . . .*Syzygium aromaticum*

Copaiba/Copal . . .*Copaiba reticulata (langsdorfii)*

Coriander . . . .*Coriandrum sativum*

Cumin . . . .*Cuminum cyminum*

Cypress . . . .*Cupressus sempervirens*

Davana . . . . *Artemesia pallens*

Dill . . . . *Anethum graveolens*

Douglas Fir . . . .*Pseudotsuga menziesii*

Elemi . . . .*Canarium luzonicum*

Eucalyptus dives . . . .*Eucalyptus dives*

Eucalyptus citriodora . . . . . .*Eucalyptus citriodora*

Eucalyptus globulus . . . .*Eucalyptus globulus*

Eucalyptus polybractea . . .*Eucalyptus polybractea*

Eucalyptus radiata . . . .*Eucalyptus radiata*

Fennel . . . .*Foeniculum vulgare*

Fleabane . . . .*Conyza canadensis*

Frankincense . . . .*Boswellia carteri*

Galbanum . . . .*Ferula gummosa*

Geranium . . . .*Pelargonium graveolens*

Ginger . . . .*Zingiber officinale*

Goldenrod . . . .*Solidago canadensis*

Grapefruit . . . .*Citrus x paradisi*

Helichrysum . . . .*Helichrysum italicum*

Hyssop . . . .*Hyssopus officinalis*

Jasmine . . . .*Jasminum officinale*

Juniper . . . .*Juniperus communis*

Juniper . . . .*Juniperus osteosperma*

Bay Laurel . . . .*Laurus nobilis*

Lavandin . . . .*Lavandula x hybrida*

Lavender . . . .*Lavandula angustifolia*

Ledum . . . .*Ledum groenlandicum*

Lemon . . . .*Citrus limon*

Lemongrass . . . .*Cymbopogon flexuosus*

Lime . . . .*Citrus aurantifolia*

Mandarin . . . .*Citrus reticulata*

Manuka . . . .*Leptospermum scoparium*

Marjoram . . . .*Origanum majorana*

Melissa . . . .*Melissa officinalis*

Mountain Savory . . . .*Satureja montana*

Myrrh . . . .*Commiphora myrrha*

Myrtle . . . .*Myrtus communis*

Neroli . . . .*Citrus aurantium*

Niaouli . . . .*Melaleuca quinquenervia*

Nutmeg . . . .*Myristica fragrans*

Orange . . . .*Citrus aurantium*

Oregano . . . .*Origanum compactum*

Palo Santo . . . .*Bursera graveolens*

Peppermint . . . .*Mentha piperita*

Pine . . . .*Pinus sylvestris*

Patchouli . . . .*Pogostemon cablin*

Ravensara . . . .*Ravensara aromatica*

Rosalina . . . .*Melaleuca ericifolia*

Rose . . . .*Rosa damascena*

Rosemary . . .*Rosmarinus officinalis CT 1, 8 cineol*

Rosewood . . . .*Aniba rosaeodora*

Sage . . . .*Salvia officinalis*

Sandalwood . . . .*Santalum album*

Spearmint . . . .*Mentha spicata*

Spikenard . . . .*Nardostachys jatamansi*

Spruce . . . .*Picea mariana*

Tangerine . . . .*Citrus nobilis*

Tansy . . . .*Tanacetum vulgare*

Tarragon . . . .*Artemisia dracunculus*

Tea Tree . . . .*Melaleuca alternifolia*

Thyme . . . .*Thymus vulgaris CT thymol*

Thyme Linalol . . . .*Thymus vulgaris CT linalol*

Tsuga . . . .*Tsuga canadensis*

Valerian . . . .*Valeriana officinalis*

Vetiver . . . .*Vetiveria zizanioides*

Western Red Cedar . . . .*Thuja plicata*

White Fir . . . .*Abies concolor*

Wintergreen . . . .*Gaultheria procumbens*

Yarrow . . . .*Achillea millefolium*

Ylang Ylang . . . .*Cananga odorata*

APPENDIX L

Plant Parts Used to Distill Essential Oils

Wood/Bark/Twigs/Needles
Balsam fir
Blue cypress
Cassia
Cedar
Cedarwood
Cinnamon
Cypress
Douglas fir
Emerald cypress
Juniper
Lemon myrtle
Manuka
Niaouli
Palo Santo
Pine
Ravensara
Rosewood
Sandalwood
Spruce
Tsuga
Western red cedar
White fir

Root
Angelica
Ginger
Mugwort
Patchouli
Spikenard
Valarian
Vetiver

Seed
Anise
Black Pepper
Cardamom
Carrot Seed
Celery Seed
Coriander
Cumin
Fennel
Nutmeg

Leaves/Stems
Basil
Cajeut
Cassia
Cistus
Citronella
Citrus Hystrix
Dill
Elemi
Eucalyptus citriodora
Eucalyptus dives
Eucalyptus globulus
Eucalyptus polybractea
Eucalyptus radiata
Fleabane
Geranium
Hyssop
Laurus nobilis
Ledum
Lemongrass
Manuka
Marjoram
Tea Tree
Melaleuca ericifolia

Melissa
Mountain savory
Myrtle
Oregano
Palmarosa
Peppermint
Petitgrain
Rosemary
Sage
Spearmint
Spikenard
Tarragon
Thyme
Wintergreen

Flowering tops
Clary sage
Clove (bud)
Davana
Geranium
German chamomile
Goldenrod
Helichrysum
Lavandin
Lavender
Ledum
Roman chamomile
Tansy
Yarrow

Flower
Jasmine *(absolute)*
Neroli *(absolute)*
Patchouli
Rose
Ylang ylang

Gum/Resin
Copaiba
Elemi
Frankincense
Galbanum
Myrrh
Styrax benzoin

Fruit/Rind
Bergamot
Grapefruit
Juniper
Lemon
Lime
Mandarin
Orange
Tangerine

Stevia: Safe, Non-caloric Supersweet Supplement with Health-giving Properties

For over 1600 years, the natives of Paraguay in South America have used this intensely sweet herb as a health agent and sweetener. Known as *Stevia rebaudiana* by botanists and yerba dulce (honey leaf) by the Guarani Indians, stevia has been incorporated into many native medicines, beverages, and foods for centuries. The Guarani used stevia separately or combined with herbs like yerba mate and lapacho.

Fifteen times sweeter than sugar, stevia was introduced to the West in 1899, when M. S. Bertoni discovered natives using it as a sweetener and medicinal herb. However, stevia never gained popularity in Europe or the United States and was only gradually adopted by several countries throughout Far East Asia.

With Japan's ban on the import of synthetic sweeteners in the 1960's, stevia began to be seriously researched by the Japanese National Institute of Health as a natural sugar substitute. After almost a decade of studies examining the safety and antidiabetic properties of the herb, Japan became a major producer, importer, and user of stevia. Japanese food companies began including stevia in hundreds of products, and eventually stevia use spread through Asia. Stevioside, the super sweet glycoside derived from stevia that is 300 times sweeter than sugar, was even used to sweeten Diet Coke sold in Japan.

Even though stevia is still relatively unknown in the United States, it has gained widespread popularity as a low-calorie sweetener throughout South America and Asia. Both the stevia leaf and stevioside are used in Taiwan, China, Korea, and Japan, with many of these same countries growing and harvesting large amounts of the raw herb.

In 1994, the U.S. Food and Drug Administration permitted the importation and use of stevia as a dietary supplement. However, its adoption by American consumers as a noncaloric sweetener has been very slow because the FDA does not currently permit stevia to be marketed as a food additive. This means that stevia cannot be sold as a sweetener (all sweeteners are classified as food additives by the FDA). Moreover, stevia faces fierce opposition by both the artificial sweetener (aspartame) and sugar industries in the U.S.

Stevia, however, is more than just a non-caloric sweetener. Several modern clinical studies have documented the ability of stevia to lower and balance blood sugar levels, support the pancreas and digestive system, protect the liver, and combat infectious microorganisms. (Oviedo et al., 1971; Suzuki et al., 1977; Ishit et al., 1986; Boeckh, 1986; Alvarez, 1986.)

In one study, Oviedo et. al. showed that oral administration of a stevia leaf extract reduced blood sugar levels by over 35 percent. Another study conducted by Suzuki et al. documented similar results. Clearly, these and other clinical evaluations indicate that stevia holds significant promise for the treatment of diabetes.

A P P E N D I X   N

MSM Research

MSM: A New Solution for Arthritis, Allergies, and Pain

MSM (Methylsulfonylmethane) is a natural sulfur-bearing nutrient that occurs widely in nature (found in everything from mother's breast milk to fresh vegetables). It is an exceptional source of nutritional sulfur—a mineral that is vital to protein synthesis and sound health.

Why is sulfur so important to the body? Because sulfur is a mineral which, like vitamin C, is constantly being used up and depleted. When we fail to replenish our reserves of nutritional sulfur, we become more vulnerable to disease and degenerative conditions. Some possible signs of sulfur deficiency are:

- Poor nail and hair growth
- Eczema
- Dermatitis
- Poor muscle tone
- Acne / Pimples
- Gout
- Rheumatism
- Arthritis
- Weakening of nervous system
- Constipation
- Impairment of mental faculties
- Lowered libido

MSM is more than just another essential nutrient. According to research compiled by Ronald Lawrence, Ph.D., M.D., and Stanley Jacob, M.D., MSM represents a safe, natural solution for chronic headaches, back pain, tendonitis, fibromyalgia, rheumatism, arthritis, athletic injuries, muscle spasms, asthma, and allergies.

In a book entitled, *The Miracle of MSM,* available through Essential Science Publishing, both Dr. Jacobs and Dr. Lawrence discuss how MSM has benefited hundred of patients. A UCLA neuropsychiatrist, Dr. Lawrence is convinced that MSM will revolutionize how millions of people deal with inflammatory autoimmune diseases like rheumatism, asthma, bursitis, and tendonitis, as well as autoimmune diseases like arthritis, lupus, scleroderma, and allergies.

Other doctors have also seen their patients dramatically improve using 2 to 4 grams of MSM daily. According to David Blyweiss, M.D., of the Institute of Advanced Medicine in Lauderhill, Florida, many patients experience a 50 percent improvement in their arthritis symptoms, along with less fatigue, better sleep, and better ability to exercise.

Dr. Lawrence has also used MSM to improve the condition of patients who were virtually crippled with arthritis and back pain. One patient was able to get out of bed for the first time after just two weeks on MSM. And after two months of MSM use, he could walk to the grocery store.

Another of Dr. Lawrence's patients was a 70-year-old woman who was suffering from severe arthritis. In this case, MSM actually postponed the need for double knee replacement. In fact, after only two months on oral MSM, she was walking again with much less pain and stiffness.

Numerous other MSM users have experienced results equivalent to cortisone—but without side effects like immune suppression, fluid retention, and weakness.

According to Stanley Jacobs, M.D., there may be no pharmaceutical back pain therapy better—or safer—than MSM. "MSM has an important role to play in the nonsurgical treatment of back pain," he said. "I have seen several hundred patients for back pain secondary to osteoarthritis, disc degeneration, spinal misalignments, or accidents. For such pain-related conditions, MSM is usually beneficial."

"I have been recommending MSM for more than six months," said Richard Shaefer, a chiropractor from Wheeling, Illinois. "The results have been excellent. I consistently see major reduction in pain and inflammation in arthritic joints, along with improved range of motion. I can't think of a single individual who isn't getting some kind of positive effect."

MSM may have other benefits aside from its pain and inflammation-reducing properties. Numerous patients have reported a surge in energy levels along with thicker hair, nails, and skin. Some have even reported a softening or disappearance of scar tissue.

One user reported a marked increase in stamina and energy after starting on MSM. "For a long while I have had the blahs," complained Lou Salyer of Tucson, Arizona. "I had no stamina. I had to force myself to get things done around the house. After two days on MSM, it was like a blast of energy. I am amazed at how much I get done now."

MSM may also do much more than relieve pain. "Prior to taking MSM (30 grams a day for 20 years), I would have a cold or flu two or three times a year," stated Dr. Jacobs. "Since I've been taking MSM, I've not had a single cold or the flu. I can't say that MSM prevented my cold or the flu, but it is a fascinating observation."

MSM contains an exceptionally bioavailable source of sulfur, one of the most neglected minerals needed by the human body. Carl Pfeiffer, M.D., Ph.D., a world-renowned expert on nutritional medicine, agrees, "Sulfur is the forgotten essential element."

Found in such foods as garlic and asparagus, the sulfur within MSM is a critical part of the amino acids cysteine and methionine, which form the building blocks of the nails, hair, and skin. Sulfur is also found in therapeutic mineral baths and hot springs that have brought relief to arthritis sufferers for centuries.

MSM is very closely related to DMSO, a powerful pain reliever that was the subject of a *60 Minutes* report in April, 1980. DMSO has been approved by the FDA for interstitial cystitis, a painful urinary tract condition.

The Youth Nutrient

Of particular importance is MSM's ability to equalize water pressure inside the cells—a considerable benefit for those plagued with bursitis, arthritis, and tendonitis. These kinds of inflammatory outbreaks are created when the water pressure inside the cells jumps past the pressure outside the cells, creating pressure and pain. MSM acts as a sort of cellular safety valve, affecting the protein envelope of the cell so that water transfers freely in and out of the cell. The result: rapid relief and less damage to tissues. And because it elasticizes the hold between the cells, MSM can restore flexibility to inflamed tissues.

When our bodies grow older and are chronically shortchanged of key minerals like sulfur and MSM, the bonds between our cells become increasingly rigid and brittle—a condition that can lead to a loss in skin flexibility and contribute to skin wrinkles. The internal manifestations of this cellular brittleness are far less visible but have a far greater negative impact on the body. MSM's ability to reintroduce flexibility into cell structures, therefore, can have widespread restorative affects.

APPENDIX O

FOS Research

FOS: Supernutrient Documented to Rebuild Intestinal Flora, Improve mineral absorption, and more.

- Minimal impact on blood sugar levels
- Glycemic index of 0
- Ideal sweetener for diabetics.
- Increases populations of beneficial bifidobacteria in the colon
- Reduces populations of harmful bacteria, such as *Clostridium perfringens*
- Improves calcium and magnesium absorption
- Improves liver function

A naturally sweet, indigestible fiber derived from chicory roots, FOS (fructooligosaccharides) are one of the best-documented, natural nutrients for promoting the growth of *Lactobacilli* and *bifidobacteria* bacteria, a key to sound health. FOS has also been clinically studied for its ability to increase magnesium and calcium absorption, lower blood glucose, cholesterol, and LDL levels, and to inhibit production of the reductase enzymes that can contribute to cancer. Because FOS can increase magnesium absorption, it can also lead to lowered blood pressure and better cardiovascular health.

FOS is one of the most powerful prebiotics to be researched in the last decade (a "prebiotic" feeds intestinal flora; a "probiotic" adds more actual cultures to existing intestinal flora). The subject of over 100 clinical studies, FOS is one of the best-documented natural nutrients for improving the healthy balance of bacteria in intestines and stimulating the growth of the beneficial *bifidobacteria*—also called "friendly flora"—that reside in the colon.

How important to good health are these so-called "friendly flora" that populate our intestines? They are our front-line defense against invading disease-causing organisms, combating premature aging caused by the toxin-producing bacteria and fungi that reside in our intestines.

FOS Builds Up Friendly Flora

Subjects	Dose g/day	Duration	Fecal *Bifidobacteria* # bacteria (log) per gram		Reference
9	1	14	9.8	10.2	Tokunaga, 92
9	3	14	9.9	10.4	Tokunaga, 92
9	5	14	9.7	10.3	Tokunaga, 92
20	12.5	12	7.9	9.1	Bouhnik, 93
38	8	14	5.2	6.2	Rochat, 94
12	4	25	9.5	9.8	Buddington, 96
			Start of Study	End of Study	

Seven Reasons Why *Bifidobacteria* Are Vital to Health

1. They produce substances that stop the growth of harmful, toxic gram-negative and positive bacteria in the intestines (Kawase 1982, Rasic 1983, Gibson and Wang 1994a&b).

2. They occupy space on the intestinal wall that could be populated by pathogenic organisms. When *Bifidobacteria* increase in numbers, they crowd out invasive toxin-generating microorganisms.

3. They slow down the production of damaging protein breakdown products, such as ammonia. This lowers blood ammonia levels that can be toxic to the human body (Bezkoravainy et al., 1989).

4. They produce B vitamins and folic acid (Nishizawa 1960, Liescher 1961).

5. They produce digestive enzymes, like phosphatases and lysozymes (Kawase 1982, Minagawa 1970).

6. They stimulate the immune system and promote immune attack against cancer cells (Mitsuoka 1980, Sekine et al., 1985).

FOS Raises Magnesium Absorption by over 75%

After 10-13 days on 5% FOS diet

FOS Raises Calcium Absorption by over 20%

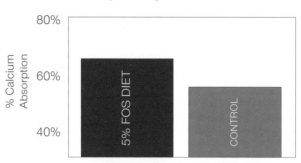

After 10-13 days on 5% FOS diet

7. They increase the absorption of essential minerals magnesium and calcium. As we age, magnesium levels in the body decline, contributing to high blood pressure and diabetes.

Technically a fiber rather than a sugar, FOS is totally unlike conventional sugars because it feeds the beneficial *bifidobacteria* while selectively starving the parasitical yeast, fungi, and bacteria that contribute to disease. Most toxin-producing microorganisms in the intestines are unable to use FOS as food. Conventional sugars, like sucrose and lactose on the other hand, work in just the opposite fashion: they tend to feed harmful bacteria more readily than it feeds beneficial bacteria.

Increases Mineral Absorption

Besides building up the beneficial bacteria in the body, FOS has also been shown to improve blood sugar control, liver function, and calcium and magnesium absorption.

A 1997 animal study conducted at the Nutritional Research Center in Japan found that a 5 percent FOS diet increased magnesium and calcium absorption substantially. A 1998 Showa University study, obtained similar results (Ohta et al., 1998, 1997, 1995; Morohashi et al., 1998).

Magnesium is one of the most important nutrients we obtain from our diet, being involved in over 300 enzyme reactions in the body. As we age, our magnesium levels drop markedly, which creates a deficiency that increases the risk of angina, atherosclerosis, cardiac arrhythmias, depression,

and diabetes (Schauss, 1998; Jansson, 1981). A study conducted by National Research Council of Canada showed that long-term marginal magnesium deficiency can reduce the life span of laboratory animals by almost 40 percent (Heroux et al., 1977).

Liver Health

FOS also improves liver health. A 1999 Louvain Catholic University study found that a 10 percent diet of FOS can protect against fat accumulating in the liver and lower both blood glucose and insulin levels.

Virtually No Effect on Blood Sugar Levels

FOS may be the ideal nutrient for diabetics. Because FOS is an indigestible sugar, it triggers no spikes in blood sugar levels the way sucrose and glucose do. About 40 to 60 percent as sweet as sugar, FOS is found in low quantities in many types of foods. However, to obtain just a quarter teaspoon of FOS from foods in your diet, you would have to consume 13 bananas, 16 tomatoes, or 16 onions. Chicory roots have one of the highest amounts of FOS of any plant, and most natural FOS supplements are commercially derived from water-extraction of the roots.

Recommended Dosages

To obtain the best results from FOS, daily intake should range between 5 and 10 grams a day. Dosages above 15 grams may cause gas or intestinal cramping from excess bifidobacteria populations.

A P P E N D I X P

Comparative Antimicrobial Activity of Essential Oils and Antibiotics

The following are test data comparing the antimicrobial ability between essential oils (cinnamon and oregano) and antibiotics (penicillin and ampicillin). The method is disk diffusion and the results are the mean value of three replicates.

These preliminary data indicate that essential oils of cinnamon and oregano are comparable with penicillin and ampicillin in inhibitory activity against *E. coli* and *Staphylococcus aureus*.

Material	**Loading amount (µl)***	*Escherichia coli* zone of inhibition (cm)	*Staphylococcus aureus* zone of inhibition (cm)
Penicillin	3	0	3.2
	6	0	3.4
	8	0	3.6
	12	0	3.6
Ampicillin	3	1.9	2.6
	6	2.1	2.6
	8	2.5	2.7
	12	2.6	2.8
Cinnamon	3	2.4	2.4
	6	2.8	2.8
	8	-	3.0
	12	3.0	3.2
Oregano	3	2.6	3.2
	6	3.3	3.6
	8	-	3.6
	12	3.3	3.8

*The concentration of penicillin = 1.76 unit / μl
The concentration of ampicillin = 5 μg / μl

Chlorine is one of the most reactive and toxic elements known to man. When put in the public water supply as a disinfectant, it creates disinfection byproducts (DBP) that can cause cancer, birth defects, and spontaneous abortions.

Besides being used in the water supply, chlorine is also chemically bonded in the manufacture of numerous industrial chemicals.

Many toxic herbicides, fungicides, and insecticides are created by attaching one or more chlorine molecules to a carbon skeleton. Once ingested or inhaled, chlorinated chemicals leach into the fat cells and become trapped.

Some of the most common and toxic of these chemicals include a quartet of chlorinated carcinogenic chemicals known as trihalomethanes (THMs): chloroform, bromoform, bromodichloromethane, and chlorobromomethane. These trihalomethanes are created when chlorine reacts with naturally occurring organic matter in raw water.

THMs are very volatile—this means they can be inhaled during bathing as well as consumed in potable water. Showering, washing dishes, and flushing a toilet can also contaminate the air with trihalomethanes.

Once inhaled or ingested, THMs accumulate in the fat cells—the same way dioxins do. Once trapped inside the body, they chemically bind with and damage DNA.

A California Department of Health study surveyed 5,144 pregnant women to determine the effects of THMs in the drinking water (Waller et al., 1998). They measured levels of THMs from water tests of public utilities, and matched these against the study group.

They found that pregnant women who consumed more than 5 glasses of water a day containing more than 75 ppb (parts per billion) had double the risk of spontaneous abortion.

Women who drank less water or who drank water with lower levels of THMs had substantially lower risk of miscarriage. Women who drank filtered water also had significantly lower risk of miscarriage.

Researchers at the University of North Carolina at Chapel Hill also examined the link between THMs and miscarriages in populations living throughout central North Carolina (Savitz et al., 1995). They found that women who suffered the highest exposure to THM in the drinking water had almost triple the risk of miscarriage.

Another study conducted by the U.S. Department of Health and Human Services examined the effect of THMs in the water supply of 75 towns throughout the state of New Jersey (Bove et al., 1995). When scientists compared levels of THMs to the frequency of birth defects, they found that women who consumed water exceeding 80 ppb THMs had triple the risk of giving birth to infants with neural tube defects.

The authors suggested that one of the reasons for this may be due to the fact that vitamin B12 may be disrupted in the body due to chloroform, a common THM.

Another statewide study in New Jersey also linked THMs in drinking water to a doubled risk of neural tube defects (Klotz et al., 1998).

An even larger epidemiological study by the National Institute of Public Health in Norway surveyed the effects of chlorinated water on 141,077 infants born in Norway between 1993 and 1995 (Magnus et al., 1999). Researchers found that the higher the chlorine content of the water and the higher the organic matter in the water, the higher the risk for birth defects including cardiac defects, respiratory tract defects, and urinary tract defects.

Murray S. Malcolm, M.D., a public health physician in New Zealand, spearheaded a countrywide study that examined the role of THMs in triggering birth defects and cancer. He concluded, "A quarter of all bladder, colon, rectal cancers, and birth defects may be preventable by reducing disinfection byproducts (i.e., THMs) exposure" (Malcolm et al., 1999; Wellington School of Medicine, New Zealand).

APPENDIX R
Body Systems Chart

Product Type Key:
- **S** Essential Oil Single
- **B** Essential Oil Blend
- **D** Dietary Supplement
- **P** Personal Care/Hair and Skin
- **L** Lotions/Creams/Massage Oils
- **G** Bath and Shower Gels/Soaps
- **A** Antiseptic/Sanitizing
- **O** Oral Care

Product	Product Type	Nervous System	Cardiovascular System	Respiratory System	Digestive/Elimination	Immune/Anti-infectious	Glandular/Hormonal	Emotional Balance	Muscle & Bone	Anti Aging	Oral Hygiene	Skin and Hair
Abundance	B			●		●		●				
Acceptance	B	●						●				
AlkaLime	D		●		●				●			
Angelica	S	●						●				
Animal Scents Pet Shampoo	G											●
Animal Scents Pet Ointment	L											●
Anise	S				●					●		
Aroma Life	B		●									
Aroma Siez	B			●					●			
A.R.T. Day Activator	P											●
A.R.T. Gentle Foaming Cleanser	P											●
A.R.T. Night Reconstructor	P											●
A.R.T. Toner	P											●
Australian Blue	B							●				
Awaken	B							●				
Balance Complete	D	●	●			●	●				●	
Basil	S		●						●			
Bath Gel Base	G											●
Be-Fit	D								●			
Bergamot	S				●			●				●
BLM Capsules	D								●			

Product Type Key:
- **S** Essential Oil Single
- **B** Essential Oil Blend
- **D** Dietary Supplement
- **P** Personal Care/Hair and Skin
- **L** Lotions/Creams/Massage Oils
- **G** Bath and Shower Gels/Soaps
- **A** Antiseptic/Sanitizing
- **O** Oral Care

Product	Product Type	Nervous System	Cardiovascular Syste	Respiratory System	Digestive/Elimination	Immune/Antiinfectious	Glandular/Hormonal	Emotional Balance	Muscle & Bone	Anti Aging	Oral Hygiene	Skin and Hair
BLM Powder	D								●			
Blue Agave Nectar	D						●		●			
BodyGize	F				●	●			●			
Boswellia Wrinkle Crème	L									●		●
Brain Power	B	●						●				
Breathe Again Roll-on	B			●								
Cajeput	S		●	●								
Carbozyme	D				●							
Cardamom	S				●							
CardiaCare	D		●									
Cassia	S		●		●					●	●	
Cedar, Western Red	S											●
Cedarwood	S	●		●								
Cel-Lite Magic	L											●
Chamomile Moisturizing Bar Soap	G											●
Chamomile, German	S	●						●				●
Chamomile, Roman	S	●						●				●
Chelex	D				●							
Christmas Spirit	B	●	●					●				
Cinnamint Lip Balm	P											●
Cinnamon Bark	S					●						
Cistus	S					●				●		
Citronella	S								●			●
Citrus Fresh	B					●		●				
ClaraDerm Spray	P											●
Clarity	B	●						●				
Clary Sage	S						●					
Clove	S		●	●	●	●				●	●	
ComforTone	D				●	●						

Product Type Key:
- **S** Essential Oil Single
- **B** Essential Oil Blend
- **D** Dietary Supplement
- **P** Personal Care/Hair and Skin
- **L** Lotions/Creams/Massage Oils
- **G** Bath and Shower Gels/Soaps
- **A** Antiseptic/Sanitizing
- **O** Oral Care

Product	Product Type	Nervous System	Cardiovascular System	Respiratory System	Digestive/Elimination	Immune/Anti-infectious	Glandular/Hormonal	Emotional Balance	Muscle & Bone	Anti Aging	Oral Hygiene	Skin and Hair
Copaiba (Copal)	S			●					●	●		
Coriander	S				●		●					
Cortistop, Women's	D						●					
Cumin	S				●	●						
Cypress	S		●						●			
Cypress, Blue	S					●						
Deep Relief Roll-on	S								●			
Dentarome	O										●	
Dentarome Plus	O										●	
Dentarome Ultra	O		●								●	
Detoxzyme Capsules	D				●	●						
Digest + Cleanse softgels	D	●			●	●				●		
Di-Gize	B				●							
Dill	S				●							
Dragon Time	B						●	●				
Dragon Time Bath Gel	G						●	●				
Dream Catcher	B							●				
Egyptian Gold	B	●				●		●				
Elemi	S											●
En-R-Gee	D	●						●				
EndoFlex	B						●					
EndoGize	D						●					
Envision	B							●				
Essential Beauty Serum (Dry Skin)	P											●
Essential Beauty Serum (Oily Skin)	P											●
Essential Beauty Serum (Acne-Prone)	P											●
Essentialzyme	D				●				●			
Estro	D						●	●				
Eucalyptus citriodora	S			●								
Eucalyptus globulus	S			●					●		●	

Product Type Key:
- **S** Essential Oil Single
- **B** Essential Oil Blend
- **D** Dietary Supplement
- **P** Personal Care/Hair and Skin
- **L** Lotions/Creams/Massage Oils
- **G** Bath and Shower Gels/Soaps
- **A** Antiseptic/Sanitizing
- **O** Oral Care

Product	Product Type	Nervous System	Cardiovascular System	Respiratory System	Digestive/Elimination	Immune/Anti-infectious	Glandular/Hormonal	Emotional Balance	Muscle & Bone	Anti Aging	Oral Hygiene	Skin and Hair
Eucalyptus polybrachtia	S			●								
Eucalyptus radiata	S			●								●
Evening Peace Bath Gel	G											●
Evergreen Essence	B							●				
Exodus	D					●						
Exodus II	B					●						
Femigen	D						●	●				
Fennel	S				●		●					
Fir, Douglas	S			●					●			
Fir, White	S			●				●	●	●		
Fleabane, Canadian (Conyza)	S		●				●					
Forgiveness	B							●				
Frankincense	S	●				●		●		●		●
Galbanum	S					●						
Gathering	B							●				
Genesis Hand and Body Lotion	L											●
Gentle Baby	B							●				●
Geranium	S							●				●
Ginger	S	●			●							
GLF	B				●	●						
Goldenrod	S		●				●					
Grapefruit	S		●							●		
Grounding	B							●				
Harmony	B							●				
Helichrysum	S		●						●			
Highest Potential	B							●				
Hope	B							●				
HRT	D		●									
Humility	B							●				
Hyssop	S	●	●	●								

Product Type Key:
- **S** Essential Oil Single
- **B** Essential Oil Blend
- **D** Dietary Supplement
- **P** Personal Care/Hair and Skin
- **L** Lotions/Creams/Massage Oils
- **G** Bath and Shower Gels/Soaps
- **A** Antiseptic/Sanitizing
- **O** Oral Care

Product	Product Type	Nervous System	Cardiovascular System	Respiratory System	Digestive/Elimination	Immune/Anti-infectious	Glandular/Hormonal	Emotional Balance	Muscle & Bone	Anti Aging	Oral Hygiene	Skin and Hair
ICP	D		●		●							
Idaho Balsam Fir	S	●			●		●					
ImmuneTune	D					●				●		
ImmuPower	B					●						
ImmuPro	D					●						
Inner Child	B							●				
Inner Defense softgels	D			●	●	●						
Inspiration	B							●				
Into the Future	B							●				
Jasmine (Absolute)	S						●	●				
Joy	B							●				
Juniper	S				●			●				
JuvaFlex	B				●			●				
JuvaTone	D				●	●						
Juva Cleanse	B				●					●		
Juva Power	D				●					●		
Juva Spice	D				●					●		
K & B	D				●							
KidScents Bath Gel	G											●
KidScents Lotion	L											●
KidScents Mighty Mist	D	●	●	●	●	●	●		●			
KidScents Mighty Vites	D	●	●	●	●	●	●		●			
KidScents Shampoo	P											●
KidScents Tender Tush	L											●
KidScents Toothpaste	O										●	
Lady Sclareol	B						●	●				
Laurus nobilus (Bay Laurel)	S			●	●	●						
LavaDerm Cooling Mist	P							●				●
Lavender	S	●	●					●				●
Lavender-Rosewood Moisturizing Bar Soap	G											●

Product Type Key:
- **S** Essential Oil Single
- **B** Essential Oil Blend
- **D** Dietary Supplement
- **P** Personal Care/Hair and Skin
- **L** Lotions/Creams/Massage Oils
- **G** Bath and Shower Gels/Soaps
- **A** Antiseptic/Sanitizing
- **O** Oral Care

Product	Product Type	Nervous System	Cardiovascular System	Respiratory System	Digestive/Elimination	Immune/Anti-infectious	Glandular/Hormonal	Emotional Balance	Muscle & Bone	Anti Aging	Oral Hygiene	Skin and Hair
Lavender Volume Shampoo	P											●
Lavender Volume Nourishing Rinse	P											●
Ledum	S				●	●				●		●
Lemon	S			●	●	●				●		
Lemon-Sage Clarifying Shampoo	P											●
Lemon-Sage Clarifying Nourishing Rinse	P											●
Lemon-Sandalwood Cleansing Bar Soap	G											●
Lemongrass	S					●			●			
Lime	S			●	●	●				●		
Lipozyme	D				●							
Life 5	D				●	●				●		
Longevity	B									●		
Longevity softgels	D		●							●		
M-Grain	B	●										
Magnify Your Purpose	B	●						●				
Mandarin	S				●					●		●
Manuka	S			●	●	●			●			
Marjoram	S		●						●			
Mega Cal	D		●						●			
Melaleuca alternifolia (Tea Tree)	S			●		●			●		●	●
Melaleuca ericifolia (Rosalina)	S			●								●
Melaleuca-Geranium Moisturizing Bar Soap	G											●
Melaleuca quinquenervia (Niaouli)	S			●					●			
Melissa	S						●			●		●
Melrose	B			●								●
Mineral Essence	D	●	●			●	●	●	●			
Mister	B						●					
Morning Start Bath and Shower Gel	G											●
Morning Start Moisturizing Bar Soap	G							●				●
Motivation	B	●						●				

Product Type Key:
- **S** Essential Oil Single
- **B** Essential Oil Blend
- **D** Dietary Supplement
- **P** Personal Care/Hair and Skin
- **L** Lotions/Creams/Massage Oils
- **G** Bath and Shower Gels/Soaps
- **A** Antiseptic/Sanitizing
- **O** Oral Care

Product	Product Type	Nervous System	Cardiovascular System	Respiratory System	Digestive/Elimination	Immune/Anti-infectious	Glandular/Hormonal	Emotional Balance	Muscle & Bone	Anti Aging	Oral Hygiene	Skin and Hair
Mountain Savory	S					●						
MultiGreens	D	●	●		●	●			●			
Myrrh	S	●				●	●					●
Myrtle	S			●	●		●		●			
Niaouli	S			●					●			
Neroli	S				●							●
NeuroGen cream	L	●					●		●			
Ningxia Wolfberries	D	●	●			●	●			●		
Ningxia Red	D	●	●			●	●			●		
Nutmeg	S	●				●	●					
Omega Blue softgels	D	●	●			●	●		●	●		●
Orange	S				●	●				●		●
Orange Blossom Facial Wash	P											●
Oregano	S			●		●			●	●		
Ortho Sport Massage Oil	L								●			
Ortho Ease Massage Oil	L								●			●
Palmarosa	S		●					●				●
Palo Santo	S	●				●						
PanAway	B	●							●			
ParaFree softgels	D				●	●						
Patchouli	S											●
PD 80/20	D						●	●	●			
Peace & Calming	B	●						●				
Pepper, Black	S	●			●							
Peppermint	S	●		●	●				●		●	●
Peppermint-Cedarwood Moisturizing Bar Soap	G								●			●
Petitgrain	S							●				
Pine	S			●					●			
Polyzyme	D				●				●	●		
Power Meal	D		●		●	●			●			

Product Type Key:
- **S** Essential Oil Single
- **B** Essential Oil Blend
- **D** Dietary Supplement
- **P** Personal Care/Hair and Skin
- **L** Lotions/Creams/Massage Oils
- **G** Bath and Shower Gels/Soaps
- **A** Antiseptic/Sanitizing
- **O** Oral Care

Product	Product Type	Nervous System	Cardiovascular System	Respiratory System	Digestive/Elimination	Immune/Anti-infectious	Glandular/Hormonal	Emotional Balance	Muscle & Bone	Anti Aging	Oral Hygiene	Skin and Hair
Prenolone cream	L	●					●	●	●	●		
Prenolone + cream	L	●					●	●	●	●		
Present Time	B							●				
ProGen	D						●					
Progessence cream	L						●					●
ProTec	B						●					
Pure Protein Complete	D								●	●		
Purification	B				●			●				●
R.C.	B			●								
Ravensara	S			●		●						
Regenolone cream	L	●					●		●			●
Rehemogen	D		●		●							
Relaxation Massage Oil	L							●				●
Release	B							●				
Relieve It	B								●			
Rose	S							●				●
Rose Ointment	P											●
Rosemary (CT cineol)	S		●		●				●			
Rosewood	S											●
Rosewood Moisturizing Shampoo	P											●
Rosewood Moisturizing Nourishing Rinse	P											●
RutaVaLa	B	●						●				
Sacred Mountain	B							●				
Sacred Mountain Moisturizing Bar Soap	G							●				●
Sage	S					●	●					
Sandalwood	S	●						●	●			●
Sandalwood Moisture Creme	P											●
SARA	B							●				
Satin Facial Scrub-Mint	P											●
SclarEssence	B/D				●		●					

Product Type Key:
- **S** Essential Oil Single
- **B** Essential Oil Blend
- **D** Dietary Supplement
- **P** Personal Care/Hair and Skin
- **L** Lotions/Creams/Massage Oils
- **G** Bath and Shower Gels/Soaps
- **A** Antiseptic/Sanitizing
- **O** Oral Care

Product	Product Type	Nervous System	Cardiovascular System	Respiratory System	Digestive/Elimination	Immune/Anti-infectious	Glandular/Hormonal	Emotional Balance	Muscle & Bone	Anti Aging	Oral Hygiene	Skin and Hair
Sensation	B						●	●				
Sensation Bath and Shower Gel	G											●
Sensation Hand and Body Lotion	L											●
Sensation Massage Oil	L											●
Spearmint	S				●			●				
Spikenard	S							●				●
Spruce	S	●		●				●				
Stevia Extract	D		●		●	●						
Sulfurzyme Capsules or Powder	D	●				●			●	●		●
Super B	D	●	●						●			
Super C	D			●		●				●		
Super C Chewable	D					●				●		
Super Cal	D	●	●					●	●			
Surrender	B	●						●				
Tangerine	S					●		●		●		●
Tansy, Blue	S	●										
Tansy, Idaho	S					●						
Tarragon	S	●			●							
Tea Tree (Melaleuca alternifolia)	S			●		●			●		●	●
ThermaBurn	D								●			
Thieves	A					●				●	●	
Thieves Antiseptic Spray	A					●					●	●
Thieves Cleansing Bar Soap	A					●						●
Thieves Dental Floss	O										●	
Thieves Fresh Essence Plus mouthwash	O					●					●	●
Thieves Hand Sanitizer	A					●						●
Thieves Foaming Hand Soap	A					●						●
Thieves Household Cleaner	A					●						
Thieves Lozenges	O			●							●	

Product Type Key:
- **S** Essential Oil Single
- **B** Essential Oil Blend
- **D** Dietary Supplement
- **P** Personal Care/Hair and Skin
- **L** Lotions/Creams/Massage Oils
- **G** Bath and Shower Gels/Soaps
- **A** Antiseptic/Sanitizing
- **O** Oral Care

Product	Product Type	Nervous System	Cardiovascular System	Respiratory System	Digestive/Elimination	Immune/Anti-infectious	Glandular/Hormonal	Emotional Balance	Muscle & Bone	Anti Aging	Oral Hygiene	Skin and Hair
Thieves Waterless Hand Purifier	A					●						●
Thieves Wipes	A					●						
3 Wise Men	B							●				
Thyme	S					●			●	●		
Thyromin	D						●					
Trauma Life	B							●				
Tranquil Roll-on	B	●						●				
Transformation	B	●					●	●				
True Source Multivitamin	D	●	●	●	●	●	●	●	●	●		●
Tsuga	S		●	●								
Ultra Young +	D						●			●		
V-6 Enhanced Vegetable Oil Complex	L								●			●
Valerian	S	●										
Valor	B	●						●	●			●
Valor Moisturizing Bar Soap	P	●										●
Valor Roll-on	B	●						●	●			●
Vetiver	S	●					●	●				●
White Angelica	B							●				
Wintergreen	S								●			
Wolfberry Crisp Bars	D				●	●			●	●		
Wolfberry Eye Creme	L									●		●
Yarrow, Blue	S						●	●				
Ylang Ylang	S		●				●	●				
YL Manna	D				●	●			●	●		

APPENDIX S
Single Oil Data

Single Oil Name	Botanical Name	Safety Data	Products containing Single Oil
Angelica	*Angelica archangelica* (Umbelliferae)	GRAS, FA, P, PH, DS	Awaken, Forgiveness, Grounding, Harmony, Surrender
Anise	*Pimpinella anisum* (Umbelliferae)	GRAS, FA, DS	Awaken, Di-Gize, Dream Catcher, ICP, Essentialzyme, ParaFree Softgels, Power Meal, Polyzyme, Detoxzyme, ComforTone
Basil	*Ocimum basilicum* (Labiatae)	GRAS, FA, E+, CH, P+, SI, DS	Aroma Siez, Clarity, M-Grain Super Cal
Bergamot	*Citrus bergamia* (Rutaceae)	GRAS, FA, SI, DS, CH+	Awaken, Clarity, Forgiveness, Gentle Baby, Harmony, Joy, White Angelica, Progessence, Genesis Lotion, Prenolone Cream, Prenolone+, Regenolone Cream, NeuroGen, Rosewood Shampoo/ Conditioner, Dream Catcher, Dragon Time Bath Gel, Evening Peace Bath Gel
Blue Cypress	*Callitris intratropica*		Brain Power, Highest Potential
Cajeput	*Melaleuca leucadendra* (Myrtaceae)	SI	
Calamus	*Acorus calamus* (Araceae)	SI, P+, CH+	Exodus II
Cardamom	*Elettaria cardamomum* (Zingiberaceae)	GRAS, FA, DS SI	Clarity, Transformation
Carrot Seed Oil	*Daucus carota* (Umbelliferae)	GRAS, FA, DS	Rose Ointment
Cassia	*Cinnamomum cassia* (Lauraceae)	GRAS, FA, DS, P, CH, SI+	Exodus II, Oils of Ancient Scripture
Cedar, Western Red	*Thuja plicata* (Cupressaceae)	SI	Evergreen Essence
Cedarwood	*Cedrus atlantica* (Pinaceae)		Australian Blue, Brain Power, SARA, Grounding, Highest Potential, Inspiration, Into the Future, Oils of Ancient Scripture, KidScents Lotion, Sacred Mountain, Sacred Mountain Bar Soap, Peppermint-Cedarwood Bar Soap, Cel-Lite Magic

Single Oil Name	Botanical Name	Safety Data	Products containing Single Oil
Celery Seed		P, SI, DS	JuvaCleanse
Chamomile (German/Blue)	*Matricaria chamomilla/recutita* (Compositae)	GRAS, FA, DS, PH	EndoFlex, Surrender, K&B Tincture, JuvaTone, ComforTone
Chamomile (Roman)	*Chamaemelum nobile* (Compositae)	GRAS, FA, DS	Awaken, Clarity, Forgiveness, Gentle Baby, Harmony, Joy, JuvaFlex, Surrender, M-Grain, Motivation, Genesis Lotion, Lemon Sage Shampoo/Conditioner, Sandalwood Toner, Satin Body Lotion, Wolfberry Eye Creme, Dragon Time Bath Gel, Evening Peace Bath Gel, Chelex Tincture, K&B Tincture, Tender Tush Ointment, Rehemogen Tincture, Clara Derm
Cinnamon Bark	*Cinnamomum verum* (Lauraceae)	GRAS, FA, DS, P, SI+, CH	Abundance, Christmas Spirit, Exodus II, Gathering, Highest Potential, Magnify Your Purpose, Oils of Ancient Scripture, Thieves, Cinnamint Lip Balm, Thieves Bar Soap, Mineral Essence, Carbozyme, Dentarome Plus/Ultra Toothpaste, Thieves Antiseptic Spray, Thieves Wipes, Thieves Household Cleaner
Cistus	*Cistus ladanifer* (Cistaceae)	FA	ImmuPower, ImmuneTune, KidScents Lotion
Citronella	*Cymbopogon nardus* (Gramineae)	GRAS, FA, DS, P, SI	Purification, Sunsation Suntan Oil
Citrus Hystrix		DS, SI, PH, CH	Trauma Life
Clary Sage	*Salvia sclarea* (Labiatae)	GRAS, FA, P, DS	Into the Future, Progessence, Lavender Shampoo/Conditioner, Prenolone Cream, Prenolone+, Rosewood Shampoo/Conditioner, Dragon Time EO/Bath Gel/Massage Oil, EveningPeace Bath Gel, SclarEssence, Cel-Lite Magic, Cortistop WOMEN, Lady Sclareol, Transformation
Clove	*Syzygium aromaticum* (Myrtaceae)	GRAS, FA, DS, A, SI+	Abundance, BLM Capsules & Powder, Carbozyme, En-R-Gee, ImmuPower, Longevity, Longevity Caps, Melrose, PanAway, Thieves, Dentarome Plus/Ultra Toothpaste, Kidscent Toothpaste, Fresh Essence Plus, Thieves Bar Soap, K&B Tincture, Essentialzyme, ParaFree Softgels, AromaGuard Stick Deodorant, Thieves Antiseptic Spray, Thieves Wipes, Thieves Household Cleaner

Single Oil Name	Botanical Name	Safety Data	Products containing Single Oil
Copaiba (Copal)	*Copaiba langsdorfii*	GRAS, FA, DS	Breath Again Roll-on, Deep Relief Roll-on
Coriander	*Coriandrum sativum L.* (Umbelliferae)	GRAS, FA,DS	
Cumin	*Cuminus cyminum* (Umbelliferae)	GRAS, FA, DS, SI	ImmuPower, ParaFree Softgels, Detoxzyme
Cypress	*Cupressus sempervirens* (Cupressaceae)		Aroma Life, Aroma Siez, RC, H-R-T Tincture, Cel-Lite Magic, BodyGize, Power Meal, Super Cal
Davana	*Artemisia pallens* (Compositae)		Trauma Life
Dill	*Anethum graveolens* (Umbelliferae)	GRAS, FA, DS, E	
Elemi	*Canarium luzonicum* (Burseraceae)		Ortho Sport
Eucalyptus citriodora	*Eucalyptus citriodora* (Myrtaceae)		RC
Eucalyptus dives	*Eucalyptus dives* (Myrtaceae)	SI, P	
Eucalyptus globulus	*Eucalyptus globulus* (Myrtaceae)	FA, FL, DS	RC, Dentarome Plus/Ultra Toothpaste, Chelex Tincture, Ortho Sport
Eucalyptus polybractea	*Eucalyptus polybractea* (Myrtaceae)		
Eucalyptus radiata	*Eucalyptus radiata* (Myrtaceae)		RC, Thieves, AromaGuard Stick Deodorant, Thieves Bar Soap, Thieves Antiseptic Spray, Dentarome Plus/Ultra Toothpaste, Carbozyme, Thieves Wipes, Thieves Household Cleaner
Fennel	*Foeniculum vulgare* (Umbelliferae)	GRAS, FA, DS, E, P	Di-Gize, JuvaFlex, Mister, Progessence, Detoxzyme, Prenolone Cream, Prenolone+, Dragon Time EO/Bath Gel/ Massage Oil, K&B Tincture, ICP, SclarEssence, Essentialzyme, ParaFree Softgels, Power Meal, ProGen, Cortistop WOMEN
Fir, Douglas	*Pseudotsuga menziesii* (Pinaceae)	SI	Regenolone Cream
Fir, Idaho Balsam	*Abies grandis* (Pinaceae)	FA, FL, SI, DS	Gratitude, BLM Powder & Capsules, Sacred Mountain, Believe, En-R-Gee, Sacred Mountain Bar Soap, Transformation
Fir, White	*Abies grandis* (Pinaceae)	SI	ImmuneTune, AromaGuard Stick Deodorant, Evergreen Essence, Grounding, Australian Blue, Into the Future

Single Oil Name	Botanical Name	Safety Data	Products containing Single Oil
Fleabane	*Conyza canadensis* (Compositae)		Progessence, ProMist, ThermaBurn, Cortistop WOMEN
Frankincense	*Boswellia carteri* (Burseraceae)	FA, FL, DS	Abundance, Acceptance, Awaken, Believe, Brain Power, Clara Derm, Exodus II, Forgiveness, Gathering, Harmony, Humility, ImmuPower, Gratitude, Inspiration, Into the Future, Longevity, Oils of Ancient Scripture, 3 Wise Men, Trauma Life, Valor, Valor Bar Soap, Boswellia Wrinkle Creme, Wolfberry Eye Creme, Exodus, ThermaBurn, Cortistop WOMEN, Tender Tush Ointment, A.R.T Day Activator, A.R.T. Night Reconstructor, A.R.T Gentle Foaming Cleanser
Galbanum	*Ferula gummosa* (Umbelliferae)	FA, FL, DS	Exodus II, Gathering, Gratitude, Highest Potential, Oils of Ancient Scripture
Geranium	*Pelargonium graveolens* (Geraniaceae)	GRAS, FA, DS, FL	Acceptance, Clarity, EndoFlex, Envision, Forgiveness, Gathering, Lady Sclareol, Highest Potential, Gentle Baby, Harmony, Humility, Joy, JuvaFlex, Release, SARA, Trauma Life, White Angelica, AromaGuard Stick Deodorant, Boswellia, Wrinkle Creme, Progessence, Genesis Lotion, Lemon-Sage Shampoo/Conditioner, Prenolone Cream, Prenolone+, Rosewood Shampoo/Conditioner, KidScents Lotion, Satin Body Lotion, Wolfberry Eye Creme, Dragon Time Bath Gel, Evening Peace Bath Gel, Melaleuca-Geranium Bar Soap, K&B Tincture, JuvaTone, KidScents Liquid Soap
Ginger	*Zingiber officinale* (Zingiberaceae)	GRAS, FA, DS, A, PH	Abundance, Di-Gize, ComforTone, ICP, Magnify Your Purpose
Goldenrod	*Solidago canadensis* (Asteraceae)	DS	
Grapefruit	*Citrus x paradisi* (Rutaceae)	GRAS, FA, DS	Citrus Fresh, Cel-Lite Magic, Bodygize, Power Meal, ProMist, Super C
Helichrysum	*Helichrysum italicum* (Compositae)	GRAS, FA, DS	Aroma Life, Brain Power, Forgiveness, Awaken, JuvaFlex, JuvaCleanse, M-Grain, PanAway, Trauma Life, Chelex Tincture, CardiaCare, Clara Derm
Hyssop	*Hyssopus officinalis* (Labiatae)	GRAS, FA, DS, E+, HBP+, P+	Exodus II, Harmony, ImmuPower, Relieve It, White Angelica, Exodus, Oils of Ancient Scripture

Single Oil Name	Botanical Name	Safety Data	Products containing Single Oil
Jasmine (Absolute)	*Jasminum officinale* (Oleaceae)		Awaken, Clarity, Dragon Time, Forgiveness, Gentle Baby, Harmony, Highest Potential, Inner Child, Joy, Lady Sclareol, Into the Future, Lavender Shampoo/Conditioner, Genesis Lotion, Satin Body Lotion, Dragon Time Bath Gel/Massage, Evening Peace Bath Gel, Sensation EO/Lotion/Bath Gel/Message Oil
Juniper	*Juniperus osteosperma* and/or *J. scopulorum* (Cupressaceae)	GRAS, FA, DS SI	Awaken, Di-Gize, Dream Catcher, En-R-Gee, Grounding, Hope, Into the Future, 3 Wise Men, NeuroGen, Cel-Lite Magic,Ortho Ease, Morning Start Bath Gel, Morning Start Bar Soap, K&BTincture
Laurel	*Laurus nobilis* (Lauraceae)	GRAS, FA, DS, SI	Exodus, ParaFree Softgels
Lavandin	*Lavandula x hybrida* (Labiatae)	GRAS, FA, DS,	Purification, Release
Lavender	*Lavandula angustifolia* CT linalol (Labiatae)	GRAS, FA, DS	Aroma Siez, Awaken, Brain Power, RC, Envision, Forgiveness, Gentle Baby, Harmony, Gathering, Highest Potential, M-Grain, Mister, Motivation, SARA, Surrender, Trauma Life, ProGen LavaDerm Cooling Mist, AromaGuard Stick Deodorant, Lavender Shampoo/ Conditioner, Tender Tush Ointment, Orange Blossom Facial Wash, Sunsation Suntan Oil, Sandalwood Moisture Creme, Wolfberry Eye Creme, Juniper Satin Scrub, Lavender Rosewood Bar Soap, Dragon Time EO/Bath Gel/Massage Oil Relaxation Massage Oil, Clara Derm
Ledum	*Ledum groenlandicum* (Ericaceae)	DS	JuvaCleanse
Lemon	*Citrus limon* (Rutaceae)	GRAS, FA, DS, PH, SI	Citrus Fresh, Clarity, Thieves, Forgiveness, Gentle Baby, Harmony, Joy, RC, Surrender, Genesis Lotion, Lavender Shampoo/Conditioner, Lemon-Sage Shampoo/Conditioner, KidScents Shampoo, Orange Blossom Facial Wash, Dragon Time Bath Gel, Evening Peace Bath Gel, AromaGuard Stick Deodorant, Thieves Bar Soap, Lemon-Sandalwood Bar Soap, H-R-T Tincture, AlkaLime, AminoTech, Bodygize, CardiaCare, Carbozyme, ImmuneTune,

Single Oil Name	Botanical Name	Safety Data	Products containing Single Oil
Lemon *(continued)*			JuvaTone, MegaCal, Mineral Essence, Power Meal, Super C, Super C Chewable, Multi Greens, KidScents Detangler, Dentarome Plus/Ultra Toothpaste, Fresh Essence Plus Mouthwash, Thieves Antiseptic Spray, Thieves Wipes, Thieves Household Cleaner, Transformation, A.R.T. Gentle Foaming Cleanser
Lemongrass	*Cymbopogon flexuosus* (Gramineae)	GRAS, FA, DS, CH, SI+	ICP, Di-Gize, En-R-Gee, Inner Child, Purification, NeuroGen, Sunsation Suntan Oil, Morning Start Bath Gel, Morning Start Bar Soap, Ortho Ease, Ortho Sport, Bodygize, Be-Fit, MultiGreens
Lime	*Citrus aurantifolia* (Rutaceae)	GRAS, FA, DS, PH+	Lemon-Sage Shampoo/Conditioner AlkaLime, Super C, AminoTech,
Mandarin	*Citrus reticulata* (Rutaceae)	GRAS, FA, DS, PH	Awaken, Citrus Fresh, Joy, Dragon Time Bath Gel, Super C, Bodygize
Manuka	*Leptospormum scoparium*		Essential Beauty Serum (Acne Prone)
Marjoram	*Origanum majorana* (Labiatae)	GRAS, FA, DS, P	Aroma Life, Aroma Siez, Dragon Time, M-Grain, RC, Dragon Time Bath Gel, Ortho Ease, Ortho Sport CardiaCare, Super Cal
Melaleuca ericifolia (formerly Rosalina)	*Melaleuca ericifolia* (Myrtaceae)		Melaleuca-Geranium Bar Soap
Melissa	*Melissa officinalis* (Labiatae)	GRAS, FA, DS	Brain Power, Forgiveness, Hope, Humility, White Angelica, MultiGreens
Mountain Savory	*Satureja montana* (Labiatae)	GRAS, FA, DS, CH, SI+	ImmuPower, Surrender
Mugwort		GRAS, FA, DS P, CH	Comfortone
Myrrh	*Commiphora myrrha* (Burseraceae)	FA, FL, DS	Abundance, Exodus II, Gratitude, Hope, Humility, Oils of Ancient Scripture, 3 Wise Men, White Angelica, Boswellia Wrinkle Creme, Rose Ointment, Sandalwood Moisture Creme, Sandalwood Toner, Thyromin, Clara Derm
Myrtle	*Myrtus communis* (Myrtaceae)	FA, FL, DS	EndoFlex, Inspiration, Mister, Purification, RC, JuvaTone, ProGen, ThermaBurn, Thyromin
Neroli	*Citrus aurantium bigaradia* (Rutaceae)	GRAS, FA, DS	Acceptance, Awaken, Humility, Inner Child, Present Time

Single Oil Name	Botanical Name	Safety Data	Products containing Single Oil
Niaouli	*Melaleuca quinquenervia* (Myrtaceae)		Melrose, AromaGuard Stick Deodorant
Nutmeg	*Myristica fragrans* (Myristicaceae)	GRAS, FA, DS, SI, E, P, CH+	EndoFlex, En-R-Gee, Magnify Your Purpose, Royal Essence Tincture, Be-Fit, ParaFree Softgels, Power Meal, ThermaBurn
Onycha	*Styrax benzoin* (Styracaceae)		Oils of Ancient Scripture
Orange	*Citrus aurantium* (Rutaceae)	GRAS, FA, DS, PH	Abundance, Christmas Spirit, Citrus Fresh, Envision, Harmony, Inner Child, Peace & Calming, SARA, Bodygize, ImmuneTune, ImmuPro, Lady Sclareol, Mighty Vites, Longevity, Longevity Caps, Power Meal, Super C, Wolfberry Bar
Oregano	*Origanum compactum* (Labiatae)	GRAS, FA, DS, SI+	ImmuPower, Regenolone Cream, Ortho Sport Massage Oil
Palmarosa	*Cymbopogon martinii* (Gramineae)	GRAS, FA, DS	Awaken, Clarity, Forgiveness, Gentle Baby, Harmony, Joy, Genesis Lotion, Rose Ointment, Dragon Time Bath Gel, Evening Peace Bath Gel
Palo Santo	*Bursera graveolens*	CH, P, SI	
Patchouli	*Pogostemon cublin* (Labiatae)	FA, FL, DS	Abundance, Di-Gize, Magnify Your Purpose, Peace & Calming, Orange Blossom Facial Wash, Rose Ointment
Pepper (black)	*Piper nigrum* (Piperaceae)	GRAS, FA, DS, SI	Dream Catcher, En-R-Gee, Relieve It, Cel-Lite Magic
Peppermint	*Mentha piperita* (Labiatae)	GRAS, FA, DS, SI+, HBP, CH+	Aroma Siez, Clarity, Di Tone, M-Grain, Mister, PanAway, Raven, RC, Relieve It, AromaGuard Stick Deodorant, Cinnamint Lip Balm, Dentarome Plus/Ultra Toothpaste, Detoxzyme, Peppermint Satin Scrub MINT, NeuroGen, Regenolone Cream, Satin Body Lotion, Morning Start Bath Gel, Peppermint-Cedarwood Bar Soap, Morning Start Bar Soap, Ortho Ease, Ortho Sport, Relaxation Massage Oil, Polyzyme, BLM Powder, Cortistop WOMEN, ComforTone, Thyromin, SclarEssence, Satin Scrub, Essentialzyme, Transformation, Mineral Essence, Pro-Gen, ProMist
Petitgrain	*Citrus aurantium* (Rutaceae)	GRAS, FA, DS	

Single Oil Name	Botanical Name	Safety Data	Products containing Single Oil
Pine	*Pinus sylvestris* (Pinaceae)	FA, FL, SI, DS	Evergreen Essence, Grounding, RC, Lemon-Sage Shampoo/Conditioner, ImmuneTune
Pine, Ponderosa	*Pinus ponderosa* (Pinaceae)	SI	Evergreen Essence
Ravensara	*Ravensara aromatica* (Lauraceae)		ImmuPower, Respiratory S, ImmuneTune
Rose	*Rosa damascena* (Rosaceae)	GRAS, FA, DS,	Awaken, Envision, Forgiveness, Gathering, Gentle Baby, Harmony, Joy, Humility, Highest Potential, SARA, Trauma Life, White Angelica, Rose Ointment
Rosemary	*Rosmarinus officinalis* CT cineol (Labiatae)	GRAS, FA, DS, E+, HBP, P+ CH+	Clarity, En-R-Gee, JuvaFlex, Melrose, Purification, Thieves, Morning Start Bath Gel, Multi Greens, AromaGuard Stick Deodorant, Thieves Bar Soap, Morning Start Bar Soap, Chelex Tincture, Rehemogen Tincture, Sandalwood Moisture Creme, Be-Fit, Carbozyme, ComforTone, Polyzyme, ICP, JuvaTone, Orange Blossom Facial Wash, Thieves Antiseptic Spray, Thieves Wipes, Thieves Household Cleaner, Transformation, Dentarome Plus/Ultra Toothpaste
Rosewood	*Aniba rosaeodora* (Lauraceae)		Acceptance, Awaken, Believe, Clarity, Forgiveness, Gentle Baby, Joy, Gratitude, Harmony, Humility, Valor, Inspiration, Magnify Your Purpose, White Angelica, Genesis Lotion, Rose Ointment, AromaGuard Stick Deodorant, Rosewood Shampoo/Conditioner, KidScents Lotion, Sandalwood Moisture Creme, Sandalwood Toner, Satin Body Lotion, Wolfberry Eye Creme, Dragon Time Bath Gel, Evening Peace Bath Gel, Sensation EO/Lotion/Bath Gel/Massage Oil, Lavender Rosewood Bar Soap, Valor Bar Soap, H-R-T Tincture, Relaxation Massage Oil, Lady Sclareol, Tender Tush Ointment
Sage	*Salvia officinalis* (Labiatae)	GRAS, FA, DS, E+, P+, CH+ HBP	EndoFlex, Envision, Magnify Your Purpose, Mister, Lemon Sage Shampoo/Conditioner, Dragon Time Massage Oil/Bath Gel, K&B Tincture, Progen
Sage Lavender	*Salvia lavandulifolia*		Awaken, Harmony, Lady Sclareol, SclarEssence

Single Oil Name	Botanical Name	Safety Data	Products containing Single Oil
Sandalwood	*Santalum album* (Santalaceae)	FA, FL, DS	Acceptance, Awaken, Brain Power, Dream Catcher, Forgiveness, Gathering, Harmony, Highest Potential, Inner Child, Inspiration, MagnifyYour Purpose, Oils of Ancient Scripture, Release, 3 Wise Men, Trauma Life, White Angelica, Boswellia Wrinkle Creme, Rosewood Shampoo/ Conditioner, Sandalwood Moisture Creme, Sandalwood Toner, Satin Body Lotion, Evening Peace Bath Gel, Lemon-Sandalwood Bar Soap, Tender Tush Ointment, Lady Sclareol, A.R.T Day Activator, A.R.T Gentle Foaming Cleanser, A.R.T Night Reconstructor
Spearmint	*Mentha spicata* (Labiatae)	GRAS, FA, DS SI, CH+	Citrus Fresh, EndoFlex, Cinnamint Lip Balm, Relaxation Massage Oil, Mint Condition, ProMist, ThermaBurn, Thyromin
Spikenard	*Nardostachys jatamansi* (Valerianaceae)		Exodus II, Humility, Exodus, Oils of Ancient Scripture
Spruce	*Picea mariana* (Pinaceae)	FA, FL, DS SI	Abundance, Christmas Spirit, Envision, Gathering, Grounding, Harmony, Hope, Highest Potential, Inner Child, Inspiration, Motivation, Present Time, RC, Relieve It, Sacred Mountain, Surrender, 3 Wise Men, Trauma Life, Valor, White Angelica, Sacred Mountain Bar Soap, Valor Bar Soap
Tangerine	*Citrus nobilis* (Rutaceae)	GRAS, FA, DS SI, PH	Awaken, Citrus Fresh, Dream Catcher, Inner Child, Peace & Calming, Bodygize, Relaxation Massage Oil, ComforTone KidScents Detangler, KidScents Shampoo
Tansy, Blue	*Tanacetum annum* (Compositae)		Acceptance, Australian Blue, Awaken, Dream Catcher, Highest Potential, JuvaFlex, Peace & Calming, Release, SARA, Valor, Dragon Time Bath Gel, Evening Peace Bath Gel, Valor Bar Soap, JuvaTone, Tender Tush Ointment KidScents Shampoo,
Tansy, Idaho	*Tanacetum vulgare* (Compositae)	E+, P+. CH+	Awaken, ImmuPower, Into the Future, ParaFree Softgels, Lady Sclareol
Tarragon	*Artemisia dracunculus* (Compositae)	GRAS, FA, DS, E+, P+, CH+	Di-Gize, ComforTone, ICP, Essentialzyme

Single Oil Name	Botanical Name	Safety Data	Products containing Single Oil
Tea Tree	*Melaleuca alternifolia* (Myrtaceae)		Melrose, Purification, AromaGuard Stick Deodorant, Rose Ointment, Sunsation Suntan Oil, Melaleuca-Geranium Bar Soap, Rehemogen Tincture, ParaFree Softgels, Clara Derm
Thyme, Red	*Thymus vulgaris* (Labiatae)	GRAS, FA, DS, HBP, SI+, CH	Longevity, Longevity Caps, Kidscent Toothpaste, ParaFree Softgels, Rehemogen, Ortho Ease
Tsuga	*Tsuga canadensis* (Pinaceae)	SI+	
Valerian	*Valeriana officinalis* (Valerianaceae)	FA, FL, DS	Trauma Life
Vetiver	*Vetiveria zizanoides* (Gramineae)	FA, FL, DS	Lady Sclareol, Melaleuca-Geranium Bar Soap, Ortho Ease, Ortho Sport, ParaFree Softgels
Wintergreen	*Gaultheria procumbens* (Ericaceae) *Betula alleghaniensis*	E+, P+, CH+ A	PanAway, Dentarome Plus/Ultra Toothpaste Regenolone, Be-Fit, Super Cal, ArthoTune, Rosewood Shampoo/Conditioner, BLM Capsules & Powder, Ortho Ease, Ortho Sport
Yarrow	*Achillea millefolium* (Compositae)		Dragon Time, Mister, Dragon Time Massage Oil, Prenolone Cream, Prenolone+, ProGen
Ylang Ylang	*Cananga odorata* (Annonaceae)	GRAS, FA, DS,	Aroma Life, Awaken, Clarity, Dream Catcher, Forgiveness, Gathering, Gentle Baby, Gratitude, Grounding, Harmony, Humility, Australian Blue Highest Potential, Inner Child, Joy, Motivation, Peace & Calming, Present Time, Release, Sacred Mountain, SARA, White Angelica, Boswellia Wrinkle Creme, Progessence, Genesis Lotion, Lemon Sage Shampoo/Conditioner, Prenolone Cream, Prenolone+, Satin Body Lotion, CardiaCare, Sensation EO/Lotion/Bath Gel/Massage Oil, Dragon Time Bath Gel/Massage Oil, Evening Peace Bath Gel, Sacred Mountain Bar Soap, H-R-T Tincture, Relaxation Massage Oil, Lady Sclareol

Safety Data Legend:

A	Anti-coagulant – May enhance the effects of blood thinners; avoid using with Aspirin, heparin, Warfarin, etc)
CH	Do not use on children younger than 18 months of age
CH+	Do not use on children younger than 5 years of age
DS	Dietary supplement
E	Use with **caution** if susceptible to **epilepsy** (small amounts or in dilution)
E+	**Avoid** if susceptible to **epilepsy** (can trigger a seizure)
FA	Food additive
FL	Flavoring agent
GRAS	Generally regarded as safe
HBP	Use with **caution** if dealing with **high blood pressure** (small amounts)
HBP+	**Avoid** if dealing with **high blood pressure**
P	Use with **caution** during pregnancy
P+	**Avoid** during pregnancy
PH	**Photosensitivity** – direct exposure to sunlight within 24 hours after use could cause dermatitis (test first)
PH+	**Extreme Photosensitivity** – direct exposure to sunlight after use within 72 hours can cause severe dermatitis (avoid exposing affected area of skin to direct sunlight for 48-72 hours)
SI	Could possibly result in **skin irritation** (dilution may be necessary)
SI+	Can cause **extreme skin irritation** (dilution highly recommended)

Blend Name	Single Oil Contents	Safety Data	Uses/Application Areas
Abundance	Myrrh, Cinnamon Bark, Patchouli, Orange, Clove, Ginger, Spruce, Frankincense	SI, CH	Diffuse; wrists, ears, neck, face; wallet/purse; painting; direct inhalation
Acceptance	Geranium, Blue Tansy, Frankincense, Sandalwood, Neroli, Rosewood (Carrier: Almond Oil)		Diffuse; liver, heart, chest, face, ears, neck, thymus, wrists; sacral chakra; direct inhalation
Aroma Life	Cypress, Marjoram, Helichrysum, Ylang Ylang (Carrier: Sesame Seed Oil)		Heart; Vita Flex heart points, under left ring finger, under left ring toe, above left elbow, neck; spine; direct inhalation
Aroma Siez	Basil, Marjoram, Lavender, Peppermint, Cypress	SI, CH	Muscles; neck; heart; Vita Flex points; full body massage; bath; direct inhalation
Australian Blue	Blue Cypress, Ylang Ylang Cedarwood, Blue Tansy, White Fir		Diffuse; chest, heart, forehead, neck, temples, wrists; direct inhalation
Awaken	Lemon, Mandarin, Bergamot, Ylang Ylang, Rose, Rosewood, Geranium, Palmarosa, Roman Chamomile, Jasmine, Hyssop, Frankincense, Sandalwood, Helichrysum, Juniper, Blue Tansy, Tangerine, Black Pepper, Anise Neroli, Spruce, Lavender, Orange, Angelica, Sage Lavender (Carrier: Almond Oil)	PH	Diffuse; chest, heart, forehead, neck, temples, wrists; full body massage; bath
Believe	Idaho Balsam Fir, Rosewood, Frankincense		Diffuse; heart, forehead, neck, temples, wrists; bath; direct inhalation
Brain Power	Cedarwood, Sandalwood, Frankincense, Melissa, Australian Blue Cypress, Lavender, Helichrysum		Diffuse; neck, throat, nose; inside of cheeks, wrists; direct inhalation

Blend Name	Single Oil Contents	Safety Data	Uses/Application Areas
Breath Again Roll-on	*Eucalyptus Staigeriana, Eucalyptus Globulus, Eucalyptus radiata,* Eucalyptus Blue (Azul), Myrtle, Bay Laurel, Peppermint, Manuka (Carrier: Virgin and Fractionated Coconut Oil)	CH	Topical; throat; neck; chest
Christmas Spirit	Orange, Cinnamon Bark, Spruce	SI, CH	Diffuse; crown; neck, wrists; heart, temple; bath; direct inhalation
Citrus Fresh	Orange, Tangerine, Mandarin, Grapefruit, Lemon, Spearmint	SI, PH DS	Diffuse; ears, heart, wrists; neck, wrists; full body massage; bath; purify drinking water
Clarity	Basil, Cardamom, Rosemary cineol, Peppermint, Rosewood, Geranium, Lemon, Palmarosa, Ylang Ylang, Bergamot, Roman Chamomile, Jasmine	SI, P, PH+, CH, DS	Diffuse; forehead, neck, temples, wrists, neck; bath direct inhalation
Deep Relief Roll-on	Peppermint, Lemon, Idaho Balsam Fir, Copaiba, Clove, Wintergreen, Helichrysum, Vetiver, Palo Santo (Carrier: Virgin and Fractionated Coconut Oil)	SI, P, E,	Topical on location; temples; forehead
Di-Gize	Tarragon, Ginger, Peppermint, Juniper, Anise, Fennel, Lemongrass, Patchouli	SI, P, E, CH+, DS	Vita Flex points, compress ankles; stomach; abdomen, bottom of throat; direct inhalation
Dragon Time	Clary Sage, Fennel, Lavender, Jasmine, Yarrow, Marjoram	P	Vita Flex points; diffuse; abdomen, lower back, location direct inhalation
Dream Catcher	Sandalwood, Bergamot, Ylang Ylang, Juniper, Blue Tansy, Tangerine, Black Pepper, Anise	PH	Diffuse; forehead, eye brows, temples, ears, throat chakra; neck, wrists; bath; direct inhalation
Egyptian Gold	Frankincence, Lavender, Blasam Fir, Myrrh, Spikenard, Hyssop, Rose, Cedarwood, Cinnamon Bark	SI, P, CH	Vita Flex points; diffuse; wrists, temples; massage direct inhalation
EndoFlex	Spearmint, Sage, Geranium, Myrtle, Nutmeg, German Chamomile (Carrier: Sesame Seed Oil)	SI, E, CH	Thyroid, kidneys, liver, pancreas, glands; Vita Flex points; direct inhalation
En-R-Gee	Rosemary cineol, Juniper, Nutmeg, Idaho Balsam Fir, Black Pepper, Lemongrass, Clove	SI, E	Diffuse; wrists, ears, neck, temples, feet; full body massage; direct inhalation
Envision	Spruce, Sage, Rose, Geranium, Orange, Lavender	HBP, E, P	Vita Flex points; diffuse; wrists, temples; bath; massage direct inhalation

Blend Name	Single Oil Contents	Safety Data	Uses/Application Areas
Evergreen Essence	Colorado Blue Spruce, Ponderosa Pine, Pine, Red Fir Cedar, White Fir, Black Pine, Piñon Pine, Lodge Pole Pine	SI	Diffuse; forehead, heart, temples, neck, thymus, direct inhalation
Exodus II	Cinnamon Bark, Cassia, Calamus, Myrrh, Hyssop, Frankincense, Spikenard, Galbanum (Carrier: Olive Oil)	SI+, P+, CH+	Diffuse; Direct Inhale; Chest, ears, wrist, spine, (Raindrop style); VitaFlex direct inhalation
Forgiveness	Frankincense, Sandalwood, Lavender, Melissa, Angelica, Helichrysum, Rose, Rosewood, Geranium, Lemon, Palmarosa, Ylang Ylang, Bergamot, Roman Chamomile, Jasmine (Carrier: Sesame Seed Oil)		Diffuse; navel, heart, ears, wrists; direct inhalation
GLF	Grapefruit, Helichrysum, Clery Seed, Ledum, Hyssop, Spearmint	CH+, P+	Take 1 capsule size 0 diluted 80-20 1-2 times daily
Gathering	Galbanum, Frankincense, Sandalwood, Lavender, Cinnamon Bark, Rose, Spruce, Geranium, Ylang Ylang		Diffuse; forehead, heart, temples, neck, thymus, face, chest; direct inhalation
Gentle Baby	Geranium, Rosewood, Palmarosa, Lavender, Roman Chamomile, Ylang Ylang, Rose, Lemon, Bergamot, Jasmine		Diffuse; ankles, lower back, abdomen, feet, face, neck; massage; bath; direct inhalation direct inhalation
Gratitude	Idaho Balsam Fir, Frankincense, Rosewood, Myrrh, Galbanum Ylang Ylang		Diffuse; ears; chest, heart, temples, neck, feet, wrists direct inhalation
Grounding	Juniper, Angelica, Ylang Ylang, Cedarwood, Pine, Spruce, White Fir	SI	Diffuse; brain stem, back of neck, sternum, temples direct inhalation
Harmony	Hyssop, Spruce, Lavender, Frankincense, Geranium, Ylang Ylang, Orange, Sandalwood, Angelica, Sage Lavender, Rose, Rosewood, Lemon, Palmarosa, Bergamot, Roman Chamomile, Jasmine	P, E+, HBP, PH	Diffuse; Vita Flex points; ears, feet, heart; energy meridians, crown direct inhalation
Highest Potential	Galbanum, Frankincense, Sandalwood, Lavender, Cinnamon Bark, Rose, Spruce, Geranium, Ylang Ylang, Blue Cypress, Cedarwood, Blue Tansy, White Fir, Jasmine		Diffuse; ears; chest, heart, temples, wrists, neck, feet; direct inhalation

Blend Name	Single Oil Contents	Safety Data	Uses/Application Areas
Hope	Melissa, Myrrh, Juniper, Spruce (Carrier: Almond Oil)		Diffuse; ears; chest, heart, temples, solar plexus, neck, feet, wrists; direct inhalation
Humility	Geranium, Ylang Ylang, Frankincense, Spikenard, Myrrh, Rose, Rosewood, Melissa, Neroli (Carrier: Sesame Seed Oil)		Diffuse; heart, neck, temples; direct inhalation
ImmuPower	Cistus, Frankincense, Hyssop, Ravensara, Mountain Savory, Oregano, Clove, Cumin, Idaho Tansy	SI, P, E, CH	Diffuse; throat, chest, spine, feet; thymus; neck, under arms direct inhalation
Inner Child	Orange, Tangerine, Jasmine, Ylang Ylang, Spruce, Sandalwood, Lemongrass, Neroli	PH,SI	Diffuse; navel, chest, temples nose; direct inhalation
Inspiration	Cedarwood, Spruce, Rosewood, Sandalwood, Frankincense, Myrtle, Mugwort		Diffuse; temples, crown, shoulders, back of neck direct inhalation
Into the Future	Frankincense, Jasmine, Clary Sage, Juniper, Idaho Tansy, White Fir, Orange, Cedarwood, Ylang Ylang, White Lotus (Carrier: Almond Oil)		Diffuse; bath; heart, wrists neck; compress; full body massage; direct inhalation
Joy	Lemon, Mandarin, Bergamot, Ylang Ylang, Rose, Rosewood, Geranium, Palmarosa, Roman Chamomile, Jasmine	PH, CH	Diffuse; heart, ears, neck, thymus, temples, forehead, wrists; bath; compress; massage; direct inhalation
Juva Cleanse	Helichrysum, Celery Seed, Ledum	CH+	Take 1 capsule size 0 diluted 80-20 1-2 times daily
JuvaFlex	Fennel, Geranium, Rosemary cineol, Roman Chamomile, Blue Tansy, Helichrysum (Carrier: Sesame Seed Oil)	SI	Vita Flex points; feet, spine, liver; full body massage direct inhalation
Lady Sclareol	Rosewood, Vetiver, Geranium, Orange, Clary Sage, Ylang Ylang, Sandalwood, Sage Lavender Jasmine (absolute), Idaho Tansy	P, CH	Apply 2-4 drops to Vita Flex Points
Longevity	Clove, Orange, Thyme Frankincense	DS, CH+	Take 1 capsule size 00 1-2 x daily
M-Grain	Basil, Marjoram, Lavender, Peppermint, Roman Chamomile, Helichrysum	SI, CH, P	Diffuse; forehead, crown, shoulders, neck, temples; Vita Flex points; massage; direct inhalation
Magnify Your Purpose	Sandalwood, Nutmeg, Patchouli, Rosewood, Cinnamon Bark, Ginger, Sage	E, P, SI, CH	Vita Flex points; feet, wrists, temples; diffuse; bath; massage; direct inhalation

Blend Name	Single Oil Contents	Safety Data	Uses/Application Areas
Melrose	Melaleuca (Alternifolia & Quinquenervia), Rosemary cineol, Clove	SI	Topically on location diffuse; forehead, liver; direct inhalation
Mister	Sage, Fennel, Lavender, Myrtle, Yarrow, Peppermint (Carrier: Sesame Seed Oil)	P+, E, CH	Vita Flex points; ankles, lower pelvis, prostate (dilute); compress; direct inhalation
Motivation	Roman Chamomile, Ylang Ylang, Spruce, Lavender		Diffuse; chest, neck; solar plexus, sternum, feet, navel, ears; wrists, palms; direct inhalation
PanAway	Wintergreen, Helichrysum, Clove, Peppermint	SI, CH	Apply on location of pain; Vitaflex feet; direct inhalation
Peace & Calming	Tangerine, Orange, Ylang Ylang, Patchouli, Blue Tansy	PH	Diffuse; navel, nose, neck, feet; bath; wrists; direct inhalation
Present Time	Neroli, Spruce, Ylang Ylang (Carrier: Almond Oil)		Thymus; neck, forehead direct inhalation
Purification	Citronella, Lemongrass, Rosemary cineol, Melaleuca, Lavandin, Myrtle	SI	Diffuse; Vita Flex points; ears, feet, temples; on location of injury; direct inhalation
Raven	Ravensara, Eucalyptus radiata, Peppermint, Wintergreen, Lemon	SI, CH	Diffuse; compress; Vita Flex points; lungs, throat; pillow; suppository; direct inhalation
R.C.	Eucalyptus (E. globulus, E. radiata, E. australiana, E. citriodora), Myrtle, Marjoram, Pine, Cypress, Lavender, Spruce, Peppermint	CH	Compress; diffuse; chest, back, feet; sinuses, nasal passages; ears, neck, throat; massage; direct inhalation
Release	Ylang Ylang, Lavandin, Geranium, Sandalwood, Blue Tansy (Carrier: Olive Oil)		Compress on liver; ears, feet, Vita Flex points; wrists
Relieve It	Spruce, Black Pepper, Hyssop, Peppermint	SI, P, E, HBP, CH	Apply on location of pain; direct inhalation; Raindrop Technique
RutaVaLa	Ruta graveolens, Valerian, Lavender	PH, P, CH	Aromatic use only. Diffuse or inhale
Sacred Mountain	Spruce, Ylang Ylang, Cedarwood Idaho Balsam Fir	SI	Diffuse; solar plexus, brain stem, crown, neck ears, thymus, wrists; direct inhalation
SARA	Blue Tansy, Rose, Lavender, Geranium, Orange, Cedarwood, Ylang Ylang, White Lotus (Carrier: Almond Oil)		En-R-Gee centers; Vita Flex points; temples, nose; places of abuse; direct inhalation
SclarEssence	Clary Sage, Peppermint, Sage Lavender, Fennel	DS, P+, CH	1-10 drops in capsule with VO, Ingest 1 capsule daily as needed
Sensation	Rosewood, Ylang Ylang, Jasmine		Diffuse; apply on location; massage; bath; direct inhalation

Blend Name	Single Oil Contents	Safety Data	Uses/Application Areas
Surrender	Lavender, Roman Chamomile, German Chamomile, Angelica, Mountain Savory, Lemon, Spruce	SI, DS	Forehead, rim of ears, nape of neck, chest, solar plexus; bath direct inhalation
Thieves	Clove, Lemon, Cinnamon Bark, Eucalyptus radiata, Rosemary cineol	SI+, P, CH	Diffuse; feet, throat, stomach, intestines; thymus, under arms; direct inhalation
3 Wise Men	Sandalwood, Juniper, Frankincense, Spruce, Myrrh (Carrier: Almond Oil)		Diffuse; crown of head; neck, forehead, solar plexus, thymus direct inhalation
Tranquil Roll-on	Lavender, Cedarwood, Blue Tansy Frankincense (Carrier: Virgin and Fractionated Coconut Oil)		Topical; forehead, back of neck, temples, over heart
Transformation	Lemon, Peppermint, Sandalwood, Clary Sage, Frankincense, Idaho Balsam Fir, Rosemary, Cardamom	P, PH, CH	Diffuse or apply to Vita Flex points
Trauma Life	Citrus Hystrix, Davana, Geranium, Spruce, Helichrysum, Rose, Sandalwood, Frankincense, Lavender, Valerian		Diffuse; spine; feet, chest, ears, neck, forehead direct inhalation
Valor	Spruce, Rosewood, Blue Tansy, Frankincense (Carrier: Almond Oil)		Feet; diffuse; heart, wrists, solar plexus, neck to thymus, spine; direct inhalation
Valor Roll-on	Spruce, Rosewood, Blue Tansy, Frankincense (Carrier: Virgin and Fractionated Coconut Oil)		Topical; forehead, back of neck, temples, over heart
White Angelica	Geranium, Spruce, Myrrh, Ylang Ylang, Hyssop, Bergamot, Melissa, Sandalwood, Rose, Rosewood (Carrier: Almond Oil)	PH	Diffuse; shoulders, crown, chest, ears, neck, forehead, wrists; bath; direct inhalation; compress

Safety Data Legend:

A	Anti-coagulant – May enhance the effects of blood thinners
CH	Do not use on children younger than 18 months of age
CH+	Do not use on children younger than 5 years of age
DS	Dietary supplement
E	Use with **caution** if susceptible to **epilepsy** (small amounts or in dilution)
E+	**Avoid** if susceptible to **epilepsy** (can trigger a seizure)
FA	Food additive
FL	Flavoring agent
GRAS	Generally regarded as safe
HBP	Use with **caution** if dealing with **high blood pressure** (small amounts)

HBP+	**Avoid** if dealing with **high blood pressure**
P	Use with **caution** during pregnancy
P+	**Avoid** during pregnancy
PH	**Photosensitivity** – direct exposure to sunlight within 24 hours after use could cause dermatitis (test first)
PH+	**Extreme Photosensitivity** – direct exposure to sunlight after use within 72 hours can cause severe dermatitis (avoid exposing affected area of skin to direct sunlight for 48-72 hours)
SI	Could possibly result in **skin irritation** (dilution may be necessary)
SI+	Can cause **extreme skin irritation** (dilution highly recommended)

INDEX